Multichannel Time Series
Analysis with Digital
Computer Programs

NOBERT WIENER
1894-1964

MULTICHANNEL TIME SERIES ANALYSIS

WITH DIGITAL COMPUTER PROGRAMS

Second Edition

Enders A. Robinson

Distinguished Professor of Geophysics
University of Tulsa

Goose Pond Press
11600 Southwest Freeway, Suite 179
Houston, Texas 77031

Multichannel Time Series Analysis
with Digital Computer Programs

First Edition 1967
Revised Edition 1978
Second Edition 1983

Library of Congress Cataloging in Publication Data

Robinson, Enders A.
    Multichannel time series analysis with digital
computer programs.

    Includes bibliographical references and index.
    1. Time-series analysis—Data processing. 2. Time-
series analysis—Computer programs. I. Title.
QA280.R63 1983   519.5'5'0285425   83-1497
ISBN 0-910835-03-9

Preface

During the past decade an important new approach to waveform manipulation, or signal processing, has come into importance in electrical engineering. It became practical to represent information-bearing waveforms digitally, and to do signal processing on the digital representation of the waveform. The flexibility of the digital computer thus became available for the processing of waveforms. One can now manipulate waveforms digitally in ways that would have been totally impractical with continuous representations. For example, once the digital representation of a transient waveform is in computer memory, the waveform acquires a permanence which permits a wide range of processing operations, even a time reversal, and at any point the waveform can be restored to a continuous form with a new time base.

Two basic operations in digital signal processing are spectral analysis and digital filtering. One of the major events in digital signal processing was the publication in 1965 of a paper by J. S. Cooley and J. W. Tukey that gave an algorithm for computing Fourier transforms. The paper was concerned not with the computation of the Fourier series of continuous periodic waveforms, but instead with the computation of the discrete Fourier transform. The discrete Fourier transform is the form of Fourier transformation that is amenable to digital computation. The Cooley-Tukey paper showed that there was an algebraic structure in the computation of discrete Fourier transforms that could be exploited to speed up the computation of an n point transform from the order of n^2 arithmetic operations to the order of only n log n arithmetic operations. (A computer program for the Cooley-Tukey method of fast Fourier transformation is subroutine NLOGN on page 63.) The Cooley-Tukey method made it practical to do signal processing on waveforms in either the time or the frequency domains, something never practical with continuous systems. The Fourier transform became not just a theoretical description, but a tool. With the development of the fast Fourier transform the field of digital signal processing grew from obscurity to importance, and is now a major discipline in electrical engineering.

Digital filtering has also been a major area of research in signal processing. The mathematical analysis of dynamic systems has been a matter of concern for many years. The problem has been pursued with great interest since the invention of the digital computer. The analysis of the outputs of dynamic systems was largely the concern of the field of time series analysis which was developed mainly within the sciences of statistics, econometrics, and communications theory. However, in recent years great advances in the analysis of dynamic systems have been made in the field of control theory based on state-space concepts and time domain analysis. As a result there is renewed interest in time series analysis, and in particular predictive techniques. The method of predictive deconvolution has been used for many years in the digital processing of seismic data taken in the exploration of oil and natural gas, (as described on pages 104-112). In this method, a least-squares prediction-error filter is designed from the data. The determination of this operator depends upon the solution of a set of Toeplitz normal equations. Except for short filters, the requirements for computer storage space and computer time for solving these equations by use of a standard simultaneous equations routine are prohibitive. Levinson is a classic paper in 1947 applied the Toeplitz recursion to the solution of these equations. For an operator of length m, the Toeplitz recursion reduces the requirements for computer storage space from m^2 to m and for computer time from m^3 to m^2, as compared to conventional methods. (A computer program for the Toeplitz recursion is given as subroutine EUREKA on page 44.) This recursion makes economic the large scale use of predictive deconvolution in many scientific areas today. Predictive deconvolution (which often is called prediction-error filtering or linear prediction) has found extensive application in speech processing and sonar analysis in the last few years.

The analysis and synthesis of human speech represents an important application of deconvolution. Speech represents the spoken word, whereas text represents the written word. When one reads, he converts text to speech; when one writes, he converts speech to text. However, there is an intermediate point between speech and text; this intermediate point is characterized by numbers called the parameters. Speech analysis is defined as the conversion of speech to the numerical parameters; speech synthesis is defined as the conversion of the numerical parameters to speech. Text analysis is the conversion of text to the numerical parameters, whereas text synthesis is the conversion of the numerical parameters to text. Speech analysis and synthesis are now successfully carried out by means of deconvolution and reconvolution, respectively. Text analysis and text synthesis are not yet perfected but may be within the next few years. At that time an automatic reading machine could be constructed for which the input is printed text and the output is speech. Such an automatic reading machine would be made up of a text analysis machine followed by a speech synthesis machine. Even more useful would be an automatic typewriter for which the input is speech and the output is typewritten text. The automatic typewriter would be made up of a speech analysis machine followed by a text synthesis machine.

Human speech is produced as the result of passing air from the lungs through the vocal tract. The vocal tract is a non-uniform acoustic tube that extends from the glottis to the lips. Each sound produced at the lips is the resultant of two factors, namely (1) the type of wave motion used to excite the vocal tract and (2) the shape of the vocal tract. For example, in order to produce a voiced sound, the excitation function is a series of periodic pulses generated by the vocal cords. In order to produce an unvoiced sound, the excitation function is white random noise generated by turbulent air. These are the two main types of excitation functions that are inputs into the vocal tract at the glottis. The various sounds that are outputs from the vocal tract at the lips are produced by changing the shape of the vocal tract by moving the lips, jaw, tongue, and velum. A particular sound at the lips represents a segment of a stationary time series that is produced by a given type of excitation function and a given shape of the vocal tract. More specifically, a particular sound is equal to the convolution of its excitation function with the impulse response function of the vocal tract shape. We can make this statement because the vocal tract acts like a linear filter in producing speech.

The problem of deconvolution is one of decomposing the observed output sound into its excitation function and its vocal-tract impulse response. As it turns out, the actual shape of the excitation function is not important, so only the gross features of the excitation function need to be saved, such as (1) its r.m.s. amplitude, (2) knowledge of whether it is a pulse train (in case of a voiced sound) or whether it is random (in case of an unvoiced sound) and (3) the period of the pulses (in case of a voiced sound). That is, the excitation function can be characterized by three parameters, namely (1) r.m.s. value, (2) a binary voiced-unvoiced parameter, and (3) in case of a voiced sound, the pitch period. It also turns out that the vocal-tract impulse response can be characterized by as few as 12 numbers. Thus the result of the deconvolution of a particular sound can be as few as 15 parameters, namely 3 excitation parameters and 12 vocal-tract parameters. Since the sound in question would be represented by a time series of several hundreds or thousands of observations, and since deconvolution would replace these observations by 15 parameters characterizing that sound, this approach results in a considerable reduction of the data. In fact, a reduction of 50 to 1 seems to be a goal in speech analysis that is within reach. Another goal is text synthesis, that is, the identification of the parameters representing a sound with the phonetic symbol for that sound, so that an automatic typewriter could be constructed that would type out printed text from the spoken word.

The fidelity of speech analysis can be tested by speech synthesis. In other words, the results of the deconvolution of speech can be evaluated by reconvolution. For each sound an excitation function is generated from its parameters. This excitation function is convolved with the vocal-tract impulse response function to produce the output time-series segment for that sound. This convolution process is called reconvolution because we are not using the original excitation function but a reconstructed one which agrees with the original in its gross features only. The result of this process is the reconvolved sound. By attaching together all these reconvolved sound segments, we obtain the reconvolved speech signal which can be compared to the original speech signal. Experimental listening tests with various auditors establish that the quality of the reconvolved speech is very close to that of the original speech for a wide range of spoken messages and for many different speakers both male and female.

Thus the basic problem of speech analysis is one of the decomposition, or deconvolution, of each sound segment to separate its excitation function from its vocal tract shape. In order to solve this problem, it is first necessary to obtain a good working model of the vocal tract. The model is based on an approximation to the vocal tract made up of a set of interconnected sections. Such a model is called an acoustic tube model. If we assume that the thickness of each section is the same, then the acoustic tube model is specified by the cross-sectional area of each section. At each interface between two adjacent sections, a traveling wave will be partially reflected and partially transmitted, the division of energy between the reflected and transmitted waves being governed by the reflection coefficient associated with that interface. The acoustic tube can support travelling wave-motion from the glottis to the lips, which we call upgoing waves, and also travelling wave-motion from the lips to the glottis, which we call downgoing waves. The upgoing wave and the downgoing wave in any section will be generally different from the respective upgoing wave and downgoing wave in any other section, because of the effects of the reflections and transmissions at each interface. In other words, the vocal tract represents a reverberating system with the full array of multiple reflections and transmissions. This acoustic tube model of the human vocal tract is in fact identical to the model of layered media which is treated in detail in Chapter 3 of this book. The speech-producing acoustic tube model of the vocal tract is a deep-source (i.e. the lungs) model, whereas the marine seismic model given in Section 3.12 is a surface-source model.

In summary, the essence of the entire processes of speech analysis and synthesis is based respectively on deconvolution and reconvolution methods in which the concept of prediction error is the key. The essence of the physical process of speech can be unraveled by a separation of the predictable and unpredictable components. In fact, in the analysis of almost any physical process, prediction theory plays an essential role.

The single channel methods given in this book are finding extensive application. With the success of these single channel methods established, the multichannel methods which comprise the bulk of the book take on new importance. In fact some of the multichannel ideas are actually being used in single-channel analysis. In particular we refer to the concept of the prediction-error operator and the hindsight-error operator given in Section 6.3. In the multichannel case these two operators are in fact different, whereas in the single channel case they reduce to the same thing. However for estimation purposes in the single channel case the distinction between these two operators can indeed be important. It is the balanced use of the Toeplitz recursion with respect to these two operators that is the essence of the Burg method of computing the maximum entropy spectrum. Maximum-entropy methods are intimately connected with the concept of deconvolution. The maximum entropy power spectrum is proportional to the inverse of the energy spectrum of the deconvolution operator. The multichannel method of the Toeplitz recursion for computing deconvolution operators as well as more general type operators is given in mathematical form as well as in programs for digital computers in Chapter 6. In particular subroutine NORMEQ on page 247 is the multichannel counterpart of subroutine EUREKA for the Toeplitz recursion.

In 1942 Norbert Wiener produced his greatest work *Extrapolation, Interpolation and Smoothing of Stationary Time Series with Engineering Applications*. Wiener envisaged the application of his work to result in the construction of hardware devices to be used on ensembles of time series. During those same wartime years, John von Neumann examined, from its foundations, the problem of computing on electronic machines, and during 1944 and 1945 he formulated the now fundamental methods of translating a set of mathematical procedures into a language of instruction for a computing machine. Von Neumann's great contribution was the idea of a fixed and rather universal set of connections or circuits in the machine, a flow diagram, and a code so as to enable a fixed set of connections in the machine to have a means of solving a great variety of problems. The engineering of the digital computer owes a great deal to von Neumann. The logical schemata of the machines, the planning of the relative roles of their memory, their speed, the selection of fundamental orders and their circuits bear heavily the imprint of his ideas. The multichannel computer program WIENER on page 253 represents the union of the ideas of these two great mathematicians, namely Wiener's concept of the unity of time series and communications engineering and von Neumann's concept of the stored-program digital computer and its realization as an engineering device.

Professor Norbert Wiener (1894–1964) was generous with his ideas and always glad to talk about time series analysis and applications. His original help in 1954 and 1955 at M.I.T. in going over his work on multiple time series with me had a decided influence on this book.

Let us now give a brief outline of the book. The applied aspects of time series analysis covered in the book are unified under the general philosophy presented in the *Nonmathematical Introduction*. Briefly, the approach is to link time series methods closely with the empirical and theoretical evidence provided by the subject matter under investigation. Because the writer's experience has been largely in geophysics, many of the methods are presented in their relationship to the analysis of geophysical time series recorded in the seismic exploration for oil and natural gas. However, these methods can be quite readily adapted to analyze other types of time series.

Chapter 1 introduces some of the basic ideas and computer programs which are used in subsequent chapters. Chapter 2 presents the theory of single-channel digital signal processing and spectral analysis together with the necessary computer programs. Chapter 3 gives the theory of lattice structures. The physical mechanism that embodies the lattice structure is a layered medium which admits the propagation of both upgoing and downgoing waves. Such a layered model is characterized by a sequence of reflection coefficients, one for each interface. Lattice structures give a convenient parameterization of stationary processes, and provide the rationale of many algorithms, such as the Levinson (or Toeplitz) recursion for the A polynomials as developed in the chapter. In addition a new recursion in terms of the P and Q polynomials is introduced. The main idea in the chapter is that the lattice can be used as a filter structure for the purposes of analysis and synthesis. There are two types of boundary condition commonly imposed on the top interface. One is the free-surface condition which approximately hold in the case of a marine seismogram, and the other is the non-free-surface condition. It is shown that the Levinson recursion governs the free-surface case, and a computer program is given which does both the forward process (generation of the synthetic seismogram) and the inverse process (inversion of the seismogram to obtain the reflection coefficients). On the other hand, it is the P, Q recursion which governs the non-free-surface case. Not only does the lattice approach bring out the physical significance of such concepts as minimum-delay, autocorrelation, and prediction error operators, but it leads to new methods of attack. One significant result is that the lattice can be used adaptively, and it exhibits rapid convergence and is relatively insensitive to round-off errors. The use of the lattice is a prime example of designing engineering structures as counterparts to naturally occurring phenomena (wave propagation in the sedimentary layers of the earth).

Chapter 4 treats the subject of polynomials with matrix coefficients. This material forms the mathematical basis for much of the theory of multichannel time series analysis. This same material is also used in modern control theory for the analysis of multiple-input, multiple-output systems. Chapter 5 presents methods of digital filtering and spectral analysis of multichannel time series with computer programs. Chapter 6 gives an extensive treatment of multichannel Wiener signal enhancement, filtering, and prediction together with the necessary programs.

All the computer programs in this book are written in FORTRAN IV. Because the programs are well documented a user can readily modify them to fit other computing needs. In fact, many significant results have been obtained since the original publication of this book in 1967 by people with practical needs who made use of these programs to analyze actual time series data. The best results were obtained when they made full use of their own individual know-how and ingenuity.

The programs in this book have found wide use in the petroleum industry. In the processing of seismic data one major oil company estimated how many times it made use of subroutine EUREKA, and the number came out to be one million calls each day. However the programs are also being used in many other endeavors. For example, in Chapter 6 it is shown how to predict commodity futures by means of subroutine AUGURY. Many commodity traders have reported that they are using these programs. Also major corporations that deal in commodities use these prediction programs in order to set their buy and sell prices. Previously the setting of these prices was not based on scientific principles, but was done by more or less guess work by the corporate executives. As a result many poor predictions were made with often costly consequences. Today, with the use of these programs savings of millions of dollars are realized each year. Little does one realize that when he buys a chocolate bar or a piece of copper wire that the raw material was priced by the programs in this book.

In the present book, the nonmathematical introduction, the main text, and Appendices 1, 2, and 3 are unchanged from the way they first were printed in 1967. In the present printing we have added seven additional Appendices (Appendices 4 through 10). The reason for this new printing is that the book is still in demand, and it does have a place in serving people who are entering the exciting world of computers and their applications to the sciences. However we would like to report that Professor Jack Cohen and Professor Frank Hagin of the University of Denver, both brilliant mathematicians well-known for their outstanding work in applied mathematics and physics, have joined forces with the present writer in order to write an entirely new book on this subject. An extract of their letter of January 14, 1982 reads as follows:

> We are very pleased that you are interested in having us help with a revision of ''Multichannel.'' We really cannot convey in words how excited we are by the prospect of having a joint project with you.
>
> We agree that it is important to be as far-seeing as we can, although it is really hard to keep abreast of, let alone anticipate, new developments in an area as fast moving as the computing field.
>
> Our audience would be quite different from the one that you originally addressed. Aside from its purely scientific content, your work was of great importance in showing that one did not have to be Norbert Wiener to do signal processing and that one did not have to be an ''expert'' to contemplate programming a digital computer in FORTRAN. You and your colleagues have won that battle.

A person many years from now will look back and describe the present time as the beginning of the computer age. In this sense mankind today is only starting to learn how to use and understand the great potential which lies in digital technology. We are in the midst of a digital revolution of epoch proportions and the consequences will be far reaching. We are happy to participate in this development and look forward to hearing about any ideas for the new book from our readers.

Enders A. Robinson
July, 1982

University of Tulsa
Tulsa, Oklahoma 74104

Nonmathematical Introduction

Scientific models

In time series analysis the dualism between observation and theory is recognized as fundamental. This dualism between empirical evidence and theoretical analysis is embodied in the notion of the scientific model. To develop a model it is necessary to simplify. For example, one may model an industrial firm as a system where the investments by the firm in new equipment and inventory represent the inputs to the system, and the returns on the investments represent the outputs of the system. This idealized economic situation represents a scientific model which makes description and explanation of the actual situation easier. In practice, however, such a simple model has limited usefulness, for it is usually the case that there are many competing firms, and as a result the interactions between firms must be taken into account. Hence, an ensemble of different models is required to handle the complex situations encountered in economics. Thus, the approach of scientific model-building must be pluralistic; there can never be a unique, all-embracing scientific model. The variety of types of scientific models is almost unlimited for the situations encountered in time series analysis.

A scientific model of necessity must always be a compromise between simplicity and reality. It is interesting to look at some of the factors which have influenced the evolutionary trends of the models used in time series analysis. The most important factor, of course, has been the development of statistical communication theory, which dates from the work of Norbert Wiener at M.I.T. during World War II. At one time, statistical communication theory was regarded as a potential unifier which would provide solutions of problems within many scientific disciplines in terms common to each of them. However, this ideal unification has not materialized since unifying principles have the tendency to become highly specialized subjects in themselves, thereby compounding rather than easing the problems of bridging many scientific problem areas with common methods. However, this tendency is not the only difficulty associated with unification. The most important one is that despite the similarities which exist among many scientific fields, fundamental differences also exist. Hence a detailed understanding of the physical, economic, or biological processes within each field always remains an important requirement. As a result, the models must take these factors into account, and hence we see that we must introduce meaningful subject-matter information into models in order to account for the problems we face in any scientific field.

New ideas take the form of new scientific models. There are verbal models, mathematical models, and physical models. A verbal model is simply a word description of the scientific situation. A mathematical model is one that reduces essential features of the situation into the form of mathematical equations. A physical model is a physical apparatus which represents an analog scaled-down version of the actual situation. Physical models have a long history in the sciences. In the past, mathematical models of necessity were greatly simplified. However, with the advent of the digital computer, the range of possibilities of mathematical models is greatly enhanced. No longer will mathematical models be essentially theoretical. With the large memory capacity of the new generation of computers, it is now possible to build mathematical models which indeed make use of the large body of empirical evidence which exists as data in any science. In the future, we can expect mathematical models to represent in a more equitable way both theory and observation, that is, both theoretical analysis and empirical evidence. In this way, the gap between theory and observation can be bridged, thereby forming a framework to support new ideas and new methods.

In making scientific interpretations, we are confronted in many cases not with direct problems, but with indirect or inverse problems. For example, in the physical sciences we are faced with the problems of inferring the location and properties of some unknown physical mass such as a submarine or buried ore body from physical measurements which can only be taken at a distance. In the biological sciences, we wish to determine things such as the state of health of the internal organisms of an astronaut from measurements which can be conveniently monitored while he is engaged in his normal duties. In economics, we wish to make inferences about the economic forces from measured prices and quantities. It is due to this inverse nature of many scientific problems that scientific interpretation is difficult. Knowledge and experience in addition to numerical data are needed to achieve meaningful solutions. In order to attack the interpretation problem a flexible mathematical model is required whose outcomes can be readily tested against the measurements provided by direct observation. If the agreement is not good, then the model must be altered until the values do correspond at least to within satisfactory limits. The model becomes useful when it is able to reproduce the more significant results of the actual situation. However, it may be possible to find other models which work just as accurately. At this point, any attempts to resolve the ambiguity must lie in bringing in new information. In particular, meaningful and relevant practical information should be incorporated because the final model will be interpreted in practical terms.

In summary, a scientific model represents the embodiment of theory and observation. Of necessity, it must be a compromise between simplicity and reality. There will never be one all-encompassing model; there must be many kinds of models to fit different situations. Above all, a model must incorporate practical information because the final interpretation will be based on practical needs.

Digital data processing

Why have we discussed scientific models? The reason is that a model is required before there can be any data processing. The best data processing is that which is done with the best model. Data processing of scientific evidence to achieve practical ends, therefore, needs good scientific modeling.

In this book, we are concerned with time series data, that is, data which is ordered in time. Moreover, we are concerned with digital processing of the time series data, that is, processing which is done by a digital computer.

Let us now take an example from geophysics to make these concepts more meaningful. The word *convolution* means "folding." When a signal is passed into a filter, the output is given as the convolution of the signal with the impulse response function of the filter. Likewise, when a signal is passed into the earth, the output seismogram represents the convolution of the input signal with the response function of the earth. The word *deconvolution* means "unfolding." A deconvolution operator is one which produces the inverse operation to the given convolution operator. The objective in deconvolving seismic evidence with a computer, then, is to unfold it from its original heterogeneous complexities into its simpler components so that the interpreter can see the basic structuring of the data. Thus, a deconvolution operator is one which separates specific results produced on a seismogram by earth transmission effects and data collection systems from pertinent information as to deep-reflected energy which is needed in making the geologic interpretations. For example, system deconvolution would separate out effects of the data collection systems, reverberation deconvolution would separate out the effects of reverberations, and multiple reflection deconvolution would separate out the multiple reflections from the primary reflections. In the broad sense, deconvolution may be defined as any operation that unfolds the recorded data in such a way that it separates redundant or unwanted information from desired or wanted information.

In this context, we see that the problem of deconvolving data differs from the classical problem of separating signal from noise. For example, in the classic radar situation, the received signal is masked by noise. This noise is white noise generated within the receiver and, as such, is completely independent of the signal. Hence, in such a case filters are designed to destroy as much of the noise as possible, for the noise contains no useful information about the radar environment. In contrast, nearly all the information recorded on a seismic trace represents meaningful information about the total seismic environment, and the problem is to unfold the recorded seismogram into simpler components so that an interpreter can see which energy is due to primary events and which is due to ghost events, multiple events, or to other causes. The digital processing method of deconvolution represents a way of unfolding this information.

In a similar argument, one can say that nearly all the data recorded in economic time series of share prices, commodity futures, quantities, and other economic indicators represent *meaningful* information. The problem then is to unfold this data into simpler components which can be interpreted. Nearly all the measurements taken on a human body represent valid information; the problem is to deconvolve the time series data into less complex components for medical interpretation.

Deconvolution

The concept of deconvolution is a key idea which underlies many of the developments in this book. For this reason, we want to discuss further the over-all concept in this nonmathematical introduction. For any process of deconvolution, we must construct a model which takes into account both known factors and unknown factors. The known factors are used in deterministic aspects of the model, and the unknown factors are incorporated in statistical aspects of the model. Let us now describe a basic model. The desired information consists of primary events or innovations. These innovations are unpredictable; they occur at random times and with random amplitudes. Attached to each innovation is a response. The response represents the reverberations or repercussions generated by the innovation, and each response persists over a relatively long time span before it damps out. The recorded time series consists of the sum of all the primary events with their attached responses. Because the primary events are not well separated in time, the high degree of overlap among the various responses completely masks out the onset of each primary event. As a result, a study of the recorded time series does not reveal the separate events, but only shows a highly mixed conglomeration of all the events which cannot be interpreted.

We have now described a model which generates time series data. These data represent useful information, but, as such, they are not in a form which can be interpreted. In order to interpret the data we must unfold or deconvolve the data. The basic problem then is to unfold the time series so as to separate the primary events from the reverberations. Separately these components can be interpreted, for they represent the underlying structure which makes up the recorded time series.

For example, with the process of deconvolution one can answer questions such as these: Is a certain movement of economic prices the fortuitous result of several responses adding together in phase, or does it represent some new primary event? From all the recorded data on the human body, how can we sort out any essential changes in the human state of health from effects due to previous conditions? In radar and sonar, how can environmental reverberation and clutter be separated from the true signal?

Redundancy

How does one devise a deconvolution process for the given model? In principle, every deconvolution process is based upon the cornerstone of information theory, namely, the concept of redundancy.

To bring these ideas out more clearly, let us make a small digression into the realm of information theory. The measure of information in information theory is called *entropy*. The ratio of the entropy per symbol to the maximum value it could have while still restricted to the same symbols is called the *relative entropy* ratio. One minus the relative entropy ratio is called the *redundancy*. Thus, the redundancy represents the factor by which the average lengths of messages are increased beyond the minimum necessary to transmit the desired information. *The fundamental theorem of information theory* states: A source of information can be encoded in such a way that, when transmitted over a noisy channel, the rate of transmission may approach the channel capacity with the probability of error as small as desired. This theorem is based upon the use of redundancy as a "noise-reducing" mechanism.

Let us explain. One way of reducing errors due to noise is to repeat the signal. For example, telegraph companies usually repeat numbers and names, and the sender himself sometimes repeats critical words. More generally, in many scientific situations, the symbols or parts that make up the message are linked among themselves. This linking makes the symbols partly redundant and thereby provides a check on the accuracy of the message as it is received. For this reason, every code has some overlap or redundancy. That is, its symbols do not all add their full weight of innovation, but instead they add a certain amount of internal confirmation. In this way, the reliability or accuracy of transmission over a noisy channel can be increased by means of redundancy. The source is encoded in a redundant manner, which in effect means that parts of a message tell us things already partly known. The receiver can then make use of this redundancy in order to predict the nearby succeeding parts of a message to a considerable extent. As a result, the actual reception of a message gives partly a verification or correction of the preceding prediction, in addition to any completely new ideas.

As we have just seen, redundancy is the partial or complete repetition of message content. Redundancy forms the basis upon which encoding methods can be devised to increase the transmission rate up to the channel capacity. That is, we can approach the absolute capacity of a channel, to any tolerance we fix, by putting our messages in a code whose redundancies are appropriate to the form of the noise. The redundancies show up upon reception and allow us to correct all of the errors except for the given proportion. Hence, redundancy gives the code a structure or skeleton which resists the distortion of its individual symbols. Many of the engineering aspects of information theory are concerned with building systems in which adequate redundancy is incorporated into the system in order to overcome noise.

On the other hand, in many observational systems, nature itself has built enough redundancy into the system in order to overcome noise. However, this redundancy causes so much overlapping and mutual interference that is is not possible to interpret the raw records provided by nature. The process of deconvolution in effect separates the new information from the redundant information as time progresses. This separation makes interpretation possible, for both kinds of information (new and redundant) have value in understanding the basic mechanisms involved. The new information consists of the primary events or innovations, and the redundant information the attached responses or repercussions.

Minimum delay model as a basis for deconvolution

As we have seen, a model should represent both theory and observation. It is the judicious combination of both theory and observation which makes deconvolution possible.

First, let us consider theory. By theoretical reasoning, we must arrive at some partial knowledge of the innovations and the reverberations. For example, the model for seismic deconvolution is what is called a *minimum-delay model*. The model is based upon two theoretical hypotheses, namely:

(1) The deterministic hypothesis that the reverberation attached to each primary event has the same minimum-delay shape.
(2) The statistical hypothesis that the primary events are randomly spaced in time and have random amplitudes.

The deterministic hypothesis is based upon the fact that the reverberations are caused by the vibrating physical system made up of fixed geological layers near the surface. In Chapter 3, we show that wave propagation through a layered system produces a minimum-delay response. Since each primary event passes through the same layered system at the surface, each has the same minimum-delay response attached to it. The statistical hypothesis is based on the fact that the primary events are caused by reflections from deep geological beds within the earth. These deep layers were laid down in geologic time in an unsystematic way, and thus the primary events produced by them are randomly spaced in time and amplitude.

Next, observation must be combined with theory. The empirical evidence is in the form of the time series, namely, the seismic trace. The autocorrelation of the time series is computed. The autocorrelation is a method of averaging which averages out, or destroys, the unsystematic elements of the time series but preserves features of the systematic elements. The features preserved are those contained in the autocorrelation (or, equivalently, the amplitude spectrum) of the reverberating system. We must now combine this empirical amplitude spectrum with the theoretical minimum-phase spectrum. This essential step is possible because of the minimum-delay nature of the model. Hence, using both theory and observation together, we are able to reconstruct the minimum-delay reverberating system. Having the reverberation waveform, we can then design the deconvolution operator which removes the reverberations from the seismic trace; the output is the deconvolved seismic trace consisting of the primary events only.

Such models upon which deconvolution processes are based can be only approximately true; however, the existing models are sufficiently accurate to make the deconvolution processes based upon them worthwhile in an economic sense. For a time, people will be satisfied with these results, but as time goes on, we will want to develop better processes. These better processes must be based on broader models. Hopefully, our expanded knowledge will allow us to push forward the frontier between the deterministic and the statistical; that is, some factors which we had to treat statistically before can in the future be reduced to deterministic analysis, and factors which were completely neglected before can in the future be at least encompassed within some statistical framework. As we do this, our whole frame of reference will become larger.

For example, in seismic interpretation, a geophysicist in the 1920's looked at a single trace at a time, then at a record of up to twenty-four traces in the 1930's and 1940's, then at cross sections of single coverage in the 1950's, and cross sections of multiple coverage in the 1960's. Now in the mapping of salt domes and stratigraphic traps, one must look at three-dimensional models. With this perspective, present-day reverberation-elimination deconvolution acts on a single trace; multiple-elimination deconvolution acts on several traces. We envisage that the next generation of deconvolution procedures will act on entire cross sections and will encompass three spatial dimensions. Factors which appeared random on the basis of a small amount of data will find deterministic explanations, and factors which were missed entirely on the basis of limited data will be amenable to statistical treatment on the basis of the increased data samples. The frontier will be pushed forward. The new data processing techniques must explain local space-time effects in terms of a regional model; this regional model in turn must make full use of all the pertinent information which can be derived from the data.

Time structure of data

Let us now look at the time aspects of data processing. A time series is a function of time, which can be either historical time or real time. Associated with the concept of time is the concept of prediction, for prediction represents the concept of searching for a time structuring or ordering of events which occur as time progresses. Originally it was felt that although the problem of prediction is important in many branches of science that involve real time records, such as meteorology, it is not a significant problem in the analysis of historical time records. That is, it was held that the concept of prediction does not really enter into the problem of the analysis of a time series recorded sometime in the past. As a result, it was almost universally believed that any investigation of the predictive properties of such time series would not be fruitful. However, this seeming disadvantage has been turned into an advantage by refocusing attention from the predictions to the prediction errors. If we look at the space-time complex, we see that the new information entering a time series as time progresses is from the primary (innovation) events, and hence unpredictable from the previous events. Reverberations, repercussions, and multiple reflections, however, are predictable events resulting from primary events already accounted for. Hence, a prediction-error operator represents a means of separating the unpredictable new events from the predictable reverberations, repercussions, and multiples. In Section 2.10, we discuss the prediction-error operator in the form of the deconvolution operator commonly used for the elimination of reverberations on seismic traces; however, much more general prediction-error operators can be devised to sort out new information from prior information on time series in many branches of science. This unfolding of information into the form of the dynamic structure as well as the series of innovations ordered in time and space is the essence of the deconvolution process. Deconvolution is based on the concept that new information, or innovations, are not predictable from the past and, hence, are exhibited as prediction errors. The best deconvolution of data is done from the best model, that is, the model which represents in the best way the scientific situation under consideration. The best final interpretation results from the best recognition of the validity of the model that is revealed after the unfolding process.

We want to use the term deconvolution in its larger sense, namely, as the process of unfolding the information on a time series into the predictable components such as reverberations, repercussions, and multiples and into the unpredictable components which represent the successive innovations. The next significant item in the deconvolution process which we want to discuss may be called the time-space scale of the deconvolution. On the one hand, we have deconvolution in the small where we consider at one time only a single time series. On the other hand, we have deconvolution in the large where we consider at one time ensembles of time series produced on a regional scale.

Deconvolution in the large

Let us give a specific example taken from seismology of deconvolution in the large. Let our model be the normal-incidence synthetic seismogram which includes all multiples, as described in Chapter 3.

This synthetic seismogram is based upon a parallel layered model of the earth in which plane waves travel along ray paths normal to the interfaces between the layers. The solution of the wave equation at each interface leads to the definition of a reflection coefficient associated with that interface. The reflection coefficient has several properties well known to every geophysicist. The most characteristic property is that the reflection coefficient physically cannot exceed unity in magnitude. If the reflection coefficient is equal to unity in magnitude, then the interface is a perfect reflector, and no transmission takes place through the interface. The best example of such a situation is provided by the interface representing the surface of the water in marine exploration; the reflection coefficient of the water surface is -1, or nearly so. In land exploration, the ground-to-air interface reflects nearly 100% of the energy coming up to it. Other interfaces can have high reflection coefficients; for example, it is not unusual for the base of the surface weathered layer to have a reflection coefficient of 0.5. Some interfaces, of course, have low reflection coefficients. Hence, our model is made up of a sequence of parallel interfaces where each has a reflection coefficient associated with it. Hence, in the discrete layer case, the reflection amplitudes are determined by the reflection coefficients.

Let us now consider the case of a layered system for which the upper interface is a perfect reflector. Such a case is realized in marine seismic exploration, for then the first layer is the water layer, and the surface of the water acts as a perfect reflector. Let us assume that the source is a single positive spike. This source results in a seismic trace recorded at the surface which represents all direct reflections and multiple reflections resulting from the layered system at depth.

As shown in Chapter 3, this synthetic trace itself may be regarded as one-half of an autocorrelation function. Also, from Section 2.8, we know that a prediction-error operator, or so-called deconvolution operator, of any length may be computed from any given autocorrelation function. Hence, we can compute deconvolution operators of various lengths directly from the recorded seismic trace.

Let us now take a seismic trace and, treating it as an autocorrelation function, compute deconvolution operators from it of successively increasing length. For example, if our discrete time spacing were 4 msec, we would compute deconvolution operators of length 4 msec, 8, 12, 16, 20, 24, 28, etc., up to, say, 4000 msec long. As we show in Chapter 3, we may regard this ensemble of deconvolution operators of successively increasing lengths as a means of portraying the structure of the layered earth. For example, if we convolve the deconvolution operator of length, say, 600 msec, with the trace, we obtain as output the wave motion at depth 300 msec. If we convolve the deconvolution operator of length 1400 msec with the trace, we obtain as output the wave motion at depth 700 msec. Hence, by this deconvolution process, we can obtain a three-dimensional picture of the wave motion in the earth from the two-dimensional observations at the surface. The potential value of such processes of deconvolution in the large lies in the possibility of obtaining a very detailed picture of the subsurface structure (in three dimensions) from observations taken at the surface (in two dimensions).

Thus, the computer has allowed the scientist to refocus his attention on the entire process of prediction, namely, to find time structures along time series by unfolding them into their components and seeing how the time events interlock and fit together.

Computers: digital and environmental

Today the working scientist in the normal course of commercial work is exposed to large amounts of data, and, in fact, his interpretations of these data represent research of great theoretical as well as practical value. However, in order to do meaningful research, one must have time—time to think and time to try new ideas. Usually time is strictly limited though, and hence the scientist must extract as much information as he can from the data in the limited time available to him. However, such working under a constant deadline often defeats the ultimate objective, for vital information might be missed or misinterpreted simply because of the economic pressure of getting the job done quickly. As a result, if scientists are to fullfill their expanding role, they must, of necessity, expand in number as well as talent.

Scientists are continually expanding in talent, for today a scientist can do things that were impossible just a few years ago. In the next few years, the scientist will expand his capabilities many-fold over what it is today by the expanded use of machines: data-generating machines, recording machines, computing machines, and data-display machines. This is indeed a stimulating prospect and one to encourage new people into science, thereby expanding the number of scientists as well. Until recently, most scientific data were recorded by fixed equipment, so the scientist was completely dependent in his results on the analog equipment supplied to him. Except by an involved trial-and-error process in which new equipment was designed over the years, the scientist had very limited control over the type of operation he could apply to the data in any given instance. With the advent of digital recording equipment, the scientist can now record a much more detailed band of information; he can then digitally operate on this information with a general purpose digital computer. As a result, he can design operations on the basis of the data at hand and on his present needs and ideas; he can alter or change his methods in a matter of minutes by a programming change; he can incorporate fresh ideas into the analysis and see the results immediately.

At present, this ideal situation has not fully materialized, for usually there is still a significant time gap (the so-called *turn-around time*) between the original data collection and the final interpretation in most scientific work. However, with the new generation of computers and with such programming advances as time-sharing and the new computer languages, it is within our grasp to overcome the problem of turn-around time in most cases.

The computing machine will have a tremendous impact on science. Computer science represents an entirely new scientific discipline. Computer science is the science of the future. The computer by its handling of great masses of information allows man to spend more of his time on the edge of the unknown and thus lets him apply his unique talents to the field of the unknown. This ability of the computer to save time and manipulate large amounts of information has given new scope to the application of man's talents.

In this sense, the computer must be incorporated in the total environment of science. As an example, again taken from seismology, the earth itself can be used as a computer. Through the use of high-powered electro-mechanical vibrators, signals of specific types can be impressed in the earth. By the use of directional detectors, signals can be picked up, and coded signals can then be fed back into the earth under the control of a digital computer on the surface, all in real time. Hence, the earth itself becomes a computing machine which can effect the deconvolution process as the time series are recorded. Thus, we can use the earth itself to analyze the data from the earth. In this way, we can utilize seismic recording systems more efficiently; our equipment will not be idle a good part of the time as it is now, but will be used at great efficiency by incorporating the environment itself into our computing system. In the biomedical sciences, the human body itself will be used as a computer under control of digital computers, and thereby the final data recorded will already be deconvolved and hence in a form ready for interpretation. Thus, man can make his enviroment a computer which in turn is linked to the digital computer. Energy is recycled into the environmental computer in accordance with the needs determined by sampling the original energy return from the environment. It is possible for man to see the results of his own ideas at the time of recording by such use of the environment as a computer. The information from the environment can be unfolded or de-convolved during the recording process itself, for man can link the digital computer to the environmental computer to acquire such information.

In closing this introduction, let us be careful to point out that such use of computers does not mean that the machine decides for us all the vital decisions to be made, for at the present time it would be very difficult or im-possible to provide the machine with all the information which is germane to such decisions. The chief use of the machine is to prepare the information and to display it to the human interpreter who then incorporates into the decision such highly significant information as only the human mind has available. The logical development of such a use of the computer is as follows. As more and more of the unknown factors become better understood, they can be incorporated into the machine programs, and hence the scientific interpreter will always be able to concentrate his attention on the unknown factors. The computer will be used as a machine to always keep the scientist at the fore-front of human knowledge, for it is at the edge of the unknown that the human mind has the comparative advantage over the computer and will produce the significant contributions.

Contents

Multichannel Time Series
Analysis with Digital
Computer Programs

1

Some Basic Computer Programs

1.1 Introduction

There are essentially an unlimited number of approaches to signal analysis. Each approach has certain merits; in the final analysis we do not want to be restricted to any given approach but want to make use of a variety of different ones.

The approach which we want to develop falls under what may be called multichannel time series analysis. This assumes that the signals of interest will appear simultaneously on several different channels. These signals will not be independent of each other but will be interrelated or correlated; this cross correlation is regarded as a major factor in the understanding and analysis of the signals. Also it is assumed that the signals will be digitized so that they appear not as continuous functions but as a discrete series of numbers ordered in time, that is, as multichannel time series. These multichannel time series will be stored in the memory of a high-speed digital computer; the computer will be programmed to act on this data for specific purposes; the output will then be used for the description, explanation, or control of the biological, physical, or behavioral process under investigation.

In this monograph we restrict ourselves to specific types of operations which can be programmed in the computer to process the data. Thus we are concerned with only part of one step in a chain of operations from the initial measurements to the final results. However, an exposition of this area at this time, it is hoped, will help other investigators understand some of the basic data processing methods which are available and what information they can extract.

1.2 Stimulus-response: single-channel case

One of the basic concepts used in time series analysis is that of stimulus-response. If we stimulate a biological, physical, or behavioral system, a certain response will occur. This response will necessarily follow the stimulus in time; that is, no response can occur prior to its stimulus. This property is described by saying that the system is causal (or physically realizable). The response is said to be one-sided (in time), for it is necessarily zero for all times up to the initiation of the stimulus.

A few examples should help to clarify this point. We often use simple numerical examples with only a few points; from these one can extrapolate the basic ideas to more complicated physical situations.

Suppose that a unit spike impulse is applied to an input channel of some biological or physical system, and the response resulting from this input is measured on an output channel. This output is called the impulse response of the system for the given input and output channels. For example, suppose a unit spike is imposed on input channel 1; this spike would look like the following:

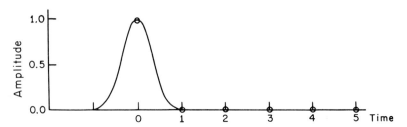

Fig. 1. A "unit spike" as might be observed in an actual situation.

The resulting response on output channel 1 might be

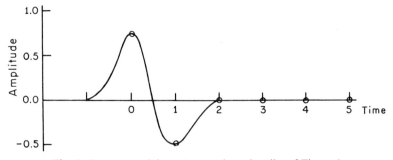

Fig. 2. Response of the system to the unit spike of Figure 1.

If we very roughly digitize these two analog signals (as shown by the circles), we would get the following digital signals. The unit spike input would be represented by a unity at time zero; that is, the input could be represented as

$$(1, 0, 0, 0, \ldots).$$

$$\uparrow \ \uparrow \ \uparrow \ \uparrow$$

Discrete time: 0 1 2 3

The output would be represented by an amplitude of 0.75 at time 0 and an amplitude of -0.50 at time 1; that is, the output could be represented as

$$(0.75, \quad -0.50, 0, 0, \ldots).$$

$$\uparrow \qquad \uparrow \ \uparrow \ \uparrow$$

Discrete time: 0   1 2 3

More compactly we can represent the output as simply the 2-term row vector

$$(0.75, \quad -0.50).$$

At first glance, this 2-term case seems somewhat trivial, for in most situations we would want to digitize with closer spacing so that the output would consist of a series of many discrete terms. However, as it turns out, it is very valuable to study carefully such simple 2-term responses, as many of the basic principles of multichannel time series analysis can be illustrated by such simple cases.

Let us look at the 2-term response

$$(0.75, \quad -0.50).$$

$$\uparrow \qquad \uparrow$$

Time: 0   1

We see that in this case the first coefficient is larger in magnitude than the second coefficient; that is,

$$|0.75| > |-0.50|.$$

In other words, the energy of the response is greater at the beginning and tapers off at the end. We expect this type of response in many physical situations. Thus we give a name to this type of response. We say that a 2-term response is *minimum delay*, provided the magnitude of its initial term is greater than the magnitude of its final term.

On the other hand, suppose we had a system whose impulse response is the 2-term signal

$$(-0.10, \quad 0.80).$$

Here we see that the magnitude of the first term, namely 0.10, is less than the magnitude of the second, namely, 0.80. In this case we see that the energy has been delayed, for most of the energy is associated with the last term. Such a 2-term signal is called a *maximum-delay* signal.

1.3 The z-transform

At this point it is useful to introduce the concept of z-transform. The z-transform of a digital signal, say,

$$(6, 7, 4) ,$$

$$\uparrow \uparrow \uparrow$$

Time: 0 1 2

is defined as the polynomial formed from the signal, in this case,

$$6 + 7z + 4z^2 .$$

The letter z is chosen as the variable used to define the polynomial. The coefficients of the digital signal become the coefficients of the polynomial, and the relative times become the powers to which z is raised. Thus the term $4z^2$ represents the fact that the signal has amplitude 4 at time 2.

Any polynomial can be factored into a product of binomials. Thus the polynomial given above can be factored as

$$6 + 7z + 4z^2 = (2 + z)(3 + 4z) .$$

Each binomial represents a 2-term signal. Thus the binomial $2 + z$ represents the signal (2, 1), and the binomial $3 + 4z$ represents the signal (3, 4).

It is now possible to extend the concepts of minimum delay and maximum delay to signals of any length as follows. Factor the z-transform of the signal into binomials. If each binomial is minimum delay, then the signal is called *minimum delay*. If each binomial is maximum delay, then the signal is called *maximum delay*. If there is a mixture of minimum-delay and maximum-delay binomials, then the signal is called *mixed delay*. In our example, the 2-term signal (2, 1) is minimum delay, and the 2-term signal (3, 4) is maximum delay; hence the signal (6, 7, 4) is mixed delay.

1.4 Stimulus-response: multichannel case

So far we have only considered one input channel and one output channel. Let us now consider the case of 2 input and 2 output channels. For the purposes of discussion, let us invent the following simple example. The responses to a unit spike on input channel 1 are the 2-term signal (2, 1) on output channel 1 and the 2-term signal (1, 0) on output channel 2. The responses to a unit spike on input channel 2 are the 2-term signal (0, 1) on output channel 1 and the 2-term signal (6, 1) on output channel 2. These responses may be summarized in the following matrix:

	input channel 1	input channel 2
output channel 1	(2, 1)	(0, 1)
output channel 2	(1, 0)	(6, 1)

If we look at these responses separately, we see that (2, 1), (1, 0), and (6, 1) are each minimum delay, whereas the response (0, 1) is maximum delay. We not only want to look at the responses separately, but we want to look at the response as a whole. In other words, we want to look at this multichannel situation as one integrated system.

The z-transform of the whole system is the matrix formed from the z-transform of each of the separate responses. Thus the z-transform of the above system is

$$\begin{bmatrix} 2 + z & z \\ 1 & 6 + z \end{bmatrix}.$$

This is a matrix with polynomial entries.

We ask the question whether or not this multichannel response is minimum delay. Three out of the four elements in its matrix-valued z-transform, namely $2 + z$, 1, $6 + z$, represent minimum-delay binomials; the other one, z, represents a maximum-delay binomial. Hence we might be tempted to say that this multichannel response is mixed delay. However, we must restrain ourselves from looking at each matrix element separately. Instead, as it turns out, we must look at the *determinant* of this matrix-valued z-transform. Its determinant is

$$(2 + z)(6 + z) - (1)(z),$$

which equals

$$12 + 8z + z^2 - z$$

or

$$12 + 7z + z^2.$$

This determinant is a polynomial; this polynomial represents the 3-term signal

$$(12, 7, 1).$$

If we factor this polynomial, we obtain

$$12 + 7z + z^2 = (3 + z)(4 + z).$$

The binomials $3 + z$ and $4 + z$ represent the minimum-delay signals (3, 1) and (4, 1), respectively; hence the determinant $12 + 7z + z^2$ represents a minimum-delay response. We therefore say that this multichannel system is minimum delay. That is, *a multichannel response is called minimum delay whenever the determinant of its z-transform represents a single-channel minimum-delay response.*

Likewise, a multichannel response is called maximum delay whenever the determinant of its z-transform represents a single-channel maximum-delay response. A multichannel response is called mixed delay whenever the determinant of its z-transform represents a single-channel mixed-delay response.

1.5 Subroutines

A computer program represents a plan of activities to be carried out by a digital computer where these activities are structured according to certain motivating factors so as to have logical completeness. Especially useful in the structuring of large or complicated programs is the concept of the *subroutine*. A subroutine can be used, or called, by the main program as many times as needed. Often subroutines will call other subroutines, so that several levels of subroutines are utilized. At the lowest levels there are certain basic subroutines which perform mathematical operations that are used in many different situations; at the highest levels there are master subroutines designed to fulfill complex but specialized tasks. It is our programming philosophy to keep each and every subroutine very short, that is, to require in most cases that a subroutine contains no more than about 20 lines of Fortran coding. Because they are short, these subroutines are almost self-explanatory in that they can be understood with only a small amount of description. The subroutines, then, are the basic units, or building blocks, in the make-up of computer programs.

An *array* is a sequence of memory words, or cells, having consecutive addresses; the length of the array is the number of words. The Fortran IV computer language provides for manipulating values as elements of an array. This provision has many advantages, and in particular makes the Fortran language especially powerful for time series analysis. By the use of array methods, long and cumbersome time series computations may be condensed in a few powerful Fortran statements.

An *identifier*, or *variable name*, is a string of letters and decimal digits, the first of which must be a letter. Five examples of identifiers are

X, B, X2, TEMP, MATRAN.

Identifiers are used in the Fortran language to name variables as well as subprograms, subprogram arguments, and COMMON blocks. For example, in the statement

SUBROUTINE MAINE(N,A,B)

the subroutine name MAINE and the subroutine arguments N, A, and B are all identifiers.

Information that is operated on in an object program during execution is called *data*. Each *data item* can be classified as one of six *types*, namely integer, real, double precision, complex, logical, and Hollerith. (Hollerith data are a special form of integer data.)

A *data item* may be either a constant or the value of a scalar variable. Constants and scalar variables are called *scalar quantities*.

A *constant* is a data item that cannot change during the execution of a program. A *scalar variable*, like a constant, denotes a single data item. This data item is called the value of the scalar variable. Unlike a constant, however, a scalar variable may take on more than one value during the execution of a program. The set of values that a scalar variable may take on is restricted to one data type.

A *constant* is referenced by naming its value; that is, its representation is both its name and its value. For example, -29 and 862 are *integer constants*, 5.0 and $-7.3E5$ are *real constants*, $562.2\,D-2$ is a *double precision constant*, $(5.6, -1.)$ is a *complex constant*, .TRUE. is a *logical constant*, and 4HTIME is a *Hollerith constant*.

Reference is made to a *scalar variable* by a name, which may be a simple name or a subscripted name. We discuss the naming of scalar variables shortly.

An *array variable*, or *array*, denotes an ordered set of data items, all of the same data type. This set of data items is called the value of the array variable. Like a scalar variable, an array variable may take on more than one value during the execution of a program. The set of values that any array variable may take on is restricted to one data type. Associated with an array variable is the property of dimension; for example, we may have a one-dimensional array, a two-dimensional array, etc. Reference is made to an *array* by a simple name.

An *array element* is a scalar variable that denotes a specified data item of an array. Reference is made to an *array element* by a subscripted name.

Let us now describe the naming of scalar variables, arrays, and array elements. A *simple name* is an identifier that refers to a scalar variable or an array. For example, suppose that we have the scalar variable m and the one-dimensional array variable given by the ordered set $(x_1, x_2, \ldots, x_n)$. We could use the identifier M to name the scalar variable m and the identifier X to name the array $(x_1, x_2, \ldots, x_n)$, as depicted in the table:

Name of variable	*Variable*
M	m
X	$(x_1, x_2, \ldots, x_n)$.

Throughout this book we present various subroutines; in our description of these subroutines we give the correspondence between the mathematical variables used in the text and the identifiers (i.e., the names of these variables) used in the Fortran programs. Ideally we should construct a table, as the one given above; for practical reasons, however, it is simpler to express the relationship between the names and the variables simply as

$$M = m$$
$$X = (x_1, x_2, \ldots, x_n).$$

Also in our description of these subroutines we give numerical examples, such as the case when the scalar variable m is equal to 5, and the array variable $(x_1, x_2, \ldots, x_n)$ is equal to (2, 4, 6, 8, 10). Ideally we should write the table as

Name of variable	Value of variable
M	5
X	(2, 4, 6, 8, 10),

but we will simply write

$$M = 5$$
$$X = (2, 4, 6, 8, 10).$$

Thus we want to emphasize that the equal signs appearing in expressions such as $M = m$ or $M = 5$ *in our comments describing Fortran programs* are not the same as the equal signs used in other ways, such as the equality sign in a mathematical equation, or as the replacement operator in a Fortran replacement statement *within the program itself.*

A *subscripted name* is used to refer to an element of an array. A subscripted name is made up of the array identifier followed by a subscript. The subscript of a one-dimensional array assumes the form (s), and the subscript of a two-dimensional array assumes the form (s_1, s_2), where s, s_1, and s_2 are expressions that are evaluated and converted to integers before use. Subscripts are discussed further in Sec. 1.7. Each element in the array is indicated by the order in which it appears in the set of elements which make up the array. The subscripted name X(I) refers to the Ith element of the one-dimensional array X; the subscripted name Y(I,J) refers to the (I, J)th element of the two-dimensional array Y.

Scalar variables and array variables may be of any of the data types of integer, real, double precision, complex, or logical. (There is no such thing as a Hollerith variable, since Hollerith data are a special form of integer data.) If a variable has not been assigned to a particular data type, the following conventions are assumed:

(a) Variables whose names begin with the letters I, J, K, L, M, or N are integer data.

(b) Variables whose names begin with any other letter are real data.

An array is directly appropriate for the storage of a single-channel time series without ambiguity, but an option arises for the storage of a multichannel time series in a single array. There are two modes in which a multichannel time series may be stored in an array, namely the *trace* mode and the *multi-plexed* mode. Suppose we have a two-channel time series, given by

$$
\begin{array}{lcccc}
\text{Channel 1:} & -3 & -1 & 2 & 0 \\
\text{Channel 2:} & 4 & 0 & -5 & -2 \\
\text{Time:} & 1 & 2 & 3 & 4 \,.
\end{array}
$$

In the trace mode we store the tracing of the first channel, namely $-3, -1,$ 2, 0 followed by the tracing of the second channel, namely 4, 0, $-5, -2$; thus the time series in the trace mode would appear in storage as the array

$$ X = (-3, -1, 2, 0, 4, 0, -5, -2). $$

In the multiplexed mode we store the values at time 1 of channel 1 followed by channel 2, the values at time 2 of channel 1 followed by channel 2, etc.; thus the time series in the multiplexed mode would appear in storage as the array

$$ X = (-3, 4, -1, 0, 2, -5, 0, -2). $$

Let the subscript K denote the channel and the subscript I denote the time. Then in the trace mode a multichannel time series would be referred to as the two-dimensional array $X(I,K)$. In the multiplexed mode a multichannel time series would be referred to as the two-dimensional array $X(K,I)$. This notation is in accord with the Fortran convention that although an array may have several dimensions, it is placed in storage as a linear string. This linear string is made up of the array elements in sequence (from the low-address storage toward the high-address storage). The sequence is such that the left-most dimension varies most rapidly, the next left-most dimension varies the next most rapidly, and so forth. In standard mathematical usage, a doubly subscripted quantity, say $X(K,I)$, can represent the element of a matrix where the first subscript designates the row of the matrix and the second subscript designates the column of the matrix. Thus the array X written out as a matrix would be

$$
\begin{bmatrix}
X(1,1) & X(1,2) & X(1,3) & X(1,4) \\
X(2,1) & X(2,2) & X(2,3) & X(2,4)
\end{bmatrix},
$$

whereas it would appear in machine storage as the linear sequence (according to the rule that the subscript K varies the most rapidly)

$$ X(1,1), \ X(2,1), \ X(1,2), \ X(2,2), \ X(1,3), \ X(2,3), \ X(1,4), \ X(2,4). $$

That is, the first column of the matrix is stored, followed by the second column, followed by the third column, etc., which is the reason it is said that two-dimensional Fortran arrays are stored "columnwise." It is seen that the relationship between the trace mode and the multiplexed mode for the storage of a multichannel time series is simply one of matrix transpose; that is, the trace mode representation $X(I,K)$ is the matrix transpose of the multiplexed mode representation X(K,I). Because the number of channels is usually different from the number of time points, we cannot assume that the matrices in question will be square. Hence to convert from one mode to the other, we need a subroutine for the transposition of a rectangular matrix. Moreover, because ordinarily we want to conserve machine storage space, our subroutine for matrix transpose should be one which transposes the rectangular matrix on top of itself. Such a subroutine is subroutine MATRAN, standing for matrix transpose, which is described in Sec. 1.10.

1.6 Dimension statements

The DIMENSION statement defines the dimensions of an array variable. It is a nonexecutable specification statement. A single DIMENSION statement may be used to dimension any number of arrays. A typical example would be

DIMENSION A(50), B(3,25), C(40,30,20)

which specifies arrays A, B, and C. The DIMENSION statement must appear in the source program before any executable reference to the arrays, for example, before any subscripted variable names, such as A(31), B(2,4), C(1,1,2), referred to in the program. The array A as dimensioned here is called a one-dimensional array, the array B a two-dimensional array, and the array C a three-dimensional array.

At first glance it might appear that we would always want to represent a multichannel time series as two-dimensional array, where one dimension represents the channel number and the other dimension represents the time index. For example, if we were dealing with a three-channel time series with 100 time points, we could write the statement

DIMENSION X(3,100)

in the main program for storage of this time series in multiplexed form in array X. Such a procedure would be fine provided we always used the main program to analyze three-channel time series with 100 time points. However, such a limitation is too restrictive in those cases where the program is used consecutively for time series with various numbers of channels and various numbers of time points. For example, we might want to use the program to analyze a 5-channel 50 time-point time series, then a 2-channel 350 time-point time series, etc., one after another. In such a case, which is the usual case in most applications, it is expedient to store the time series in a one-dimensional array, and thus write the dimension statement as

DIMENSION X(2000),

where in this case the number 2000 would represent the largest number of data points (= product of the number of channels and the number of time points) in any of the multichannel time series contemplated. The multichannel time series can be stored in this array in either the trace mode or the multiplexed mode, and this storage convention must be borne in mind whenever reference is made to the one-dimensional array X. The reason for using a one-dimensional array for multichannel time series data is that it allows us to always *closely pack* the data. For example, suppose we have the 2-channel 3 time-point time series

$$\text{Channel 1:} \quad -1, \quad -3, \quad -2$$
$$\text{Channel 2:} \quad 5, \quad 7, \quad 6.$$

If we stored this time series in array X dimensioned as

DIMENSION X(3, 5)

where the first dimension refers to channel and the second dimension to time, then the array X would contain the string

$$-1, \quad 5, \quad u, \quad -3, \quad 7, \quad u, \quad -2, \quad 6, \quad u, \quad u, \quad u, \quad u, \quad u, \quad u, \quad u,$$

where the u's denote unspecified entries. We thus see that gaps appear between the numbers, due to the fact that we are storing a 2-channel time series in an array dimensioned for 3 channels. These gaps are troublesome in designing a system of subroutines for time series analysis. As a result, in our work we would dimension the array X as

DIMENSION X(15)

and store the multiplexed time series in closely packed form (i.e., no gaps between data points) as

$$-1, \quad 5, \quad -3, \quad 7, \quad -2, \quad 6, \quad u, \quad u, \quad u, \quad u, \quad u, \quad u, \quad u, \quad u, \quad u,$$

where again the u's denote unspecified entries.

As a specific example, let us write a main program for the inversion of a symmetric matrix. Such a program would make use of a subroutine such as subroutine MAINE. Two versions of this subroutine exist; both versions have the same calling sequence and perform the same computations. The program for version 1 is the following:

```
      SUBROUTINE  MAINE(N,A,B)
C     VERSION 1 OF SUBROUTINE MAINE
C     SYMMETRIC MATRIX INVERSION BY ESCALATOR
C     1METHOD
      DIMENSION  A(2),B(3)
      B(1)=1.0/A(1)
      IF(N.EQ.1) RETURN
      NN=N*N
      DO 5 I=2,NN
```

```
    5 B(I)=0.0
      DO 50  M=2,N
      K=M-1
      MM=M+(M-1)*N
      EK=A(MM)
      DO 10  I=1,K
      DO 10  J=1,K
      MI=M+(I-1)*N
      IJ=I+(J-1)*N
      JM=J+(M-1)*N
   10 EK=EK-A(MI)*B(IJ)*A(JM)
      B(MM)=1.0/EK
      DO 30  I=1,K
      IM=I+(M-1)*N
      DO 20  J=1,K
      IJ=I+(J-1)*N
      JM=J+(M-1)*N
   20 B(IM)=B(IM)-B(IJ)*A(JM)/EK
      MI=M+(I-1)*N
   30 B(MI)=B(IM)
      DO 40  I=1,K
      IM=I+(M-1)*N
      DO 40  J=1,K
      MJ=M+(J-1)*N
      IJ=I+(J-1)*N
   40 B(IJ)=B(IJ)+B(IM)*B(MJ)*EK
   50 CONTINUE
      RETURN
      END
```

The program for version 2 is

```
      SUBROUTINE  MAINE(N,A,B)
C     VERSION 2 OF SUBROUTINE MAINE
C     SYMMETRIC MATRIX INVERSION BY ESCALATOR
C     1METHOD
      DIMENSION  A(N,N),B(N,N)
      DO 5 I=1,N
      DO 5 J=1,N
    5 B(I,J)=0.0
      B(1,1)=1./A(1,1)
      IF(N.EQ.1)  RETURN
      DO 40 M=2,N
```

```
    K = M − 1
    EK = A(M,M)
    DO 10 I = 1,K
    DO 10 J = 1,K
10  EK = EK − A(M,I)*B(I,J)*A(J,M)
    B(M,M) = 1./EK
    DO 30 I = 1,K
    DO 20 J = 1,K
20  B(I,M) = B(I,M) − B(I,J)*A(J,M)/EK
30  B(M,I) = B(I,M)
    DO 40 I = 1,K
    DO 40 J = 1,K
40  B(I,J) = B(I,J) + B(I,M)*B(M,J)*EK
    RETURN
    END
```

(*Note.* Both versions of subroutine MAINE assume that all matrices are closely packed as arbitrary square matrices, that is, without any recognition of the fact that both the given matrix and the inverse are symmetric. By taking advantage of the symmetry, it is possible to omit the elements on one side of the main diagonal and closely pack the remaining elements. We do not do this because usually we will be working with nonsymmetric matrices, and so it is not worth the trouble for our purposes to make special storage provision for those cases when we encounter a symmetric matrix. Nevertheless, it is easy to envision cases when such provision would be very valuable.)

A main program which makes use of subroutine MAINE is

```
    DIMENSION X(400),Y(400)
5   READ 6,M
6   FORMAT(I5)
    MM = M*M
    READ 8,(X(I),I = 1,MM)
8   FORMAT(10F8.3)
    CALL RITE(1,M,M,1,X)
    CALL MAINE(M,X,Y)
    CALL RITE(1,M,M,1,Y)
    GO TO 5
    END
```

We may use either version of subroutine MAINE with the main program; it does not matter in the final result. Both versions of subroutine MAINE have the same arguments, namely N,A,B, and both versions assume that the matrices A and B are closely packed (and stored columnwise in the usual

Fortran manner). The call statement for subroutine MAINE which appears in the main program is

CALL MAINE(M, X, Y).

The subroutine inputs are

$$M = \text{order of matrix}$$
$$X = \text{matrix}$$

and the subroutine output in

$$Y = \text{inverse matrix}.$$

In examining version 1 of subroutine MAINE, we find the dimension statement

DIMENSION A(2), B(3),

whereas version 2 has the dimension statement

DIMENSION A(N,N), B(N,N).

That is, version 1 has A and B as one-dimensional arrays, whereas version 2 has A and B as two-dimensional arrays. Because arrays A and B appear as subroutine arguments, these arrays are necessarily *dummy arrays;* that is, arrays A and B are not actual arrays. A dummy array, say A, does not actually occupy any storage space in the subroutine; instead, the subroutine assumes that the argument X [that is, X(1)] supplied in the calling statement

CALL MAINE(M,X,Y)

defines the first element of the actual array to be used by the subroutine and calculates subscripts from that location. Likewise the dummy array B does not occupy any storage space in subroutine MAINE; the subroutine assumes that the argument Y [that is, Y(1)] supplied in the calling statement defines the first element of the actual array to be used and calculates subscripts from that location.

The calling argument X represents a one-dimensional array in the main program, as seen by the dimension statement

DIMENSION X(400), Y(400).

In version 1 of subroutine MAINE, the dummy array A to which the calling argument X corresponds also represents a one-dimensional array, as seen by the dimensions statement

DIMENSION A(2), B(3).

Since A and B are each one-dimensional dummy arrays, the integers 2 and 3 are not needed to locate their elements and so have no function other than to indicate that A and B are each one-dimensional; as a result any other positive integers could have been used in their place, such as

DIMENSION A(1), B(1000).

[As we will see shortly we could also use the scalar variable N; that is, we could have used the dimension statement

DIMENSION A(N), B(N)

in version 1.]

However, it is not necessary for the actual array in the calling statement to have the same number of dimensions as the dummy array to which it corresponds. Version 2 represents a case where different numbers of dimensions are defined for the dummy and actual arrays; namely, the dummy arrays A and B are two-dimensional, and the actual arrays X and Y are one-dimensional, as seen by the respective statements

DIMENSION A(N,N), B(N,N)

and

DIMENSION X(400), Y(400).

The dummy array A does not actually occupy any storage space in the subroutine; instead, the subroutine assumes via the call statement

CALL MAINE(M,X,Y)

that the argument X(1) defines the first element of the actual array used by the subroutine and calculates the subscripts of the other elements from that location. A further point is illustrated by this example. As we have said, a dummy array does not actually occupy any storage space, which means that its dimension statement is not used to allocate storage for the array, but only used to locate its elements. As a result, the dimensions of a dummy array do not have to be defined within the subroutine in the normal manner of specifying the length of the array in each dimension by a constant integer. Instead, any or all the dimensions of a dummy array may be specified by scalar variables, for example, the N in the statement

DIMENSION A(N,N), B(N,N)

in version 2. The use of scalar variables permits the calling program to supply the size of the dummy array each time the subroutine is called. Only a dummy array may be given an adjustable size, and the scalar variables used must be subroutine arguments. Note that in version 2 we could equally well have used the statement

DIMENSION A(N,3), B(N,1000)

as the size of the last dimension of a *n*-dimensional array does not matter when it comes to locating the elements of an array. More is said on this subject in the next section.

1.7 Standard subroutines

In this section we describe some basic subroutines which we will make use of throughout our work. The first is subroutine ZERO whose purpose is to store the floating-point number zero 0.0 in each storage location of an array. If A is an array of floating-point numbers, which is dimensioned as DIMENSION A(100) in the calling program, then the statements

$$N = 100$$
$$\text{CALL ZERO}(N,A)$$

would result in each element in the array A being replaced by 0.0, that is,

$$A(1) = 0.0, \ A(2) = 0.0, \ \ldots , \ A(100) = 0.0.$$

The program for subroutine ZERO is

```
      SUBROUTINE ZERO(LX,X)
      DIMENSION X(LX)
C     FOR COMPLEX VERSION REMOVE THE C FROM
C     1COLUMN 1 OF NEXT CARD
C     COMPLEX X
      IF(LX.LE.0) RETURN
      DO 1 I=1,LX
    1 X(I)=0.0
      RETURN
      END
```

This subroutine is extremely simple, yet with it we can illustrate some basic Fortran principles. For example, suppose that in the calling program the array B is dimensioned as DIMENSION B(10), so that 10 cells are allocated to B. Suppose further that we wish to make elements B(5), B(6), B(7), and B(8) each equal to 0.0. We can do so by the call statement

$$\text{CALL ZERO}(4, \ B(5)).$$

This call statement results in $B(5) = 0.0$, $B(6) = 0.0$, $B(7) = 0.0$, and $B(8) = 0.0$; the other elements, namely $B(1)$, $B(2)$, $B(3)$, $B(4)$, $B(9)$, and $B(10)$ are unaffected. Note that the arguments in the CALL statement, namely 4, $B(5)$, must match the arguments in the SUBROUTINE statement, namely LX,X in number (2 arguments in each) and in type [4 and LX are integer type, $B(5)$ and X are real type]. Moreover, there must be agreement between the calling program and the subroutine as to which arguments represent single variables and which represent arrays. The argument 4 in the calling program and the corresponding argument LX in the subroutine represent single values; the argument $B(5)$ in the calling program and the corresponding argument X in the subroutine represent arrays. The machine knows that B(5) and X represent arrays because of the dimension statement DIMENSION B(10) in the calling program and the dimension statement DIMENSION X(LX) in the sub-routine. In this case both dimension statements agree as to the number of sub-scripts (that is, both B and X are one-dimensional arrays); however, as we have seen in the last section this agreement is not necessary. What is necessary is that both the calling program and the subroutine agree on the absolute machine location of a subscripted variable. If we let LOC [   ] stand for "absolute machine location of," and if we assume a dimension statement of the form

DIMENSION A(L1), B(M1, M2), C(N1,N2,N3),

then the following rules must be obeyed by both programs:

$$\text{LOC } [A(I)] \quad = \text{LOC } [A(1)] \quad + (I - 1)$$
$$\text{LOC } [B(I,J)] \quad = \text{LOC } [B(1,1)] \quad + (I - 1) + (J - 1) * M1$$
$$\text{LOC } [C(I,J,K)] = \text{LOC } [C(1,1,1)] + (I - 1) + (J - 1) * N1 + (K-1)* N2.$$

(Note that the size L1 of the last dimension of the one-dimensional array A, the size M2 of the last dimension of the two-dimensional array B, and the size N3 of the last dimension of the three-dimensional array C do not matter in the location of the elements of the arrays, as we have mentioned in the last section.)

    The call statement CALL ZERO(4,B(5)) passes the absolute location of B(5) to the subroutine; this absolute location becomes the absolute location of the first element X(1) of the dummy array X occuring in the program for SUBROUTINE ZERO. Likewise, the absolute location of B(6) becomes the absolute location of the second element X(2) of the dummy array X in SUB-ROUTINE ZERO, etc.

    The next basic subroutine is MOVE. The purpose of subroutine move is to move an array from one storage location to another. The call statement is

CALL MOVE(L,A,B).

The result is that the values (L in number) originally in array A have been moved to array B. Provided the two arrays do not overlap, array A is left in-tact. A tentative program[1] for subroutine MOVE might be

```
      SUBROUTINE MOVE(LX,X,Y)
      DIMENSION X(LX),Y(LX)
C        FOR COMPLEX VERSION REMOVE THE C FROM
C        1COLUMN 1 OF NEXT CARD
```

---

[1] This program for subroutine MOVE works satisfactorily in all the programs in this book which call subroutine MOVE.

```
C     COMPLEX X,Y
      DO 1 I=1,LX
    1 Y(I)=X(I)
      RETURN
      END
```

Suppose a given array C has 10 elements, with the numerical values 1, 2, 3, 4, 5, 6, 7, 8, 9, 10, stored in C(1), C(2), . . . , C(10), that is, the given array C is

$$C = (1, \quad 2, \quad 3, \quad 4, \quad 5, \quad 6, \quad 7, \quad 8, \quad 9, \quad 10).$$

Let us now consider three cases, each of which has the given C as input. In the first case (case of no overlap), the given C is transformed by the call statement

$$\text{CALL MOVE}(4,C(2),C(7))$$

into the array

$$C = (1, \quad 2, \quad 3, \quad 4, \quad 5, \quad 6, \quad 2, \quad 3, \quad 4, \quad 5).$$

In the second case (case of overlap), the given C is transformed by the call statement

$$\text{CALL MOVE}(4,C(4),C(2))$$

into the array

$$C = (1, \quad 4, \quad 5, \quad 6, \quad 7, \quad 6, \quad 7, \quad 8, \quad 9, \quad 10).$$

Thus the 4 values starting with C(4), namely, (4, 5, 6, 7), have been moved to the 4 cells starting with C(2), as required. In the third case (case of overlap), the given C is transformed by the call statement

$$\text{CALL MOVE}(4,C(2),C(4))$$

into the array

$$C = (1, \quad 2, \quad 3, \quad 2, \quad 3, \quad 2, \quad 3, \quad 8, \quad 9, \quad 10).$$

Thus the 4 values starting with C(2), namely (2, 3, 4, 5), have not been moved to the 4 cells starting with C(4), which instead contain (2, 3, 2, 3). Thus the above program for subroutine MOVE has given us an incorrect result in the third case, and hence represents a subroutine with a built-in bobby trap. A program for subroutine MOVE which works properly in all cases is

```
      SUBROUTINE MOVE(LX,X,Y)
      DIMENSION X(LX),Y(LX)
C     FOR COMPLEX VERSION REMOVE THE C FROM
C     1COLUMN 1 OF NEXT CARD
C     COMPLEX X,Y
      IF(XLOCF(X)-XLOCF(Y)) 3,5,1
```

```
  1 DO 2 I=1,LX
  2 Y(I)=X(I)
    GO TO 5
  3 K=LX
    DO 4 I=1,LX
    Y(K)=X(K)
  4 K=K−1
  5 RETURN
    END
```

The purpose of subroutine SCALE is to multiply each element of an array X, of length LX, by a scale factor *c*. The call statement is

$$\text{CALL SCALE(S,LX,X)},$$

where the subroutine inputs are

$$\text{S} = \text{constant scale factor} = c$$
$$\text{LX} = \text{length of X} = n$$
$$\text{X} = (x_1, x_2, \ldots, x_n),$$

and the subroutine output is

$$\text{X} = (cx_1, cx_2, \ldots, cx_n).$$

The program is

```
    SUBROUTINE SCALE(S,LX,X)
    DIMENSION X(LX)
C       FOR COMPLEX VERSION REMOVE THE C FROM
C       1COLUMN 1 OF NEXT CARD
C       COMPLEX X
    DO 1 I=1,LX
  1 X(I)=S*X(I)
    RETURN
    END
```

The *dot product* of the vector $(x_1, x_2, \ldots, x_n)$ with the vector $(y_1, y_2, \ldots, y_n)$ is defined as

$$x_1 y_1 + x_2 y_2 + \cdots + x_n y_n.$$

The purpose of subroutine DOT is to compute the dot product of two vectors. The call statement is

$$\text{CALL DOT(L,X,Y,P)},$$

where the subroutine inputs are

$$L = \text{length of } X = \text{length of } Y = n$$
$$X = (x_1, x_2, \ldots, x_n)$$
$$Y = (y_1, y_2, \ldots, y_n),$$

and where the subroutine output is

$$P = \text{the dot product.}$$

The program is

```
SUBROUTINE DOT(L,X,Y,P)
DIMENSION X(L),Y(L)
P=0.0
IF(L.LE.0) RETURN
DO 1 I=1,L
1 P=P+X(I)*Y(I)
RETURN
END
```

The dot product reverse of the vector $(x_1, x_2, \ldots, x_n)$ with the vector $(y_1, y_2, \ldots, y_n)$ is defined as

$$x_1 y_n + x_2 y_{n-1} + \cdots + x_{n-1} y_2 + x_n y_1.$$

The purpose of subroutine DOTR is to compute the dot product reverse of two vectors. The call statement is

CALL DOTR(LX,X,Y,P),

where the subroutine inputs are

$$L = \text{length of } X = \text{length of } Y = n$$
$$X = (x_1, x_2, \ldots, x_n)$$
$$Y = (y_1, y_2, \ldots, y_n),$$

and where the subroutine output is

$$P = \text{the dot product reverse.}$$

The program is

```
SUBROUTINE DOTR(L,X,Y,P)
DIMENSION X(L),Y(L)
P=0.0
IF(L.LE.0) RETURN
DO 1 I=1,L
J=L-I+1
1 P=P+X(I)*Y(J)
RETURN
END
```

The purpose of subroutine MINSN is to find the minimum element of an array, taking into account the algebraic signs of the elements. The calling statement is

CALL MINSN(LX,X,XMIN,INDEX),

where the subroutine inputs are

$$LX = \text{length of } X = n$$
$$X = (x_1, x_2, \ldots, x_n),$$

and where the subroutine outputs are

$$XMIN = X(INDEX) = \text{the smallest element in array } X$$
$$INDEX = \text{Fortran subscript of the smallest element XMIN.}$$

The program is

```
SUBROUTINE MINSN(LX,X,XMIN,INDEX)
DIMENSION X(LX)
INDEX=1
DO 1 I=1,LX
IF(X(INDEX).GT.X(I)) INDEX=I
1 CONTINUE
XMIN=X(INDEX)
RETURN
END
```

Subroutine MAXSN is like MINSN, except that it finds the maximum element XMAX. The program is

```
SUBROUTINE MAXSN(LX,X,XMAX,INDEX)
DIMENSION X(LX)
INDEX=1
DO 1 I=1,LX
IF(X(INDEX).LT.X(I)) INDEX=I
1 CONTINUE
XMAX=X(INDEX)
RETURN
END
```

Subroutine REMAV removes the arithmetic average from a numerical sequence $y_1, y_2, \ldots, y_n$. The call statement is

CALL REMAV(LY,Y,AVERAG),

where the subroutine inputs are

$$LY = \text{length of } Y = n$$
$$Y = (y_1, y_2, \ldots, y_n),$$

and where the subroutine outputs are

$$\text{AVERAG} = \bar{y} = (y_1 + y_2 + \cdots + y_n)/n$$
$$Y = (y_1 - \bar{y}, y_2 - \bar{y}, \ldots, y_n - \bar{y}).$$

The program is

```
       SUBROUTINE REMAV(LY,Y,AVERAG)
       DIMENSION Y(2)
       S=0.
       DO 10 I=1,LY
   10  S=S+Y(I)
       AVERAG=S/FLOAT(LY)
       DO 20 I=1,LY
   20  Y(I)=Y(I)-AVERAG
       RETURN
       END
```

The purpose of subroutine REVERS is to reverse the order of the elements of an array. The call statement is

$$\text{CALL REVERS(LX,X)},$$

where the subroutine inputs are

$$\text{LX} = \text{length of } X = n$$
$$X = (x_1, x_2, \ldots, x_{n-1}, x_n),$$

and where the subroutine output is

$$X = (x_n, x_{n-1}, \ldots, x_2, x_1).$$

The program is

```
       SUBROUTINE REVERS(LX,X)
       DIMENSION X(LX)
       L=LX/2
       DO 1 I=1,L
       J=LX-I
       TEMP=X(I)
       X(I)=X(J+1)
    1  X(J+1)=TEMP
       RETURN
       END
```

The purpose of subroutine NORMEN is to normalize an array by dividing each element by the RMS energy of the array. The call statement is

$$\text{CALL NORMEN(LX,X)},$$

where the subroutine inputs are

$$LX = \text{length of } X = n$$
$$X = (x_1, x_2, \ldots, x_n),$$

and where the subroutine output is

$$X = (x_1/\sigma, x_2/\sigma, \ldots, x_n/\sigma),$$

where σ is the RMS energy given by

$$\sigma = \sqrt{x_1^2 + x_2^2 + \cdots + x_n^2}.$$

The program is

```
      SUBROUTINE NORMEN(LX,X)
      DIMENSION X(LX)
      E=0.
      DO 10 I=1,LX
  10  E=E+X(I)*X(I)
      E=SQRT (E)
      DO 20 I=1,LX
  20  X(I)=X(I)/E
      RETURN
      END
```

A similar program is NORM1, which normalizes an array by its first element. The program is

```
      SUBROUTINE NORM1(LX,X)
      DIMENSION X(LX)
      X1=X(1)
      IF(LX.LE.0) RETURN
      DO 1 I=1,LX
   1  X(I)=X(I)/X1
      RETURN
      END
```

Another similar program is NORMAG, which normalizes an array by the magnitude of the element which is greatest in magnitude. The program is

```
      SUBROUTINE NORMAG(LX,X)
      DIMENSION X(LX)
      B=0.0
      DO 10 I=1,LX
  10  B=AMAX1(ABS(X(I)),B)
      DO 20 I=1,LX
  20  X(I)=X(I)/B
      RETURN
      END
```

As we have stated earlier, in the programming of methods for time series analysis, one makes use of arrays. An array element is a member of the set of data associated with the corresponding array variable. Array elements are referenced by the array identifier followed by a subscript. For example, in the foregoing pages we have often made use of the array identifier X, where the array contains the set of data denoted by $x_1, x_2, \ldots, x_n$, and we have written this relationship as

$$X = (x_1, x_2, \ldots, x_n).$$

That is, the array element x_1 is referenced by $X(1)$, the array element x_2 is referenced by $X(2)$, the array element x_3 is referenced by $X(3)$, etc. Subscripts assume the following form:

(s_1)	for a one-dimensional array
(s_1, s_2)	for a two-dimensional array
$(s_1, s_2, \ldots, s_n)$	for an n-dimensional array.

In the Fortran IV language for the SDS 9300 digital computer, the s_1, $s_2, \ldots, s_n$ may be any expressions of integer, real, or double-precision mode, where real and double-precision expressions used as subscripts are truncated to integer values. Moreover, nested subscription is permissible; that is, subscripts themselves may be subscripted, where there is no limit on the level of subscription. For example, we might refer to the array element

$$K(K(K(K(K(K(J))))))$$

or the array element

$$X(I(A(M)/B(M*N)),J(C(N*K-1)))$$

in a program written for the SDS 9300 computer. Such flexibility in the use of subscripts is extremely useful in time series analysis. However, in the programs given in this book we have not made use of the flexibility offered by the SDS Fortran, despite the fact that the company with which the writer is associated owns an SDS 9300 computer. The reason is simple; the programs appearing in this book are designed to be used on any digital computer that has a standard Fortran IV capability. We have run the subroutines given in this book interchangeably on the IBM 7094 computer, the SDS 9300 computer, the CDC 3600 computer, and the UNIVAC 1108 computer. Of course, some minor adjustments in the programs must be made for smaller computers which admit only restricted versions of Fortran IV.

Because we use standard Fortran IV, the subscripts in our programs assume the form:

(s_1)	for a one-dimensional array
(s_1, s_2)	for a two-dimensional array
(s_1, s_2, s_3)	for a three-dimensional array,

where the s_1, s_2, s_3 must be constants, variables, or arithmetic expressions in the integer mode, whose numerical values may never be zero or negative. The subscript expressions may assume the five forms:

$$v$$
$$c$$
$$v + c \quad \text{or} \quad v - c$$
$$c * v$$
$$c * v + c' \quad \text{or} \quad c * v - c',$$

where the symbols c and c' denote integer constants, and v denotes an integer variable. For example, J, 5, K+2, M−10, 3∗L, 4∗I+5, 2∗N−12 are admissible as subscripts, whereas −J, K∗N, N∗M, K∗N+5, I∗4+5, N∗2−12, and N∗(M−1) are not.

For our purposes, the most inconvenient restriction on subscripts in standard Fortran IV is the restriction that numerical values of subscripts can never be zero or negative. In fact, it is the banishment of zero as a subscript which causes many of the Fortran expressions in our programs to be out of step with their mathematical counterparts. It is said that there was a time when no one could imagine a numeral that stands for nothing you can see, or touch, or count, and it was the Hindus who brought to the court of Baghdad the first zero, a real digit, that could be used in addition or subtraction. However, as we have seen, the zero still has not found its way into the standard Fortran IV language as a subscript. As a result, whenever a mathematical vector starts with a subscript 0, we have no choice but to make the corresponding Fortran array start with the subscript 1. For example, the set of data denoted by $x_0, x_1, x_2, \ldots, x_n$ would be stored in array X of length LX $= n + 1$ as

$$X = (x_0, x_1, x_2, \ldots, x_n),$$

where

$$X(1) = x_0, X(2) = x_1, X(3) = x_2, \ldots, X(LX) = x_n$$

so the Fortran subscripts are one greater than the corresponding mathematical subscripts. Although personally we find this an inconvenience, we have adhered to it; however, some people we know prefer it. The standard Fortran subscript convention corresponds to the American practice of starting to count with the number 1. For example, the ground floor in an American building is number 1, the next floor is number 2, etc. On an American telephone dial the first number is number 1, the next is number 2, etc., and the last is number 0. Such a counting system is not universal, however, for in Europe the ground floor is number 0, the next is number 1, etc., and, on a Swedish telephone dial, the first number is number 0, the next is number 1, etc., and the last is number 9. (Also there are no letters on the Swedish telephone dial, so there is no possibility of mixing up the numeral 0 with the letter O as on the American dial. However, when it comes to key-punching computer programs, there is always the universal danger of mixing up the numeral 0 and the letter O. Except for putting a slash through the numeral 0 as the teletypewriter does, or putting a slash through the letter O as some computer printers do, or shaping the 0 and O slightly differently, there seems to be no solution to this troublesome problem.)

The purpose of subroutine impulse is to store an impulse function in an array. The call statement is

$$\text{CALL IMPULS(LD,D,K)},$$

where the subroutine inputs are

$$\text{LD} = \text{length of } D = n + 1$$
$$\text{K} = k + 1,$$

and the subroutine output is

$$D = (d_0, d_1, \ldots, d_n),$$

where

$$d_t = \begin{cases} 0 & \text{for } t \neq k \\ 1 & \text{for } t = k. \end{cases}$$

The program is

```
SUBROUTINE IMPULS(LD,D,K)
DIMENSION D(LD)
DO 1 I=1,LD
1 D(I)=0.0
D(K)=1.0
RETURN
END
```

The cross-correlation coefficient g_s for time-shift s of the vector $(x_0, x_1, \ldots, x_m)$ with the vector $(y_0, y_1, \ldots, y_n)$ is defined as

$$g_s = \sum_{t=0}^{m} x_t y_{t-s},$$

where values of x_t outside the range $t=0,1,2, \ldots, m$ and values of y_i outside the range $i=0,1,2, \ldots, n$ are assumed to be zero.

The purpose of subroutine CROSS is to compute the cross correlation of two vectors. Subroutine CROSS needs subroutine DOT. The call statement is

$$\text{CALL CROSS(LX,X,LY,Y,LG,G)},$$

where the subroutine inputs are

$$LX = \text{length of } X = m + 1$$
$$X = (x_0, x_1, \ldots, x_m)$$
$$LY = \text{length of } Y = n + 1$$
$$Y = (y_0, y_1, \ldots, y_n)$$
$$LG = \text{desired length of cross correlation} = k + 1,$$

and the subroutine output is

$$G = (g_0, g_1, \ldots, g_k).$$

We see that the subroutine output is the center point g_0 and k values, namely, $g_1, g_2, \ldots, g_k$, of the right-hand side of the cross-correlation function g_s, where $-\infty < s < \infty$. However, in order to obtain the center point g_0 and k values, namely $g_{-1}, g_{-2}, \ldots, g_{-k}$, of the left-hand side of the cross-correlation function, we would make use of the same arrays X and Y as before, but now with the call statement

CALL CROSS(LY,Y,LX,X,LG,G)

for this statement yields the subroutine output

$$G = (g_0, g_{-1}, \ldots, g_{-k}).$$

The program is

```
SUBROUTINE CROSS(LX,X,LY,Y,LG,G)
DIMENSION X(LX),Y(LY),G(LG)
DO 1 J=1,LG
1 CALL DOT(MIN0(LY,LX−J+1),X(J),Y,G(J))
RETURN
END
```

To obtain the autocorrelation of the signal $x_0, x_1, \ldots, x_m$ one may

CALL CROSS(LX,X,LX,X,LR,R)

with the subroutine inputs

$$LX = m + 1$$
$$X = (x_0, x_1, \ldots, x_m)$$
$$LR = k + 1.$$

The subroutine output is

$$R = (r_0, r_1, \ldots, r_k),$$

where

$$r_s = \sum_{t=0}^{m-s} x_{t+s} x_t \qquad \text{for } s = 0, \cdots, k$$

are the (unnormalized) autocorrelation coefficients.

1.8 Polynomial subroutines

A polynomial is an expression of the form

$$A(z) = a_0 + a_1 z + a_2 z^2 + \ldots + a_m z^m ,$$

where the coefficients, in particular, may be real or complex constants or real or complex matrices, and where z is any symbol. Since nothing is assumed known about z, the symbol z is usually called an *indeterminate*. Using only the rules for adding, subtracting, and multiplying the coefficients, one can add, subtract, and multiply any two polynomials. Thus the polynomial written above can be multiplied with the polynomial

$$B(z) = b_0 + b_1 z + b_2 z^2 + \cdots + b_n z^n$$

to yield the polynomial

$$\begin{aligned}
C(z) &= A(z)\, B(z) \\
&= (a_0 + a_1 z + \cdots + a_m z^m)(b_0 + b_1 z + \cdots + b_n z^n) \\
&= c_0 + c_1 z + c_2 z^2 + \cdots + c_{m+n} z^{m+n}
\end{aligned}$$

with coefficients

$$\begin{aligned}
c_0 &= a_0 b_0 \\
c_1 &= a_0 b_1 + a_1 b_0 \\
&\cdots \\
c_k &= a_0 b_k + a_1 b_{k-1} + \cdots + a_k b_0 \\
&\cdots \\
c_{m+n-1} &= a_{m-1} b_n + a_m b_{n-1} \\
c_{m+n} &= a_m b_m ,
\end{aligned}$$

where $a_i = 0$ if $i > m$ and $b_j = 0$ if $j > n$.

The coefficients $(a_0, a_1, \cdots, a_m)$ of the polynomial $A(z)$ can represent the values of a signal or an operator; then the polynomial $A(z)$ is called the z-transform of the signal or operator. The index i on the signal coefficient a_i represents the time index. When we write a signal as $(a_0, a_1, \cdots, a_m)$ it is understood that its coefficients outside of the indicated time interval are zero, that is, $a_i = 0$ for $i < 0$ and for $i > m$.

The convolution of two signals a_i and b_i of indefinite time extent (i.e., $-\infty < i < \infty$) is defined as the signal c_k given by the formula

$$c_k = \sum_{i=-\infty}^{\infty} a_i b_{k-i} ,$$

where $-\infty < k < \infty$. In case of signals $(a_0, a_1, \cdots, a_m)$ and $(b_0, b_1, \cdots, b_n)$ of finite time length, the convolution formula reduces to

$$c_k = \Sigma a_i b_{k-1} ,$$

where the summation is over all i such that $0 \leqslant i \leqslant m$ and $0 \leqslant k - i \leqslant n$. Hence the coefficients are

$$c_k = \begin{cases} 0 & \text{for } k < 0 \\ a_0 b_k + a_1 b_{k-1} + \cdots + a_k b_0 & \text{for } 0 \leqslant k \leqslant m+n \\ 0 & \text{for } k > 0, \end{cases}$$

where $a_i = 0$ if $i > m$ and $b_j = 0$ if $j > n$. But these coefficients c_k are the the same as those obtained by polynomial multiplication. Thus we have arrived at the important result that the convolution of two signals corresponds to the multiplication of their z-transforms. The signal

$$(c_0, c_1, \cdots, c_{m+n})$$

is called the *complete transient convolution* of the signals $(a_0, a_1, \cdots, a_m)$ and $(b_0, b_1, \cdots, b_n)$.

Subroutine FOLD performs polynomial multiplication, or equivalently the complete transient convolution of two signals. Subroutine FOLD needs subroutine ZERO. The call statement is

CALL FOLD(LA,A,LB,B,LC,C),

where the subroutine inputs are

$$\begin{aligned} \text{LA} &= \text{length of A} = m + 1 \\ \text{A} &= (a_0, a_1, \cdots, a_m) \\ \text{LB} &= \text{length of B} = n + 1 \\ \text{B} &= (b_0, b_1, \cdots, b_n), \end{aligned}$$

and the subroutine outputs are

$$\begin{aligned} \text{LC} &= \text{length of C} = m + n + 1 \\ \text{C} &= (c_0, c_1, c_2, \cdots, c_{m+n}). \end{aligned}$$

The program is

```
SUBROUTINE FOLD(LA,A,LB,B,LC,C)
DIMENSION A(LA),B(LB),C(LC)
LC=LA+LB−1
CALL ZERO(LC,C)
DO 1  I=1,LA
DO 1   J=1,LB
K=I+J−1
1 C(K)=C(K)+A(I)*B(J)
RETURN
END
```

It is seen that this program is based on the analogy of multiplication of polynomials. As an illustration, suppose the subroutine inputs to FOLD are

$$LA = 2$$
$$A = (1.0, 2.0)$$
$$LB = 3$$
$$B = (1.0, -1.0, 0.5).$$

Then the subroutine outputs are

$$LC = 4$$
$$C = (1.0, 1.0, -1.5, 1.0).$$

The purpose of subroutine POLYDV is to divide one polynomial by another, that is, to deconvolve one signal by another. Given the divisor polynomial

$$B(z) = b_0 + b_1 z + \cdots + b_n z^n$$

and the dividend polynomial

$$A(z) = a_0 + a_1 z + \cdots + a_m z^m ,$$

we define their quotient as

$$\frac{A(z)}{B(z)} = q_0 + q_1 z + \cdots + q_k z^k + \text{remainder} .$$

Subroutine POLYDV needs subroutine ZERO and MOVE. The call statement is

CALL POLYDV(N,DVS,M,DVD,L,Q),

where the subroutine inputs are

$$N = n + 1$$
$$DVS = (b_0, b_1, \cdots, b_n) \qquad \text{where } b_0 \neq 0$$
$$M = m + 1$$
$$DVD = (a_0, a_1, \cdots, a_m)$$
$$L = k + 1 ,$$

and where the subroutine output is

$$Q = (q_0, q_1, \cdots, q_k) .$$

As a numerical example, suppose

$$N = 2$$
$$DVS = (1, -0.5) \qquad \text{(minimum-delay signal)}$$
$$M = 1$$
$$DVD = (1)$$
$$L = 5.$$

Then

$$Q = (1, 0.5, 0.25, 0.125, 0.0625).$$

The program is

```
      SUBROUTINE POLYDV(N,DVS,M,DVD,L,Q)
      DIMENSION DVS(N),DVD(M),Q(L)
C     FOR COMPLEX VERSION REMOVE THE C FROM
C   1 COLUMN 1 OF NEXT CARD
C     COMPLEX DVS,DVD,Q
      CALL ZERO (L,Q)
      CALL MOVE (MIN0(M,L),DVD,Q)
      DO 10  I=1,L
      Q(I)=Q(I)/DVS(1)
      IF (I.EQ.L) RETURN
      K=I
      ISUB=MIN0(N-1,L-I)
      DO 10  J=1,ISUB
      K=K+1
   10 Q(K)=Q(K)-Q(I)*DVS(J+1)
      RETURN
      END
```

Given the polynomial

$$c_0 + c_1 z + \cdots + c_n z^n \qquad \text{(where } c_0 > 0\text{)},$$

subroutine PSQRT finds the first $m + 1$ coefficients of the square-root power series

$$\sqrt{c_0 + c_1 z + \cdots + c_n z^n} = a_0 + a_1 z + a_2 z^2 + \cdots.$$

The call statement is

$$\text{CALL PSQRT(N,C,M,A)},$$

where the subroutine inputs are

$$N = n + 1$$
$$C = (c_0, c_1, \cdots, c_n) \qquad \text{(where } c_0 > 0\text{)}$$
$$M = m + 1,$$

and where the subroutine output is

$$A = (a_0, a_1, \cdots, a_m).$$

Note that the program requires that both N and M must be greater than or equal to 4. However, this is no essential restriction since any of c_1, c_2, and/or c_3 may be zero. As an example, if

$$N = 4$$
$$C = (1, 4, 1, 0)$$
$$M = 5,$$

then

$$A = (1, 2, 0, 0, 0).$$

As another example, if

$$N = 4$$
$$C = (1, 2, 0, 0)$$
$$M = 6,$$

then

$$A = (1, 1, -0.5, 0.5, -0.625, 0.875).$$

The program is

```
      SUBROUTINE  PSQRT(N,C,M,A)
      DIMENSION  C(N),A(M)
      A(1)=SQRT(C(1))
      TA=2.*A(1)
      A(2)=C(2)/TA
      A(3)=(C(3)-A(2)*A(2))/TA
      DO 100  I=4,M
      IF(I-N)  20,20,10
   10 PA=0.
      GO TO 30
   20 PA=C(I)
   30 CONTINUE
      PS=0.
      IH=I/2
      DO 40  J=2,IH
      K=I-J
   40 PS=PS+A(J)*A(K+1)
      PA=PA-2.*PS
      IF(2*IH-1)  50,60,50
   50 PA=PA-A(IH+1)*A(IH+1)
   60 A(I)=PA/TA
  100 CONTINUE
      RETURN
      END
```

Subroutine POLYEV performs complex polynomial evaluation. Given the polynomial

$$a_0 + a_1 z + \cdots + a_m z^m$$

with real coefficients, subroutine POLYEV computes the value of the polynomial at the complex point

$$z = z_1.$$

Note that if

$$z_1 = e^{-2\pi i f} = \cos 2\pi f - i \sin 2\pi f,$$

where f is frequency (in cycles per time unit), then this polynomial evaluation is equivalent to taking the discrete Fourier transform

$$\sum_{t=0}^{m} a_t \, e^{-2\pi i f t}$$

of the signal $(a_0, a_1, \cdots, a_m)$ at the frequency f. The call statement is

$$\text{CALL POLYEV(LA,A,Z,AZ)},$$

where the subroutine inputs are

$$\begin{aligned}
&\text{LA} = m + 1 \\
&\text{A} = (a_0, a_1, \cdots, a_m) \quad \text{(real numbers)} \\
&\text{Z} = z_1 \quad\quad\quad\quad\quad\;\; \text{(complex number)},
\end{aligned}$$

and the subroutine output is

$$\text{AZ} = a_0 + a_1 z_1 + \cdots + a_m z_1^m \quad \text{(complex number)}.$$

For example, if $m = 4$, this formula is evaluated in the following way:

$$\text{AZ} = (a_0 + z_1 (a_1 + z_1 (a_2 + z_1 (a_3 + z_1 a_4)))).$$

Thus only m additions and m multiplications are required. As a numerical example, suppose

$$\begin{aligned}
&\text{LA} = 3 \\
&\text{A} = (3, 2, 1) \\
&\text{Z} = 1 + i.
\end{aligned}$$

Then

$$\text{AZ} = 5 + 4i.$$

The program is

```
SUBROUTINE POLYEV(LA,A,Z,AZ)
DIMENSION A(LA)
COMPLEX Z,AZ
AZ=0.0
DO 1 I=1,LA
J=LA−I+1
```

```
1  AZ=Z*AZ+A(J)
   RETURN
   END
```

Subroutine POLRT is a subroutine written by IBM to compute the real and complex roots

$$z_1, z_2, \cdots, z_m$$

of a polynomial

$$a_0 + a_1 z + \cdots + a_m z^m$$

with real coefficients. The call statement is

CALL POLRT(XCOF,COF,M,ROOTR,ROOTI,IER),

where the subroutine inputs are

$$XCOF = (a_0, a_1, \cdots, a_m) \qquad \text{where } a_0 \neq 0$$
$$M = \text{order of polynomial} = m,$$

and the subroutine outputs are

$$COF = \text{working space of } m + 1 \text{ cells}$$
$$ROOTR = (\text{Re } z_1, \text{Re } z_2, \cdots, \text{Re } z_m)$$
$$ROOTI = (\text{Im } z_1, \text{Im } z_2, \cdots, \text{Im } z_m)$$
$$IER = \text{error code, where}$$

$$IER = 0 \text{ means no error}$$
$$IER = 1 \text{ means } m < 1$$
$$IER = 2 \text{ means } m > 36$$
$$IER = 3 \text{ means the program is unable to}$$
determine the root with 500 iterations on 8 starting values
$$IER = 4 \text{ means } a_m = 0.$$

Note that Re denotes "real part," and Im denotes "imaginary part," so the roots are given by

$$z_i = \text{Re } z_i + i \text{ Im } z_i \qquad \text{for } i = 1, 2, \cdots, m.$$

This subroutine is limited to polynomials of degree $m = 36$ or less. Floating-point overflow may occur for high-degree polynomials but will not affect the accuracy of the results. The method used is the Newton–Raphson iterative technique. The final iterations on each root are performed using the original polynomial instead of the reduced polynomial in order to avoid accumulated errors in the reduced polynomials. As a numerical example of the usage of subroutine POLRT suppose

$$XCOF = (36, 0, -13, 0, 1)$$
$$M = 4.$$

Then

$$ROOTR = (-3, 3, -2, 2)$$
$$ROOTI = (0, 0, 0, 0)$$
$$IER = 0.$$

If

$$XCOF = (83, -278, 720, -238, 120)$$
$$M = 4,$$

then

$$ROOTR = (0.20, 0.20, 0.79, 0.79)$$
$$ROOTI = (-0.30, 0.30, -2.15, 2.15)$$
$$IER = 0.$$

The program is

```
      SUBROUTINE POLRT(XCOF,COF,M,ROOTR,ROOTI,IER)
      DIMENSION XCOF(1),COF(1),ROOTR(1),ROOTI(1)
C         IF A DOUBLE–PRECISION VERSION OF THIS
C         ROUTINE IS DESIRED, THE C IN COLUMN 1
C         SHOULD BE REMOVED FROM THE DOUBLE–
C         PRECISION STATEMENT WHICH FOLLOWS.
C     DOUBLE PRECISION XCOF,COF,ROOTR,ROOTI,XO,YO,X,
C     1Y,XPR,YPR,UX,UY,V,YT,XT,U,XT2,YT2,SUMSQ,DX,DY,
C     2TEMP,ALPHA
C         THE C MUST ALSO BE REMOVED FROM DOUBLE–
C         PRECISION STATEMENTS APPEARING IN OTHER
C         ROUTINES USED IN CONJUNCTION WITH THIS
C         ROUTINE.
C         THE DOUBLE–PRECISION VERSION OF THIS
C         SUBROUTINE MUST ALSO CONTAIN DOUBLE–
C         PRECISION FORTRAN FUNCTIONS. ABS IN
C         STATEMENTS 78 AND 122 MUST BE CHANGED TO
C         DABS.
      IFIT=0
      N=M
      IER=0
      IF(XCOF(N+1)) 10,25,10
   10 IF(N) 15,15,32
C
C         SET ERROR CODE TO 1
C
```

```
   15 IER = 1
   20 RETURN
C
C        SET ERROR CODE TO 4
C
   25 IER = 4
      GO TO 20
C
C        SET ERROR CODE TO 2
C
   30 IER = 2
      GO TO 20
   32 IF(N − 36) 35,35,30
   35 NX = N
      NXX = N+1
      N2 = 1
      KJ1 = N+1
      DO 40   L = 1,KJ1
      MT = KJ1 − L+1
   40 COF(MT) = XCOF(L)
C
C        SET INITIAL VALUES
C
   45 XO = .00500101
      YO = 0.01000101
C
C        ZERO INITIAL VALUE COUNTER
      IN = 0
   50 X = XO
C
C        INCREMENT INITIAL VALUES AND COUNTER
C
      XO = − 10.0*YO
      YO = − 10.0*X
C
C        SET X AND Y TO CURRENT VALUE
C
      X = XO
      Y = YO
      ICT = 0
      IN = IN+1
      GO TO 60
   55 IFIT = 1
```

```
        XPR = X
        YPR = Y
C
C         EVALUATE POLYNOMIAL AND DERIVATIVES
C
    60 UX = 0.0
        UY = 0.0
        V = 0.0
        YT = 0.0
        XT = 1.0
        U = COF(N+1)
        IF(U) 65,130,65
    65 DO 70  I = 1,N
        L  = N − I + 1
        XT2 = X*XT − Y*YT
        YT2 = X*YT + Y*XT
        U = U + COF(L)*XT2
        V = V + COF(L)*YT2
        FI = I
        UX = UX + FI*XT*COF(L)
        UY = UY − FI*YT*COF(L)
        XT = XT2
    70 YT = YT2
        SUMSQ = UX*UX + UY*UY
        IF(SUMSQ) 75,110,75
    75 DX = (V*UY − U*UX)/SUMSQ
        X = X + DX
        DY = −(U*UY + V*UX)/SUMSQ
        Y = Y + DY
    78 IF( ABS(DY)+ ABS(DX)−1.0E−05) 100,80,80
C
C         STEP ITERATION COUNTER
C
    80 ICT = ICT + 1
        IF(ICT − 500) 60,85,85
    85 IF(IFIT) 115,90,115
    90 IF(IN − 5) 50,95,95
C
C         SET ERROR CODE TO 3
C
    95 IER = 3
        GO TO 20
   100 DO 105 L = 1,NXX
```

```
      MT=KJ1-L+1
      TEMP=XCOF(MT)
      XCOF(MT)=COF(L)
  105 COF(L)=TEMP
      ITEMP=N
      N=NX
      NX=ITEMP
      IF(IFIT) 120,55,120
  110 IF(IFIT) 115,50,115
  115 X=XPR
      Y=YPR
  120 IFIT=0
  122 IF(ABS(Y/X)-1.0E-04) 135,125,125
  125 ALPHA=X+X
      SUMSQ=X*X+Y*Y
      N=N-2
      GO TO 140
  130 X=0.0
      NX=NX-1
      NXX=NXX-1
  135 Y=0.0
      SUMSQ=0.0
      ALPHA=X
      N=N-1
  140 COF(2)=COF(2)+ALPHA*COF(1)
  145 DO 150 L=2,N
  150 COF(L+1)=COF(L+1)+ALPHA*COF(L)-SUMSQ*COF(L-1)
  155 ROOTI(N2)=Y
      ROOTR(N2)=X
      N2=N2+1
      IF(SUMSQ) 160,165,160
  160 Y=-Y
      SUMSQ=0.0
      GO TO 155
  165 IF(N) 20,20,45
      END
```

1.9 Matrix subroutines

In Sec. 1.6 we described subroutine MAINE which inverts a symmetric matrix by the escalator method. Subroutine SIMEQ1, which makes use of MAINE, solves a set of simultaneous equations involving a symmetric matrix. Let the set of simultaneous equations be represented by

$$a\,b = c,$$

where a is an $m \times n$ matrix of unknowns, b is an $n \times n$ symmetric matrix of knowns, and the right-hand side c is an $m \times n$ matrix of knowns. The solution is then given by

$$a = cb^{-1}.$$

The call statement is

CALL SIMEQ1(M,N,A,B,C),

where the subroutine inputs are

$$M = m$$
$$N = n$$
$$B = n \times n \text{ symmetric matrix } b$$
$$C = m \times n \text{ matrix } c,$$

and the subroutine output is

$$A = m \times n \text{ matrix } cb^{-1}.$$

The program for subroutine SIMEQ1, which requires subroutines MOVE and MAINE, is

```
      SUBROUTINE  SIMEQ1(M,N,A,B,C)
C     NMAX=LARGEST  VALUE  OF  N  TO  BE  PROCESSED
C     NONDUMMY  DIMENSION  S(NMAX,NMAX)
C     FOR  EXAMPLE,  IF  NMAX=25  THEN
      DIMENSION  S(25,25)
      DIMENSION  A(M,N),B(N,N),C(M,N)
      CALL  MOVE(N*N,B,S)
      CALL  MAINE(N,S,B)
      DO  1  I=1,M
      DO  1  J=1,N
      A(I,J)=0.0
      DO  1  K=1,N
    1 A(I,J)=A(I,J)+C(I,K)*B(K,J)
      CALL  MOVE(N*N,S,B)
      RETURN
      END
```

Note that this program has a nondummy DIMENSION S(NMAX, NMAX), where NMAX denotes the order of the largest matrix b that is anticipated.

Subroutine FADDEJ inverts a (not necessarily symmetric) $n \times n$ matrix a by a method given by Faddeev and Sominskii.[2] The method is described in

---

[2] Faddeev, D. K., and I. S. Sominskii, *Problems in Higher Algebra*, Gostekhizdat, Moscow, 1954, 5th ed.

Gantmacher.[3] In addition to the inverse matrix a^{-1}, the method also yields the determinant, det a, the adjugate, adj a, and the coefficients, $p_1, p_2, \ldots, p_n$, of the characteristic polynomial

$$\det (\lambda I - a) = \lambda^n - p_1\lambda^{n-1} - p_2\lambda^{n-2} - \cdots - p_n .$$

The call statement is

CALL FADDEJ(N, A, AINV, DET, ADJUG, P),

where the subroutine inputs are

N = order of matrix = n
A = $n \times n$ matrix a ,

and the subroutine outputs are

AINV = inverse matrix a^{-1}
DET = determinant = det a
ADJUG = adjugate = adj a = (det a) a^{-1}
P = coefficients of characteristic polynomial
   = $(p_1, p_2, \ldots, p_n)$.

As a numerical example, suppose

N = 4
A = (2, 0, −1, 1, −1, 1, 1, 1, 1, 1, 1, 1, 2, 0, 1, 0).

Then

AINV = (0, −0.5, 0.5, 0, −1, −2.5, 3.5, −2, 0,1, −1,1,1,2,−2,1)
DET = 2
ADJUG = (0, −1, 1, 0, −2, −5, 7, −4, 0, 2, −2, 2, 2, 4, −4, 2)
P = (4, −2, −5, −2).

The real version of subroutine **FADDEJ**, which requires the real versions of subroutines MOVE, BRAINY, ZERO, and SCALE, is

```
SUBROUTINE FADDEJ(N,A,AINV,DET,ADJUG,P)
DIMENSION A(N,N),AINV(N,N),ADJUG(N,N),P(N)
CALL MOVE(N*N,A,AINV)
DO 4 K=1,N
P(K)=0.0
DO 2 I=1,N
2 P(K)=P(K)+AINV(I,I)
P(K)=P(K)/FLOAT(K)
```

[3] Gantmacher, F. R., *The Theory of Matrices*, vol. 1, Chelsea, New York, 1959, pp. 87–89.

```
      IF(K.EQ.N) GO TO 5
      CALL MOVE(N*N,AINV,ADJUG)
      DO 3 I=1,N
    3 ADJUG(I,I)=AINV(I,I)−P(K)
    4 CALL BRAINY(N,N,1,A,N,N,1,ADJUG,AINV)
    5 CALL MOVE(N*N,ADJUG,AINV)
      IF(ABS(P(N)).GE.1.E−30) CALL SCALE(1./P(N),N*N,AINV)
    7 DET=P(N)
      IF(MOD(N,2).EQ.1) RETURN
      DET=−DET
      DO 8 I=1,N
      DO 8 J=1,N
    8 ADJUG(I,J)=−ADJUG(I,J)
      RETURN
      END
```

An advantage of this computational method is that division is used only in the last step. Even if the matrix is singular, it is possible to carry out the computations for the coefficients of the characteristic polynomial and the adjugate. The complex version of subroutine FADDEJ, which requires the complex versions of subroutines MOVE, BRAINY, and ZERO, is

```
      SUBROUTINE FADDEJ(N,A,AINV,DET,ADJUG,P)
      COMPLEX A,AINV,DET,ADJUG,P
      DIMENSION A(N,N),AINV(N,N),ADJUG(N,N),P(N)
      CALL MOVE(N*N,A,AINV)
      DO 4 K=1,N
      P(K)=0.0
      DO 2 I=1,N
    2 P(K)=P(K)+AINV(I,I)
      P(K)=P(K)/FLOAT(K)
      IF(K.EQ.N) GO TO 5
      CALL MOVE (N*N,AINV,ADJUG)
      DO 3 I=1,N
    3 ADJUG(I,I)=AINV(I,I)−P(K)
    4 CALL BRAINY(N,N,1,A,N,N,1,ADJUG,AINV)
    5 CALL MOVE(N*N,ADJUG,AINV)
      IF(CABS(P(N)).LT.1.0E−30) GO TO 7
      DO 6 I=1,N
      DO 6 J=1,N
    6 AINV(I,J)=AINV(I,J)/P(N)
    7 DET=P(N)
      IF(MOD(N,2).EQ.1) RETURN
      DET=−DET
```

```
      DO 8 I=1,N
      DO 8 J=1,N
    8 ADJUG(I,J)= -ADJUG(I,J)
      RETURN
      END
```

Subroutine MAINV computes the inverse of a (not necessarily symmetric) matrix *a*. The call statement is

$$\text{CALL MAINV(N,A,B),}$$

where the subroutine inputs are

$$N = \text{order of matrix} = n$$
$$A = \text{given } n \times n \text{ matrix } a,$$

and where the subroutine output is

$$B = \text{inverse matrix } a^{-1}.$$

The program for the real version of subroutine MAINV, which requires the real versions of subroutines FADDEJ, MOVE, BRAINY, ZERO, and SCALE, is

```
      SUBROUTINE MAINV(N,A,B)
C     NMAX=LARGEST VALUE OF N TO BE PROCESSED
C     NONDUMMY DIMENSION ADJUG(NMAX*NMAX),
C     1P(NMAX)
C     FOR EXAMPLE, IF NMAX=25 THEN
      DIMENSION ADJUG(625),P(25)
C     DIMENSION A(N*N),B(N*N)
      DIMENSION A(1),B(1)
      CALL FADDEJ(N,A,B,DET,ADJUG,P)
      RETURN
      END
```

The program for the complex version of subroutine MAINV, which requires the complex versions of subroutines FADDEJ, MOVE, BRAINY, and ZERO, is

```
      SUBROUTINE MAINV(N,A,B)
      COMPLEX A,B,DET,ADJUG,P
C     NMAX=LARGEST VALUE OF N TO BE PROCESSED
C     NONDUMMY DIMENSION ADJUG(NMAX*NMAX),
C     1P(NMAX)
C     FOR EXAMPLE, IF NMAX=25 THEN
      DIMENSION ADJUG(625),P(25)
C     DIMENSION A(N*N),B(N*N)
```

```
DIMENSION A(1),B(1)
CALL FADDEJ(N,A,B,DET,ADJUG,P)
RETURN
END
```

Subroutine EUREKA finds the solution of the so-called single-channel *normal equations* which arise in least-squares filtering and prediction problems for single-channel time series. Given the set of simultaneous equations,

$$\sum_{s=0}^{m} f_s r_{t-s} = g_t \qquad \text{for } t = 0, 1, 2, \cdots, m ,$$

where the matrix

$$\begin{bmatrix} r_0 & r_1 & \cdots & r_m \\ r_{-1} & r_0 & \cdots & r_{m-1} \\ & \cdots & & \\ r_{-m} & r_{-m+1} & \cdots & r_0 \end{bmatrix}$$

is symmetric, positive definite, and *Töplitz* (i.e., has equal elements along any diagonal). In time series applications, the coefficients r_t are the *autocorrelation coefficients*. The coefficients $r_t = r_{-t}$ for $t = 0,1,2, \ldots , m$ are assumed to be known, as well as the right-hand side coefficients g_t for $t = 0, 1, 2, \ldots , m$. The coefficients f_s for $s = 0, 1, 2, \ldots , m$, which are called the *filter coefficients*, represent the unknowns. The solution is accomplished by a recursive process given by Levinson[4]; the counterpart of this recursive method for the multi-channel case is described in Sec. 6.3, where subroutine NORMEQ, which is the multichannel counterpart of EUREKA, is given. The machine time required to solve the normal equations for a filter with m coefficients is proportional to m^2 for the recursive method, as compared to m^3 for conventional methods of solving simultaneous equations. Another advantage of using the recursive method is that it only requires computer storage space proportional to m, rather than m^2 as in the case of conventional methods. An additional output of EUREKA is the set of coefficients a_s for $s = 0, 1, 2, \ldots , m$ which represent the solution of the equations

$$\sum_{s=0}^{m} a_s r_{t-s} = v\delta_t \qquad \text{for } t = 0, 1, 2, \ldots , m ,$$

where

$$a_0 = 1$$
$$\delta_t = \begin{cases} 1 & \text{when } t = 0 \\ 0 & \text{when } t \neq 0 \end{cases}$$
$$v = a_0 r_0 + a_1 r_{-1} + \cdots + a_m r_{-m} .$$

[4] Levinson, N., "The Wiener RMS (root mean square) error criterion in filter design and prediction," *J. Math. Phys.* **25**, 261–278 (1946).

In time series applications, the coefficients $a_0 = 1$, a_1, a_2, $\cdots$, a_m are the coefficients of the *prediction error operator* (or, equivalently, the *hindsight error operator*, as these two operators coincide in the single-channel case). The call statement is

CALL EUREKA(LR,R,G,F,A),

where the subroutine inputs are

LR = length of filter = $m + 1$
R = autocorrelation coefficients = $(r_0, r_1, \ldots, r_m)$
G = right-hand side coefficients = $(g_0, g_1, \ldots, g_m)$,

and where the subroutine outputs are

F = filter coefficients = $(f_0, f_1, \ldots, f_m)$
A = prediction error operator = $(a_0 = 1, a_1, a_2, \ldots, a_m)$.

As a numerical example, suppose

$$LR = 2$$
$$R = (2.5625, -1.25)$$
$$G = (-1.25, 0) .$$

Then

$$F = (-0.64012, -0.31226)$$
$$A = (1, 0.48780) .$$

As a second example, suppose

$$LR = 2$$
$$R = (10, 4)$$
$$G = (2, 0) .$$

Then

$$F = (0.23810, -0.09524)$$
$$A = (1, -0.40) .$$

Subroutine EUREKA requires no subroutine. The program is

```
SUBROUTINE EUREKA(LR,R,G,F,A)
DIMENSION R(LR),G(LR),F(LR),A(LR)
V=R(1)
D=R(2)
A(1)=1.
F(1)=G(1)/V
Q=F(1)*R(2)
IF(LR.EQ.1) RETURN
DO 4 L=2,LR
```

```
      A(L)=-D/V
      IF(L.EQ.2) GO TO 2
      L1=(L-2)/2
      L2=L1+1
      IF(L2.LT.2) GO TO 5
      DO 1 J=2,L2
      HOLD=A(J)
      K=L-J+1
      A(J)=A(J)+A(L)*A(K)
    1 A(K)=A(K)+A(L)*HOLD
    5 IF(2*L1.EQ.L-2) GO TO 2
      A(L2+1)=A(L2+1)+A(L)*A(L2+1)
    2 V=V+A(L)*D
      F(L)=(G(L)-Q)/V
      L3=L-1
      DO 3 J=1,L3
      K=L-J+1
    3 F(J)=F(J)+F(L)*A(K)
      IF(L.EQ.LR) RETURN
      D=0.0
      Q=0.0
      DO 4 I=1,L
      K=L-I+2
      D=D+A(I)*R(K)
    4 Q=Q+F(I)*R(K)
      END
```

One example of the use of subroutine EUREKA is for the calculation of the inverse of a Töplitz matrix. This is accomplished by subroutine INVTOP, which calls EUREKA. The calling statement is

CALL INVTOP(LR,R,Q,SPACE),

where the subroutine inputs are

$\qquad$ LR = order of the Töplitz matrix = m
$\qquad$ R = first row of Töplitz matrix = $(r_0, r_1, \ldots, r_m)$,

and the subroutine outputs are

Q = inverse matrix
SPACE = working space .

Three numerical examples computed by subroutine INVTOP are:

EXAMPLE (a)

$\qquad$ LR = 5
$\qquad$ R = (10.00000,   4.00000,   −1.00000,   −4.00000,   −4.00000)

Q = (0.14899,   −0.05657,   0.02727,   0.03232,   0.02677,
     −0.05657,   0.16566,   −0.07273,   0.01010,   0.03232,
      0.02727,   −0.07273,   0.16364,   −0.07273,   0.02727,
      0.03232,   0.01010,   −0.07273,   0.16566,   −0.05657,
      0.02677,   0.03232,   0.02727,   −0.05657,   0.14899).

EXAMPLE (b)

  LR = 5

  R = (10.00000,   4.00000,   1.00000,   4.00000,   4.00000)

  Q = (0.15323,   −0.06452,   0.03763,   −0.06452,   −0.01344,
       −0.06452,   0.17921,   −0.08602,   0.06810,   −0.06452,
        0.03763,   −0.08602,   0.16129,   −0.08602,   0.03763,
       −0.06452,   0.06810,   −0.08602,   0.17921,   −0.06452,
       −0.01344,   −0.06452,   0.03763,   −0.06452,   0.15323).

EXAMPLE (c)

  LR = 5

  R = (16.72605,   0.   ,   10.75437,   0.   ,   2.44141)

  Q = (0.12867,   0.   ,   −0.12045,   −0.   ,   0.05867,
          0.   ,   0.10192,   −0.   ,   −0.06553,   0.   ,
         −0.12045,   −0.   ,   0.21468,   0.   ,   −0.12045,
         −0.   ,   −0.06553,   0.   ,   0.10192,   −0.   ,
          0.05867,   0.   ,   −0.12045,   −0.   ,   0.12867).

The program for subroutine INVTOP, which requires subroutines IMPULS and EUREKA, is

```
      SUBROUTINE INVTOP(LR,R,Q,SPACE)
C     DIMENSION Q(LR*LR),SPACE(2*LR)
      DIMENSION R(LR),Q(2),SPACE(2)
      DO 1 K=1,LR
      CALL IMPULS(LR,SPACE,K)
      J=LR*(K−1)+1
      CALL EUREKA(LR,R,SPACE,Q(J),SPACE(LR+1))
    1 CONTINUE
      RETURN
      END
```

The purpose of subroutine TRIANG is to factor a positive definite symmetric matrix a into the product

$$a = s^T s,$$

where s is a triangular matrix, and s^T is the transpose of s. Given a, the subroutine computes s. The call statement is

$$\text{CALL TRIANG(N,TOP,S,SPACE)},$$

where the subroutine inputs are

$$N = n = \text{order of given matrix}$$
$$\text{TOP} = \text{given } n \times n \text{ matrix } a,$$

and where the subroutine outputs are

$$S = \text{triangular matrix } s$$
$$\text{SPACE} = \text{working space needed for the computations.}$$

For example, suppose a is the matrix

$$a = \begin{bmatrix} 64 & -48 \\ -48 & 37 \end{bmatrix}.$$

Then the subroutine inputs would be

$$N = 2$$
$$\text{TOP} = (64, -48, -48, 37),$$

and the subroutine output would be

$$S = (8, 0, -6, 1).$$

Hence

$$a = s^T s = \begin{bmatrix} 8 & 0 \\ -6 & 1 \end{bmatrix} \begin{bmatrix} 8 & -6 \\ 0 & 1 \end{bmatrix}.$$

The real version of subroutine TRIANG, which requires the real version of subroutine ZERO, is

```
SUBROUTINE TRIANG(N,TOP,S,SPACE)
DIMENSION  TOP(N,N),S(N,N),SPACE(N)
CALL ZERO(N,SPACE)
CALL ZERO(N*N,S)
DO 30 I=1,N
IP=I+1
IM=I−1
S(I,I)=SQRT(TOP(I,I)−SPACE(I))
IF(N.EQ.I) RETURN
DO 30 K=IP,N
E=0.
IF(IM.EQ.0) GO TO 20
DO 10 L=1,IM
```

```
10 E=E+S(L,I)*S(L,K)
20 X=(TOP(I,K)−E)/S(I,I)
   SPACE(K)=SPACE(K)+X*X
30 S(I,K)=X
   RETURN
   END
```

The complex version of subroutine TRIANG, which requires the complex version of subroutine ZERO, is

```
   SUBROUTINE TRIANG(N,TOP,S,SPACE)
   DIMENSION TOP(N,N),S(N,N),SPACE(N)
   COMPLEX TOP,S,SPACE
   CALL ZERO(N,SPACE)
   CALL ZERO(N*N,S)
   DO 30 I=1,N
   IP=I+1
   IM=I−1
   S(I,I)=CSQRT(TOP(I,I)−SPACE(I))
   IF(N.EQ.I) RETURN
   DO 30 K=IP,N
   E=0.
   IF(IM.EQ.0) GO TO 20
   DO 10 L=1,IM
10 E=E+S(L,I)*S(L,K)
20 X=(TOP(I,K)−E)/S(I,I)
   SPACE(K)=SPACE(K)+X*X
30 S(I,K)=X
   RETURN
   END
```

Given the $n \times n$ matrix $a = [a_{ij}]$, its *trace* or *spur* is defined as the sum of its diagonal elements, that is,

$$\text{tr } a = \sum_{i=1}^{n} a_{ii}.$$

Fortran FUNCTION SPUR(N,A) computes the trace of a square matrix. The function inputs are

$$N = \text{order of matrix} = n$$
$$A = \text{matrix } a,$$

and the value of the function is

$$SPUR(N,A) = \text{tr } a.$$

The program is

```
FUNCTION SPUR(N,A)
DIMENSION A(N,N)
SPUR=0.0
DO 1 I=1,N
1 SPUR=SPUR+A(I,I)
RETURN
END
```

1.10 Transposition of rectangular matrices

A permutation is a one-to-one transformation of a finite set into itself. For instance, the set might consist of 5 digits 1, 2, 3, 4, 5. One permutation might be the transformation T, where

$$1T = 2, \quad 2T = 3, \quad 3T = 4, \quad 4T = 5, \quad 5T = 1 .$$

Another permutation might be the transformation T′ with

$$1T' = 2, \quad 2T' = 3, \quad 3T' = 1, \quad 4T' = 5, \quad 5T' = 4 .$$

In general, permutations do not commute; in this case, one can compute T T′ and T′ T and verify that T T′ $\neq$ T′ T. Permutations, which, like the permutation T defined above, give a circular rearrangment of the symbols permuted, are called cyclic permutations. A convenient notation for cyclic permutations is one in which we write down inside parentheses first any symbol involved, then its transform, . . . , and finally the symbol transformed into the original symbol. Thus the permutation T given above might be written as (1, 2, 3, 4, 5) or as (2, 3, 4, 5, 1). Another example is the permutation $n \rightarrow n + 1$ (modulo 8); this permutation may be written as (0, 1, 2, 3, 4, 5, 6, 7) or as (5, 6, 7, 0, 1, 2, 3, 4).

Let us now consider a cyclic permutation of n symbols, say C = (a_1, a_2, . . . , a_n), which carries a_i into a_{i+1}. Hence C^2 has the doubled effect of carrying each a_i into a_{i+2}, and in general C^k carries each a_i into a_{i+k}, where all subscripts are to be reduced modulo n. Hence C^k is equal to the identity transformation I if and only if a_{i+k} equals a_i; that is, if and only if $k \equiv 0$ (modulo n). The smallest value of k with $C^k = I$ is then n itself, so n represents the order of the permutation. Thus a cyclic permutation of n symbols has order n.

The notational convention for a cyclic permutation can be extended to any permutation. For example, the permutation T′ defined above cyclically permutes the digits 1, 2, 3 by themselves, and 4, 5 by themselves. Hence it is a product of these two cycles:

$$(1, 2, 3)(4, 5) = (4, 5)(1, 2, 3) .$$

This product can be written in either order, since the symbols permuted by (1, 2, 3) are left unchanged by (4, 5), which means that the successive application of these permutations in either order gives the same result.

Now let us consider any permutation of n symbols, say P. Let us select any symbol and denote it by a_1. Let us denote a_1P by a_2, a_2P by $a_3, \ldots, a_{q-1}P$ by a_q, until $a_qP = a_i$ is some element already named. Because the antecedent of any a_i (where $i > 1$) is a_{i-1} and because a permutation is a one-to-one transformation, it follows that a_qP can only be a_1. Thus the effect of P on the letters $a_1, a_2, \ldots, a_q$ is the cycle $(a_1, a_2, \ldots, a_q)$. Moreover, $(a_1, a_2, \ldots, a_q)$ contains with any symbol a_i its antecedent; hence P permutes the remaining symbols among themselves. By induction it follows that any permutation P can be written as a product of cycles, no two of which alter the same symbols. More briefly, any permutation P can be written as a product of disjoint cycles. Conversely, any product of disjoint cycles represents a permutation. More-over, it may be shown that the order of any permutation P is the least common multiple of the lengths of its disjoint cycles.

In the Fortran IV language, arrays are stored in column order in increasing storage locations, with the first of their subscripts varying most rapidly and the last varying least rapidly. Thus a rectangular (i.e., $m \times n$) matrix $[a_{ij}]$ can be stored as a two-dimensional array as follows, from the lowest core storage location to the highest:

$$a_{11}, a_{21}, \ldots, a_{m1}, a_{12}, a_{22}, \ldots, a_{m2}, \ldots, a_{mn} .$$

For example, the rectangular matrix

$$\mathbf{A} = \begin{bmatrix} a_{11} & a_{12} & a_{13} \\ a_{21} & a_{22} & a_{23} \end{bmatrix}$$

and its transpose

$$\mathbf{A}^\mathrm{T} = \begin{bmatrix} a_{11} & a_{21} \\ a_{12} & a_{22} \\ a_{13} & a_{23} \end{bmatrix}$$

are stored in core as:

Location	A	Location	$\mathbf{A}^\mathrm{T}$
1	a_{11}	1	a_{11}
2	a_{21}	2	a_{12}
3	a_{12}	3	a_{13}
4	a_{22}	4	a_{21}
5	a_{13}	5	a_{22}
6	a_{23}	6	a_{23}

Hence the transposition of the matrix A represents the permutation of the storage locations given by

$$\begin{array}{llll} a_{11} & : & 1 & \to & 1 \\ a_{21} & : & 2 & \to & 4 \\ a_{12} & : & 3 & \to & 2 \end{array}$$

$$
\begin{aligned}
a_{22} &: \quad 4 \;\rightarrow\; 5 \\
a_{13} &: \quad 5 \;\rightarrow\; 3 \\
a_{23} &: \quad 6 \;\rightarrow\; 6 \,.
\end{aligned}
$$

This permutation breaks down into the 3 disjoint cycles:

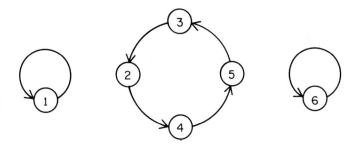

Similarly the permutation representing the transposition of a 3×4 matrix breaks down into the disjoint cycles:

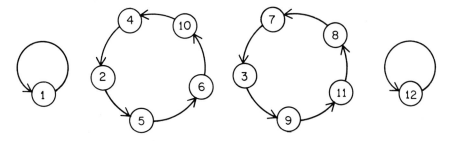

The relative storage location for the element a_{ij} of an $m \times n$ matrix $\mathbf{A} = [a_{ij}]$ is given by $i + (j-1)\, m$, whereas the storage location for the element a_{ij} when the matrix $\mathbf{A}$ is transposed becomes $j + (i-1)\, n$. Hence the required permutation is defined by

$$
i + (j-1)\, m \rightarrow j + (i-1)\, n \,.
$$

Subroutine MATRAN makes use of this permutation in order to transpose a rectangular matrix on top of itself in storage. A typical calling statement would be

$$
\text{CALL MATRAN(M,N,A),}
$$

where the subroutine inputs are

$$
\begin{aligned}
\text{M} &= \text{number of rows in matrix A} \\
\text{N} &= \text{number of columns in matrix A} \\
\text{A} &= \text{matrix A,}
\end{aligned}
$$

and the subroutine output is

$$A = \text{matrix } A^T \text{ (i.e., A transpose).}$$

Both M and N are of integer type, whereas A is of real type although sub-routine MATRAN looks at A as if it were of integer type. Subroutine MATRAN is machine-dependent in that it requires that the integers are right-adjusted in the storage cell, and that the right bit is the most insignificant in a real type number. The right bit is lost for each element in A. The subroutine code is

```
      SUBROUTINE MATRAN(M,N,MATRIX)
      DIMENSION MATRIX(1)
      K=M*N-1
      DO 1 I=2,K
    1 MATRIX(I)=(MATRIX(I)/2)*2
      DO 3 L=2,K
      IF(MATRIX(L).NE.(MATRIX(L)/2)*2) GO TO 3
      KEEP=MATRIX(L)
      IJ=L
    2 JLESS1=(IJ-1)/M
      I=IJ-JLESS1*M
      J=JLESS1+1
      JI=J+(I-1)*N
      KATCH=MATRIX(JI)
      MATRIX(JI)=KEEP+1
      KEEP=KATCH
      IJ=JI
      IF(IJ.NE.L) GO TO 2
    3 CONTINUE
      RETURN
      END
```

1.11 Input and output subroutines

The purpose of subroutine INDATA is to read a set of data values from cards into the computer. The first card contains the number of data points punched as I5 followed by the data FORMAT starting in column 7. More specifically, this FORMAT is made up of the beginning left parenthesis character, the final right parenthesis character, and the specifications enclosed therein. The data values are punched on the following cards according to the FORMAT statement given on the first card. The call statement is

CALL INDATA(LD,D)

which reads the given cards, thereby yielding as subroutine output the quan-tities

$$LD = \text{length of data} = n$$
$$D = \text{data} = (x_1, x_2, \ldots, x_n)$$

stored in the computer. Moreover, these quantities are also printed out by the computer; this *echo-print* feature of subroutine INDATA enables the programmer to know what specific data values were read in at that point. As an example, suppose the data cards are

Card 1 $b\ b\ b\ b\ 5\ b\ (\ 1\ X\ ,\ 3\ F\ 4\ .\ 1\ )\ b\ b\ b\ b\ \ldots$
Card 2 $b\ b\ b\ 3\ .\ b\ -\ 4\ .\ b\ 6\ .\ 1\ b\ b\ b\ b\ b\ b\ b\ \ldots$
Card 3 $b\ 2\ .\ 2\ b\ b\ b\ 1\ .\ b\ b\ b\ b\ b\ b\ b\ b\ b\ b\ b\ \ldots.$

Then the call statement above would cause

$$LD = 5$$
$$D = (3, -4, 6.1, 2.2, 1)$$

to be stored in the machine and

$b\ b\ b\ 5\ b\ b\ b\ b\ b\ b\ b\ b\ b\ b\ b\ \ldots$
$b\ 3\ .\ 0\ -\ 4\ .\ 0\ b\ 6\ .\ 1\ b\ b\ \ldots$
$b\ 2\ .\ 2\ b\ 1\ .\ 0\ b\ b\ b\ b\ b\ b\ \ldots$

to be printed out. Here the b characters indicate blanks. The program for subroutine INDATA is

```
      SUBROUTINE INDATA(LD,D)
C     FOR COMPLEX VERSION REMOVE THE C FROM
C     1COLUMN 1 OF NEXT CARD
C     COMPLEX D
C     NONDUMMY DIMENSION FMT(9)
      DIMENSION FMT(9)
      DIMENSION D(LD)
      READ 1,LD,(FMT(I),I=1,9)
    1 FORMAT(I5,1X,9A8)
      READ FMT,(D(I),I=1,LD)
      PRINT 2,LD
    2 FORMAT(1H0,I4)
      PRINT FMT,(D(I),I=1,LD)
      RETURN
      END
```

This program is machine-dependent to the extent that the form A8 appears in statement 1, and hence this version of the program is valid for a computer with 48 bits per word. For computers with 36 bits per word, the A8 must be changed to A6.

The purpose of subroutine OUTDAT is to print out an array as a sequence of numbers. The call statement is

CALL OUTDAT(LD,D),

where the subroutine inputs are

$$LD = \text{length of data} = n$$
$$D = \text{data} = (x_1, x_2 \ldots, x_n).$$

The subroutine output would be the printed values of the data. The program is

```
      SUBROUTINE OUTDAT(LD,D)
      DIMENSION D(LD)
C     FOR COMPLEX VERSION REMOVE THE C FROM
C     1COLUMN 1 OF NEXT CARD
C     COMPLEX D
      PRINT 1,(D(I),I=1,LD)
C     FOR COMPLEX VERSION REPLACE NEXT CARD BY A
C     1COMPLEX FORMAT SPECIFICATION
    1 FORMAT(4F15.4)
C     THE FOREGOING FORMAT SPECIFICATION SHOULD
C     1BE CHANGED TO MEET THE INDIVIDUAL REQUIRE-
C     2MENTS OF SPECIFIC JOBS.
      RETURN
      END
```

The purpose of subroutine RITE is to print out an array as a sequence of matrices. The call statement is

CALL RITE(NB,M,N,L,A),

where the subroutine inputs are

NB = number of matrices printed per line = u
M = number of rows in each matrix a_k
N = number of columns in each matrix a_k
L = number of matrices = q
A = $(a_1, a_2, \ldots, a_q)$ stored in the multiplexed mode, i.e., stored as
A(I, J, K), where I denotes the row, J denotes the column, and
K denotes the matrix index.

The subroutine output would be the printed matrices

$$
\begin{array}{cccc}
a_1 & a_2 & \cdots & a_u \\
a_{u+1} & a_{u+2} & \cdots & a_{2u} \\
\cdots & & \cdots & \cdots \\
& \cdots & a_{q-1} & a_q .
\end{array}
$$

For example, suppose that the array A contains

$$A = (1 \ \ 2, 3, 4, 5, \ldots, 98, 99, 100) .$$

Then the statement

$$\text{CALL RITE}(2,1,1,3,A)$$

would produce the output

[1.] [2.]
[3.] .

The statement

$$\text{CALL RITE}(4,3,2,10,A)$$

would produce the output

$$\begin{bmatrix} 1. & 4. \\ 2. & 5. \\ 3. & 6. \end{bmatrix} \begin{bmatrix} 7. & 10. \\ 8. & 11. \\ 9. & 12. \end{bmatrix} \begin{bmatrix} 13. & 16. \\ 14. & 17. \\ 15. & 18. \end{bmatrix} \begin{bmatrix} 19. & 22. \\ 20. & 23. \\ 21. & 24. \end{bmatrix}$$

$$\begin{bmatrix} 25. & 28. \\ 26. & 29. \\ 27. & 30. \end{bmatrix} \begin{bmatrix} 31. & 34. \\ 32. & 35. \\ 33. & 36. \end{bmatrix} \begin{bmatrix} 37. & 40. \\ 38. & 41. \\ 39. & 42. \end{bmatrix} \begin{bmatrix} 43. & 46. \\ 44. & 47. \\ 45. & 48. \end{bmatrix}$$

$$\begin{bmatrix} 49. & 52. \\ 50. & 53. \\ 51. & 54. \end{bmatrix} \begin{bmatrix} 55. & 58. \\ 56. & 59. \\ 57. & 60. \end{bmatrix} .$$

In both of the above examples, we have blocked off the matrices with square brackets for clarity; subroutine RITE would produce only the numbers shown. The program is

```
      SUBROUTINE RITE(NB,M,N,L,A)
C     NONDUMMY DIMENSION B(30)
      DIMENSION B(30)
      DIMENSION A(M,N,L)
C     FOR COMPLEX VERSION REMOVE THE C FROM
C     1COLUMN 1 OF NEXT CARD
C     COMPLEX A,B
      LL=L
      K1=-NB+1
      K2=0
    1 LLL=LL-NB
      IF(LLL.LT.0) GO TO 4
      K1=K1+NB
      K2=K2+NB
      DO 3 I=1,M
      II=0
      DO 2 K=K1,K2
      DO 2 J=1,N
      II=II+1
```

```
   2 B(II) = A(I,J,K)
     NBN = NB*N
   3 PRINT 100,(B(II),II = 1,NBN)
     PRINT 25
  25 FORMAT(1H0)
     LL = LLL
     IF(LL.EQ.0) GO TO 7
     GO TO 1
   4 K1 = K1+NB
     K2 = K2+LL
     DO 6 I = 1,M
     II = 0
     DO 5 K = K1,K2
     DO 5 J = 1,N
     II = II+1
   5 B(II) = A(I,J,K)
     LLN = LL*N
   6 PRINT 100,(B(II),II = 1,LLN)
   7 PRINT 25
C    FOR COMPLEX VERSION REPLACE NEXT CARD BY A
C    1COMPLEX FORMAT SPECIFICATION
 100 FORMAT(1X,12F9.3)
C    THE FOREGOING FORMAT SPECIFICATION SHOULD BE
C    1CHANGED TO MEET THE INDIVIDUAL REQUIREMENTS
C    2OF SPECIFIC JOBS.
     RETURN
     END
```

2

Single-Channel Digital
Filtering and Spectral Analysis

2.1 Single-channel operators

Any variable which is generated sequentially in time constitutes a single-channel time series. The use of digital computers to process time series is now well established. Our purpose in this chapter is to give a systematic presentation of digital filtering and spectral analysis of single-channel time series, and by so doing bring out some techniques and interpretations which deserve further attention.

A *discrete operator* (or *discrete filter*) is one by which a discrete input is transformed into a discrete output. The input and output are *digital signals*, or *time series*, which are defined at discrete, equally spaced time points $t = n \Delta t$, where n is an integer-valued time index and Δt is the time spacing. Usually it is convenient to define the time unit equal to the time spacing, that is, to define $\Delta t = 1$ time unit, in which case the time parameter t takes on integer values: $t = \ldots, -1, 0, 1, 2, \ldots$. We will consider only time series defined at equally spaced instants one unit apart. A time series, say $\ldots, x_{-1}, x_0, x_1, x_2, \ldots$, may arise naturally, as an economic time series of daily prices or quantities, or it may arise from sampling a continuous function, such as an electric voltage in a radar receiver.

A *linear time-invariant discrete operator* may be characterized by a sequence of numerical coefficients $(. . . , a_{-1}, a_0, a_1, a_2, . . .)$, which are called the *impulse response function* of the system. The system transforms the input x_t into the output y_t by means of the *moving summation*, or (discrete) *convolution*, formula[5]

$$y_t = \cdots + a_{-1}x_{t+1} + a_0x_t + a_1x_{t-1} + a_2x_{t-2} + \cdots$$

which holds for all discrete time points (integers) t. Briefly, we denote this convolution formula as $y_t = a_t * x_t$. This formula may be divided into two terms, namely

$$y_t = \sum_{s=-\infty}^{-1} a_s x_{t-s} + \sum_{s=0}^{\infty} a_s x_{t-s} .$$

If we regard the time instant t as the present time, then the first term involves the future values $. . . , x_{t+2}, x_{t+1}$ of the input time series, whereas the second term involves the present and past values $x_t, x_{t-1}, x_{t-2}, . . .$ of the input time series. As a result the coefficients involved in the first term, namely $(. . . , a_{-2}, a_{-1})$, represent the *anticipation component* of the impulse response function, and the coefficients involved in the second term, namely $(a_0, a_1, a_2, . . .)$, represent the *memory component* of the impulse response function. If time t represents historical, or so-called nominal, time, in which case all time points are in actuality past events, then an operator with both an anticipation component and a memory component may be used in order to transform an input time series to an output time series. However, if time t represents real time, then, of course, the future values $. . . , x_{t+2}, x_{t+1}$ of the input time series are not available at the present time instant t, and hence only an operator with a memory component, and no anticipation component, can be used. Of course, if we are willing to tolerate a time delay between input and output, then those future values which occur during this time delay become available, and hence that portion of the anticipation component corresponding to this delay can be used in order to transform the input to the output. In radar systems such a time delay is usually introduced, so that although the system is operating in real time, some portion of the anticipation component may be used, thereby improving the information handling capacity of the system. An operator with only a memory component is said to be *realizable* (in real time), whereas an operator which involves an anticipation component is *nonrealizable*. This is the same definition of realizability as that given in electrical engineering.

Prediction operators by their very nature are designed to operate in real time and hence must be realizable. On the other hand, various types of smoothing operators are designed to operate in historical time, or else in real

---

[5] This convolution formula may be computed by means of subroutine FOLD given in Sec. 1.8.

time with a sufficiently long time delay, and hence need not be realizable in real time.

The *z-transform* of a discrete sequence $(. . . , a_{-1}, a_0, a_1, a_2, . . .)$ is defined as the expression

$$A(z) = \sum_{t=-\infty}^{\infty} a_t z^t$$

whose coefficient for z^t is the value a_t of the sequence at the tth time index. In case the sequence is one-sided (that is, $a_t = 0$ for $t < 0$), then the z-transform becomes the power series

$$A(z) = \sum_{t=0}^{\infty} a_t z^t .$$

In the case of a realizable operator $(a_0, a_1, a_2, . . . , a_m)$ with a finite number $(= m + 1)$ of coefficients, the z-transform is the polynomial

$$A(z) = a_0 + a_1 z + a_2 z^2 + \cdots + a_m z^m .$$

Two important properties of the z-transform which are used frequently are:

(1) Convolution in the time domain corresponds to multiplication in the z-domain; that is, if $X(z)$, $A(z)$, and $Y(z)$ are the z-transforms of the sequences x_t, a_t, and y_t, respectively, then the convolution $y_t = a_t * x_t$ in the time domain corresponds to the multiplication $Y(z) = A(z)X(z)$ in the z-domain.

(2) The z-transform evaluated on the unit circle $z = e^{-2\pi i f}$ corresponds to the Fourier transform; that is, the (discrete) Fourier transform of the sequence a_t is

$$A(e^{-2\pi i f}) = \sum_{t=-\infty}^{\infty} a_t e^{-2\pi i f t} .$$

This expression is called the *transfer function* or *filter characteristics* of the operator. Frequency f in cycles per discrete time unit and angular frequency ω in radians per discrete time unit are related by the equation

$$\omega = 2\pi f .$$

2.2 Single-channel spectral subroutines

Two basic subroutines are COSTAB, which generates a full wavelength cosine table, and SINTAB, which generates a full wavelength sine table. The call statement for COSTAB is

CALL COSTAB(M,TABLE) ,

where the subroutine input is

$$M = m + 1,$$

and the subroutine output is the full wavelength cosine table of length $2*M - 1 = 2m + 1$ given by

$$\text{TABLE} = (\cos 0, \cos \theta, \cos 2\theta, \cos 3\theta, \ldots ,$$
$$\cos (2m-1)\theta, \cos 2m\theta),$$

where $\theta = \pi/m$. Note that

$$\text{TABLE}(1) = \text{TABLE}(2*M-1) = 1$$
$$\text{TABLE}(M-1) = -1.$$

The call statement for SINTAB is

$$\text{CALL SINTAB(M,TABLE)},$$

where the subroutine input is

$$M = m+1,$$

and the subroutine output is the full wavelength sine table of length $2*M-1 = 2m+1$ given by

$$\text{TABLE} = (\sin 0, \sin \theta, \sin 2\theta, \sin 3\theta, \ldots ,$$
$$\sin (2\ m-1)\theta, \sin 2\ m\theta),$$

where $\theta = \pi/m$. Note that

$$\text{TABLE}(1) = \text{TABLE}(M-1) = \text{TABLE}(2*M-1) = 0.0.$$

The programs are

```
      SUBROUTINE  COSTAB(M,TABLE)
C     DIMENSION  TABLE(M+M-1)
      DIMENSION  TABLE(2)
      FM=M+M-2
      MM=M+M-1
      DO 10 I=1,MM
   10 TABLE(I)=COS(FLOAT(I-1)*6.2831853/FM)
      RETURN
      END

      SUBROUTINE  SINTAB(M,TABLE)
C     DIMENSION  TABLE(M+M-1)
      DIMENSION  TABLE(2)
      FM=M+M-2
      MM=M+M-1
      DO 10 I=1,MM
   10 TABLE(I)=SIN(FLOAT(I-1)*6.2831853/FM)
      RETURN
      END
```

Subroutine COSP computes the kth value of either a cosine transform or a sine transform. The call statement is

CALL COSP(N,DATA,TABLE,M,K,C),

where the subroutine inputs are

$\quad\quad$ N = $n+1$
$\quad$ DATA $= (x_0, x_1, x_2, \ldots, x_n)$
$\quad$ TABLE $=$ either a full wavelength cosine table of length
$\quad\quad\quad\quad$ $2*M-1$ with TABLE (1) $=$ TABLE ($2*M-1$) $= 1.0$,
$\quad\quad\quad\quad$ or a full wavelength sine table of length
$\quad\quad\quad\quad$ $2*M-1$ with TABLE (1) $=$ TABLE ($2*M-1$) $= 0.0$
$\quad\quad$ M $= m+1$
$\quad\quad$ K $= k+1$, where $0 \leqslant k \leqslant m$,

and where the subroutine output is either

$$C = c_k \equiv \sum_{i=0}^{n} x_i \cos\left(\frac{\pi i k}{m}\right)$$

if TABLE is the cosine table, or

$$C = s_k \equiv \sum_{i=0}^{n} x_i \sin\left(\frac{\pi i k}{m}\right)$$

if TABLE is the sine table. TABLE is conveniently generated subroutine COSTAB in the case of the cosine table, or by subroutine SINTAB in the case of the sine table. The program for subroutine COSP is

```
      SUBROUTINE  COSP(N,DATA,TABLE,M,K,C)
C     DIMENSION  DATA(N),TABLE(2*M-1)
      DIMENSION  DATA(2),TABLE(2)
      J=1
      C=0.
      KK=K-1
      MM=M+M-1
      MMM=MM-1
      DO 20 I=1,N
      C=C+DATA(I)*TABLE(J)
      J=J+KK
      IF(J-MM) 20,20,10
   10 J=J-MMM
   20 CONTINUE
      RETURN
      END
```

Subroutine NLOGN computes the discrete Fourier transform by the n log n method, also known as the fast Fourier transform method.[6,7] This extremely efficient method requires that the data consists of 2^n values where n is some positive integer. Subroutine NLOGN makes use of no subroutines. The call statement is

$$\text{CALL NLOGN(N,X,SIGN),}$$

where the subroutine inputs are

$$N = n$$
$$X = (x_0, x_1, x_2, \ldots, x_{q-1}), \text{ where } q = 2^n$$
$$\text{(complex numbers)}$$
$$\text{SIGN} = -1.0 \text{ or } 1.0,$$

and the subroutine output is

$$X = (y_0, y_1, y_2, \ldots, y_{q-1})$$
$$\text{(complex numbers),}$$

where

$$y_j = \sum_{k=0}^{q-1} x_k e^{-2\pi ikj/q} \qquad \text{if SIGN} = -1.0$$

or

$$y_j = \frac{1}{q} \sum_{k=0}^{q-1} x_k e^{2\pi ikj/q} \qquad \text{if SIGN} = 1.0.$$

If x_k for $k = 0, 1, \ldots, q-1$ represents a time function, then the subroutine output y_j for $j = 0, 1, \ldots, q-1$ in the case of SIGN $= -1.0$ represents the frequency spectrum at frequencies $f = j/q$ cycles per time unit, where $j = 0, 1, \ldots, q-1$. In particular, if x_k is real-valued, then

$$\text{Re}\{y_j\} = \sum_{k=0}^{q-1} x_k \cos (2\pi ikj/q)$$

is the cosine spectrum and

$$\text{Im}\{y_j\} = -\sum_{k=0}^{q-1} x_k \sin (2\pi ikj/q)$$

is the sine spectrum. To recover the time function x_k we may call NLOGN again, but this time with SIGN $= +1.0$. That is, given the array X, the call statements one after the other

$$\text{CALL NLOGN(N,X,-1.0)}$$
$$\text{CALL NLOGN(N,X,1.0)}$$

---

[6] Cooley, J. S., and J. W. Tukey, "An algorithm for the machine calculation of complex Fourier series," *Math. Computation* **19**, 297–301 (1965).
[7] Simpson, S. M., *Time Series Computations in FORTRAN and FAP*, Addison-Wesley, Reading, Mass., 1966.

yield the same X as final output, for

$$\frac{1}{q}\sum_{j=0}^{q-1}\left[\sum_{k=0}^{q-1} x_k\, e^{-2\pi i k j/q}\right] e^{2\pi i jm/q} = x_m\,.$$

Likewise, given the array X, the call statements one after the other

CALL NLOGN(N,X,1.0)
CALL NLOGN(N,X,−1.0)

yield the same X as final output.
    As a numerical example, suppose we have the function

X = (1, 2, 3, 4).

Then the call statement

CALL NLOGN(2,X,1.0)

would yield the Fourier transform

X = (2.5, −0.5 − 0.5i, −0.5, −0.5 + 0.5i) .

If we then execute the call statement

CALL NLOGN(2,X,−1.0),

we return to given function

X = (1, 2, 3, 4) .

    The program for the fast Fourier transform method is

```
      SUBROUTINE NLOGN(N,X,SIGN)
C     NMAX=LARGEST VALUE OF N TO BE PROCESSED
C     NONDUMMY DIMENSION M(NMAX)
C     FOR EXAMPLE, IF NMAX=25 THEN
      DIMENSION M(25)
C     DIMENSION X(2**N)
      DIMENSION X(2)
      COMPLEX X,WK,HOLD,Q
      LX=2**N
      DO 1 I=1,N
    1 M(I)=2**(N−I)
      DO 4 L=1,N
      NBLOCK=2**(L−1)
      LBLOCK=LX/NBLOCK
      LBHALF=LBLOCK/2
      K=0
      DO 4 IBLOCK=1,NBLOCK
      FK=K
```

```
      FLX=LX
      V=SIGN*6.2831853*FK/FLX
      WK=CMPLX(COS(V),SIN(V))
      ISTART=LBLOCK*(IBLOCK−1)
      DO 2 I=1,LBHALF
      J=ISTART+1
      JH=J+LBHALF
      Q=X(JH)*WK
      X(JH)=X(J)−Q
      X(J)=X(J)+Q
    2 CONTINUE
      DO 3 I=2,N
      II=I
      IF (K.LT.M(I)) GO TO 4
    3 K=K−M(I)
    4 K=K+M(II)
      K=0
      DO 7 J=1,LX
      IF (K.LT.J) GO TO 5
      HOLD=X(J)
      X(J)=X(K+1)
      X(K+1)=HOLD
    5 DO 6 I=1,N
      II=I
      IF(K.LT.M(I)) GO TO 7
    6 K=K−M(I)
    7 K=K+M(II)
      IF(SIGN.LT.0.0) RETURN
      DO 8 I=1,LX
    8 X(I)=X(I)/FLX
      RETURN
      END
```

Subroutine TRIG computes one value of the Fourier transform by the sum-of-angles trigonometric formulas for sine and cosine. The call statement is

CALL TRIG(LX,X,W,S,C),

where the subroutine inputs are

$$LX = \text{length of } X = n$$
$$X = (x_0, x_1, \ldots , x_n)$$
$$W = \text{angular frequency} = \omega$$
$$\text{(in radians per time unit)},$$

and the subroutine outputs are

$$S = \sum_{k=0}^{n-1} x_k \sin \omega k = \text{sine transform at } \omega$$

$$C = \sum_{k=0}^{n-1} x_k \cos \omega k = \text{cosine transform at } \omega \ .$$

The program is

```
      SUBROUTINE  TRIG(LX,X,W,S,C)
      DIMENSION  X(LX)
      COSNW=1.
      SINNW=0.
      SINW=SIN(W)
      COSW=COS(W)
      S=0.0
      C=0.0
      DO  10  I=1,LX
      C=C+COSNW*X(I)
      S=S+SINNW*X(I)
      T=COSW*COSNW−SINW*SINNW
      SINNW=COSW*SINNW+SINW*COSNW
  10  COSNW=T
      RETURN
      END
```

Subroutine DRUM makes a phase curve continuous; it is used by sub-routine CAST. The program for DRUM is

```
      SUBROUTINE  DRUM(LPHZ,PHZ)
      DIMENSION  PHZ(LPHZ)
      PJ=0.
      DO  40   I=2,LPHZ
      IF(ABS(PHZ(I)+PJ−PHZ(I−1))−3.14159265)  40,40,10
  10  IF(PHZ(I)+PJ−PHZ(I−1))   20,40,30
  20  PJ=PJ+3.14159265*2.
      GO  TO  40
  30  PJ=PJ−3.14159265*2.
  40  PHZ(I)=PHZ(I)+PJ
      RETURN
      END
```

Subroutine POLAR computes polar coordinates; it is also used by sub-routine CAST. The program is

```
      SUBROUTINE POLAR(L,RE,XIM,AMP,PHZ)
      DIMENSION RE(L),XIM(L),AMP(L),PHZ(L)
      PI=3.14159265
      DO 110  I=1,L
      AMP(I)=SQRT(RE(I)**2+XIM(I)**2)
      IF(XIM(I))  10,20,30
  10  IF(RE(I))  40,50,60
  20  IF(RE(I))  70,80,60
  30  IF(RE(I))  90,100,60
  40  PHZ(I)=ATAN(XIM(I)/RE(I))-PI
      GO TO 110
  50  PHZ(I)=-PI/2.0
      GO TO 110
  60  PHZ(I)=ATAN(XIM(I)/RE(I))
      GO TO 110
  70  PHZ(I)=-PI
      GO TO 110
  80  PHZ(I)=0.0
      GO TO 110
  90  PHZ(I)=ATAN(XIM(I)/RE(I))+PI
      GO TO 110
 100  PHZ(I)=PI/2.0
 110  CONTINUE
      RETURN
      END
```

Given a finite operator or wavelet $(a_0, a_1, \ldots, a_m)$, subroutine CAST computes its cosine and sine transforms

$$C(f) = \sum_{s=0}^{m} a_s \cos 2\pi fs$$

$$S(f) = \sum_{s=0}^{m} a_s \sin 2\pi fs$$

and the amplitude and phase-lag spectra

$$|A(f)| = [C^2(f) + S^2(f)]^{1/2}$$
$$\theta(f) = \arctan[S(f)/C(f)]$$

each for $f = 0, \Delta f, 2\Delta f, \ldots, n\Delta f$, where $\Delta f = (1/2n)$ cycles per time unit. Subroutine CAST requires subroutines POLYEV, POLAR, and DRUM. The call statement is

CALL CAST(LW,W,LT,TCOS,TSIN,AMP,PHZ),

where the subroutine inputs are

LW = length of W = $m + 1$
W = $(a_0, a_1, \ldots, a_m)$
LT = length of TCOS,TSIN,AMP, or PHZ = $n + 1$,

and where the subroutine outputs are

TCOS = cosine transform
TSIN = sine transform
AMP = amplitude spectrum
PHZ = phase-lag spectrum .

As a numerical example, suppose

LW = 7
W = (50, −65, 28, 68, 6, −9, −2)
LT = 19 .

Then we would have

AMP = (77, 75, 70, 63, 58, 63, 80, 104, 127, 146,
156, 158, 152, 141, 126, 112, 99, 90, 88)
PHZ = (0, 0.38, 0.81, 1.34, 2.03, 2.81, 3.52, 4.07,
4.53, 4.92, 5.26, 5.56, 5.82, 6.04, 6.20,
6.30, 6.34, 6.33, 6.28) ,

where the values of AMP and PHZ correspond to the frequencies

f = 0, 10, 20, 30, . . . , 170, 180 degrees per time unit.

The program is

```
SUBROUTINE  CAST(LW,W,LT,TCOS,TSIN,AMP,PHZ)
DIMENSION  W(LW),TCOS(LT),TSIN(LT),AMP(LT),PHZ(LT)
COMPLEX  X,A
DANG=3.14159265/FLOAT(LT−1)
ANG=0.0
DO 10  I=1,LT
X=CMPLX(COS(ANG),SIN(ANG))
CALL  POLYEV(LW,W,X,A)
TCOS(I)=REAL(A)
TSIN(I)=AIMAG(A)
10 ANG=ANG+DANG
```

```
      CALL POLAR(LT,TCOS,TSIN,AMP,PHZ)
      CALL DRUM(LT,PHZ)
      RETURN
      END
```

2.3 Minimum delay, mixed delay, and maximum delay

In order to study the characteristic properties of a finite discrete realizable operator, we may factor the operator into simpler components and then use the properties of these components to classify the given operator. The z-transform of the finite discrete operator $(a_0, a_1, a_2, \ldots, a_m)$ can be factored into the form

$$A(z) = a_0 + a_1 z + a_2 z^2 + \cdots + a_m z^m$$
$$= a_m(z - z_1)(z - z_2) \ldots (z - z_m),$$

where z_i (for $i = 1, 2, \ldots, m$) are the zeros (or roots) of the polynomial $A(z)$. Some or all of these roots may be complex; in the case when the coefficients $(a_0, a_1, \ldots, a_m)$ are real, then all complex roots must occur in complex conjugate pairs. In the time domain, this factorization exhibits the operator as the result of cascaded convolutions of *two coefficient operators*, or *couplets*, as given by

$$(a_0, a_1, a_2, \ldots, a_m) = a_m(-z_1, 1) * (-z_2, 1) * \cdots * (-z_m, 1).$$

A couplet (c_0, c_1) is said to be *minimum delay*, provided the magnitude of its first coefficient equals or exceeds the magnitude of its second coefficient that is, provided $|c_0| \geqslant |c_1|$. On the other hand, a couplet (c_0, c_1) is said to be *maximum delay*, provided the magnitude of its second coefficient equals or exceeds the magnitude of its first coefficient, that is, provided $|c_1| \geqslant |c_0|$. Thus an *equi-delay* couplet (that is, one whose two coefficients have the same magnitude) may be regarded as both minimum delay and maximum delay. For example, the couplet $(2, 1)$ is minimum delay, the couplet $(3, 4)$ is maximum delay, and the couplet $(1, -1)$ is equi-delay. The concepts of minimum delay and maximum delay can be extended to longer operators as follows. If each couplet appearing in the factorization of a realizable operator is minimum delay, then the operator is called *minimum delay*. If each couplet appearing in the factorization of a realizable operator is maximum delay, then the operator is called *maximum delay*. However, if the couplets appearing in the factorization of a realizable operator are a mixture of minimum-delay and maximum-delay ones, then the operator is called *mixed delay*. As we have defined them, the concepts of minimum delay, maximum delay, and mixed delay apply only in the case of realizable operators.

In summary let us give the following definitions. A sequence a_t of numerical coefficients defined for integer time indices t represents:

(1) a *realizable operator*, provided that it is one-sided in the sense that its coefficients for negative time indices vanish (that is, provided $a_t = 0$ for $t < 0$).

(2) a *stable operator*, provided that it has finite energy in the sense that the sum of squares of its coefficients is finite (that is, provided $\cdots + a_{-2}^2 + a_{-1}^2 + a_0^2 + a_1^2 + a_2^2 + \cdots$ is finite).

(3) a *wavelet*, provided that it is realizable and stable.

(4) a *minimum-delay operator*,[8] provided that it is realizable and stable, and provided that all the zeros of its z-transform lie on or outside the unit circle in the z-plane [that is, provided that $A(z) \neq 0$ for $|z| < 1$].

For example, the operator $(a_0, a_1, a_2) = (6, 5, 1)$ is minimum delay because $A(z) = 6 + 5z + z^2$ has zeros $z_1 = -2$ and $z_2 = -3$, both of which have magnitude greater than unity. On the other hand, the operator $(1, 5, 6)$ is maximum delay because $A(z) = 1 + 5z + 6z^2$ has zeros $z_1 = -\frac{1}{3}$ and $z_2 = -\frac{1}{2}$, both of which have magnitude less than unity. The operator $(3, 7, 2)$ is mixed delay because $A(z) = 3 + 7z + 2z^2$ has zeros $z_1 = -\frac{1}{2}$ and $z_2 = -3$, one of which has magnitude less than unity and the other greater than unity.

2.4 Inverse digital filters

One objective of signal analysis is to increase the resolution of overlapping pulses, that is, to diminish the width of a given wavelet to the point that it can be clearly distinguished from neighboring wavelets. A way to accomplish this goal is through the use of so-called inverse digital filters (or inverse operators). Inverse digital filters have many practical applications. Their proper use allows information smeared over a broad portion of a time series to be shrunk into a narrower region, with resulting over-all increase in resolution.

The *inverse* of the finite discrete realizable operator (or finite wavelet) $(a_0, a_1, a_2, \ldots, a_m)$ is defined as the *stable* operator $(\ldots, b_{-2}, b_{-1}, b_0, b_1, b_2, \ldots)$ such that

$$a_t * b_t = \delta_t ,$$

where δ_t is the Kronecker delta function. The Kronecker delta function is defined as $\delta_t = 1$ when $t = 0$ and $\delta_t = 0$ when $t \neq 0$; hence δ_t represents a

---

[8] In this definition we rule out the presence of the so-called type 3 all-pass system. For the general definition of minimum delay, see Robinson, E. A., "Structural properties of stationary stochastic processes with applications," in *Time Series Analysis*, M. Rosenblatt, ed., Wiley, New York, 1962, pp. 170–196.

sequence $(\ldots, 0, 0, 1, 0, 0, \ldots)$, where the unit spike 1 occurs at time index 0. In terms of z-transforms, the inverse relationship is

$$A(z)B(z) = 1$$

since the z-transform of δ_t is equal to unity. Solving this equation we have the expression for the z-transform of the inverse operator given by

$$B(z) = \frac{1}{A(z)} \, .$$

Using the factorization of $A(z)$, we can write this expression as

$$B(z) = \frac{1}{a_m(z - z_1)(z - z_2) \ldots (z - z_m)} \, .$$

For convenience, let us assume that all the zeros $z_1, z_2, \ldots, z_m$ are distinct. Then $B(z)$ has the partial fraction expansion

$$B(z) = \frac{u_1}{z - z_1} + \frac{u_2}{z - z_2} + \cdots + \frac{u_m}{z - z_m} \, ,$$

where the constant u_1 is defined as

$$u_1 = [(z - z_1)B(z)]_{z=z_1} = \frac{1}{a_m(z_1 - z_2)(z_1 - z_3) \ldots (z_1 - z_m)} \, ,$$

and where the constants $u_2, u_3, \ldots, u_m$ are similarly defined. Relabeling the zeros if necessary, we may suppose that $z_1, z_2, \ldots, z_h$ have magnitudes greater than unity, and $z_{h+1}, z_{h+2}, \ldots, z_m$ have magnitudes less than unity. (For simplicity, we assume that no roots have magnitude unity.) In order to obtain a stable sequence we must make use of one or the other of two possible expansions for each term $u_j/(z - z_j)$ of $B(z)$. If the root z_j has magnitude greater than unity, then we should expand in positive powers of z, that is, we should use the expansion

$$\frac{u_j}{z - z_j} = -u_j(z_j^{-1} + z_j^{-2}z + z_j^{-3}z^2 + \cdots) \, .$$

On the other hand, if the root z_j has magnitude less than unity, then we should expand in negative powers of z, that is, we should use the expansion

$$\frac{u_j}{z - z_j} = u_j(z^{-1} + z_j z^{-2} + z_j^2 z^{-3} + \cdots) \, .$$

In other words, roots greater than one in magnitude contribute to the memory component of the inverse, whereas roots less than one in magnitude contribute to the anticipation component of the inverse. From the partial fraction expansion of $B(z)$ we therefore obtain Table 1.

TABLE 1. Type of operator and the corresponding inverse operator

Finite realizable operator $(a_0, a_1, \ldots, a_m)$	Inverse operator b_t
Minimum delay (Roots $z_1, z_2, \ldots, z_m$ have magnitude greater than unity.)	Minimum delay realizable $$b_s = \begin{cases} -\sum_{j=1}^{m} u_j z_j^{-s-1} & \text{for } s \geqslant 0 \\ 0 & \text{for } s < 0 \end{cases}$$
Mixed delay (Roots $z_1, \ldots, z_h$ have magnitude greater than unity and roots $z_{h+1}, \ldots, z_m$ have magnitude less than unity.)	Nonrealizable (two-sided) $$b_s = \begin{cases} -\sum_{j=1}^{h} u_j z_j^{-s-1} & \text{for } s \geqslant 0 \\ \sum_{j=h+1}^{m} u_j z_j^{-s-1} & \text{for } s < 0 \end{cases}$$
Maximum delay (Roots $z_1, z_2, \ldots, z_m$ have magnitude less than unity.)	Purely nonrealizable $$b_s = \begin{cases} 0 & \text{for } s \geq 0 \\ \sum_{j=1}^{m} u_j z_j^{-s-1} & \text{for } s < 0 \end{cases}$$

2.5 Spike filters and waveshaping filters

A major difficulty in signal interpretation is the lack of resolution of overlapping pulse-shaped events. As a result, increased attention is being given to the problem of designing high-resolution filters that can increase the amount of detail available on the recorded time series. One type of filter available for this purpose is the *spike filter*. Spike filters are designed to compress as well as possible a wavelet into a knife-sharp spike.

Before we enter into a discussion of high-resolution spike filters, we first wish to discuss the energy characteristics of wavelets. The energy characteristic of a wavelet provides a basis for understanding how high-resolution filters work.

In Figure 3, three different wavelets are shown. Each of the wavelets shown has exactly the same frequency content, that is, the amounts of high frequencies, intermediate frequencies, and low frequencies are precisely the same in each wavelet, and shown by their common frequency amplitude spectrum as given in Figure 4.

Although the three wavelets of Figure 3 all have the same amplitude spectrum, they differ in their time distributions of energy. Wavelet A has its spectral energy concentrated as much as possible at the front of the wavelet.

In other words, the spectral energy is *delayed* in time the *smallest* possible amount for any wavelet with the frequency spectrum shown in Figure 4. It is not possible to make wavelet A have its energy concentrated any further to the front, *under the restriction* that the frequency content of the wavelet is fixed. For this reason wavelet A is called a *minimum-delay wavelet*. (Of course, if we were allowed to add additional high-frequency content to wavelet A, we could make it have a sharper leading edge. But under the restriction that we must hold the amplitude spectrum constant, the minimum-delay wavelet, i.e., wavelet A, has the *sharpest leading edge* of any wavelet with the given spectrum.)

At the other extreme, we have wavelet C. This wavelet has its energy concentrated as much as possible at the back. In other words, the spectral energy is *delayed* in time the *greatest* possible amount for any wavelet with

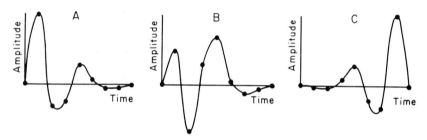

Fig. 3. Wavelets with the same amplitude spectrum and same pulse width. A is the minimum-delay wavelet; B is a mixed-delay wavelet; C is the maximum-delay wavelet.

the same breadth as wavelet A and with the given amplitude spectrum. It is not possible to make wavelet C have its energy concentrated any further to the back, *under the restriction* that the breadth and frequency content of the wavelet is fixed. For this reason wavelet C is called a *maximum-delay wavelet*.

It is easy to see that wavelet C is nothing more than the time reverse of wavelet A. That is, the maximum-delay wavelet is the time reverse of the minimum-delay wavelet. Also, it follows that wavelet C has the sharpest possible trailing edge of any wavelet with the given frequency content.

Intermediate between the minimum-delay wavelet and the maximum-delay wavelet are the mixed-delay wavelets. As we would expect, there are many possible different mixed-delay wavelets as we run through the transition of energy from the front to the back. In Figure 3 we show one of the possible mixed-delay wavelets with the frequency content shown in Figure 4. As we see, the energy in wavelet B is delayed with respect to the minimum-delay wavelet A, but not delayed so much as the maximum-delay wavelet C.

Now we wish to consider the design problem for what we might call a prototype filter, namely, the spike filter. We want to consider one isolated

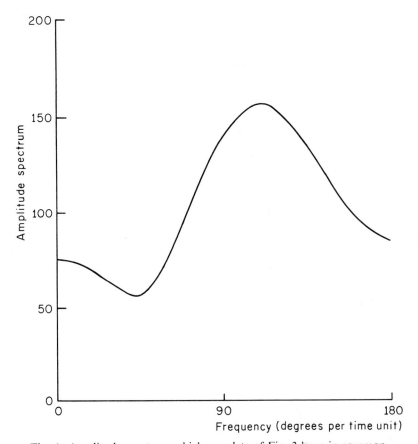

Fig. 4. Amplitude spectrum which wavelets of Fig. 3 have in common.

event, say the mixed-delay wavelet B shown in Figure 3. Our problem is to find a filter that contracts this wavelet to a spike. Now theoretically we can achieve our purpose *exactly* if we can use the exact inverse filter for the given wavelet. The exact inverse filter for a mixed-delay wavelet is a two-sided, infinitely long filter. However, in practice we must restrict outselves to filters of finite length, and hence at best we can only achieve our purpose approximately.

More generally, we want to consider the design problem for the *waveshaping filter*. As we will see, the spike filter is a special case of the shaping filter. Hence let us derive the mathematical equations for the waveshaping filter. Suppose that we are given an input wavelet

$$(b_0, b_1, b_2, \ldots, b_n)$$

and a desired output wavelet

$$(d_0, d_1, d_2 \ldots, d_k).$$

Then we want to find a filter

$$(f_0, f_1, f_2, \ldots, f_m)$$

such that when we pass the input wavelet into the filter we obtain an actual output wavelet

$$(c_0, c_1, c_2, \ldots, c_{m+n})$$

which is as close as possible to the desired output wavelet in the least-squares sense. Such a filter is called a shaping filter, for it shapes the input wavelet into the desired output wavelet as well as theoretically possible.

According to the least-squares principle, the filter coefficients f_0, f_1, $\ldots, f_m$ are determined so that the sum of squared errors given by

$$I = \sum_{t=0}^{\infty} (d_t - c_t)^2$$

is a minimum. Because

$$c_t = \sum_{s=0}^{m} f_s b_{t-s} \qquad \text{for } t = 0, 1, \ldots, m+n$$

and

$$c_t = 0 \qquad \text{for } t = m+n+1, m+n+2, \ldots,$$

we have

$$I = \sum_{t=0}^{m+n} \left(d_t - \sum_{s=0}^{m} f_s b_{t-s} \right)^2 + \sum_{t=m+n+1}^{\infty} d_t^2 .$$

The value of I is a minimum if its partial derivatives with respect to each of the coefficients $f_0, f_1, \ldots, f_m$ are equal to zero. Setting the partial derivative of I with respect to f_j $(j = 0, 1, \ldots, m)$ equal to zero, we obtain the set of equations

$$\frac{\partial I}{\partial f_j} = \sum_{t=0}^{m+n} 2 \left(d_t - \sum_{s=0}^{m} f_s b_{t-s} \right)(-b_{t-j}) = 0 \quad (j = 0, 1, \ldots, m),$$

which is

$$\sum_{s=0}^{m} f_s \left(\sum_{t=0}^{m+n} b_{t-s} b_{t-j} \right) = \sum_{t=0}^{m+n} d_t b_{t-j} \qquad (j = 0, 1, \ldots, m).$$

We recognize

$$\sum_{t=0}^{m+n} b_{t-s} b_{t-j} \equiv r_{j-s}$$

as being the autocorrelation of the input wavelet $(b_0, b_1, \ldots, b_n)$, and

$$\sum_{t=0}^{m+n} d_t b_{t-j} \equiv g_j \qquad (j = 0, 1, 2, \ldots, m)$$

as being the cross correlation of the desired output with the input, so the set of equations may be written as

$$\sum_{s=0}^{m} f_s r_{j-s} = g_j \qquad (j = 0, 1, 2, \ldots \; m).$$

This set of $m + 1$ simultaneous linear equations in the $m + 1$ unknowns $f_0, f_1, \ldots, f_m$ is the discrete time analog of the Wiener-Hopf integral equation. This set of simultaneous equations, whose solution gives the required shaping filter, is called the set of *normal equations* for the filter. The minimum value attained by the sum of squared errors is

$$I_{min} = \sum_{t=0}^{k} d_t^2 - \sum_{s=0}^{m} f_s g_s .$$

Subroutine SHAPE computes the waveshaping filter. Subroutine SHAPE needs subroutines CROSS, EUREKA, DOT, FOLD, and ZERO. The call statement is

CALL SHAPE(LB,B,LD,D,LA,A,LC,C,ASE,SPACE),

where the subroutine inputs are

LB = length of B = $n + 1$
B = wavelet that is input to shaping filter = $(b_0, b_1, \ldots, b_n)$
LD = length of D = $k + 1$
D = wavelet that is desired output of filter = $(d_0, d_1, \ldots, d_k)$
LA = length of A = $m + 1$,

and the subroutine outputs are

A = coefficients of shaping filter = $(f_0, f_1, \ldots, f_m)$
LC = length of C = $m + n + 1$
C = wavelet that is actual output of filter = $(c_0, c_1, \ldots, c_{m+n})$
ASE = average squared error between desired and actual

outputs of filter = $I_{min} / \sum_{t=0}^{k} d_t^2$

SPACE = working space.

The program is

SUBROUTINE SHAPE (LB,B,LD,D,LA,A,LC,C,ASE,SPACE)
DIMENSION B(LB),D(LD),A(LA),C(LC),SPACE(2)

```
C      DIMENSION  SPACE(3*LA)
       CALL  CROSS(LB,B,LB,B,LA,SPACE)
       CALL  CROSS(LD,D,LB,B,LA,SPACE(LA+1))
       CALL  EUREKA(LA,SPACE,SPACE(LA+1),A,SPACE(2*LA+1))
       CALL  DOT(LD,D,D,DD)
       CALL  DOT(LA,A,SPACE(LA+1),AG)
       ASE=(DD-AG)/DD
       CALL  FOLD(LA,A,LB,B,LC,C)
       RETURN
       END
```

Some numerical examples computed by subroutine SHAPE are the following.

EXAMPLE (a)

$$LB = 2$$
$$B = (-1.25000, \quad 1.00000) \quad \text{(minimum delay)}$$
$$LD = 5$$
$$D = (2.00, \quad 1.00, \quad 0.00, \quad 1.00, \quad 2.00)$$
$$LA = 2$$
$$A = (-1.08041, \quad -1.01483)$$
$$LC = 3$$
$$C = (1.35051, \quad 0.18813, \quad -1.01483)$$
$$ASE = 0.71109$$
$$SPACE = (2.56250, \quad -1.25000, \quad -1.50000, \quad -1.25000).$$

EXAMPLE (b)

$$LB = 2$$
$$B = (1.00000, \quad -1.25000) \quad \text{(maximum delay)}$$
$$LD = 5$$
$$D = (2.00, \quad 1.00, \quad 0.00, \quad 1.00, \quad 2.00)$$
$$LA = 2$$
$$A = (0.63388, \quad 0.69945)$$
$$LC = 3$$
$$C = (0.63388, \quad -0.09290, \quad -0.87432)$$
$$ASE = 0.88251$$
$$SPACE = (2.56250, \quad -1.25000, \quad 0.75000, \quad 1.00000).$$

The above two examples show that it is more difficult to shape the maximum-delay input into this particular desired output than the minimum-delay input.

EXAMPLE (c)

$$LB = 3$$
$$B = (1.56250, \quad -1.76770, \quad 1.00000) \quad \text{(minimum delay)}$$
$$LD = 5$$
$$D = (2.00, \quad 1.00, \quad 0.00, \quad 1.00, \quad 2.00)$$

        LA = 2
         A = (0.90811,   1.01672)
        LC = 4
         C = (1.41892,   −0.01663,   −0.88916,   1.01672)
       ASE = 0.61621
     SPACE = (6.56617,   −4.52973,   1.35730,   2.56250).

EXAMPLE (*d*)

       LB = 3
        B = (1.00000,   −1.76770,   1.56250) (maximum delay)
       LD = 5
        D = (2.00,   1.00,   0.00,   1.00,   2.00)
       LA = 2
        A = (0.58120,   0.79120)
        C = (0.58120,   −0.23618,   −0.49049,   1.23625)
      ASE = 0.78375
    SPACE = (6.56617,   −4.52973,   0.23230,   2.56250).

The preceding two examples show again that the minimum-delay input does a better job of shaping for this particular desired output.

EXAMPLE (*e*)

        LB = 5
         B = (2.00,   1.00,   0.00,   −1.00,   −2.00)
        LD = 5
         D = (2.00,   1.00,   0.00,   1.00,   2.00)
        LA = 2
         A = (−0.,   0.)
        LC = 6
         C = (−0.,   0.,   0.,   0.,   0.,
              −0.)
       ASE = 1.00000
     SPACE = (10.00000,   4.00000,   0.,   0.).

Here it is not possible to shape the input into the desired output; the average square error is 100 percent.

Let us now return to the case of a spiking filter. This is the special case of a shaping filter in which all the coefficients of the desired output are zero, except a single coefficient which is unity. As we will see, the position of the spike is an important factor as to the fidelity that the actual output resembles the desired spike. Provided that the filter length is sufficiently great, it will turn out that:

(1) in the case of a *minimum-delay* input wavelet, the best result is ob-

tained when the spike is at the initial point of the desired output, that is, the optimum spike position is given by

$$(d_0 = 1, d_1 = 0, d_2 = 0, \ldots, d_{m+n} = 0);$$

(2) in the case of a *maximum-delay* input wavelet, the best result is obtained when the spike is at the $(m + n)$th point of the desired output, that is, the optimum spike position is given by

$$(d_0 = 0, d_1 = 0, d_2 = 0, \ldots, d_{m+n} = 1);$$

(3) in the case of a *mixed-delay* input wavelet, the best result is obtained when the spike is at some intermediate position p, that is, somewhere between $t = 0$ and $t = m + n$.

The actual value of this intermediate point which gives the optimum spike position is most easily found by computation. For example, suppose the input wavelet is the mixed-delay wavelet B shown in Fig. 3. This wavelet is

$$(b_0, b_1, \ldots, b_6) = (50, -65, 28, 68, 6, -9, -2),$$

where $n = 6$. If we compute the least-squares spike filter (with $m = 4$) for each spike position from $t = 0$ to $t = m + n = 10$ in the desired output, we obtain the following results for the values of the minimum sums of squared errors:

Spike position t	Minimum sum of squared errors $I_{min}(t)$
0	0.75
1	0.50
2	0.44
3	0.20
4	0.09
5	0.18
6	0.29
7	0.54
8	0.98
9	0.99
10	0.99

The minimum value in this column is for spike position $t = 4$, so the optimum spike position is $p = 4$. Thus we see that for the given mixed-delay input wavelet the best result is obtained by that spike filter for which the desired output was chosen to be

$$(0, 0, 0, 0, 1, 0, 0, 0, 0, 0, 0).$$

We can compare this desired output with the actual output, which is

$$(0.18, 0.07, -0.04, -0.03, 0.91, 0.06, -0.09, 0.16, 0.03, -0.02, -0.01).$$

Subroutine SPIKE computes the spiking filter for the optimum spike position. Subroutine SPIKE needs subroutines IMPULS, SHAPE, CROSS, EUREKA, DOT, FOLD, ZERO, and MINSN. The call statement is

$$\text{CALL SPIKE(LB,B,LA,A,INDEX,ASE,S)},$$

where the subroutine inputs are

$\text{LB} = \text{length of } B = n + 1$
$B = \text{wavelet that is input to spiking filter}$
$= (b_0, b_1, \ldots, b_n)$
$\text{LA} = \text{length of } A = m + 1,$

and the subroutine outputs are

$A = \text{coefficients of spiking filter for optimum spike position}$
$= (f_0, f_1, \ldots, f_m)$
$\text{INDEX} = \text{optimum spike position plus unity} = p + 1$
$\text{ASE} = \text{average squared error}$
$\text{for filter for optimum spike position} = I_{min}(p)$
$S = \text{working space}.$

The values of $I_{min}(t)$ for each spike position from $t = 0$ to $t = m + n$ are found in the first $\text{LD} = \text{LA} + \text{LB} - 1$ cells of S. The program is

```
      SUBROUTINE SPIKE(LB,B,LA,A,INDEX,ASE,S)
C     DIMENSION B(LB),A(LA),S(2*LD+3*LA)
      DIMENSION B(4),A(3),S(21)
      LD=LA+LB-1
      DO 10 I=1,LD
      CALL IMPULS(LD,S(LD+1),I)
      CALL SHAPE(LB,B,LD,S(LD+1),LA,A,LD,S(LD+1),S(I),
     1S(2*LD+1))
   10 CONTINUE
      CALL MINSN(LD,S,ASE,INDEX)
      CALL IMPULS(LD,S(LD+1),INDEX)
      CALL SHAPE(LB,B,LD,S(LD+1),LA,A,LD,S(LD+1),ASE,
     1S(2*LD+1))
      RETURN
      END
```

Two numerical examples computed by subroutine SPIKE are the following.

EXAMPLE (*a*)

$\text{LB} = 5$
$B = (2.00000, \quad 1.00000, \quad 0. \qquad 1.00000, \quad 2.00000)$
$\text{LA} = 8$

A = (0.10995,   −0.03986,   0.09315,   −0.10514,   −0.15317,
          0.07600,   −0.15306,   0.35695)
INDEX = 12
ASE = 0.28610
S = (0.28610,   0.35022,   0.35150,   0.35908,   0.30458,
        0.34852,   0.34852,   0.30458,   0.35908,   0.35150,
        0.35022,   0.28610).

EXAMPLE (b)

LB = 5
B = (2.00000,   1.00000,   0.   ,   −1.00000,   −2.00000)
LA = 8
A = (−0.02714,   −0.11459,   0.11508,   −0.11487,   −0.09633,
        −0.07348,   0.16259,   −0.35686)
INDEX = 12
ASE = 0.28627
S = (0.28627,   0.28899,   0.38070,   0.38788,   0.32764,
        0.32851,   0.32851,   0.32764,   0.38788,   0.38070,
        0.28899,   0.28627).

A computationally more efficient spiking filter subroutine is SPIKER. It makes use of Simpson sideways recursion,[9] as performed by subroutine SIDE. Subroutine SIDE is designed to be used in conjunction with subroutine EUREKA to perform sideways recursion. Subroutine SIDE calls no subroutines. Its program is

```
SUBROUTINE SIDE(H,LF,F,A,R)
DIMENSION F(LF),A(LF),R(LF)
V=R(1)
S=0.0
T=0.0
IF(LF.EQ.1) GO TO 2
DO 1 I=2,LF
J=LF+2−I
S=S+F(I−1)*R(I)
T=T+A(J)*R(I)
1 V=V+A(I)*R(I)
2 FLF=F(LF)
W=(H−S+FLF*T)/V
IF(LF.EQ.1) GO TO 4
```

[9] cf. Wiggins, R. A., and E. A. Robinson, "Recursive solution to the multichannel filtering problem," J. Geophys. Research 70, 1885–1891 (1965).

```
      DO 3 I=2,LF
      J=LF−I+2
    3 F(J)=F(J−1)+W*A(J)−FLF*A(I)
    4 F(1)=W
      RETURN
      END
```

Subroutine SPIKER needs IMPULS, SHAPE, CROSS, EUREKA, DOT, FOLD, ZERO, MINSN, and SIDE. The call statement for subroutine SPIKER is

CALL SPIKER (LB,B,LA,A,LC,C,INDEX,ERRORS,SPACE),

where the subroutine inputs are

$$LB = n + 1$$
$$B = (b_0, b_1, \ldots, b_n)$$
$$LA = m + 1,$$

and where the subroutine outputs are

$$A = \text{coefficients of spiking filter for optimum spike position}$$
$$= (f_0, f_1, \ldots, f_m)$$
$$LC = m + n + 1 = \text{length of actual output}$$
$$C = \text{actual output} = (c_0, c_1, \ldots, c_{m+n})$$
$$INDEX = \text{optimum spike position plus unity} = p + 1$$
$$ERRORS = [I_{\min}(0), I_{\min}(1), \ldots, I_{\min}(m + n)]$$
$$SPACE = \text{working space}.$$

As a numerical example, suppose the subroutine inputs are

$$LB = 7$$
$$B = (50, -65, 28, 68, 6, -9, -2) \quad \text{(a mixed-delay wavelet)}$$
$$LA = 5.$$

Then SPIKER gives as subroutine outputs

$$A = (0.0036, 0.0061, 0.0051, -0.0024, 0.0034)$$
$$LC = 11$$
$$C = (0.18, 0.07, -0.04, -0.03, 0.91, 0.07,$$
$$-0.09, 0.16, 0.03, -0.03, -0.01)$$

INDEX = 5, so the unit spike occurs at the same time as c_4, and hence the actual output C represents the least-squares approximation to the optimum positioned desired output

$$(0, 0, 0, 0, 1, 0, 0, 0, 0, 0, 0)$$

$$ERRORS = (0.75, 0.50, 0.44, 0.21, 0.09, 0.18, 0.30,$$
$$0.54, 0.99, 0.99, 0.999).$$

The program is

```
      SUBROUTINE  SPIKER(LB,B,LA,A,LC,C,INDEX,ERRORS,
     1SPACE)
      DIMENSION  B(LB),A(LA),C(LC),ERRORS(LC),SPACE(2)
C     DIMENSION  SPACE(3*LA)
      LC=LA+LB−1
      CALL  CROSS(LB,B,LB,B,LA,SPACE)
      DO 4 I=1,LC
      CALL  IMPULS(LC,C,I)
      CALL  CROSS(LC,C,LB,B,LA,SPACE(LA+1))
      IF(I.GE.2) GO TO 2
      CALL  EUREKA(LA,SPACE,SPACE(LA+1),A,SPACE(2*LA+1))
      GO TO 3
    2 CALL  SIDE(SPACE(LA+1),LA,A,SPACE(2*LA+1),SPACE)
    3 CALL  DOT(LA,A,SPACE(LA+1),Q)
      CALL  FOLD(LA,A,LB,B,LC,C)
    4 ERRORS(I)=1.−Q
      CALL  MINSN(LC,ERRORS,EMIN,INDEX)
      CALL  IMPULS(LC,C,INDEX)
      CALL  SHAPE(LB,B,LC,C,LA,A,LC,C,EMIN,SPACE)
      RETURN
      END
```

Subroutine SHAPER computes the waveshaping filter for the optimum positioning in time of the desired output waveform with respect to the input waveform. For example, suppose that we are given the input waveform

$$(b_0, b_1, b_2, \ldots, b_n)$$

and the desired output waveform

$$(d_0, d_1, d_2, \ldots, d_k) .$$

We restrict ourselves to a finite-length realizable filter $(a_0, a_1, \ldots, a_m)$. Let us consider a series of cases.

   Case 0. The last coefficient d_k of the desired output waveform precedes in time the first coefficient b_0 of the input waveform. In this case, all the coefficients of the desired output waveform represent irreducible error.

   Case 1. The last coefficient d_k of the desired output waveform occurs at the same time as the first coefficient b_0 of the input waveform. In this case, the first coefficient c_0 of the actual output can approximate the last coefficient d_k of the desired output, so now only the coefficients $d_0, d_1, \ldots, d_{k-1}$ of the desired output waveform represent irreducible error.

   Case 2. The last coefficient d_k of the desired output waveform occurs at the same time as the second coefficient b_1 of the input waveform. In this case, the first two coefficients c_0, c_1 of the actual output can approximate the last two coefficients d_{k-1}, d_k of the desired output waveform, so now only the coefficients $d_0, d_1, \ldots, d_{k-2}$ of the desired output waveform represent irreducible error.

These cases are continued, where each case is obtained from the preceding one by lagging the desired output waveform one time unit from its time position in the preceding case. The final case of overlap of the actual output with the desired output waveform is case number $m + n + k + 1$. For the cases after this one, the desired output waveform has been lagged to such a point that the entire waveform represents irreducible error.

Subroutine SHAPER needs subroutines CROSS, DOT, EUREKA, FOLD, MINSN, SHAPE, SIDE, and ZERO. The call statement is

CALL SHAPER(LB,B,LD,D,LA,A,LC,C,INDEX,ERRORS,S),

where the subroutine inputs are

LB = length of B = $n + 1$
B = input waveform = $(b_0, b_1, \ldots, b_n)$
LD = length of D = $k + 1$
D = desired output waveform = $(d_0, d_1, \ldots, d_k)$
LA = length of A = $m + 1$,

and where the subroutine outputs are

A = coefficients of shaping filter for optimum positioning
= $(a_0, a_1, \ldots, a_m)$
LC = $m + n + 1$ = length of C
C = actual output = $(c_0, c_1, \ldots, c_{m+n})$
$INDEX$ = number of optimum case (as described above)
(This number lies in the range 1 through $m + n + k + 1$.)
$ERRORS$ = $[e(1), e(2), \ldots, e(m + n + k + 1)]$, where

$$e(j) = I_{min}(j) / \sum_{t=0}^{k} d_t^2$$

denotes the relative mean square error
for case number j
S = working space .

As a numerical example, suppose the subroutine inputs are

LB = 7
B = (50, −65, 28, 68, 6, −9, −2) (a mixed-delay wavelet)
LD = 5
D = (0.5, 0.8, 1.0, 0.8, 0.5)
LA = 5 .

Then the outputs from subroutine SHAPER are

$$A = (0.0059, 0.0116, 0.0133, 0.0112, 0.0060)$$
$$LC = 11$$
$$C = (0.30, 0.20, 0.07, 0.43, 0.78, 0.85, 0.90,$$
$$0.33, -0.09, -0.08, -0.01)$$

INDEX $= 8$, so d_0 occurs at the same time as c_3, and
hence the actual output C represents the
least-squares approximation to the optimum
positioned desired output

$$(0, \quad 0, \quad 0, \quad 0.5, \quad 0.8, \quad 1.0, \quad 0.8, \quad 0.5, \quad 0, \quad 0, \quad 0)$$
$$\quad\quad t=0 \quad t=1 \quad t=2 \quad\quad t=3$$

ERRORS $= (0.98, 0.97, 0.95, 0.91, 0.74, 0.51, 0.17, 0.08,$
$0.20, 0.52, 0.78, 0.97, 0.996, 0.9985, 1.000)$.

The program is

```
      SUBROUTINE SHAPER(LB,B,LD,D,LA,A,LC,C,INDEX,
     1ERRORS,S)
      DIMENSION B(LB),D(LD),A(LA),C(2),ERRORS(2),S(2)
C     DIMENSION C(LCD),ERRORS(LCD),S(3*LA)
      LC=LA+LB-1
      LCD=LC+LD-1
      CALL DOT(LD,D,D,DD)
      CALL CROSS(LB,B,LB,B,LA,S)
      DO 4 I=1,LCD
      CALL ZERO(LCD,C)
      LDI=LD-I+1
      IF(I.LE.LD) CALL MOVE(I,D(LDI),C)
      ILD=I-LD+1
      IF(I.GT.LD) CALL MOVE(LD,D,C(ILD))
      CALL CROSS(LC,C,LB,B,LA,S(LA+1))
      IF(I.GE.2) GO TO 2
      CALL EUREKA(LA,S,S(LA+1),A,S(2*LA+1))
      GO TO 3
    2 CALL SIDE(S(LA+1),LA,A,S(2*LA+1),S)
    3 CALL DOT(LA,A,S(LA+1),AG)
      CALL FOLD(LA,A,LB,B,LC,C)
    4 ERRORS(I)=(DD-AG)/DD
      CALL MINSN(LCD,ERRORS,EMIN,INDEX)
      CALL ZERO(LCD,C)
      LDIND=LD-INDEX+1
      IF(INDEX.LE.LD) CALL MOVE(INDEX,D(LDIND),C)
```

```
INDLD=INDEX-LD+1
IF(INDEX.GT.LD) CALL MOVE(LD,D,C(INDLD))
CALL SHAPE(LB,B,LC,C,LA,A,LC,C,EMIN,S)
RETURN
END
```

2.6 Autocorrelation and power spectral computations

A single-channel *stochastic process* x_t (where t is an integer denoting the discrete evenly spaced time index) is called (covariance) *stationary*, provided that the *autocorrelation*

$$ E\{ x_{t+s}\, x_t^* \} $$

depends only upon s, and not upon absolute time t. Let us denote this auto-correlation by ϕ_s, where the subscript s indicates the time shift between x_{t+s} and x_t. A realization of a stationary stochastic process, that is, the time sequence of numerical data which is observed, is called a *stationary time series*. As is common practice in statistics, the same symbol x_t is used for the numerical observations (the time series) as for the parent random variables (the stochastic process).

The Wiener[10]–Khintchine[11] theorem states that the autocorrelation function of an entirely nondeterministic stationary stochastic process has the representation

$$ \phi_s = \int_{-0.5}^{0.5} e^{2\pi i f s} \Phi(f) \, df, $$

where the spectral density function, or power spectrum, $\Phi(f)$ is a non-negative function of frequency f. The real variable f, where $-0.5 \leqslant f \leqslant 0.5$, represents frequency in cycles per time unit, where the time unit is defined as the amount of time that elapses between two successive observations x_t and x_{t+1} of the time series. For example, if the observations x_t were recorded at a sampling rate of 1000 observations per sec, then the time unit would be 0.001 sec (per observation), and hence the frequency variable f would be expressed in units of cycles per 0.001 sec, or equivalently in units of 1000 cps. The frequency

$$ f_0 = 0.5 \text{ cycles per time unit} $$

is called the Nyquist frequency. Hence for a sampling rate of 1000 observations per sec, the Nyquist frequency would be

---

[10] Wiener, N., "Generalized harmonic analysis," *Acta Math.* **55**, 117–258 (1930).
[11] Khintchine, A., "Korrelationstheorie der stationären stochastischen Prozesse," *Math. Annal.* **109**, 604–615 (1934).

$$f_0 = 0.5 \text{ cycles per } 0.001 \text{ sec}$$
$$= 0.5 \, (1000 \text{ cps})$$
$$= 500 \text{ cps} \, .$$

In engineering it is usual to think of the parent signal as being a function of continuous time, in which case the time series x_t would be obtained by sampling the parent signal at uniformly spaced time instants. We do not want to enter upon a discussion of the aliasing problem here, as it is well treated in many books; however, let us state the main result, namely, in order to avoid the aliasing problem, the sampling frequency must exceed twice the highest frequency present in the parent signal. Our sampling frequency (by definition of the time unit) is one observation per time unit; one half the sampling frequency is called the Nyquist frequency, so the Nyquist frequency is

$$f_0 = 0.5 \text{ cycles per time unit} \, .$$

Hence the engineering definition of Nyquist frequency is the same as the definition which follows from the Wiener–Khintchine theorem, as given in the foregoing paragraph. As an example, if the highest frequency in the parent signal were 500 cps, then a sampling rate of 1000 observations per sec would be (theoretically) adequate in order to avoid aliasing.

The empirical autocorrelation c_s of a finite-length (real) time series

$$x_0, x_1, \ldots, x_{n-1}$$

is given by the formula

$$c_s = \frac{1}{n} \sum_{t=0}^{n-1-|s|} x_{t+|s|} x_t \, . \tag{1}$$

With the subroutine inputs

$$LX = n$$
$$X = (x_0, x_1, \ldots, x_{n-1}) \quad \text{(Assume } x_t \text{ is real.)}$$
$$LR = k + 1 \, ,$$

the call statement

$$\text{CALL CROSS(LX,X,LX,X,LR,R)}$$

yields as subroutine output

$$R = (r_0, r_1, \ldots, r_k) \, ,$$

where

$$r_s = nc_s = \sum_{t=0}^{n-1-|s|} x_{t+|s|} x_t \, .$$

This subroutine is good for educational purposes and for experimental computations involving short time series; however, for extensive computations involving long time series, some more efficient method must be used for the computation of correlation functions. The same remarks also apply in the computation of convolutions; subroutine **FOLD** would not be economically feasible for extensive data-processing applications. One solution to this economic problem is through the use of additional hardware attached to the main frame of the computer. For example, the SDS 9300 computer[12] has an SDS Correlation and Filtering Unit CFE 1 attached to it. This is a special purpose device which enables the SDS 9300 computer to perform a series of multiply–add operations at speeds and costs which cannot be attained on conventional general purpose, stored program computers. Effective multiply–add times of 146 nsec (i.e., over 6,800,000 multiply–add operations per sec) can be achieved with this device. The CFE 1 has direct access to the computer's memory, independent of the central processor. With such a device it is economically feasible to compute the correlations and convolutions required in the application of digital technology to the field of geophysical exploration for oil.

Another solution to this economic problem of reducing the costs of computing correlations and convolutions is through the development of programming systems, that is, software. The most extensive development available in the literature is that documented by Simpson.[13] In his introduction, Simpson states that cost studies of programming systems of this size (about 40,000 registers) might predict a developmental price tag of about a quarter of a million dollars for his set of programs. His subroutine **PROCOR** writes a machine language program designed to compute at high speed a single, fixed-point cross product of a given series X (of length n) with an arbitrary series Y (also of length n) which can be lagged arbitrarily. The speed of one cross product approaches $2 n$ machine cycles, as n gets large with respect to the maximum magnitude of the numerical values of the given series (considered as 35 bit-plus-sign integers). The user provides space for the object program which is somewhat longer than the given series X. Once the program is generated, the given series X is no longer needed and the program is reusable. High speed is attained by grouping multipliers so as to substitute summation for multiplication and by carrying out the summation by a straight line program. For example, if

$$N = n = 8$$
$$X = (1, 2, -1, 0, -2, 0, 1, 2)$$
$$Y = (2, -1, 2, 0, 1, 2, -2, 1),$$

the cross product

---

[12] Owned by Digital Consultants, Inc., Houston, Texas.
[13] Simpson, S. M., *Time Series Computations in FORTRAN and FAP, Volume 1, A Program Library*, Addison-Wesley, Reading, Mass., 1966.

$$1 \cdot 2 + 2 \cdot (-1) - 1 \cdot 2 + 0 \cdot 0 - 2 \cdot 1 + 0 \cdot 2 + 1 \cdot (-2) + 2 \cdot 1$$

would be computed by the object program in the form

$$(2 - 2 - 2) \cdot 1 + (-1 - 1 + 1) \cdot 2 .$$

Another way to speed up the computation of convolutions and correlations by software is through the use of fast Fourier transforms as developed by Simpson,[14] Cooley–Tukey,[15] and others. In order to describe this approach let us review a basic principle, namely that convolution in the time domain corresponds to multiplication in the frequency domain.

Suppose that we are given two series a_t and x_t, each of which is assumed to be zero outside of some finite time interval. As we have seen, the convolution

$$y_t = \sum_{s=-\infty}^{\infty} a_s x_{t-s} \tag{2}$$

in the time domain corresponds to the multiplication

$$Y(z) = A(z)X(z)$$

in the z-domain, where the z-transforms are defined as

$$A(z) = \sum_{t=-\infty}^{\infty} a_t z^t$$

$$X(z) = \sum_{t=-\infty}^{\infty} x_t z^t$$

and

$$Y(z) = \sum_{t=-\infty}^{\infty} y_t z^t .$$

If we let $z = e^{-2\pi i f}$, the z-transforms become the corresponding frequency spectra; hence convolution in the time domain corresponds to the multiplication

$$Y(f) = A(f) X(f)$$

in the frequency domain. Note that we have written $A(e^{-2\pi i f})$ simply as $A(f)$ for there should be no possibility of confusion whenever this simplified notation is used.

In Sec. 2.2 we gave subroutine NLOGN which performs fast Fourier transformation.

[14] Simpson, S. M., *op. cit.*
[15] Cooley, J. S., and J. W. Tukey, "An algorithm for the machine calculation of complex Fourier series," *Math. Computation* **19**, 297–301 (1965).

In order to perform the convolution (2) by the fast Fourier transform method we call NLOGN twice with SIGN = −1.0, once for the array containing a_t which yields $A(f)$, and once for the array containing x_t which yields $X(f)$. We form the array containing $A(f)X(f)$, and then call NLOGN with SIGN = 1.0 which yields the required convolution y_t.

Let x_t be a time series which is assumed to be zero outside some finite time interval. The autocorrelation

$$r_s = \sum_{t=-\infty}^{\infty} x_{t+s} x_t^*$$

in the time domain corresponds to the multiplication

$$R(f) = X(f)[X(f)]^* = |X(f)|^2$$

in the frequency domain, where

$$R(f) = \sum_{t=-\infty}^{\infty} r_t e^{-2\pi i f t}$$

and

$$X(f) = \sum_{t=-\infty}^{\infty} x_t e^{-2\pi i f t} .$$

Hence to perform the autocorrelation by the fast Fourier transform method, we call NLOGN with SIGN = −1.0 for the array containing x_t which gives $X(f)$. We form the array $X(f)[X(f)]^*$, and then call NLOGN with SIGN = 1.0 which gives the required autocorrelation r_t.

Let us now discuss estimation of the power spectrum. Given the finite-length time series

$$x_0, x_1, \ldots, x_{n-1} ,$$

we may compute its empirical autocorrelation c_s given by eq. (1). The Fourier transform of the empirical correlation is

$$C(f) = \sum_{s=-n+1}^{n-1} c_s e^{-2\pi i f s} .$$

The frequency function $C(f)$ is called the *periodogram*. Equivalently, the periodogram is given by the formula

$$C(f) = \frac{1}{n} \left| \sum_{t=0}^{n-1} x_t e^{-2\pi i f t} \right|^2 = \frac{1}{n} \left| X(f) \right|^2 .$$

The periodogram is an asymptotically unbiased estimate of the power spectrum $\Phi(f)$. However, the periodogram is not a consistent estimate of the spectral density; that is, the variance of the periodogram at any given frequency does not tend to zero as the sample size n tends to infinity. Thus the periodogram is a very erratic function of frequency f, and hence some method of averaging the available information must be used in order to obtain a consistent spectral estimate. One way of doing the averaging would be to compute the periodogram and then perform a smoothing operation on the periodogram to obtain the required estimate. Another way is to weight the empirical autocorrelation function, and then take the Fourier transform of the weighted autocorrelation to obtain the required estimate. The choice between these two ways is a computational choice, as they are mathematically equivalent. The second way is computationally more direct in most cases. However, the first way has historical interest, dating back to the early work of Hamming and Tukey.[16]

Subroutine COSTR computes the cosine transform given by

$$\Psi(f) = \psi_0 + 2 \sum_{s=0}^{n} \psi_s \cos 2\pi f s .$$

If ψ_s is the empirical autocorrelation c_s given by eq. (1), then $\Psi(f)$ is the periodogram. If ψ_s is the weighted empirical autocorrelation $w_s c_s$ (the weighting function w_s is soon discussed), then $\Psi(f)$ is the spectral estimate associated with the given weighting function. Subroutine COSTR requires no subroutines. The call statement is

CALL COSTR(LR,R,W,S),

where the subroutine inputs are

LR = length of R = $n + 1$
R = $(\psi_0, \psi_1, \ldots, \psi_n)$
W = angular frequency = $\omega = 2\pi f$,

and the subroutine output is

S = $\Psi(f)$ = cosine transform at frequency f.

The program is

```
SUBROUTINE  COSTR(LR,R,W,S)
DIMENSION  R(LR)
COSNW=1.
SINNW=0.
COSW=COS(W)
SINW=SIN(W)
S=R(1)
```

---

[16] Hamming, R. W., and J. W. Tukey, *Measuring Noise Color*, Bell Telephone Lab., Murray Hill, N.J., 1949.

```
       DO 1 I=2,LR
       T=COSW*COSNW-SINW*SINNW
       SINNW=COSW*SINNW+SINW*COSNW
       COSNW=T
    1  S=S+2*R(I)*COSNW
       RETURN
       END
```

Subroutine SMOOTH computes the spectral estimate by performing a smoothing operation on the periodogram by the Hamming–Tukey formula.[17] Subroutine SMOOTH requires no subroutines. The call statement is

$$\text{CALL SMOOTH(LS,SPECT)},$$

where the subroutine inputs are

$$\text{LS} = \text{length of SPECT} = m + 1$$
$$\text{SPECT} = [C(0),\, C(\Delta f),\, C(2\Delta f),\, \ldots,\, C(m\,\Delta f)],$$

where $C(f)$ is the periodogram and $\Delta f = \dfrac{1}{2m}$,

and the subroutine output is

$$\text{SPECT} = [S(0),\, S(\Delta f),\, S(2\,\Delta f),\, \ldots,\, S(m\,\Delta f)],\text{ where}$$
$S(f)$ is the spectral estimate, i.e., the periodogram smoothed by the Hamming–Tukey formula.

The program is

```
       SUBROUTINE SMOOTH(LS,SPECT)
       DIMENSION SPECT(LS)
       MM=LS-1
       A=.54*SPECT(1)+.46*SPECT(2)
       B=.54*SPECT(LS)+.46*SPECT(MM)
       SJ=SPECT(1)
       SK=SPECT(2)
       DO 10 J=2,MM
       SI=SJ
       SJ=SK
       SK=SPECT(J+1)
   10  SPECT(J)=.54*SJ+.23*(SI+SK)
       SPECT(1)=A
       SPECT(LS)=B
       RETURN
       END
```

---

[17] Hamming, R. W., and J. W. Tukey, *op. cit.*

Because the problem of the choice of the weighting function w_t is so adequately treated in the work of Parzen,[18] Jenkins,[19] Blackman and Tukey,[20] and others, we do not wish to enter upon it here. One simple yet effective weighting function is the *triangular* (or *Fejer*, or *Bartlett*) *weighting function*

$$w_t = \begin{cases} 1 - \dfrac{|t|}{m+1} & \text{for } |t| = 0, 1, 2, \ldots, m \\ 0 & \text{for } |t| > m, \end{cases}$$

where the parameter m is called the truncation point. The parameter m would be chosen to be a fraction, say 10 or 20%, of the number n of observations in the finite-length time series $x_0, x_1, \ldots, x_{n-1}$. Thus in using the triangular weighting function there is a computational saving made in forming the spectral estimate, for the empirical autocorrelation coefficients c_s need not be computed for $|s| > m$. A weighting function with extremely good properties is the *Parzen weighting function*, which for m even is

$$w_t = \begin{cases} 1 - 6\left(\dfrac{t}{m}\right)^2 + 6\left|\dfrac{t}{m}\right|^3 & \text{for } |t| = 0, 1, \ldots, \dfrac{m}{2} \\ 2\left(1 - \left|\dfrac{t}{m}\right|\right)^3 & \text{for } |t| = \dfrac{m}{2} + 1, \ldots, m \\ 0 & \text{for } |t| > m. \end{cases}$$

The truncation point m is chosen to be a fraction, say 10 or 20%, of the number n of observations in the finite-length time series, so there is a computational saving made in forming the Parzen spectral estimate.

2.7 Linear least-squares estimation

The underlying concept in the problem of linear least-squares estimation is the *orthogonality principle*. Two (real) random variables y and x are said to be *orthogonal*, provided that the expected value of their product yx is zero, that is, provided that

$$E\{yx\} = 0.$$

It follows that if a random variable y is orthogonal to each of the random variables $x_1, x_2, \ldots, x_n$, then the random variable y is orthogonal to any linear combination of the random variables $x_1, x_2, \ldots, x_n$. In other words, if

$$E\{yx_i\} = 0 \quad \text{for } i = 1, 2, \ldots, n,$$

[18] Parzen, E., "Mathematical considerations in the estimation of spectra," *Technometrics* **3**, 167–190 (1961). This is one paper of an extensive literature by Professor Parzen on the estimation of power spectra.

[19] Jenkins, G. M., "General considerations in the analysis of spectra," *Technometrics* **3**, 133–166 (1961).

[20] Blackman, R. B., and J. W. Tukey, *The Measurement of Power Spectra*, Dover, New York, 1958.

then

$$E\{y(a_1x_1 + a_2x_2 + \cdots + a_nx_n)\} = 0 \,,$$

where $a_1, a_2, \ldots, a_n$ are any constants because

$$E\{y(a_1x_1 + \cdots + a_nx_n)\} = a_1E\{yx_1\} + \cdots + a_nE\{yx_n\} = 0 + \cdots + 0 = 0 \,.$$

Let us now consider the *linear least-squares estimation problem.* Suppose that we are given the n random variables $x_1, x_2, \ldots, x_n$ each with zero mean and with covariances

$$r_{ij} = E\{x_ix_j\} \,.$$

The problem is to estimate the random variable z by a linear combination of the random variables $x_1, x_2, \ldots, x_n$ in the least-squares sense. That is, we wish to determine constants $a_1, a_2, \ldots, a_n$ such that the mean-square-error between the desired output z and the estimate (or actual output)

$$y = a_1x_1 + a_2x_2 + \cdots + a_nx_n$$

is a minimum. The error is

$$e = z - y = z - (a_1x_1 + a_2x_2 + \cdots + a_nx_n)$$

so the mean-square-error is

$$I = E\{(z - y)^2\} = E\{[z - (a_1x_1 + a_2x_2 + \cdots + a_nx_n)]^2\} \,.$$

In order to minimize this expression, we may set the derivatives of I with respect to each of the coefficients $a_1, a_2, \ldots, a_n$ equal to zero. We obtain the set of equations

$$\frac{\partial I}{\partial a_1} = -2E\{[z - (a_1x_1 + a_2x_2 + \cdots + a_nx_n)]x_1\} = 0$$

$$\frac{\partial I}{\partial a_2} = -2E\{[z - (a_1x_1 + a_2x_2 + \cdots + a_nx_n)]x_2\} = 0$$

$$\cdots$$

$$\frac{\partial I}{\partial a_n} = -2E\{[z - (a_1x_1 + a_2x_2 + \cdots + a_nx_n)]x_n\} = 0 \,.$$

The set of equations may be written as

$$E\{[z - (a_1x_1 + a_2x_2 + \cdots + a_nx_n)]x_1\} = 0$$
$$E\{[z - (a_1x_1 + a_2x_2 + \cdots + a_nx_n)]x_2\} = 0$$
$$\cdots$$
$$E\{[z - (a_1x_1 + a_2x_2 + \cdots + a_nx_n)]x_n\} = 0 \,.$$

This set of equations states that the required constants $a_1, a_2, \ldots, a_n$ are such that the error

$$e = z - (a_1x_1 + a_2x_2 + \cdots + a_nx_n)$$

is orthogonal (or normal) to each of the input random variables $x_1, x_2, \ldots, x_n$. This is the *orthogonality principle,* namely, the linear least-squares estimate y of z is the one whose constants $a_1, a_2, \ldots, a_n$ are determined by the condition that the error $z - y$ be orthogonal to each of the input random variables. The above set of equations, which are called the *orthogonal equations*, or *normal equations*, may be written in terms of the covariances as

$$a_1 r_{11} + a_2 r_{21} + \cdots + a_n r_{n1} = g_1$$
$$a_1 r_{12} + a_2 r_{22} + \cdots + a_n r_{n2} = g_2$$
$$\cdots$$
$$a_1 r_{1n} + a_2 r_{2n} + \cdots + a_n r_{nn} = g_n,$$

where g_i is defined as

$$g_i = E\{z x_i\} \qquad \text{for } i = 1, 2, \ldots, n.$$

Given the covariances r_{ij} and g_i for $i, j = 1, 2, \ldots, n$, we can determine the constants a_i for $i = 1, 2, \ldots, n$ by solving the normal equations. The resulting estimate

$$y = a_1 x_1 + a_2 x_2 + \cdots + a_n x_n$$

is called the projection of the random variable z onto the linear space spanned by the input random variables $x_1, x_2, \ldots, x_n$. Since the error $z - y$ is orthogonal to $x_1, x_2, \ldots, x_n$, it is also the orthogonal to y, since y is a linear combination of $x_1, x_2, \ldots, x_n$; that is,

$$E\{(z - y)y\} = 0 = E\{zy\} - E\{y^2\}.$$

Hence it follows that the *minimum mean-square-error* I_0 is

$$I_0 = E\{e^2\} = E\{(z - y)^2\} = E\{(z - y)z\}$$

which gives

$$E\{e^2\} = E\{z^2\} - E\{y^2\}.$$

This last equation is a statement of the Pythagorean theorem, as seen in Figure 5:

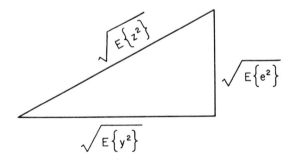

Fig. 5. Right triangle with lengths of its sides indicated.

In terms of covariances, the last equation is

$$I_0 = h - (a_1 g_1 - a_2 g_2 - \cdots - a_n g_n),$$

where h is defined as $E\{z^2\}$.

2.8 Prediction

Prediction is perhaps the most exciting and most rewarding aspect encountered in most cases of time series analysis. Prediction is an art based upon the skillful weighting of many seen and unseen factors. Some of the factors can be measured explicitly and quantitatively; others can only be included in some qualitative way. In many cases there are past data, and the prediction is based upon these data. Here we are concerned with the prediction of entirely nondeterministic stationary time series. In particular we do not address ourselves to problems of predicting time series with trends and cyclical components; such problems are treated in the excellent book of Jenkins and Box.[21] Specifically we address ourselves to problems of linear least-squares prediction and signal enhancement as put forth in the pioneering work of Wiener.[22] Our Fortran programs may be described as the software embodiment of Wiener's work for use on a digital computer, as opposed to the hardware embodiment in lumped electrical networks which he envisaged and described in his book in 1942, and which has actually taken place in engineering practice since that time.

Given the stationary stochastic process x_t for $-\infty < t < \infty$, we would like to estimate (that is, predict) the random variable $x_{t+\alpha}$ by a linear combination of the past random variables $x_t, x_{t-1}, \ldots, x_{t-m}$. Let us denote the predicted value of $x_{t+\alpha}$ by

$$y_t = f_0 x_t + f_1 x_{t-1} + \cdots + f_m x_{t-m}.$$

The parameter α is called the *prediction distance* or *span*. By the orthogonality principle, the mean-square-error

$$I = E\{(x_{t+\alpha} - y_t)^2\}$$

is minimized when

$$E\{[x_{t+\alpha} - (f_0 x_t + f_1 x_{t-1} + \cdots + f_m x_{t-m})]x_{t-s}\} = 0$$

for $s = 0, 1, 2, \ldots, m$. Hence the coefficients of the *prediction operator* $(f_0, f_1, \ldots, f_m)$ are given as the solution of the *normal equations*

$$f_0 \phi_s + f_1 \phi_{s-1} + \cdots + f_m \phi_{s-m} = \phi_{\alpha+s}$$

---

[21] Jenkins, G. M., and G. E. P. Box, *Models for Forecasting and Control*, Holden-Day, San Francisco, 1968.

[22] Wiener, N., *Extrapolation, Interpolation, and Smoothing of Stationary Time Series with Engineering Applications*, M.I.T. Press, Cambridge, Mass., 1942.

for $s = 0, 1, 2, \ldots, m$, where $\phi_s = E\{x_{t+s}x_t\}$ is the autocorrelation. The *minimum mean-square-error* is

$$I_0 = \phi_0 - (f_0\phi_\alpha - f_1\phi_{\alpha+1} - \cdots - f_m\phi_{\alpha+m}) .$$

The *prediction error time series* $\epsilon_{t+\alpha}$ for $-\infty < t < \infty$ is given by

$$\epsilon_{t+\alpha} = x_{t+\alpha} - y_t = x_{t+\alpha} - f_0 x_t - \cdots - f_m x_{t-m} .$$

If we define the *prediction error operator* (of length $m + \alpha + 1$) as

$$(a_0, a_1, \ldots, a_{m+\alpha}) = (1, 0, \ldots, 0, -f_0, -f_1, \ldots, -f_m) ,$$

then we have

$$\epsilon_t = a_0 x_t + a_1 x_{t-1} + \cdots + a_{m+\alpha} x_{t-m-\alpha} .$$

In terms of the prediction error operator the minimum mean-square-error is

$$I_0 = a_0\phi_0 + a_1\phi_1 + a_2\phi_2 + \cdots + a_{m+\alpha}\phi_{m+\alpha} .$$

The *normalized mean-square-error* $Q_0 = I_0/\phi_0$ is a non-negative number that lies between zero (perfect prediction) and one (completely unpredictable).

Whenever the term "prediction error operator" is used without explicit reference to the prediction distance α, it is assumed that the prediction distance $\alpha = 1$.

Subroutine AUGURY is a multichannel Wiener prediction program; it can be used for single-channel prediction by setting the parameter N which designates the number of channels equal to one. Subroutine AUGURY requires subroutines OMEN, FORM, MAINE, MOVE, ZERO, BRAINY, and HEAT. The call statement is

CALL AUGURY(N,LX,X,LR,R,SPIKE,FLOOR,LF,F,LY,Y,ERROR),

where the subroutine inputs are

      N = number of channels = p
    LX = length of time series = n
      X = given time series = $(x_1, x_2, \ldots, x_n)$
        (multiplexed in multichannel case)
    LR = maximum possible length of prediction operator = $m + 1$
SPIKE = white noise parameter = non-negative number which is 0 in the absence of white noise
FLOOR = non-negative number between 0 and 1 which represents a lower bound on the normalized mean-square-error in the sense that the recursion to a longer filter is stopped once the normalized mean-square-error falls to or below this level,

and the subroutine outputs are

R = autocorrelation = $(r_0, r_1, \ldots, r_m)$
(multiplexed in multichannel case)

LF = length of prediction error operator = $k + 1$, where $k \leqslant m$

F = prediction error operator for unit prediction distance
= $(a_0, a_1, \ldots, a_k)$ (multiplexed in multichannel case)

LY = length of prediction error series = $n + k$

Y = prediction error time series = $(\epsilon_1, \epsilon_2, \ldots, \epsilon_{n+k})$
(multiplexed in multichannel case)

$ERROR$ = normalized mean-square-error sequence for prediction error operators of length 1, length 2, ..., length $k + 1$. Note: $ERROR(LF)$ is the normalized mean-square-error for the computed prediction error operator $F = (a_0, a_1, \ldots, a_k)$.

The prediction error time series $(\epsilon_1, \epsilon_2, \ldots, \epsilon_{n+k})$ is the complete transient convolution of the given time series $(x_1, x_2, \ldots, x_n)$ with the prediction error operator $(a_0, a_1, \ldots, a_k)$. In particular, since the unknown future value x_{n+1} is zero in the given time series, it follows that the predicted value of x_{n+1} is equal to $-\epsilon_{n+1}$.

As a numerical example, suppose that the given time series is the series of Friday closing prices of Control Data Corporation common stock from Friday, October 8, 1965 to Friday, June 17, 1966, namely, the time series of 37 observations given by

October	:33 1/2,	33 1/2,	34 1/4,	37	,	
November	:39	,	43	,	41 1/2,	39 1/4,
December	:38 3/4,	38 1/4,	38 1/8,	38 5/8,	37 1/2,	
January	:33	,	32 3/4,	30 1/2,	28 7/8,	
February	:29 3/8,	28 3/4,	32 3/8,	31 5/8,		
March	:29 3/4,	28 3/4,	27 5/8,	28	,	
April	:26 7/8,	28 5/8,	29 1/2,	30	,	29 1/8,
May	:32 7/8,	28 1/2,	28 3/8,	30 1/8,		
June	:30 3/4,	34 5/8,	37 1/4.			

The time unit is one week. We wish to predict one week ahead, that is, predict the Control Data common stock price for June 24, 1966. The following computations were done on the SDS 9300 computer previously mentioned.

By subroutine REMAV, the average, which is \$32.98, was removed from the time series; the resulting zero-average time series was stored in array X of length

$$LX = 37 .$$

We also set

$$N = 1$$
$$SPIKE = 0.0$$
$$FLOOR = 0.0001 .$$

With these values as subroutine inputs, we called AUGURY successively with LR = 2, LR = 3, and LR = 4. For LR = 2 we obtained as subroutine outputs

$$R = (712, 628)$$
$$LF = 2$$
$$F = (1, -0.88)$$
$$LY = 38$$
$$ERROR = (1, 0.223),$$

and Y, which we will not list here except for one value, namely, the prediction error

$$Y(LX + 1) = \epsilon_{38} = -3.76 .$$

Hence the predicted value of x_{38} is $3.76. In order to obtain the prediction of the Control Data common stock price for Friday, June 24, we must add the average of $32.98 to the predicted value of $3.76. Therefore, the predicted common stock price for June 24, 1966 (= time index 38) is

$$\$32.98 + \$3.76 = \$36.74 .$$

With the same subroutine inputs to AUGURY, except that now we let LR = 3, we obtained the subroutine outputs

$$R = (712, 628, 539)$$
$$LF = 3$$
$$F = (1, -0.96, 0.09)$$
$$LY = 39$$
$$Y(LX + 1) = \epsilon_{38} = -3.95$$
$$ERROR = (1, 0.223, 0.221) .$$

Hence the predicted value of x_{38} is 3.95, so the predicted value of the Control Data common stock price for June 24, 1966 (= time index 38) is

$$\$32.98 + \$3.95 = \$36.93 .$$

Again with the same subroutine inputs, except now with LR = 4, we obtained as output from AUGURY

$$R = (712, 628, 539, 451)$$
$$LF = 4$$
$$F = (1, -0.95, 0.03, 0.07)$$
$$LY = 40$$
$$Y(LX+1) = \epsilon_{38} = -4.19$$
$$ERROR = (1, 0.223, 0.221, 0.220) .$$

Hence the predicted value of x_{38} is 4.19, so the predicted value of the Control Data common stock price for June 24, 1966 (= time unit 38) is

$$\$32.98 + \$4.19 = \$37.17 .$$

It turned out a week after these predictions were made that the actual price of Control Data common stock on June 24, 1966 was 37 1/8 = $37.13.

The programs are

```
      SUBROUTINE AUGURY(N,LX,X,LR,R,SPIKE,FLOOR,LF,F,
     1LY,Y,ERROR)
C     NMAX=LARGEST VALUE OF N TO BE PROCESSED
C     NNMAX=NMAX*NMAX
C     NONDUMMY DIMENSION VF(NNMAX),VB(NNMAX)
C     FOR EXAMPLE, IF NMAX=9 THEN
      DIMENSION VF(81),VB(81)
C     DIMENSION X(N*LX),R(N*N*LR),F(N*N*LR),Y(N*LY),
C    1ERROR(LR)
      DIMENSION X(1),R(1),F(1),Y(1),ERROR(1)
      CALL HEAT(N,1,LX,X,N,1,LX,X,LR,R)
      RT=0.0
      DO 1  I=1,N
      J=(I-1)*N+I
      R(J)=R(J)*(1.+SPIKE)
      RT=RT+R(J)
    1 CONTINUE
      NNLR=N*N*LR
      DO 3  L=1,LR
      CALL OMEN(N,L,R,F,Y,VF,VB,Y(NNLR+1))
      Q=0.0
      DO 2  I=1,N
      J=(I-1)*N+I
    2 Q=Q+VF(J)
      ERROR(L)=Q/RT
      LF=L
      IF(ERROR(L).LE.FLOOR) GO TO 4
    3 CONTINUE
    4 LY=LX+LF-1
      CALL BRAINY(N,N,LR,F,N,1,LX,X,Y)
      RETURN
      END

      SUBROUTINE OMEN(N,L,R,AF,AB,VF,VB,SP)
C     NMAX=LARGEST VALUE OF N TO BE PROCESSED
C     NNMAX=NMAX*NMAX
C     NONDUMMY DIMENSION DF(NNMAX),DB(NNMAX),
C    1CF(NNMAX),CB(NNMAX)
```

```
C     FOR EXAMPLE, IF NMAX=9 THEN
      DIMENSION DF(81),DB(81),CF(81),CB(81)
C     DIMENSION R(N,N,L)
      DIMENSION AF(N,N,L),AB(N,N,L),VF(N,N),VB(N,N),
     1R(N,N,1),SP(N,N,L)
      IF(L.NE.1) GO TO 20
      CALL MOVE(N*N,R,VF)
      CALL MOVE(N*N,R,VB)
      CALL ZERO(N*N,AF)
      DO 10  I=1,N
   10 AF(I,I,1)=1.
      CALL MOVE(N*N,AF,AB)
      RETURN
   20 CALL HEAT(N,N,L-1,AB,N,N,L-1,R(1,1,2),1,DB)
      DO 30  I=1,N
      DO 30  J=1,N
      IJ=(I-1)*N+J
      JI=(J-1)*N+I
   30 DF(IJ)=DB(JI)
      CALL MAINE(N,VB,SP)
      CALL BRAINY(N,N,1,DF,N,N,1,SP,CF)
      CALL MAINE(N,VF,SP)
      CALL BRAINY(N,N,1,DB,N,N,1,SP,CB)
      CALL MOVE(N*N*(L-1),AB,SP(1,1,2))
      CALL ZERO(N*N,SP)
      CALL MOVE(N*N*L,SP,AB)
      CALL ZERO(N*N,AF(1,1,L))
      CALL FORM(N,N,L,AB,CB,AF)
      CALL FORM(N,N,L,AF,CF,SP)
      CALL FORM(N,N,1,VF,CF,DB)
      CALL FORM(N,N,1,VB,CB,DF)
      RETURN
      END

      SUBROUTINE FORM(M,N,L,A,B,C)
      DIMENSION A(M,N,L),B(M,N),C(N,N,L)
      DO 10  I=1,M
      DO 10  J=1,N
      DO 10  II=1,N
      DO 10   K=1,L
   10 A(I,J,K)=A(I,J,K)-B(I,II)*C(II,J,K)
      RETURN
      END
```

Subroutine BRAINY is given in Sec. 4.4, and subroutine HEAT in Sec. 5.5.

2.9 *Minimum-delay factorization of power spectrum*

An entirely nondeterministic (covariance) stationary stochastic process x_t has infinitely many representations as a convolution of the general form

$$x_t = \sum_{s=0}^{\infty} a_s \, \epsilon_{t-s} , \tag{1}$$

where a_t is a wavelet (i.e., a_t is a one-sided stable operator), and ϵ_t is a white noise time series (i.e., ϵ_t satisfies $E\{\epsilon_t \epsilon_s\} = 0$ when $t \neq s$ and $= \sigma^2$ when $t = s$). In terms of this representation, the autocorrelation of x_t becomes

$$E\{x_{t+s} x_t\} = \sigma^2 \sum_{j=0}^{\infty} a_{j+s} a_j . \tag{2}$$

Hence *the autocorrelation of the stationary time series x_t, namely, $E\{x_{t+s} x_t\}$, is equal to the autocorrelation of the wavelet a_t, namely, $\sum_{j=0}^{\infty} a_{j+s} a_j$, except for* the scale factor σ^2. Without loss of generality, we may normalize the amplitude unit of ϵ_t so that $\sigma^2 = 1$. Also let us denote the autocorrelation of x_t by ϕ_s. With these conventions, eq. (2) becomes

$$\phi_s = \sum_{j=0}^{\infty} a_{j+s} a_j , \tag{3}$$

which corresponds in the frequency domain to the equation

$$\Phi(e^{-2\pi i f}) = |A(e^{-2\pi i f})|^2, \tag{4}$$

where

$$\Phi(e^{-2\pi i f}) = \sum_{t=-\infty}^{\infty} \phi_t \, e^{-2\pi i f t}$$

is the power spectrum of the time series and

$$A(e^{-2\pi i f}) = \sum_{t=0}^{\infty} a_t \, e^{-2\pi i f t}$$

is the transfer function of the operator a_t. In terms of z-transforms, eq. (4) becomes

$$\Phi(z) = A(z)A(1/z)$$
$$= (a_0 + a_1 z + \cdots + a_m z^m)(a_0 + a_1 z^{-1} + \cdots + a_m z^{-m}). \tag{5}$$

Given a stationary time series x_t, we can estimate its autocorrelation ϕ_t and its power spectrum $\Phi(e^{-2\pi i f})$ as outlined in Sec. 2.6. From this information we would like to determine the wavelet a_t which appears in the representation (1). Without further restrictions, this problem is by no means unique, for there are infinitely many such wavelets. However, in many physical situations, we know from the physical structure that the wavelet a_t must be minimum delay. This minimum-delay restriction makes the problem of determining the wavelet a_t from knowledge of the autocorrelation ϕ_t have a unique solution, except for a constant of magnitude unity.

The problem may thus be stated as follows. Given $\Phi(z)$, the problem is to find the minimum-delay factor $A(z)$ which satisfies eq. (5); this problem is called the *problem of factoring the power spectrum*. In this section we assume that the autocorrelation ϕ_t is of finite length, that is, $\phi_t = 0$ for $|t| > m$. The autocorrelation z-transform $\Phi(z)$ contains negative powers of z. However, $\Phi(z)$ can be transformed into a polynomial merely by multiplying it by z^m; that is,

$$G(z) = z^m \Phi(z)$$

is a polynomial of degree $2m$. For the purposes of this discussion, it is just as easy to consider the complex case, that is, the case when the autocorrelation may be complex, for this immediately brings out the symmetry of the roots of $G(z)$ with respect to the unit circle. In the complex case, $\phi(-t)$ is equal to $\phi^*(t)$; hence it follows that the polynomial $G(z)$ is equal to its reverse polynomial,[23] which we denote by $G^R(z)$. It therefore follows that the roots of $G(z)$ must be symmetrical with respect to the unit circle. That is, for every root z_0 lying outside the unit circle (i.e., $1 < |z_0| < \infty$), there is a corresponding root given by $1/z_0^*$ lying inside the unit circle (i.e., $0 < |1/z_0^*| < 1$). By differentiation we can ascertain that the roots z_0 and $1/z_0^*$ are of the same multiplicity. Moreover, the roots of $G(z)$ on the unit circle, if they exist, are of even multiplicity, so again we can pair z_0 and $1/z_0^*$, even though they now overlap (i.e., $z_0 = 1/z_0^*$ if and only if z is on the unit circle). Finally, if zero is a root[24] of order i of $G(z)$, then infinity is a root[25] of the same order, so even here we can pair roots (i.e., $z_0 = \infty$ corresponds to $1/z_0^* = 0$). Because $G(z)$ is a polynomial of degree $2m$, it has $2m$ roots, where we agree to count a root of multiplicity j as j roots of multiplicity one. Taking the above facts into account, we can divide these $2m$ roots into pairs; if we arbitrarily take one member of each pair and label these m roots as

---

[23] Let

$$K(z) = k_0 + k_1 z + k_2 z^2 + \cdots + k_n z^n$$

be a polynomial of degree n. Then its reverse polynomial is defined as

$$K^R(z) = k_n^* + k_{n-1}^* z + k_{n-2}^* z^2 + \cdots + k_0^* z^n = z^n [K(1/z^*)]^* = z^n K^*(1/z),$$

where the superscript asterisk denotes the complex conjugate.

[24] A polynomial has zero as a root of order i if its first i coefficients (namely, those of $1, z, z^2, \ldots, z^{i-1}$) vanish.

[25] A polynomial has infinity as a root of order i if its last i coefficients vanish.

$$z_1, z_2, z_3, \ldots, z_m,$$

then the remaining m roots will be

$$1/z_1^*, 1/z_2^*, 1/z_3^*, \ldots, 1/z_m^*.$$

Because there are m pairs of roots, there are 2^m possible choices of the roots $z_1, z_2, z_3, \ldots, z_m$. Of course, if some of the roots are not distinct, then some of these possible choices will not be distinct either. Now, one of the two roots in each pair corresponds to a minimum-delay factor, and the other to a maximum-delay factor, of the polynomial $G(z)$. For example, the root z_1 corresponds to the factor $z - z_1$ and the root $1/z_1^*$ corresponds to the factor $1 - z_1^* z$. The factor $z - z_1$, which can be written as $-z_1 + z$, is the z-transform of the couplet $(-z_1, 1)$. Likewise, the factor $1 - z_1^* z$ is the z-transform of the couplet $(1, -z_1^*)$. We may summarize this information in the form of the table:

Root	Couplet	z-transform
z_1	$(-z_1, 1)$	$z - z_1$
$1/z_1^*$	$(1, -z_1^*)$	$1 - z_1^* z.$

We immediately see that the couplet $(1, -z_1^*)$ is the reverse[26] of the couplet $(-z_1, 1)$. Hence each of the two roots, z_1 and $1/z_1^*$, corresponds to a couplet, where one couplet is the reverse of the other. If the magnitude of the root z_1 is greater than or equal to unity (i.e., $|z_1| \geqslant 1$), then the couplet corresponding to this root, namely, the couplet $(-z_1, 1)$, is minimum delay; the other couplet, namely, the couplet $(1, -z_1^*)$, is maximum delay. Hence if we choose the m roots $z_1, z_2, z_3, \ldots, z_m$ all greater than or equal to unity (i.e., all outside of or on the unit circle), then the resulting polynomial

$$A(z) = c(z - z_1)(z - z_2) \ldots (z - z_m)$$

is minimum delay (where the scale factor $c = a_m$). It then follows that the polynomial formed from the factors corresponding to the remaining roots, namely,

$$1/z_1^*, 1/z_2^*, 1/z_3^*, \ldots, 1/z_m^*,$$

is maximum delay. This maximum-delay polynomial so formed is recognized to be equal to the reverse polynomial of $A(z)$, that is,

$$A^R(z) = z^m[A(1/z^*)]^* = c^*(1 - z_1^* z)(1 - z_2^* z) \cdots (1 - z_m^* z).$$

Moreover, we see that the polynomial with which we started, namely, $G(z)$, is equal to

---

[26] The reverse of the couplet (c_0, c_1) is defined as the couplet (c_1^*, c_0^*). Note that a couplet has the same autocorrelation coefficients as its reverse.

$$G(z) = A(z)A^R(z) = z^m A(z)[A(1/z^*)]^*$$

for $A(z)A^R(z)$ by construction has the same roots as $G(z)$.

So far we have considered the case where the polynomial $G(z)$ could have complex coefficients [i.e., $\phi(-t) = \phi^*(t)$]. If we now specialize to the case of real coefficients [i.e., $\phi(-t) = \phi(t)$], then to every complex root there must correspond a root equal to its complete conjugate. It therefore follows that the minimum-delay polynomial $A(z)$ has real coefficients, so our final equation may be written simply as

$$G(z) = z^m A(z)A(1/z) .$$

We recall that $G(z)$ was defined as

$$G(z) = z^m \Phi(z).$$

Hence the above two equations immediately give

$$\Phi(z) = A(z)A(1/z).$$

Because we have shown how to construct $A(z)$ we have therefore solved the problem we set out to solve, namely, the problem of factoring the power spectrum so as to obtain a minimum-delay operator. However, this method involves finding the roots of the polynomial $G(z)$; if the degree $2m$ of this polynomial is large, then the amount of computation required would be excessive. In the design of least-squares digital filters in practice, the factorization of the power spectrum is avoided since one can determine the filter coefficients directly as the solution of the normal equations (see Secs. 6.2 and 6.3).

2.10 Predictive deconvolution of seismic traces in petroleum exploration

The continental shelves and other water-covered regions of the world contain deposits of oil buried deep in the subsurface rocks. These areas can be explored for petroleum by marine seismic methods. For example, oil exploration is now being carried out in such places as the Gulf of Mexico, the Persian Gulf, the North Sea, the continental shelf of eastern North America, off-shore Africa, and off-shore Alaska.

The marine seismic method can be described briefly as follows. One ship sets off an explosion (or, in the case of marine *Vibroseis*,[27] a vibration) a few feet below the surface of the water. A nearby ship drags a string of detecting instruments which record the resulting seismic waves on magnetic tape in the form of traces. With present-day digital recording systems, these seismic traces are recording directly in the form of time series (i.e., discrete sequences of data points equally spaced in time). The recorded waves will have taken a great

---

[27] Trademark of the Continental Oil Company, Ponca City, Oklahoma.

variety of paths, each requiring a different time of travel from shot to detector. In fact, for about five to six seconds after the first arrival of energy at a detector, the instrument will record meaningful information in the form of the continual motion of the water under the impact of seismic waves that have traveled along the various paths. The most pertinent information, of course, is contained in those seismic waves which have been reflected upward from the (5,000 to 20,000 feet) deep geological interfaces, for this information can be used to map the potentially oil-producing beds. The seismic interpreter, therefore, must be able to pick out the deep reflections, and their arrival times, from the mass of other information recorded on the seismic trace. The ability of the seismic interpreter to identify the deep reflections on a marine seismogram, however, until recently has been severely limited by multiple reflections (that is, reverberations) occurring within the water layer itself. The water layer, which is less than a few hundred feet deep in most cases of active interest, thus presented a very serious problem in marine seismic interpretation. The water reverberation problem was first recognized in the 1940's in the Persian Gulf where the seismic traces assumed the appearance of a sine wave or a simple combination of sine waves; such seismograms were described as "singing" records. In the absence of singing, the desired reflected events would appear as an identifiable sequence of pulse-like wavelets occuring at the arrival times dictated by the deep geological structure. However, in the presence of singing the desired reflected events are completely masked. In the 1950's, singing records were observed in many other water-covered regions; it was recognized that the water reverberation problem represented a serious and widespread limitation as to the acquisition of valid deep structural information. As a result, large water-covered areas could not be explored for oil.

The water reverberation problem in marine seismic exploration operations may be described as follows. The water–air interface is a strong reflector, with reflection coefficient nearly -1. If the water–bottom interface is also a strong reflector, then the water layer represents a non-attenuating medium bounded by two strong reflecting interfaces and hence represents an energy trap. A seismic pulse generated in this energy trap will be successively reflected between the two interfaces. Consequently, reflections from deep horizons below the water layer will be obscured by the water reverberations.

Let us consider a downward traveling impulse plane wave (i.e., we assume that the source wavelet is a unit spike), and let us suppose that we have a transducer which measures only downward motion in the water layer. The signal received by the transducer represents the successive reflections from the air–water interface. We assume that we are dealing with discrete time so that successive sampled data points are separated by a fixed sampling time increment; for example, the sampling time unit might be 4 ms (where ms stands for millisecond = 0.001 sec.). We let the integer n represent the two-way travel time in the water measured in terms of the sampling time unit;

for example, if the water depth is 100 feet and the water velocity is 5000 feet per sec, then the two-way travel time would be 40 ms so for a 4-ms sampling increment the value of n would be 10. The *water-confined reverberation spike train* is of the form

$$(1, 0, 0, \ldots, 0, \quad -c, 0, 0, \ldots, 0,$$
$$\uparrow \uparrow \uparrow \qquad\qquad \uparrow$$

time: $\quad 0, 1, 2, \ldots \qquad\qquad n$

$$c^2, 0, 0, \ldots, 0, \quad -c^3, 0, 0, \ldots). \quad (1)$$
$$\uparrow \qquad\qquad\qquad \uparrow$$
$$2n \qquad\qquad\qquad 3n$$

In this spike train, we see that the coefficient 1 occurs at time 0 and represents the initial downgoing spike. The coefficient $-c$ occurs at discrete time n and represents the second downgoing spike, which has suffered a reflection at the bottom (reflection coefficient c) and a reflection at the surface (reflection coefficient -1). The coefficient c^2 occurs at discrete time $2n$ and represents the third downgoing spike, which has suffered two reflections at the bottom (c^2) and two reflections at the surface $[(-1)^2]$. The coefficient $-c^3$ occurs at discrete time $3n$ and represents the fourth downgoing spike, which has suffered three reflections at the bottom (c^3) and three reflections at the surface $[(-1)^3]$, etc. The reflection coefficient c cannot exceed unity in magnitude; generally c will be less than unity in magnitude, for otherwise the water layer would represent a perfect energy trap, and no energy would penetrate to the deeper layers. Thus in the case where $|c| < 1$, the water-confined reverberation spike train (1) represents a convergent sequence and is a wavelet (according to the mathematical definition of a discrete wavelet as being a one-sided stable time sequence). The z-transform of the water-confined reverberation spike train is

$$1 - cz^n + c^2z^{2n} - c^3z^{3n} + \cdots.$$

This expression is in the form of a geometric series which can be summed to give

$$\frac{1}{1 + cz^n}.$$

The *water-confined reverberation elimination filter* would be the inverse filter, and thus would have the z-transform

$$1 + cz^n$$

so that the impulse response function would be the couplet

$$(1, 0, 0, \ldots, c)$$
$$\uparrow \uparrow \uparrow \qquad \uparrow .$$

time: $\quad 0, 1, 2 \qquad n$

$$(2)$$

Because $|c| < 1$, this couplet is minimum delay, and it also follows that the water-confined reverberation spike train (1) is minimum delay because the inverse of a minimum-delay wavelet is also minimum delay. To verify that the water-confined reverberation elimination filter (2) does indeed convert the water-confined reverberation spike train (1) into a spike (and thereby eliminates the reverberation) we may convolve (1) with (2) and thereby obtain the spike $(1, 0, 0, 0, \ldots)$, which represents the impulse plane wave without the water reverberation.

In our analysis thus far we have considered only the water reverberation effect itself, and have not considered the effect of the water layer on deep subsurface reflections. To do so, we must take into account that the water layer acts as a filter, and the seismic energy passes through this filter once as it goes down to the deep reflecting horizon, and again as it returns to the surface. That is, the water layer acts on the deep reflection data twice, once going down to the deep strata and once again coming back to the surface. Hence we have, in effect, a situation where the deep reflection data pass through two cascaded sections of the water layer, so that the over-all z-transform of the filtering introduced by the water layer is the square of the z-transform due to a single pass, as given in the foregoing paragraph. That is, the z-transform of the reverberation spike train resulting from a deep reflecting horizon is

$$(1 - cz^n + c^2z^{2n} - c^3z^{3n} + \cdots)^2$$

or

$$\frac{1}{(1 + cz^n)^2}.$$

In the time domain, we see that the *deep-reflection reverberation spike train* is given by

$$(1, 0, 0, \ldots, 0, \quad -2c, 0, 0, \ldots, 0,$$

$$\uparrow \uparrow \uparrow \qquad\qquad \uparrow$$

time: $\quad 0, 1, 2, \ldots \qquad\qquad n$

$$3c^2, 0, 0, \ldots, 0, \quad -4c^3, 0, 0, \ldots). \quad (3)$$

$$\uparrow \qquad\qquad\qquad \uparrow$$

$$2n \qquad\qquad\qquad 3n$$

This expression may be obtained by convolving the water-confined reverberation spike train (1) with itself. Since spike train (1) is minimum delay, it follows that spike train (3) is also minimum delay. The reverberation spike train (3) may be interpreted as being made up of the deep reflection spike at time 0, and the attached reverberation spikes at times $n, 2n, 3n, 4n, \ldots$. To eliminate the reverberation part of spike train (3) we must pass spike train (3) through the *inverse filter* whose z-transform is given by

$$(1 + cz^n)^2$$

or

$$1 + 2cz^n + c^2z^{2n} .$$

The impulse response function of this inverse filter is

$$(1, 0, 0, \ldots, 0, 2c, 0, 0, \ldots, 0, c^2) . \qquad (4)$$

$$\uparrow \uparrow \uparrow \qquad\quad \uparrow \qquad\qquad\quad \uparrow$$

time: 0, 1, 2 n $2n$

Convolving spike train (3) with spike train (4), we see that the output is indeed a spike $(1, 0, 0, 0, \ldots)$ which represents the direct deep reflection spike (at time 0) with the attached reverberation spikes eliminated.

In practice the reverberations are often generated by a more complicated physical situation than the one we have described, so the reverberation elimination operator (4) is not adequate in many field applications. However, there is an important principle which we can extract from the foregoing deterministic reverberation model, namely, the fact that the deep-reflection reverberation spike train (3) is minimum delay. This minimum-delay property of reverberation spike trains is also valid in other more complicated reverberation models, and, moreover, it is upheld on recorded data from various field situations. As a result, we would want to use a deconvolution method which exploits this minimum-delay property.

Thus far, for simplicity we have assumed that the seismic source pulse is a spike. In practice it will not be a spike but will have some more complicated shape. Let us designate the pulse-train waveform due to a deep reflection by the symbol b_t. The pulse-train waveform b_t is given by the convolution of the deep-reflection reverberation spike train (whatever it is) with the seismic source wavelet (whatever it is). For example, in the reverberation model which we have described, the deep-reflection reverberation spike train was given by (3). As we have just noted, the deep-reflection reverberation spike train in many instances is minimum delay, or at least approximately so. Hence, if the seismic source is sufficiently sharp so that the source wavelet is also approximately minimum delay, then it follows that the waveform b_t is also approximately minimum delay. (This follows from the fact that the signal resulting from the convolution of two minimum-delay signals is minimum delay.)

Let us designate the received seismic trace by x_t (where it is assumed that the filtering effect of the recording instruments has already been removed from x_t by some restoring filtering operation). The received seismic trace x_t is the resultant of many deep reflections; each reflection contributes a pulse-train waveform of shape b_t. However, because of the fact that all the pulse-train waveforms are overlapping to various degrees with each other, it is not possible to obtain a direct measurement of the individual waveform shape b_t. In such a physical situation, the method of predictive decomposition of seismic traces[28] can be used to eliminate the reverberations, and thus better bring out the true reflection pulses. (The word "composition" is the old term for "convolution"; because of the prevalence of the coined word "deconvolution" it is appropriate now to use the term "predictive deconvolution" in place of "predictive decomposition.") The method of predictive deconvolution is based upon a minimum-delay interpretation of the fundamental Wold decomposition theorem.[29]

There are two basic approaches to seismology, namely, the deterministic approach and the statistical approach. The deterministic approach is concerned with the building of mathematical and physical models of the layered earth in order to better understand seismic wave propagation. These models involve no random elements; they are completely deterministic. The statistical approach is concerned with the building of seismic models involving random components. For example, in the statistical model which we will discuss, the depths and reflectivities of the deep reflecting horizons are considered to have a random distribution. A major justification for using the statistical approach in seismology is due to the fact that large amounts of data must be processed; any data in large enough quantities takes on a statistical character, even if each individual piece of data is of a deterministic nature.

The predictive deconvolution method is based on the following statistical model. The received seismic trace x_t (included within an appropriately chosen time gate) is considered to be the result of convolving the waveform b_t with a random spike series ϵ_t; that is, $x_t = b_t * \epsilon_t$. The spike series ϵ_t represents the reflections from the deep reflecting horizons in the sense that the timing of a spike represents the direct arrival time of a reflection, and the amplitude of the spike represents the strength of the reflection. For data-processing purposes, this spike series ϵ_t is considered as a random uncorrelated (i.e., white noise) series. Hence the autocorrelation of the received seismic trace x_t is the same as the autocorrelation of the individual waveform b_t, except for a constant scale factor. This scale factor will not affect the final results, so it may be neglected. We can therefore compute the autocorrelation of the waveform b_t from the received seismic trace x_t. From the autocorrelation we can compute the prediction operator for the waveform b_t. Because the waveform b_t is minimum delay, a prediction operator for prediction distance n ($=$ two-way travel time in the water) will predict the reverberation component of the wave-

[28] Robinson, E. A., "Predictive decomposition of seismic traces," *Geophys.* **22**, 767–778 (1957); Robinson, E. A., *An Introduction to Infinitely Many Variates*, Griffin, London, and Hafner, New York, 1959, pp. 105–110.

[29] For a recent discussion of this theorem, see Wold, H., "A graphic introduction to stochastic processes," in *Bibliography on Time Series and Stochastic Processes*, H. Wold, ed., Oliver and Boyd, Edinburgh, 1965, p. 61.

form b_t. (This would not be true if the waveform were not minimum delay. For an illustration of this principle, see Robinson.[30]) A delay of n time units will line up this predicted reverberation with the reverberation portion of the waveform b_t; by subtracting this delayed predicted reverberation from the waveform b_t we obtain the prediction error. Because the delayed predicted reverberation cancels the reverberation part of the waveform b_t, it follows that the prediction error represents the nonreverberation part of the waveform b_t. Hence the prediction error operator (for prediction distance n) eliminates the reverberation part of the waveform b_t. Since the prediction error operator is linear, we can apply it to the received seismic trace $x_t = b_t * \epsilon_t$ (which represents many overlapping waveforms b_t with arrival times and strengths given according to the spike series ϵ_t). In so doing, we eliminate the reverberations from each of the waveforms b_t, but leave intact the initial nonreverberation portions, thereby increasing seismic resolution. If more resolution is desired, the prediction distance can be lessened, which will have the effect of further compressing the energy in the waveform. Also some type of band-pass filtering or shaping operation can be applied as a post-filtering operation to yield a cleaned-up deconvolved seismic trace. As an extra result, we can obtain the shape of the waveform b_t.[31]

The model required for the application of the predictive deconvolution is a statistical model. This model depends upon two basic hypotheses, namely, (1) the statistical hypothesis that the strengths and arrival times of the information-bearing events on seismic trace can be represented as a random spike series, and (2) the deterministic hypothesis that the basic waveform associated with each of these events is minimum phase. There are various ways of checking a model to see if it conforms with the physical situation. In the writing of my thesis at M.I.T. during 1953 and 1954, some checks of the above model were made but were necessarily of a limited nature because of the data and computing facilities (the M.I.T. Whirlwind digital computer) then available. Despite these limitations, however, this model seemed a reasonable one in many instances.

From a theoretical point of view, the concept of minimum phase provided much fertile ground for mathematical research. We recall that minimum phase was originally introduced as a frequency-domain concept; the definition is that a system is minimum phase provided it produces the minimum possible phase shift for its gain. This concept has proven to be vital in the design of feedback control systems. Our research was aimed at taking the concept of minimum phase out of the frequency domain and transferring it into the time

[30] Robinson, E. A., *Random Wavelets and Cybernetic Systems*, Griffin, London, and Hafner, New York, 1962, pp. 90–91.

[31] Robinson, E. A., *Predictive Decomposition of Time Series with Application to Seismic Exploration*, Ph.D. thesis, M.I.T. Press, Cambridge, Mass., 1954. Reprinted in *Geophys.* **32**, 418–484 (1967).

domain; by so doing we arrived at the identical concept in the time domain, which we called "minimum delay."[32] (That is, the terms "minimum phase" and "minimum delay" are synonymous, except that the former connotes frequency domain and the latter time domain.) A minimum-delay waveform is one which has its largest concentration of energy in the early part of the waveform. In this section we have given a fundamental example of a minimum-delay pulse-train waveform, namely, that occurring in the model of water reverberation generation. The reason we can often expect minimum-delay pulse-train waveforms in the layered earth situation is that reflection coefficients are less than unity in magnitude. Hence the more times a seismic pulse is reflected and transmitted, the more it is delayed and attenuated. Thus the concentration of energy in a seismic pulse-train waveform appears at its beginning rather than at its end; this is the condition that the pulse-train waveform be minimum delay.

The reverberation model which we described represents a special case of much more general deterministic layered-earth models. From these models it is not difficult to show that in many instances certain basic seismic pulse-train waveforms generated by such models are minimum delay. These results have done much from a theoretical point of view to justify the deterministic hypothesis required by our statistical model, namely, that the basic waveform is minimum delay. With the advent of routine digital field recording and extensive digital computer processing of seismic data in the last few years, it has been possible to test statistical models on a large-scale basis with high quality data. Because a seismic trace is made up of many overlapping waveforms, it is usually not possible to obtain a direct measurement of the individual waveform shape. Hence the minimum-delay nature of a pulse-train waveform must be verified indirectly. This indirect verification can be carried out by applying the method of predictive deconvolution to seismic data; if the method works satisfactorily, then we can conclude that the minimum-delay hypothesis is upheld.

The method of predictive deconvolution has been highly successful in deconvolving seismic exploration records, especially marine records with reverberations. The general success of the method shows that the minimum-delay hypothesis is valid over a wide range of field situations. The next step, therefore, is to categorize these various field situations in order to be able to predict those cases where the minimum-delay hypothesis does not apply. For such nonminimum-delay cases, adaptive procedures must be devised whereby some measure of the deviations from minimum delay can be determined. With such

---

[32] Robinson, E. A., "Extremal representation of stationary stochastic processes," *Arkiv för Matematik* **4**, 379–384 (1962); Robinson, E. A., "Properties of the Wold decomposition of stationary stochastic processes," *Teoriya Veroyatnostei i ee Primeneniya* **8**, 201–211 (1963); also in *The Theory of Probability and its Applications* **8**, 187–194 (1963).

information it is then possible to design the necessary deconvolution operators.

In summary, we may say that in the standard deterministic model of water reverberation generation, the reverberation pulse train resulting from a deep reflection is minimum delay. Even in the more complex physical situations encountered in the field, there is evidence that in many cases the reverberation pulse-train waveforms are minimum delay, or at least approximately so. The reason for this minimum-delay property is that a pulse-train waveform results from multiple reflections and transmissions within the layered earth; because reflection coefficients are less than unity in magnitude, the concentration of energy in a pulse train must appear at its beginning rather than its end; this early concentration of energy is the condition that pulse-train waveform be minimum delay. Each deep reflection horizon contributes a minimum-delay reverberation pulse-train waveform to a seismic trace. If we let a spike series represent the deep horizons in the sense that the timing of a spike represents the direct arrival time of a reflection and the amplitude of the spike represents the strength of the reflection, then the seismic trace may be considered as the convolution of the spike series with the reverberation pulse-train waveform. Because the reverberation pulse-train waveform is minimum delay, and because at least approximately the deep horizon spike series represents a statistically uncorrelated series, the two conditions required for the application of the method of predictive deconvolution[33] are met, and hence this method can be used as a practical digital data-processing method to eliminate water reverberations on exploration seismic traces. As a result large water-covered areas of the globe can now be explored for oil, which hitherto had to be classified as "no-good" seismic regions because of the destructive interference of the water reverberations with the desired deep reflection signals.

2.11 Signal approximation and adaptive detection

In signal analysis one seeks a representation of a signal which corresponds to the basic physical mechanisms involved in the generation of the signal. One set of fundamental parameters that characterize a signal are the complex natural frequencies of the basic resonating system. In discrete time (i.e., $t = $ integer) these natural frequencies appear as components of the form

$$A_k a_k^{t-\tau} \qquad (\text{for } t \geqslant \tau),$$

where a_k is a constant of magnitude less than unity. When the signal involves the sum of several such components (say, for $k = 1, 2, \ldots, N$), the determina-

    [33] Robinson, E. A., "Multichannel z-transforms and minimum delay," *Geophys.* **31**, 482–500 (1966).

tion of the constants a_k involves the solution of a set of nonlinear equations whose solution is difficult at best. On the other hand, the amplitude coefficients A_k can be readily determined as the solution of linear equations, given that the exponential factors a_k are known. If we do not know these factors, then we should try to select another set which provides a suitable approximation to the first set. In other words, we should try to use a fairly small number of damped exponentials a_k^t ($t \geqslant 0$) which span the region of interest. Then we would represent the signal f_t (for $t \geqslant 0$) by the summation

$$f_t = \sum_{k=1}^{N} A_k a_k^t .$$

Now the component functions $A_k a_k^t$ are correlated with each other; hence a change in the amplitude of one affects the amplitudes of the others, which means that the solution of the equations is sensitive to numerical errors. To eliminate this difficulty we can form an orthonormal set, say, $\phi_{1t}, \phi_{2t}, \ldots, \phi_{Nt}$ from the given set $a_1^t, a_2^t, \ldots, a_N^t$. The Gram–Schmidt procedure can be used; however, in this case we can use a simpler procedure based upon Parseval's equality. This equality states that the inner product of two time functions is equal to the inner product of their transforms. Let one time function be f_t with z-transform $F(z)$; let the other be g_t with z-transform $G(z)$. Then Parseval's equality states that

$$\sum_{t=-\infty}^{\infty} f_t g_t^* = \frac{1}{2\pi i} \oint_{|z|=1} F(z) G^*(z^{-1}) \frac{dz}{z} .$$

Two time functions are orthogonal if their inner product vanishes. Hence from Parseval's equality it follows that if two time functions are orthogonal, then these transforms are also orthogonal.

If the time functions are given as the sum of exponentials, then their transforms will be rational functions of z. Hence the integral on the right-hand side of Parseval's equality can be evaluated in terms of the residues of the integrand contained within the unit circle. If we can choose the poles of $F(z) G^*(z^{-1})/z$ so that it is analytic in either the outside or inside of the unit circle, then the integral must vanish, and hence f_t will be orthogonal to g_t. This observation permits us to write down the orthogonal functions constructed from a prescribed set of exponential components.

Given a set $a_1, a_2, \ldots, a_N$ of constants, each less than unity in magnitude, belonging to the exponential functions

$$q_{kt} = \begin{cases} 0 & \text{for } t < 0 \\ a_k^t & \text{for } t \geqslant 0, \end{cases}$$

we may construct a set of orthogonal functions as follows. We write

$$\Phi_1(z) = M(a_1, z)$$
$$\Phi_2(z) = A(a_1, z)M(a_2, z)$$
$$\Phi_3(z) = A(a_1, z)A(a_2, z)M(a_3, z)$$
$$\cdots$$
$$\Phi_N(z) = A(a_1, z)A(a_2, z)\cdots A(a_{N-1}, z)M(a_N, z),$$

where $A(a_k, z)$ is an all-pass z-transform defined as

$$A(a_k, z) = \frac{-a_k^* + z}{1 - a_k z},$$

and $M(a_k, z)$ is a minimum-delay z-transform defined as

$$M(a_k, z) = \frac{\sqrt{1 - a_k a_k^*}}{1 - a_k z}.$$

We can verify that

$$\frac{1}{2\pi i} \oint_{|z|=1} \Phi_j(z)\,\Phi_k^*\,(z^{-1})\,z^{-1}\,dz = \delta_{jk}\,.$$

In the case when $j < k$, all the poles of $\Phi_j(z)$ are cancelled by the zeros of $\Phi_k^*(z^{-1})$ so that the integrand is analytic outside the unit circle (including the point at infinity) so the value of the integral around the unit circle must vanish. Similarly, when $j > k$, the integrand is analytic inside the unit circle so the value of the integral must vanish. When $j = k$, the value of the integral is equal to one. We have thus established the fact that the $\Phi_k(z)$, and hence ϕ_{kt}, form orthonormal sets.

As an example, let us construct a set of orthonormal functions from the components

$$\left(\frac{1}{2}\right)^t, \ \left(\frac{1}{3}\right)^t, \ \left(\frac{1}{4}\right)^t.$$

We have

$$\Phi_1(z) = \frac{\sqrt{3}}{2 - z}$$

$$\Phi_2(z) = \frac{-1 + 2z}{2 - z}\,\frac{\sqrt{8}}{3 - z}$$

$$\Phi_3(z) = \frac{-1 + 2z}{2 - z}\,\frac{-1 + 3z}{3 - z}\,\frac{\sqrt{15}}{4 - z}.$$

To transform these orthogonal functions to the time domain we must evaluate the integrals

$$\phi_{kt} = \frac{1}{2\pi i} \oint_{|z|=1} \Phi_k(z)\,z^{-t}\,\frac{dz}{z}\,.$$

The residue at a simple pole z_k is given by

$$\lim_{z \to z_k} [(z - z_k)\Phi_k(z) z^{-t}] .$$

We see that

$$\phi_{1t} = -\sqrt{3}\left(\frac{1}{2}\right)^t$$

$$\phi_{2t} = -3\sqrt{8}\left(\frac{1}{2}\right)^t + 5\sqrt{8}\left(\frac{1}{3}\right)^t$$

$$\phi_{3t} = -\frac{15}{2}\sqrt{15}\left(\frac{1}{2}\right)^t + 40\sqrt{15}\left(\frac{1}{3}\right)^t - \frac{77}{2}\sqrt{15}\left(\frac{1}{4}\right)^t .$$

We now wish to return to our basic problem, namely, to specify a time function h_t over the interval $0 \leqslant t < \infty$ when it is known from the physical situation that the signal h_t is made up of a few damped exponential components. Instead of attempting to measure the exact values of the exponential factors, we attempt to approximate h_t by a suitable combination of predetermined factors. We assume that these predetermined exponential components have been orthogonalized; we seek the amplitudes of these orthonormal components which best approximate h_t. By "best" we mean we want to determine A_k such that

$$h_t \doteq \sum_{k=1}^{N} A_k\phi_{kt}$$

in the sense that the mean-square-error

$$\sum_{t=0}^{\infty}\left[h_t - \sum_{k=1}^{N} A_k\phi_{kt}\right]^2$$

is a minimum. By standard methods the amplitude coefficients are found to be

$$A_k = \sum_{t=0}^{\infty} h_t\phi_{kt} ,$$

and the error of approximation is

$$E = \sum_{t=0}^{\infty} h_t^2 - \sum_{k=1}^{N} |A_k|^2 \geqslant 0 .$$

This set of coefficients is the set that yields the best approximation to the signal h_t.

In a variety of situations we want to detect and describe signals whose waveforms are unknown and which are masked by noise. Suppose that we are trying to follow a signal which occurs at different times as we go from trace to trace. If the waveform is known, then a digital filter can be designed to respond preferentially to that particular waveform. If only an estimate of the signal waveform is available, then we can expect a corresponding decrease in detection capability. However, because the signal recurs from trace to trace we can build up an estimate of the signal waveform which can be used to improve the detection capability of the system. This approach can be used even if the signal waveform changes between recurrences, as long as these changes are not too rapid or abrupt.

For purposes of analysis, each signal h_t will be considered as a vector in waveform space in the sense that it is described in terms of its components. That is, if we approximate the signal by

$$h_t \doteq \sum_{k=1}^{N} A_k \phi_{kt} ,$$

then the signal may be considered as the vector

$$(A_1, A_2, \ldots, A_N) .$$

As we have seen, there is generally some error of approximation, for in order to describe an arbitrary signal exactly an infinite number of orthogonal components are required. However, for practical purposes the signals can usually be adequately approximated by a fixed number of components.

Let us now consider a detection system in a situation where a pulse-like signal of unknown waveform recurs from trace to trace. It is assumed that any trend in the recurrence has been accounted for, so it may be assumed that the epoch of the signal is random. The signal on each trace is masked by noise.

The nth trace, which may be either noise or signal-plus-noise, is fed into the detection system. The system computes the coefficients A_k in the expansion of the input signal. The vector $(A_1, A_2, \ldots, A_N)$ is fed into a comparison and decision box where it is compared against available data and judged as to whether it contains a signal. If the vector is accepted as a signal, then it is sent to an arithmetic unit where it is combined with earlier data to update the signal estimates. Then the $(n + 1)$st trace is fed into the detection system.

Briefly, then, the aims of this type of adaptive system are to continuously update its parameters to achieve an optimum separation of noise-only and signal-plus-noise. The system estimates the signal vector at each stage and continues to adjust the threshold in accordance with the estimate in order to improve performance. The performance of such an adaptive detection and waveform estimation system depends primarily on how closely the estimated signal waveform approaches the true signal waveform. If the estimated signal waveform is so accurate that it essentially coincides with the true signal waveform, then the detection ability of the adaptive system would be as good as that obtained when the signal waveform is known.

3

Wave Propagation in Layered Media

3.1 Optical properties of thin solid films

If a beam of light traverses a layered medium in which there are discontinuous changes in refractive index (or changes which occur in a distance small compared with the light wavelength), then multiple reflections occur. If the distances between boundaries are small so that the beams which are multiply reflected are coherent with each other, then the intensity of light reflected or transmitted by the stratified system is obtained by the process of counting up and summing the multiple reflections, taking into account their respective time delays. The amplitudes which are summed are calculated from Maxwell's equations with the application of the appropriate boundary conditions.

Initially interest in the optical properties of layered systems of thin films was largely confined to the use of reflecting films in interferometry, but within the last few decades interest in the optical properties of thin films has grown considerably. Mathematical developments in the techniques of studying thin films, some of which we outline in this chapter, give a clearer picture as to their nature and have led to a better understanding of their optical properties.

3.2 Seismic properties of stratigraphic layers in the earth

The mathematical methods given in this chapter also apply to the stratified system made up of geological layers in the earth. Much theoretical and applied geophysical research is directed at a better understanding of the reflection and transmission of seismic waves by the layered earth.

The science of seismology is concerned with the transmission of information through the means of seismic signals. A disturbance in the earth is propagated away from its source and reaches the receiving instrument, the seismograph. The range of transmission classifies the branches of seismology; teleseismology for which the range might be several thousand kilometers and exploration seismology for which the range might be several thousand meters represent the two main branches. The most important types of sources in teleseismology are the earthquakes and nuclear explosions; in exploration seismology, they are small chemical explosions, weight-dropping equipment, and vibration-inducing machines.

One of the most important characteristics of the earth as it concerns the transmission of seismic waves is that it is made up of layered strata. The layers considered in teleseismology would be the crustal layers, the mantle, and the cores; the layers considered in exploration seismology would be post-Cambrian sedimentary layers in which deposits of petroleum are found.

3.3 Model of the layered medium

In this chapter we wish to give a simplified treatment of wave propagation in layered media; the concepts illustrated in this model can be incorporated into more complicated models describing either the optical properties of thin films or the seismic properties of geological layers in the earth. Figure 6 shows the type of layered model assumed; we shall only consider plane waves which travel along ray paths normal to the parallel interfaces between the layers. Although we restrict ourselves to normal incidence, it is convenient to draw the diagrams with time displacement along the horizontal axis, so that the rays appear to be at non-normal incidence and so do not overlap one another. Hence the possible wave paths lie on a diamond-shaped grid, as depicted in Figure 7. Lines sloping downward to the right correspond to vertically down-

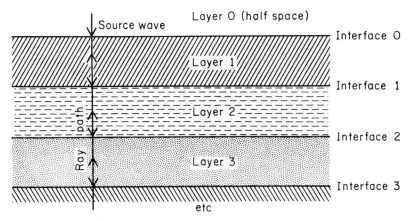

Fig. 6. System of layered media showing ray path normal to the parallel interfaces between layers.

going waves, whereas lines sloping upward to the right correspond to vertically upgoing waves.

In our treatment each layer is assumed to have the same one-way travel time for a pulse propagating from one interface to the other of the layer; this common one-way travel time in each layer is taken to be one-half unit of time. In order to obtain the effect of a layer with an arbitrary travel time, one can group several successive layers together by setting the reflection coefficients to

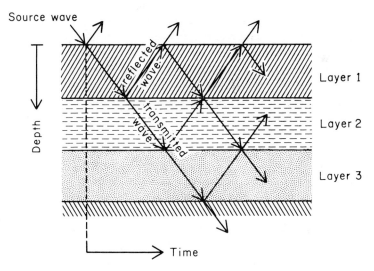

Fig. 7. Schematic diagram of vertical ray paths displaced horizontally in time.

zero and the transmission coefficients to unity at the common interfaces within the group.

3.4 Reflection and transmission coefficients

The solution of the wave equation at each interface leads to the definition of a *reflection coefficient* c_j associated with that interface. See Figure 8. The reflection coefficient c_j, which must satisfy $|c_j| < 1$, has these properties. A *downgoing wave* of amplitude A in layer j, upon striking interface j, is both re-

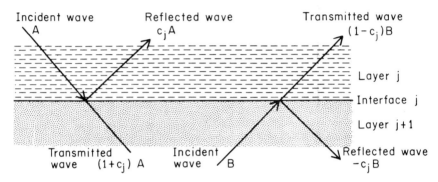

Fig. 8. The reflection coefficient c_j.

flected and transmitted. The reflected portion is an upgoing wave of amplitude c_j A in layer j, so c_j represents the *reflection coefficient*. The transmitted portion is a downgoing wave of amplitude $(1 + c_j)$ A in layer $j + 1$, so $1 + c_j$ represents the *transmission coefficient*. An *upgoing wave* of amplitude B in layer $j + 1$ is both reflected and transmitted when it strikes interface j. The reflected portion is a downgoing wave of amplitude $-c_j$ B in layer $j + 1$, and the transmitted portion is an upgoing wave of amplitude $(1 - c_j)$ B. Hence $-c_j$ and $1 - c_j$ represent, respectively, the *reflection coefficient* and the *transmission coefficient* for the upgoing wave. These properties are summarized in Table 2.

Let us denote the downgoing waveform, as a function of time t, at the top of layer j by $d_j(t)$. Then, since we assume there is no absorption in layer j, the downgoing waveform at the bottom of layer j will simply be the same waveform delayed by time equal to the travel time in the layer (which is defined as one-half time unit); hence the downgoing waveform at the bottom of layer j is $d_j(t - 0.5)$. Similarly, let us denote the upgoing waveform at the top of layer j by $u_j(t)$. Then the upgoing waveform at the bottom of layer j is the same waveform advanced by the travel time ($=$ one-half time unit), namely, $u_j(t + 0.5)$. These relations are depicted in Figure 9.

TABLE 2. Reflected and transmitted portions

	Reflected portion	Transmitted portion
Downgoing wave A in layer j	Upgoing wave $c_j A$ in layer j	Downgoing wave $(1 + c_j)A$ in layer $j + 1$
Upgoing wave B in layer $j + 1$	Downgoing wave $-c_j B$ in layer $j + 1$	Upgoing wave $(1 - c_j)B$ in layer j

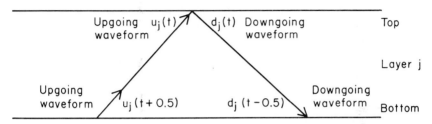

Fig. 9. Waveforms travelling through the layer suffer a delay of one-half time unit.

3.5 Relationships between the waveforms

Let us now derive the relationship between the waveforms in terms of the reflection coefficients. Figure 10 depicts the situation at the interface j (between layers j and $j + 1$) at time t. The waveform $d_{j+1}(t)$ is made up of two parts, namely, the part due to the transmitted portion of $d_j(t - 0.5)$ and the part due to the reflected portion of $u_{j+1}(t)$. Hence we have the equation

$$d_{j+1}(t) = (1 + c_j)\, d_j(t - 0.5) - c_j u_{j+1}(t) . \tag{1}$$

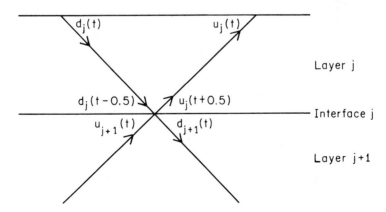

Fig. 10. Reflected and transmitted waves at interface j.

Likewise the waveform $u_j(t + 0.5)$ is made up of two parts, namely, the part due to the reflected portion of $d_j(t - 0.5)$ and the part due to the transmitted portion of $u_{j+1}(t)$. Hence we have the equation

$$u_j(t + 0.5) = c_j d_j(t - 0.5) + (1 - c_j)u_{j+1}(t) . \qquad (2)$$

If we let $D_j(s)$ be the Laplace transform of $d_j(t)$, that is,

$$D_j(s) = \int_0^\infty d_j(t) e^{-st} dt ,$$

then the Laplace transform of $d_j(t - 0.5)$ is

$$\int_0^\infty d_j(t - 0.5)e^{-st} dt = \int_0^\infty d_j(\tau)e^{-s(\tau+0.5)} d\tau = e^{-0.5s} D_j(s) .$$

If we define the parameter $z = e^{-s}$, then we may construct the following table of waveforms and their Laplace transforms.

Waveform	Laplace transform
$d_j(t)$	$D_j(s)$
$d_j(t - 0.5)$	$z^{1/2}D_j(s)$
$u_j(t)$	$U_j(s)$
$u_j(t + 0.5)$	$z^{-1/2}U_j(s)$
$d_{j+1}(t)$	$D_{j+1}(s)$
$u_{j+1}(t)$	$U_{j+1}(s)$

By taking Laplace transforms of eqs. (1) and (2) we obtain eqs. (3) and (4), respectively:

$$D_{j+1}(s) = (1 + c_j)z^{1/2} D_j(s) - c_j U_{j+1}(s) \qquad (3)$$
$$z^{-1/2}U_j(s) = c_j z^{1/2} D_j(s) + (1 - c_j)U_{j+1}(s) . \qquad (4)$$

Let us now solve eqs. (3) and (4) for $D_{j+1}(s)$ and $U_{j+1}(s)$. Equation (4) may be written as

$$U_{j+1}(s) = -\frac{c_j z^{1/2}}{1 - c_j} D_j(s) + \frac{z^{-1/2}}{1 - c_j} U_j(s) . \qquad (5)$$

Substituting eq. (5) into eq. (3), we obtain

$$D_{j+1}(s) = \frac{z^{1/2}}{1 - c_j} D_j(s) - \frac{c_j z^{-1/2}}{1 - c_j} U_j(s) . \qquad (6)$$

Writing eqs. (5) and (6) in matrix form, we have

$$\begin{bmatrix} D_{j+1}(s) \\ U_{j+1}(s) \end{bmatrix} = \begin{bmatrix} \dfrac{z^{1/2}}{1 - c_j} & -\dfrac{c_j z^{-1/2}}{1 - c_j} \\ -\dfrac{c_j z^{1/2}}{1 - c_j} & \dfrac{z^{-1/2}}{1 - c_j} \end{bmatrix} \begin{bmatrix} D_j(s) \\ U_j(s) \end{bmatrix} . \qquad (7)$$

Let us define the square matrix N_j as

$$N_j = \begin{bmatrix} z & -c_j \\ -c_j z & 1 \end{bmatrix}.$$

Then eq. (7) becomes

$$\begin{bmatrix} D_{j+1}(s) \\ U_{j+1}(s) \end{bmatrix} = \frac{z^{-1/2}}{1 - c_j} N_j \begin{bmatrix} D_j(s) \\ U_j(s) \end{bmatrix}.$$

By repeated application of this equation for $j = 1, 2, 3, \ldots, k$, we obtain

$$\begin{bmatrix} D_{k+1}(s) \\ U_{k+1}(s) \end{bmatrix} = \frac{z^{-k/2}}{(1 - c_k) \cdots (1 - c_2)(1 - c_1)} N_k \cdots N_2 N_1 \begin{bmatrix} D_1(s) \\ U_1(s) \end{bmatrix}. \quad (8)$$

This equation relates the waveforms at the top of layer $k + 1$ with those at the top of layer 1.

Let us now define $D_0(s)$ and $U_0(s)$ as the Laplace transforms of the down-going and upgoing waveforms $d_0(t)$ and $u_0(t)$, respectively, at the bottom of layer 0. To relate $D_0(s)$ and $U_0(s)$ with $D_1(s)$ and $U_1(s)$, we can use eq. (7) by setting $j = 0$, provided we set $z = 1$, for there is no time delay between the waveforms $d_0(t)$ and $u_0(t)$ at the *bottom* of layer 0 and the waveforms $d_1(t)$ and $u_1(t)$ at the *top* of layer 1. Hence in this case eq. (7) simply becomes

$$\begin{bmatrix} D_1(s) \\ U_1(s) \end{bmatrix} = \begin{bmatrix} \dfrac{1}{1 - c_0} & -\dfrac{c_0}{1 - c_0} \\ -\dfrac{c_0}{1 - c_0} & \dfrac{1}{1 - c_0} \end{bmatrix} \begin{bmatrix} D_0(s) \\ U_0(s) \end{bmatrix}. \quad (9)$$

Substituting eq. (9) into eq. (8), we obtain

$$\begin{bmatrix} D_{k+1}(s) \\ U_{k+1}(s) \end{bmatrix}$$

$$= \frac{z^{-k/2}}{(1 - c_k) \cdots (1 - c_2)(1 - c_1)(1 - c_0)} N_k \cdots N_2 N_1 N_0 \begin{bmatrix} D_0(s) \\ U_0(s) \end{bmatrix}, \quad (10)$$

where

$$N_0 = \begin{bmatrix} 1 & -c_0 \\ -c_0 & 1 \end{bmatrix}, \quad N_j = \begin{bmatrix} z & -c_j \\ -c_j z & 1 \end{bmatrix}$$

for $j = 1, 2, \ldots, k$.

3.6 Recursive generation of the fundamental polynomials

Let us define the polynomials $P_0(z)$, $Q_0(z)$, and $A_0(z)$ as

$$P_0(z) = p_0(0) = 1$$
$$Q_0(z) = q_0(0) = 0$$
$$A_0(z) = P_0(z) + Q_0(z) = 1 .$$

Next let us define the polynomials $Q_1(z)$ and $P_1(z)$ as the respective elements in the lower row of the matrix N_1, that is,

$$Q_1(z) = q_0(1) + q_1(1)z = -c_1 z$$
$$[\text{so } q_0(1) = 0, q_1(1) = -c_1] ,$$
$$P_1(z) = p_0(1) + p_1(1)z = 1$$
$$[\text{so } p_0(1) = 1, p_1(1) = 0] ,$$

and define the polynomial $A_1(z)$ as their sum

$$A_1(z) = P_1(z) + Q_1(z) = a_0(1) + a_1(1)z = 1 - c_1 z$$
$$[\text{so } a_0(1) = 1, a_1(1) = -c_1] .$$

In particular, we see that the matrix N_1 may be written as

$$N_1 = \begin{bmatrix} z & -c_1 \\ -c_1 z & 1 \end{bmatrix} = \begin{bmatrix} P_1^R(z) & Q_1^R(z) \\ Q_1(z) & P_1(z) \end{bmatrix},$$

where the *reverse polynomials* $P_1^R(z)$ and $Q_1^R(z)$ are defined as

$$P_1^R(z) = zP_1(z^{-1}) = p_1(1) + p_0(1)z = z$$
$$Q_1^R(z) = zQ_1(z^{-1}) = q_1(1) + q_0(1)z = -c_1 .$$

Likewise let us define the polynomials $Q_2(z)$ and $P_2(z)$ as the respective elements in the lower row of the matrix product $N_2 N_1$. Thus

$$N_2 N_1 = \begin{bmatrix} z & -c_2 \\ -c_2 z & 1 \end{bmatrix} \begin{bmatrix} P_1^R(z) & Q_1^R(z) \\ Q_1(z) & P_1(z) \end{bmatrix} = \begin{bmatrix} P_2^R(z) & Q_2^R(z) \\ Q_2(z) & P_2(z) \end{bmatrix}.$$

By matrix multiplication we obtain the recursion relations

$$P_2(z) = P_1(z) - c_2 z Q_1^R(z)$$
$$Q_2(z) = Q_1(z) - c_2 z P_1^R(z)$$

which gives

$$P_2(z) = p_0(2) + p_1(2)z + p_2(2)z^2 = 1 + c_1 c_2 z$$
$$[\text{so } p_0(2) = 1, p_1(2) = c_1 c_2, p_2(2) = 0] ,$$

and

$$Q_2(z) = q_0(2) + q_1(2)z + q_2(2)z^2 = -c_1 z - c_2 z^2$$
$$[\text{so } q_0(2) = 0, q_1(2) = -c_1, q_2(2) = -c_2] .$$

Likewise, we define the polynomial $A_2(z)$ as the sum

$$A_2(z) = P_2(z) + Q_2(z)$$

so

$$A_2(z) = a_0(2) + a_1(2)z + a_2(2)z^2 = 1 + (c_1c_2 - c_1)z - c_2z^2 .$$

In particular, $A_2(z)$ satisfies the recursion relation

$$A_2(z) = A_1(z) - c_2zA_1^R(z) ,$$

where

$$A_1^R(z) = P_1^R(z) + Q_1^R(z) = zA_1(z^{-1}) = a_1(1) + a_0(1)z .$$

In general, define the polynomials

$$Q_k(z) = q_0(k) + q_1(k)z + \cdots + q_k(k)z^k$$
$$P_k(z) = p_0(k) + p_1(k)z + \cdots + p_k(k)z^k$$

as the respective elements in the lower row of the matrix product $N_kN_{k-1} \cdots$
N_2N_1. Hence

$$N_kN_{k-1} \cdots N_2N_1 = \begin{bmatrix} P_k^R(z) & Q_k^R(z) \\ Q_k(z) & P_k(z) \end{bmatrix},$$

where the $P_k^R(z)$ and $Q_k^R(z)$ are the reverse polynomials

$$P_k^R(z) = z^kP_k(z^{-1}) = p_k(k) + p_{k-1}(k)z + \cdots + p_0(k)z^k$$
$$Q_k^R(z) = z^kQ_k(z^{-1}) = q_k(k) + q_{k-1}(k)z + \cdots + q_0(k)z^k .$$

In particular, we have

$$N_kN_{k-1} \cdots N_2N_1 = \begin{bmatrix} z & -c_k \\ -c_kz & 1 \end{bmatrix} \begin{bmatrix} P_{k-1}^R(z) & Q_{k-1}^R(z) \\ Q_{k-1}(z) & P_{k-1}(z) \end{bmatrix} = \begin{bmatrix} P_k^R(z) & Q_k^R(z) \\ Q_k(z) & P_k(z) \end{bmatrix}$$

which by matrix multiplication gives the recursion relations

$$P_k(z) = P_{k-1}(z) - c_kzQ_{k-1}^R(z) \tag{1}$$
$$Q_k(z) = Q_{k-1}(z) - c_kzP_{k-1}^R(z) . \tag{2}$$

By adding the above equations, we obtain for the polynomial

$$A_k(z) = a_0(k) + a_1(k)z + \cdots + a_k(k)z^k = P_k(z) + Q_k(z)$$

the recursion relation given by

$$A_k(z) = A_{k-1}(z) - c_kzA_{k-1}^R(z) . \tag{3}$$

With the initial conditions $P_1(z) = 1$ and $Q_1(z) = -c_1z$, eqs. (1) and (2) provide the recursion from step $k - 1$ to k, which allows us to compute the polynomials $P_k(z)$ and $Q_k(z)$ for $k = 2, 3, 4, 5, \ldots$. Equations (1) and (2) are, in fact, valid for $k = 1, 2, 3, 4, \ldots$ with the initial conditions $P_0(z) = 1$ and $Q_0(z) = 0$. Likewise, eq. (3) provides a recursion to determine the polynomials $A_k(z)$ for $k = 1, 2, 3, 4, \ldots$ subject to the initial condition $A_0(z) = 1$. In order to make use of these recursion relations the reflection coefficients $c_1, c_2, c_3, \ldots$ are assumed to be given.

As a numerical example, let us suppose that the given reflection coefficients are

$$c_1 = 0.1, \ c_2 = -0.2, \ c_3 = 0.3, \ c_4 = -0.4, \ c_5 = 0.5.$$

Then the polynomials $A_k(z)$ as computed by the recursion are

$$A_0(z) = 1$$
$$A_1(z) = 1 - 0.10z$$
$$A_2(z) = 1 - 0.12z + 0.2000z^2$$
$$A_3(z) = 1 - 0.18z + 0.2360z^2 - 0.3000z^3$$
$$A_4(z) = 1 - 0.30z + 0.3304z^2 - 0.3720z^3 + 0.40z^4$$
$$A_5(z) = 1 - 0.50z + 0.5164z^2 - 0.5372z^3 + 0.55z^4 - 0.5z^5 .$$

Note that in each polynomial the first coefficient is unity and the last coefficient is the negative of the kth reflection coefficient; that is, $A_k(0) = a_0(k) = 1$, $A_k^R(0) = a_k(k) = -c_k$.

3.7 Layered system subject to given boundary conditions

Now let us consider the situation where a downgoing wave $d_0(t)$ in half-space 0 is imposed on a layered system made up of k layers, and where no upgoing wave $u_{k+1}(t)$ in half-space $k + 1$ is imposed on the system. That is, we consider the situation described by the boundary conditions: $d_0(t) =$ given waveform and $u_{k+1}(t) = 0$. See Figure 11. Let us now derive the response of the system

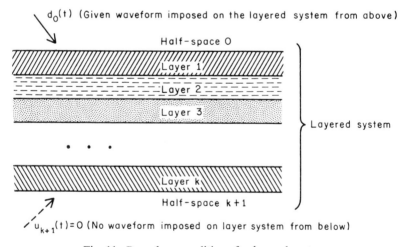

Fig. 11. Boundary conditions for layered system.

to these boundary conditions. Equation (10) of Sec. 3.5 becomes

$$
\begin{bmatrix} D_{k+1}(s) \\ 0 \end{bmatrix} = \frac{z^{-k/2}}{(1 - c_k) \dots (1 - c_1)(1 - c_0)}
$$

$$
\begin{bmatrix} z^k P_k(z^{-1}) & z^k Q_k(z^{-1}) \\ Q_k(z) & P_k(z) \end{bmatrix} \begin{bmatrix} 1 & -c_0 \\ -c_0 & 1 \end{bmatrix} \begin{bmatrix} D_0(s) \\ U_0(s) \end{bmatrix}.
$$

This matrix equation represents two scalar equations; the first is

$$
D_{k+1}(s) = \frac{z^{-k/2} z^k}{(1 - c_k) \cdots (1 - c_0)} \{[P_k(z^{-1}) - c_0 Q_k(z^{-1})] D_0(s)
$$

$$
+ [-c_0 P_k(z^{-1}) + Q_k(z^{-1})] U_0(s)\}, \quad (1)
$$

and the second is

$$
0 = [Q_k(z) - c_0 P_k(z)] D_0(s) + [-c_0 Q_k(z) + P_k(z)] U_0(s). \quad (2)
$$

Solving eq. (2) for $U_0(s)$, we obtain

$$
U_0(s) = \frac{c_0 P_k(z) - Q_k(z)}{P_k(z) - c_0 Q_k(z)} D_0(s). \quad (3)
$$

Substituting the expression for $U_0(s)$ given by eq. (3) into eq. (1), we obtain

$$
D_{k+1}(s) = \frac{z^{-k/2} D_0(s)}{(1 - c_k) \cdots (1 - c_0)} \frac{z^k P_k(z^{-1}) P_k(z) - z^k Q_k(z^{-1}) Q_k(z)}{P_k(z) - c_0 Q_k(z)} (1 - c_0^2). \quad (4)
$$

But we know that

$$
z^k P_k(z^{-1}) P_k(z) - z^k Q_k(z^{-1}) Q_k(z) = \det \begin{bmatrix} z^k P_k(z^{-1}) & z^k Q_k(z^{-1}) \\ Q_k(z) & P_k(z) \end{bmatrix}
$$

$$
= \det (N_k N_{k-1} \cdots N_1) = (\det N_k)(\det N_{k-1}) \cdots (\det N_1)
$$

$$
= \det \begin{bmatrix} z & -c_k \\ -c_k z & 1 \end{bmatrix} \det \begin{bmatrix} z & -c_{k-1} \\ -c_{k-1} z & 1 \end{bmatrix} \cdots \det \begin{bmatrix} z & -c_1 \\ -c_1 z & 1 \end{bmatrix}
$$

$$
= (z - c_k^2 z)(z - c_{k-1}^2 z) \cdots (z - c_1^2 z)
$$

$$
= z^k (1 - c_k)(1 + c_k)(1 - c_{k-1})(1 + c_{k-1}) \cdots (1 - c_1)(1 + c_1). \quad (5)
$$

Substituting eq. (5) into eq. (4), we have

$$
D_{k+1}(s) = \frac{z^{k/2}(1 + c_k) \cdots (1 + c_1)(1 + c_0)}{P_k(z) - c_0 Q_k(z)} D_0(s). \quad (6)
$$

Hence given the boundary conditions that $D_0(s)$ is arbitrary and $U_{k+1}(s)$ is zero, eqs. (3) and (6) give relations for $U_0(s)$ and $D_{k+1}(s)$, respectively, in terms of $D_0(s)$.

3.8 Optical properties of a single thin film

Let us now give two examples. The first is the reflection and transmission of light by a single film, and the second is the reflection and transmission of light by two films.

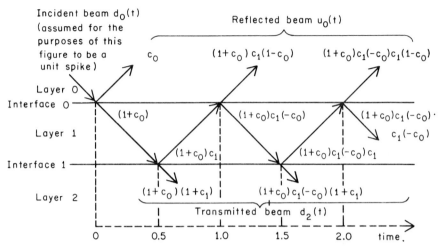

Fig. 12. Reflection and transmission of light by a single film with boundary conditions $d_0(t)$ = given waveform (which in the figure is assumed to be a unit spike at time 0) and $u_2(t) = 0$.

Figure 12 depicts the reflection and transmission of a beam of light incident on a single non-absorbing film (layer 1), bounded on either side by semi-infinite non-absorbing layers (layer 0 above and layer 2 below). We assume normal incidence, but since we draw our time scale along the horizontal axis in Figure 12 it appears as if the beam were at non-normal incidence. The light beam which is incident on the film is divided into reflected and transmitted parts. Such division happens each time the beam strikes an interface. The *transmission transfer function* $T(z)$ of the thin film, which is found by letting $k = 1$ in eq. (6) of the previous section, is

$$T(z) = \frac{D_2(s)}{D_0(s)} = \frac{z^{1/2}(1 + c_1)(1 + c_0)}{P_1(z) - c_0 Q_1(z)} .\tag{1}$$

The denominator of $T(z)$ is [since $P_1(z) = 1$ and $Q_1(z) = -c_1 z$]

$$P_1(z) - c_0 Q_1(z) = 1 + c_0 c_1 z .$$

Because the reflection coefficients c_0 and c_1 each cannot exceed unity in magnitude, it follows that

$$|c_0 c_1| < 1$$

so that the denominator $P_1(z) - c_0 Q_1(z)$ is *minimum delay*. [From strictly physical grounds we could have arrived at the same conclusion since we know that the transmission transfer function represents a physical phenomenon in real time and hence must be realizable and stable. However, apart from the factor $z^{1/2}(1 + c_1)(1 + c_0)$, $T(z)$ is the inverse of the operator represented by the z-transform $P_1(z) - c_0Q_1(z)$, and in order for this inverse to be realizable and stable it follows that $P_1(z) - c_0Q_1(z)$ must be minimum delay.] Hence $z^{-1/2}T(z)$ is minimum delay. Expanding the transmission transfer function $T(z)$ as a power series, we have

$$
\begin{aligned}
T(z) &= z^{1/2}(1 + c_1)(1 + c_0)(1 + c_0c_1z)^{-1} \\
&= z^{1/2}(1 + c_1)(1 + c_0)(1 - c_0c_1z + c_0^2c_1^2z^2 + \cdots) \\
&= (1 + c_0)(1 + c_1)z^{0.5} + (1 + c_0)c_1(-c_0)(1 + c_1)z^{1.5} + \cdots.
\end{aligned}
$$

In this expansion we recognize the coefficient of $z^{0.5}$, namely, $(1 + c_0)(1 + c_1)$, as the ray in Figure 12 occurring at time 0.5 which has been transmitted downward through interface 0 with transmission coefficient $1 + c_0$, and downward through interface 1 with transmission coefficient $1 + c_1$. Likewise we recognize the coefficient of $z^{1.5}$, namely $(1 + c_0)c_1(-c_0)(1 + c_1)$, as the ray in Figure 12 which has been transmitted downward through interface 0 with transmission coefficient $1 + c_0$, reflected upward from interface 1 with reflection coefficient c_1, reflected downward from interface 0 with reflection coefficient $-c_0$, and transmitted downward through interface 1 with transmission coefficient $1 + c_1$. In a similar way, we can identify the coefficients of the terms with $z^{2.5}, z^{3.5}, \ldots$ as the rays transmitted downward through interface 1 at times $2.5, 3.5, \ldots$.

Let us now turn our attention from the transmission transfer function to the reflection transfer function. The *reflection transfer function* $R(z)$ of a single thin film, which is found by letting $k = 1$ in eq. (3) of the previous section, is

$$
R(z) = \frac{U_0(z)}{D_0(z)} = \frac{c_0P_1(z) - Q_1(z)}{P_1(z) - c_0Q_1(z)} = \frac{c_0 + c_1z}{1 + c_0c_1z} . \tag{2}
$$

The denominator of $R(z)$ is the same as for $T(z)$; this denominator is necessarily minimum delay. The numerator $c_0 + c_1z$ may be either minimum delay or not, depending upon whether or not $|c_0| \geqslant |c_1|$. The power series expansion of the reflection transfer function is

$$
\begin{aligned}
R(z) &= (c_0 + c_1z)(1 - c_0c_1z + c_0^2c_1^2z^2 + \cdots) \\
&= c_0 + (1 + c_0)c_1(1 - c_0)z + (1 + c_0)c_1(-c_0)c_1(1 - c_0)z^2 + \cdots.
\end{aligned}
$$

Here we recognize the coefficients of $z^0, z, z^2, \ldots$ as the rays emerging upward from layer 0 in Figure 12 at times $0, 1, 2, \ldots$.

The vibration $x_0(t)$ at the bottom of layer 0 is the sum of the downgoing and upgoing waves at the bottom of layer 0, that is,

$$
x_0(t) = d_0(t) + u_0(t) .
$$

In terms of Laplace transforms, this equation is

$$
X_0(s) = D_0(s) + U_0(s) = D_0(s)[1 + R(z)] .
$$

Let us call $V(z) = 1 + R(z)$ the *surface vibration transfer function*. In the case of a single thin film, we have

$$V(z) = 1 + R(z) = 1 + \frac{c_0 + c_1z}{1 + c_0c_1z} = \frac{(1 + c_0)(1 + c_1z)}{1 + c_0c_1z}.$$

We see that $(1 + c_1z)$ is minimum delay, and hence the surface vibration transfer function

$$V(z) = 1 + R(z) = \frac{(1 + c_0)(1 + c_1z)}{1 + c_0c_1z}$$

is minimum delay.

3.9 Optical properties of two thin films

Our second example is the case of the reflection and transmission of light by two thin films, as schematically depicted in Figure 13. The *transmission transfer function* is

$$T(z) = \frac{D_3(s)}{D_0(s)} = \frac{z(1 + c_2)(1 + c_1)(1 + c_0)}{P_2(z) - c_0Q_2(z)}$$
$$= \frac{z(1 + c_2)(1 + c_1)(1 + c_0)}{1 + (c_1c_2 + c_0c_1)z + c_0c_2z^2}.$$

By the same physical reasoning as used before, we deduce that the denominator $P_2(z) - c_0Q_2(z)$ is minimum delay, so $z^{-1}T(z)$ is minimum delay. By ex-

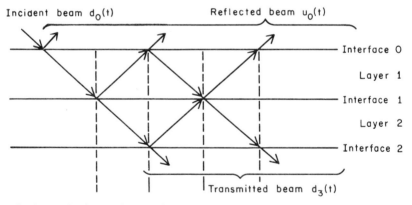

Fig. 13. Reflection and transmission of light by two films with boundary conditions $d_0(t) =$ given waveform and $u_3(t) = 0$.

panding $T(z)$ in a power series we can recognize the coefficients of z^1, z^2, z^3, ... as the rays emerging downward into the lower half-space (layer 3) at times 1, 2, 3, ..., respectively, given that $D_0(s) = 1$. Likewise, the *reflection transfer function* is

$$R(z) = \frac{U_0(z)}{D_0(z)} = \frac{c_0 P_2(z) - Q_2(z)}{P_2(z) - c_0 Q_2(z)} = \frac{c_0 + (c_0 c_1 c_2 + c_1)z + c_2 z^2}{1 + (c_1 c_2 + c_0 c_1)z + c_0 c_2 z^2}.$$

The denominator $P_2(z) - c_0 Q_2(z)$ is minimum delay, but the numerator $c_0 P_2(z) - Q_2(z)$ may or may not be minimum delay, depending upon the numerical values of the reflection coefficients c_0, c_1, c_2. By expanding $R(z)$ in a power series, we can recognize the coefficients of z^0, z, z^2, z^3, ... as the rays emerging upward into upper half-space (layer 0) at times 0, 1, 2, 3, ..., respectively, given that $D_0(s) = 1$. The *surface vibration transfer function is*

$$V(z) = 1 + R(z) = (1 + c_0) \frac{P_2(z) - Q_2(z)}{P_2(z) - c_0 Q_2(z)}$$

$$= (1 + c_0) \frac{1 + (c_1 c_2 + c_1)z + c_2 z^2}{1 + (c_1 c_2 + c_0 c_1)z + c_0 c_2 z^2},$$

which is minimum delay.

3.10 Optical properties of an arbitrary number of thin films

In summary, let us write down the formulas for the reflection and transmission of light by a system made up of k thin films. The *transmission transfer function* of the system is

$$T(z) = \frac{D_{k+1}(s)}{D_0(s)} = \frac{(1 + c_k) \cdots (1 + c_1)(1 + c_0)}{P_k(z) - c_0 Q_k(z)} z^{k/2}, \tag{1}$$

where $z^{-k/2} T(z)$ is minimum delay. The *reflection transfer function* is

$$R(z) = \frac{U_0(s)}{D_0(s)} = \frac{c_0 P_k(z) - Q_k(z)}{P_k(z) - c_0 Q_k(z)}, \tag{2}$$

which may or may not be minimum delay, depending upon whether the numerator $c_0 P_k(z) - Q_k(z)$ is or is not minimum delay. The denominator $P_k(z) - c_0 Q_k(z)$ is always minimum delay. The *surface vibration transfer function* is

$$V(z) = 1 + R(z) = (1 + c_0) \frac{P_k(z) - Q_k(z)}{P_k(z) - c_0 Q_k(z)},$$

which is minimum delay.

3.11 All-pass system or the case of a perfect reflector at the lower interface

Let us now consider the special case when the lower interface (interface k) is a *perfect reflector* (i.e., when $c_k = +1$ or $c_k = -1$). For definiteness we will take $c_k = 1$; a similar argument can be carried through in the case when $c_k = -1$. Putting $c_k = 1$ in eqs. (1) and (2) of Sec. 3.6, we have

$$P_k(z) = P_{k-1}(z) - z Q_{k-1}^R(z)$$
$$Q_k(z) = Q_{k-1}(z) - z P_{k-1}^R(z).$$

Inserting these expressions for $Q_k(z)$ and $P_k(z)$ into $R(z)$, as given in eq. (2) of Sec. 3.10, we obtain $R(z)$ in the form

$$R(z) = \frac{G(z)}{H(z)},$$

where the denominator polynomial $H(z)$ is given by

$$\begin{aligned} H(z) &= P_k(z) - c_0 Q_k(z) \\ &= P_{k-1}(z) - z Q^{R}_{k-1}(z) - c_0 Q_{k-1}(z) + c_0 z P^{R}_{k-1}(z), \end{aligned}$$

and the numerator polynomial $G(z)$ is given by

$$\begin{aligned} G(z) &= c_0 P_k(z) - Q_k(z) \\ &= c_0 P_{k-1}(z) - c_0 z Q^{R}_{k-1}(z) - Q_{k-1}(z) + z P^{R}_{k-1}(z). \end{aligned}$$

From these expressions for $H(z)$ and $G(z)$, we see that $G(z)$ is the reverse polynomial of $H(z)$, that is,

$$G(z) = H^{R}(z) = z^k H(z^{-1}),$$

and hence the reflection transfer function in the case of a perfect reflector at the lower interface is given by

$$R(z) = \frac{H^{R}(z)}{H(z)}.$$

In the expression for $R(z)$ given here, the denominator polynomial $H(z)$ is minimum delay, and hence the numerator polynomial $H^{R}(z)$, which is the reverse polynomial of $H(z)$, is maximum delay. Hence $R(z)$ is a *dispersive all-pass system*,[34] for such a system is defined as one whose z-transform is given by the ratio of a maximum-delay z-transform to the corresponding minimum-delay z-transform. Because a maximum-delay z-transform and its corresponding minimum-delay z-transform each have the same amplitude spectrum, it follows that a dispersive all-pass system has an amplitude spectrum equal to unity for all frequencies. In particular, we may verify that the amplitude spectrum of $R(z)$ is

$$|R(e^{-2\pi i f})| = \frac{|H^{R}(e^{-2\pi i f})|}{|H(e^{-2\pi i f})|} = 1.$$

Let us consider a numerical example. Suppose that we have a one-layer case so $k = 1$. Let the reflection coefficients be $c_0 = 0.5$ and $c_1 = 1$. Then the reflection transfer function is the dispersive all-pass system given by

$$R(z) = \frac{c_0 + c_1 z}{1 + c_0 c_1 z} = \frac{0.5 + z}{1 + 0.5z} = 0.5 + 0.75z - 0.375z^2 + 0.1875z^3 - \cdots.$$

---

[34] That $R(z)$ is a dispersive all-pass system was discovered experimentally by Sven Treitel in connection with experiments on a computer model of a layered system. For further discussion, see Treitel, S., and E. A. Robinson, "Seismic wave propagation in layered media in terms of communication theory," *Geophys.* **31**, 17–32 (1966).

3.12 Marine seismogram or the case of a perfect reflector at the upper interface

Let us now consider the case of a layered system for which the upper interface (i.e., interface 0) is a *perfect reflector* with reflection coefficient $c_0 = -1$. See Figure 14. Such a case is realized in marine seismic exploration, for then the

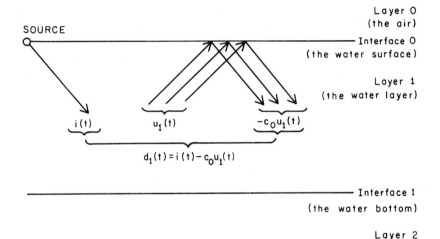

Fig. 14. Boundary condition $d_1(t) = i(t) - c_0 u_1(t)$.

first layer is the water layer and the surface of the water acts as a perfect reflector. We suppose that a source located on interface 0 gives rise to an initial downgoing waveform $i(t)$ at the top of layer 1. The upgoing waveform $u_1(t)$ at the top of layer 1 is reflected at the water surface (i.e., interface 0) to yield a downgoing waveform $-c_0 u_1(t)$ at the top of the water layer (i.e., at the top of layer 1). Hence the entire downgoing waveform at the top of layer 1 is the sum of the initial downgoing waveform and the reflected waveform, that is,

$$d_1(t) = i(t) - c_0 u_1(t) .$$

Since the water surface is a perfect reflector (i.e., $c_0 = -1$), this equation becomes

$$d_1(t) = i(t) + u_1(t) .$$

Let us assume that the initial downgoing waveform $i(t)$ is a single positive spike ϕ_0 at time 0. Then the upgoing waveform $u_1(t)$ will be a time series (starting at time 1), say,

$$\phi_1, \phi_2, \phi_3, \phi_4, \ldots ,$$

where $\phi_1 = u_1(1)$, $\phi_2 = u_1(2)$, $\phi_3 = u_1(3)$, ..., $\phi_t = u_1(t)$, ... Hence the downgoing waveform $d_1(t)$ will be the time series (starting at time 0) given by

$$\phi_0,\ \phi_1,\ \phi_2,\ \phi_3,\ \phi_4,\ \ldots,$$

where $\phi_0 = d_1(0) = i(0)$, $\phi_1 = d_1(1) = u_1(1)$, $\phi_2 = d_1(2) = u_1(2)$, ..., $\phi_t = d_1(t) = u_1(t)$. Physically the coefficients ϕ_t are defined only for non-negative integers t; if we mathematically define the coefficients ϕ_t for negative integers t by the symmetry condition

$$\phi_{-t} = \phi_t\ ,$$

then the function ϕ_t for all integers t becomes the so-called *autocorrelation function*. A seismic detector at the surface of the water records the sum of the upgoing and downgoing waveforms; that is, the recorded marine seismogram is the time series

$$\phi_0,\ 2\phi_1,\ 2\phi_2,\ 2\phi_3,\ 2\phi_4,\ \ldots.$$

The z-transforms of the upgoing and downgoing waveforms at the top of layer 1 are, respectively,

$$U_1(z) = \qquad \phi_1 z + \phi_2 z^2 + \phi_3 z^3 + \cdots,$$
$$D_1(z) = \phi_0 + \phi_1 z + \phi_2 z^2 + \phi_3 z^3 + \cdots = \phi_0 + U_1(z)\ .$$

The z-transforms of the downgoing and upgoing waveforms at the top of layer $k + 1$ are, respectively,

$$D_{k+1}(z) = d_{k+1}\left(\frac{k}{2}\right)z^{k/2} + d_{k+1}\left(\frac{k}{2} + 1\right)z^{(k/2)+1} + d_{k+1}\left(\frac{k}{2} + 2\right)z^{(k/2)+2} + \cdots$$

$$U_{k+1}(z) = \qquad\qquad u_{k+1}\left(\frac{k}{2} + 1\right)z^{(k/2)+1} + u_{k+1}\left(\frac{k}{2} + 2\right)z^{(k/2)+2} + \cdots.$$

See Figure 15. These z-transforms are related by

$$\begin{bmatrix} D_{k+1}(z) \\ U_{k+1}(z) \end{bmatrix} = \frac{z^{-k/2}}{(1 - c_k)\cdots(1 - c_2)(1 - c_1)}\begin{bmatrix} P_k^{\mathrm{R}}(z) & Q_k^{\mathrm{R}}(z) \\ Q_k(z) & P_k(z) \end{bmatrix}\begin{bmatrix} \phi_0 + U_1(z) \\ U_1(z) \end{bmatrix}.$$

This matrix equation gives the two scalar equations

$$D_{k+1}(z) = \frac{z^{-k/2}}{(1 - c_k)\cdots(1 - c_2)(1 - c_1)}\ \{[P_k^{\mathrm{R}}(z) + Q_k^{\mathrm{R}}(z)]U_1(z) + \phi_0 P_k^{\mathrm{R}}(z)\}$$

$$U_{k+1}(z) = \frac{z^{-k/2}}{(1 - c_k)\cdots(1 - c_2)(1 - c_1)}\ \{[P_k(z) + Q_k(z)]U_1(z) + \phi_0 Q_k(z)\}\ .$$

In order to reduce the amount of notation that must be carried, let us for the moment drop the (k)-designation on the coefficients of the polynomials $P_k(z)$, $Q_k(z)$, and $A_k(z)$; that is, we write for the time being

$$P_k(z) = p_0(k) + p_1(k)z + \cdots + p_k(k)z^k = p_0 + p_1 z + \cdots + p_k z^k$$
$$Q_k(z) = q_0(k) + q_1(k)z + \cdots + q_k(k)z^k = q_0 + q_1 z + \cdots + q_k z^k$$
$$A_k(z) = a_0(k) + a_1(k)z + \cdots + a_k(k)z^k = a_0 + a_1 z + \cdots + a_k z^k\ .$$

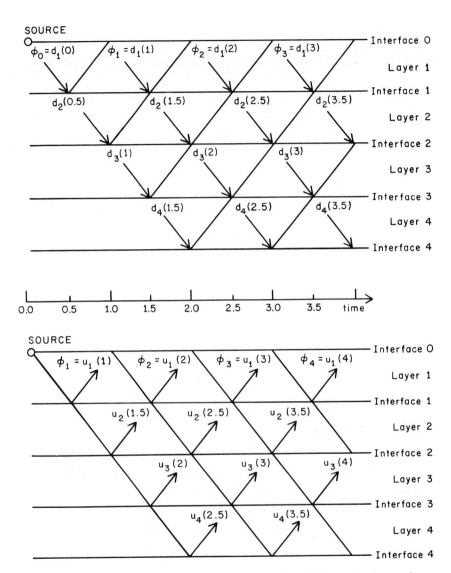

Fig. 15. The top diagram shows the notation used to designate the downgoing waveform $d_j(t)$ at the top of layer j at time t, whereas the bottom diagram shows the notation used to designate the upgoing waveform $u_j(t)$ at the top of layer j at time t. Compare with Figure 16.

The operator $[a_0(k), a_1(k), \ldots, a_k(k)]$ is the so-called *prediction-error operator* of length $k + 1$. Since $A_k(z) = P_k(z) + Q_k(z)$, the above two scalar equations become, upon multiplying each side by $z^{k/2}$,

$$d_{k+1}\left(\frac{k}{2}\right) z^k + d_{k+1}\left(\frac{k}{2} + 1\right) z^{k+1} + d_{k+1}\left(\frac{k}{2} + 2\right) z^{k+2} + \cdots$$

$$= \frac{1}{(1 - c_k) \cdots (1 - c_1)} [(a_k + \cdots + a_0 z^k)(\phi_1 z + \phi_2 z^2 + \cdots)$$
$$+ \phi_0(p_k + \cdots + p_0 z^k)] \tag{1}$$

and

$$u_{k+1}\left(\frac{k}{2} + 1\right) z^{k+1} + u_{k+1}\left(\frac{k}{2} + 2\right) z^{k+2} + \cdots = \frac{1}{(1 - c_k) \cdots (1 - c_1)}$$
$$[(a_0 + \cdots + a_k z^k)(\phi_1 z + \phi_2 z^2 + \cdots) + \phi_0(q_0 + \cdots + q_k z^k)] . \tag{2}$$

Let us now identify the coefficients of powers of z in the above two equations (1) and (2). The coefficients of $z^0, z^1, z^2, \ldots, z^k$ in eq. (2) must be zero; the coefficients of $z^0, z^1, z^2, \ldots, z^{k-1}$ in eq. (1) must be zero. Hence the coefficients of z^0 in (2) and z^k in (1) give, respectively,

$$q_0\phi_0 \qquad\qquad\qquad\qquad = 0$$
$$p_0\phi_0 + a_1\phi_1 + a_2\phi_2 + \cdots + a_k\phi_k = (1 - c_k) \cdots (1 - c_1) d_{k+1}\left(\frac{k}{2}\right),$$

which upon addition give

$$a_0\phi_0 + a_1\phi_1 + a_2\phi_2 + \cdots + a_k\phi_k = (1 - c_k) \cdots (1 - c_1) d_{k+1}\left(\frac{k}{2}\right).$$

The coefficients of z in (2) and z^{k-1} in (1) give, respectively,

$$a_0\phi_1 + q_1\phi_0 \qquad\qquad = 0$$
$$p_1\phi_0 + a_2\phi_1 + \cdots + a_k\phi_{k-1} = 0 ,$$

which upon addition give

$$a_0\phi_1 + a_1\phi_0 + a_2\phi_1 + \cdots + a_k\phi_{k-1} = 0 .$$

We continue, until finally we find that the coefficients of z^k in (2) and z^0 in (1) give, respectively,

$$a_0\phi_k + a_1\phi_{k-1} + a_2\phi_{k-2} + \cdots + q_k\phi_0 = 0$$
$$p_k\phi_0 = 0 ,$$

which upon addition give

$$a_0\phi_k + a_1\phi_{k-1} + a_2\phi_{k-2} + \cdots + a_k\phi_0 = 0 .$$

Collecting the equations obtained above by addition, we have the following set of simultaneous equations, the so-called *normal equations*,

$$a_0\phi_0 + a_1\phi_1 + a_2\phi_2 + \cdots + a_k\phi_k = v$$
$$a_0\phi_1 + a_1\phi_0 + a_2\phi_1 + \cdots + a_k\phi_{k-1} = 0$$
$$a_0\phi_2 + a_1\phi_1 + a_2\phi_0 + \cdots + a_k\phi_{k-2} = 0$$
$$\cdots$$
$$a_0\phi_k + a_1\phi_{k-1} + a_2\phi_{k-2} + \cdots + a_k\phi_0 = 0 ,$$

where we have defined the so-called *prediction-error variance* v as

$$v = v(k) = (1 - c_k)(1 - c_{k-1}) \ldots (1 - c_1) d_{k+1}\left(\frac{k}{2}\right).$$

Since $d_{k+1}(k/2)$ is the direct downward pulse that starts out at time 0 at the surface as ϕ_0, passes through interface 1 at time 1/2 with transmission coefficient $(1 + c_1)$, passes through interface 2 at time 1 with transmission coefficient $(1 + c_2)$, and finally at time $k/2$ passes through interface k with transmission coefficient $(1 + c_k)$, it follows that

$$d_{k+1}\left(\frac{k}{2}\right) = \phi_0(1 + c_1)(1 + c_2) \cdots (1 + c_k),$$

and hence the prediction-error variance is

$$v = v(k) = (1 - c_k)(1 - c_{k-1}) \cdots (1 - c_1)\phi_0(1 + c_1)(1 + c_2) \cdots (1 + c_k)$$
$$= \phi_0(1 - c_1^2)(1 - c_2^2) \cdots (1 - c_k^2).$$

Let us continue to look at the coefficients in eqs. (1) and (2) for higher powers of z, namely, for z^{k+1}, z^{k+2}, ... In general we find that the coefficients of z^{k+t} (where $t = 1, 2, 3, \ldots$) in eqs. (1) and (2) give, respectively,

$$d_{k+1}\left(\frac{k}{2} + t\right) = \frac{1}{(1 - c_k) \cdots (1 - c_1)}\left[a_k\phi_{k+1} + a_{k-1}\phi_{k+t-1} + \cdots + a_0\phi_t\right] \quad (3)$$

$$u_{k+1}\left(\frac{k}{2} + t\right) = \frac{1}{(1 - c_k) \cdots (1 - c_1)}\left[a_0\phi_{k+t} + a_1\phi_{k+t-1} + \cdots + a_k\phi_t\right], \quad (4)$$

where the expressions in square brackets are recognized, respectively, as the convolutions of the reverse prediction error operator $(a_k, a_{k-1}, \ldots, a_0)$ and the prediction error operator $(a_0, a_1, \ldots, a_k)$ each with the autocorrelation ϕ_{k+t}. Figure 16 gives numerical values of the downgoing and upgoing waves in the various layers computed by eqs. (3) and (4). The computer program used is described in the next section.

3.13 Computer program to find marine seismogram from reflection coefficients

The following *main program* computes a synthetic marine seismogram from a set of reflection coefficients, and then in turn computes the reflection coefficients from the seismogram as a numerical check.

```
      DIMENSION C(50),PHI(50),A(50),AP(50),U(50),V(50)
      DIMENSION AR(51),UP(100),DOWN(100)
    5 CALL INDATA(LC,C)
      WRITE(108,6)
    6 FORMAT (' REFLECTION COEFFICIENTS')
      WRITE(108,16)(C(K),K=1,LC)
```

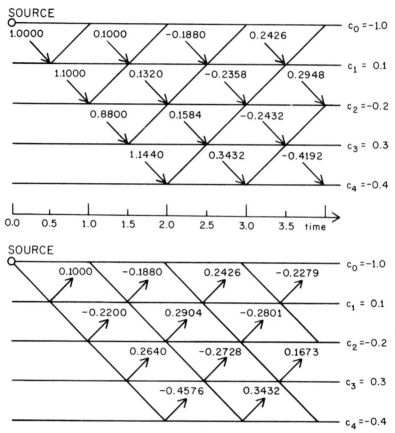

Fig. 16. The top diagram shows numerical values of the downgoing waveform
$d_j(t)$ at the top of layer j at time t, whereas the bottom diagram shows
numerical values of the upgoing waveform $u_j(t)$ at the top of layer j at
time t. Compare with Figure 15.

```
PHI(1)=C(1)
A(1)=−C(1)
V(1)=1.0−C(1)*C(1)
WRITE(108,15)
WRITE(108,16) A(1)
DO 20 I=2,LC
PHI(I)=C(I)*V(I−1)
DO 10 J=1,I−1
PHI(I)=PHI(I)−A(J)*PHI(I−J)
10 AP(J)=A(J)−C(I)*A(I−J)
DO 12 J=1,I−1
12 A(J)=AP(J)
```

```
      A(I)= -C(I)
      WRITE(108,15)
   15 FORMAT(' PREDICTION ERROR OPERATOR')
      WRITE(108,16)(A(K),K=1,I)
   16 FORMAT(1X,8F10.4)
   20 V(I)=V(I-1)*(1.0-C(I)*C(I))
      WRITE(108,25)
   25 FORMAT(' SYNTHETIC SEISMOGRAM')
      WRITE(108,16)(PHI(K),K=1,LC)
      WRITE(108,27)
   27 FORMAT(' VARIANCE CURVE')
      WRITE(108,16)(V(K),K=1,LC)
      S=1.0
      DO 40 I=1,LC
      IF(I.GE.2) GO TO 28
      C(1)=PHI(1)
      V(1)=1.0-C(1)*C(1)
      GO TO 33
   28 C(I)=U(I-1)/V(I-1)
      V(I)=V(I-1)*(1.0-C(I)*C(I))
      DO 30 J=1,I-1
   30 AP(J)=A(J)-C(I)*A(I-J)
      DO 32 J=1,I-1
   32 A(J)=AP(J)
   33 A(I)= -C(I)
      WRITE(108,15)
      WRITE(108,16)(A(K),K=1,I)
      U(I)=PHI(I+1)
      DO 35 J=1,I
   35 U(I)=U(I)+A(J)*PHI(I+1-J)
      AP(1)=1.0
      AR(I+1)=1.0
      DO 36 K=1,I
      AP(K+1)=A(K)
   36 AR(I-K+1)=A(K)
      CALL FOLD(I+1,AR,LC,PHI,L,DOWN)
      CALL FOLD(I+1,AP,LC,PHI,L,UP)
      CALL ZERO(I,DOWN)
      CALL ZERO(I,UP)
      DOWN(I)=V(I)
      S=(1.0-C(I))*S
      WRITE(108,38)
   38 FORMAT(' DOWNGOING WAVE UPGOING WAVE')
```

```
     DO 40 K=1,LC
     DOWN(K)=DOWN(K)/S
     UP(K)=UP(K)/S
     WRITE(108,39)DOWN(K),UP(K)
 39  FORMAT(2F20.6)
 40  CONTINUE
     WRITE(108,27)
     WRITE(108,16)(V(K),K=1,LC)
     WRITE(108,6)
     WRITE(108,16)(C(K),K=1,LC)
     GO TO 5
     END
```

This program was written in the Fortran IV language for the SDS 9300 computer. An example of the use of this program is illustrated by the following *printed output* sheet made by the computer.

```
      2                                                        ⎞
.10  −.20                                                      |
REFLECTION COEFFICIENTS                                        |
     .1000     −.2000                                   Printed
PREDICTION ERROR OPERATOR                               output
   −.1000                                               from
PREDICTION ERROR OPERATOR                         ⎬     first
   −.1200      .2000                                    part
SYNTHETIC SEISMOGRAM                                    of
     .1000    −.1880                                    program
VARIANCE CURVE                                                |
     .9900     .9504                                          ⎠


PREDICTION ERROR OPERATOR                                      ⎞
   −.1000                                                      |
DOWNGOING WAVE          UPGOING WAVE                           |
                1.100000               .000000          Printed
                 .132000              −.220000          output
PREDICTION ERROR OPERATOR                               from
   −.1200      .2000                                ⎬   second
DOWNGOING WAVE        UPGOING WAVE                      part
                 .000000               .000000          of
                 .880000               .000000          program
VARIANCE CURVE                                                |
     .9900      .9504                                         |
REFLECTION COEFFICIENTS                                       |
     .1000    −.2000                                          ⎠
```

A short description of the program and its output is as follows. The statement

5 CALL INDATA(LC,C)

reads in the given reflection coefficients. In the case illustrated by the printed output, there were only two reflection coefficients; this is seen by the echo-print feature of subroutine INDATA, which printed the first two lines

$$2$$
$$.10 \qquad -.20$$

indicating that LC = 2 (the number of reflection coefficients) and array C = (.10, −.20) [the given reflection coefficients (c_1, c_2)]. Note the program assumes that $c_0 = -1$, which as we have seen in the last section is the case of a marine seismogram (i.e., the case in which layer 1 is a water layer). The program prints the title REFLECTION COEFFICIENTS and again prints their numerical values. The program then computes the prediction-error operators

$$a_0(k) = 1, a_1(k), a_2(k), \ldots, a_k(k)$$

and prints the title PREDICTION ERROR OPERATOR and the numerical values of $a_1(k), a_2(k), \ldots, a_k(k)$ [note that $a_0(k)$ which is equal to unity is not printed] for $k = 1, 2, \ldots,$ LC. In the case illustrated LC = 2, so two prediction-error operators (except for their initial coefficients of unity) are printed. The program computes the coefficients

$$\phi_1, \phi_2, \phi_3, \ldots, \phi_{LC}$$

(where it is assumed that $\phi_0 = 1$), prints the title SYNTHETIC SEISMO-GRAM, and then prints the numerical values of these coefficients. Actually, as we have seen, the coefficients $\phi_1, \phi_2, \phi_3, \ldots$ are the coefficients of the upgoing wave $u_1(1), u_1(2), u_1(3), \ldots$ at the water surface; the downgoing wave at the water surface has coefficients $d_1(0) = \phi_0, d_1(1) = \phi_1, d_1(2) = \phi_2, \ldots$; and the *synthetic seismogram* is the sum of the upgoing and downgoing waves at the water surface, that is,

$$d_1(0) = \phi_0, u_1(1) + d_1(1) = 2\phi_1, u_1(2) + d_1(2) = 2\phi_2, \ldots.$$

The program computes the prediction error variances

$$v(1), v(2), v(3), \ldots, v(LC)$$

and prints VARIANCE CURVE and their numerical values. This completes the *first part* of the program, namely, the part that computes the seismogram from the reflection coefficients.

The *second part* of the program, which begins with the instruction S = 1.0, computes the reflection coefficients from the seismogram. These final reflection coefficients should be the same as those which we started with. Hence in our example the final two lines are

REFLECTION   COEFFICIENTS
.1000   − .2000,

which are the same as the original data. Before arriving at these final lines of printed output, the program prints numerical values of the following for each $k = 1, 2, \ldots,$ LC:

PREDICTION ERROR OPERATOR
$a_1(k), a_2(k), \ldots, a_k(k)$

DOWNGOING WAVE	UPGOING WAVE
.000000	.000000
.000000	.000000
. . .	. . .
.000000	.000000
$d_{k+1}\left(\dfrac{k}{2}\right)$	.000000
$d_{k+1}\left(\dfrac{k}{2}+1\right)$	$u_{k+1}\left(\dfrac{k}{2}+1\right)$
. . .	. . .
$d_{k+1}\left(\dfrac{k}{2}+\mathrm{LC}-k\right)$	$u_{k+1}\left(\dfrac{k}{2}+\mathrm{LC}-k\right),$

where there is a total of LC numbers in each column. The DOWNGOING WAVE column has its first $k − 1$ entries equal to zero, whereas the UP-GOING WAVE column has its first k entries zero. Thus in the example considered here, where LC = 2, the printed output for $k = 1$ is

DOWNGOING WAVE	UPGOING WAVE
1.100000	.000000
.132000	− .220000,

whereas for $k = 2$ it is

DOWNGOING WAVE	UPGOING WAVE
.000000	.000000
.880000	.000000.

These values of the downgoing and upgoing waves can be seen in the upper left-hand corners of the diagrams appearing in Figure 16. The computer also prints VARIANCE CURVE and its numerical values, which should agree with the values first printed.

3.14 Töplitz determinants

Let us now refer back to the normal equations given in Sec. 3.12. We re-instate the (k)-designation on the prediction error operator coefficients, so the normal equations are now written as

$$a_0(k)\phi_0 + a_1(k)\phi_1 + \cdots + a_k(k)\phi_k = v(k)$$
$$a_0(k)\phi_1 + a_1(k)\phi_0 + \cdots + a_k(k)\phi_{k-1} = 0$$
$$\cdots \tag{1}$$
$$a_0(k)\phi_k + a_1(k)\phi_{k-1} + \cdots + a_k(k)\phi_0 = 0 .$$

This set of simultaneous equations can be solved by Cramer's rule to yield the coefficients $a_0(k)$, $a_1(k)$, ..., $a_k(k)$. Then these coefficients can be substituted into the equation

$$A_k(z) = a_0(k) + a_1(k)z + \cdots + a_k(k)z^k$$

to give

$$A_k(z) = \frac{v(k)}{\Delta(k)} \begin{vmatrix} 1 & z & z^2 & \cdots & z^k \\ \phi_1 & \phi_0 & \phi_1 & \cdots & \phi_{k-1} \\ \phi_2 & \phi_1 & \phi_0 & \cdots & \phi_{k-2} \\ & & \cdots & & \\ \phi_k & \phi_{k-1} & \phi_{k-2} & \cdots & \phi_0 \end{vmatrix}, \tag{2}$$

where the *Töplitz determinant* $\Delta(k)$ is defined as

$$\Delta(k) = \begin{vmatrix} \phi_0 & \phi_1 & \phi_2 & \cdots & \phi_k \\ \phi_1 & \phi_0 & \phi_1 & \cdots & \phi_{k-1} \\ \phi_2 & \phi_1 & \phi_0 & \cdots & \phi_{k-2} \\ & & \cdots & & \\ \phi_k & \phi_{k-1} & \phi_{k-2} & \cdots & \phi_0 \end{vmatrix}. \tag{3}$$

The vertical bars used here denote as usual the determinant. By again using Cramer's rule, but now imposing the condition that $a_0(k) = 1$, we can solve the normal equations (1) for the prediction error variance $v(k)$ which gives

$$v(k) = \frac{\Delta(k)}{\Delta(k-1)}, \tag{4}$$

where the Töplitz determinant $\Delta(k-1)$ is

$$\Delta(k-1) = \begin{vmatrix} \phi_0 & \phi_1 & \cdots & \phi_{k-1} \\ \phi_1 & \phi_0 & \cdots & \phi_{k-2} \\ & \cdots & & \\ \phi_{k-1} & \phi_{k-2} & \cdots & \phi_0 \end{vmatrix}. \tag{5}$$

But from section 3.12 we know that the prediction-error variance is given by

$$v(k) = \phi_0(1 - c_1^2)(1 - c_2^2) \cdots (1 - c_k^2).$$ (6)

From eqs. (4) and (6) we have

$$\Delta(k) = \phi_0(1 - c_1^2)(1 - c_2^2) \cdots (1 - c_{k-1}^2)(1 - c_k^2) \Delta(k - 1)$$
$$\Delta(k - 1) = \phi_0(1 - c_1^2)(1 - c_2^2) \cdots (1 - c_{k-1}^2) \Delta(k - 2)$$
$$\cdots$$
$$\Delta(2) = \phi_0(1 - c_1^2)(1 - c_2^2) \Delta(1)$$
$$\Delta(1) = \phi_0(1 - c_1^2) \Delta(0)$$
$$\Delta(0) = \phi_0,$$

which gives

$$\Delta(k) = \phi_0^{k+1}(1 - c_1^2)^k(1 - c_2^2)^{k-1} \cdots (1 - c_{k-1}^2)^2(1 - c_k^2).$$

We assume that the initial spike ϕ_0 produced by the source is positive. Hence this equation shows that the condition that all the reflection coefficients be less than unity in magnitude, i.e., the condition

$$|c_k| < 1 \qquad \text{for } k = 1, 2, 3, \ldots,$$

is equivalent to the condition that all the Töplitz determinants be positive, i.e., the condition

$$\Delta(k) > 0 \qquad \text{for } k = 1, 2, 3, \ldots.$$

Now it is a physical fact that all the reflection coefficients $c_1, c_2, c_3, \ldots$ will be less than unity in magnitude, provided that we rule out the possibility of perfect reflecting horizons, in which case the corresponding reflection coefficient would be either $+1$ or -1. Hence in the absence of a perfect reflecting horizon the Töplitz determinants will all be positive. This is the case which is physically encountered in seismic prospecting for oil.

3.15 Polynomials orthogonal on the unit circle

Let us now leave the domain of applied physics and discuss the connections of the foregoing theory with pure mathematics, namely, the subject of *polynomials orthogonal on the unit circle*.[35] The positiveness of all the Töplitz determinants is equivalent to the existence of a bounded nondecreasing function $\Lambda(f)$ which has a nondenumerable set of points of increase and satisfies the condition

$$\phi_t = \int_{-0.5}^{0.5} e^{2\pi i f t} \, d\Lambda(f).$$ (1)

In sec. 3.12 we called ϕ_t an autocorrelation coefficient. Because of eq. (1), which represents the Wiener–Khintchine theorem, we see that this termi-

---

[35] The reader is referred to the excellent books on this subject: Grenander, U., and G. Szegö, *Toeplitz Forms and Their Applications*, Univ. of Calif. Press, Berkeley, 1958; and Geronimus, L., *Orthogonal Polynomials*, Consultants Bureau, New York, 1961.

nology for ϕ_t is indeed justified. The function $\Lambda(f)$ is called the *spectral distribution function*. Hence we have three equivalent representations of the information available in an autocorrelation function, namely, (1) the autocorrelation coefficients ϕ_t which describe the motion at the top of the water layer (i.e., layer 1), (2) the reflection coefficients c_k of the successive interfaces going down into the earth, and (3) the spectral distribution function.

At this point it is useful to introduce the mathematical concept of inner product (or dot product) with weighting given by the spectral distribution function. If $C(z)$ and $D(z)$ are arbitrary polynomials with real coefficients, then their *inner product* is defined as

$$[C(z), D(z)] = \int_{-0.5}^{0.5} C(e^{-2\pi if}) D(e^{2\pi if}) d\Lambda(f). \tag{2}$$

In particular, if we let $C(z) = z^m$ and $D(z) = z^n$, we have

$$[z^m, z^n] = \int_{-0.5}^{0.5} e^{-2\pi ifm} e^{2\pi ifn} d\Lambda(f),$$

which by eq. (1) is

$$[z^m, z^n] = \int_{-0.5}^{0.5} e^{2\pi if(n-m)} d\Lambda(f) = \phi_{n-m}.$$

That is, the inner product $[z^m, z^n]$ is equal to the autocorrelation coefficient ϕ_{n-m}, which in turn is equal to the autocorrelation coefficient ϕ_{m-n} because of the symmetry of the autocorrelation function.

For numerical applications, it is usually not convenient to evaluate the inner product $[C(z), D(z)]$ as given by the integral (2). Instead, the integral (2) can be converted into a quadratic form, which can be numerically evaluated quite easily. Suppose, for example, the polynomials $C(z)$ and $D(z)$ are

$$C(z) = c_0 + c_1 z + c_2 z^2 + \cdots + c_n z^n$$
$$D(z) = d_0 + d_1 z + d_2 z^2 + \cdots + d_n z^n.$$

We have written both $C(z)$ and $D(z)$ as polynomials of degree n; if one were of degree less than n, then we assume that enough zero coefficients are added to make it formally of degree n. The inner product is

$$[C(z), D(z)] = \left[\sum_{i=0}^{n} c_i z^i, \sum_{j=0}^{n} d_j z^j\right]$$

$$= \sum_{i=0}^{n} \sum_{j=0}^{n} c_i d_j [z^i, z^j]$$

$$= \sum_{i=0}^{n} \sum_{j=0}^{n} c_i \phi_{j-i} d_j,$$

which is the required quadratic form. The matrix of this quadratic form is the autocorrelation matrix $[\phi_{j-i}]$, where $i, j = 0, 1, 2, \ldots, n$; this matrix is positive definite, for its determinant is the Töplitz determinant $\Delta(n)$ which is positive (under the assumption that no reflection coefficient has magnitude unity).

The unit circle in the z-plane is defined by

$$z = e^{-2\pi i f} .$$

As frequency f runs from -0.5 to 0.5, the unit circle is traced in the clockwise direction. Hence polynomials orthogonal on the unit circle with weight given by the spectral distribution function are polynomials whose inner product vanishes. Let us form the system of polynomials

$$B_0(z), \ B_1(z), \ B_2(z), \ \ldots, \ B_k(z), \ \ldots$$

which satisfy the following conditions:

(1) $B_k(z)$ is a polynomial of degree k with real coefficients and with its coefficient for z^k equal to unity.

(2) the polynomials are mutually orthogonal, that is,

$$[B_j(z), \ B_k(z)] = 0 \qquad \text{for } j \neq k .$$

The system of orthogonal polynomials is uniquely determined by conditions (1) and (2). Let us illustrate the construction of this set $\{B_k(z), \ k = 0, 1, 2, \ldots\}$ of orthogonal polynomials in such a way that the set will be seen to be equivalent to the set $\{A_k^R(z), \ k = 0, 1, 2, \ldots\}$ of reverse prediction error polynomials. For example, let us consider the construction of

$$B_2(z) = b_0(2) + b_1(2)z + b_2(2)z^2 ,$$

where $b_2(2) = 1$. This polynomial of degree 2 must satisfy the orthogonality conditions

$$[B_2(z), \ B_0(z)] = 0$$
$$[B_2(z), \ B_1(z)] = 0 .$$

Since $B_2(z)$ is orthogonal to any linear combination of $B_0(z)$ and $B_1(z)$, it is orthogonal to any polynomial of degree less than 2. In particular, $B_2(z)$ is orthogonal to both 1 and z; that is,

$$[B_2(z), \ 1] = 0$$
$$[B_2(z), \ z] = 0 .$$

This set of orthogonality conditions may be written out as

$$[b_0(2) + b_1(2)z + z^2, \ 1] = 0$$
$$[b_0(2) + b_1(2)z + z^2, \ z] = 0 .$$

This last set becomes

$$b_0(2)[1, 1] + b_1(2)[z, 1] + [z^2, 1] = 0$$
$$b_0(2)[1, z] + b_1(2)[z, z] + [z^2, z] = 0 ,$$

which is

$$b_0(2)\phi_0 + b_1(2)\phi_1 + \phi_2 = 0$$
$$b_0(2)\phi_1 + b_1(2)\phi_0 + \phi_1 = 0 . \qquad (3)$$

We recall that the normal equations for the prediction error polynomial

$$A_2(z) = a_0(2) + a_1(2)z + a_2(2)z^2$$

with $a_0(2) = 1$ are

$$\phi_1 + a_1(2)\phi_0 + a_2(2)\phi_1 = 0$$
$$\phi_2 + a_1(2)\phi_1 + a_2(2)\phi_0 = 0 . \qquad (4)$$

Thus the set of eqs. (3) is the same as the set of eqs. (4) where we identify

$$b_0(2) = a_2(2), \ b_1(2) = a_1(2), \ b_2(2) = a_0(2) = 1 ;$$

that is, the orthogonal polynomial $B_2(z)$ is the reverse prediction error polynomial $A_2^R(z) = z^2 A_2(z^{-1})$. In summary, $B_k(z) = A_k^R(z)$ for $k = 0, 1, 2, 3, \ldots$ and the following two sets of normal equations are the same (i.e., each equation in the first column is the same as the equation beside it in the second column).

Normal equations for prediction error polynomial $A_k(z)$	Normal equations for orthogonal polynomial $B_k(z) = A_k^R(z)$
$[A_k(z), 1] = v(k)$ $[A_k(z), z] = 0$ $\cdots$ $[A_k(z), z^k] = 0$	$[B_k(z), z^k] = v(k)$ $[B_k(z), z^{k-1}] = 0$ $\cdots$ $[B_k(z), 1] = 0$

As a numerical example, let the autocorrelation function be

$$\phi_0 = 1.0000, \ \phi_1 = 0.1000, \ \phi_2 = -0.1880, \ \phi_3 = 0.2426, \ \phi_4 = -0.2279 .$$

Then the first five orthogonal polynomials are

$$B_0(z) = \quad 1.0000$$
$$B_1(z) = -0.1000 + 1.0000z$$
$$B_2(z) = \quad 0.2000 - 0.1200z + 1.0000z^2$$
$$B_3(z) = -0.3000 + 0.2360z - 0.1800z^2 + 1.0000z^3$$
$$B_4(z) = \quad 0.4000 - 0.3720z + 0.3304z^2 - 0.3000z^3 + 1.0000z^4 .$$

Since the reflection coefficient c_k is equal to $-B_k(0)$, we see that the reflection coefficients are

$$c_0 = -1.0, \ c_1 = 0.1, \ c_2 = -0.2, \ c_3 = 0.3, \ c_4 = -0.4 .$$

As a numerical check, let us evaluate the inner product

$$[B_2(z), B_1(z)] = \int_{-0.5}^{0.5} B_2(e^{-2\pi i f})B_1(e^{2\pi i f}) \, d\Lambda(f) .$$

Instead of evaluating the above integral, we evaluate the quadratic form

$$[B_2(z), B_1(z)] = [b_0(2) \quad b_1(2) \quad b_2(2)] \begin{bmatrix} \phi_0 & \phi_1 & \phi_2 \\ \phi_1 & \phi_0 & \phi_1 \\ \phi_2 & \phi_1 & \phi_0 \end{bmatrix} \begin{bmatrix} b_0(1) \\ b_1(1) \\ 0 \end{bmatrix}$$

$$= [0.20 \quad -0.12 \quad 1.00] \begin{bmatrix} 1.000 & 0.100 & -0.188 \\ 0.100 & 1.000 & 0.100 \\ -0.188 & 0.100 & 1.000 \end{bmatrix} \begin{bmatrix} -0.10 \\ 1.00 \\ 0.00 \end{bmatrix}$$

$$= [0.00 \quad 0.00 \quad 0.9504] \begin{bmatrix} -0.10 \\ 1.00 \\ 0.00 \end{bmatrix} = 0.00 ,$$

which confirms that $B_2(z)$ and $B_1(z)$ are orthogonal. Also it is easy at this point to confirm that

$$v(2) = [B_2(z), z^2] = [B_2(z), B_2(z)] = 0.9504 .$$

4

Matrix Polynomials

4.1 Matrix notation

First let us describe some of the matrix notation to be used. Generally capital letters are used in mathematics to denote matrices, such as the matrix A. However, in much of our work, we use lower-case letters to denote matrices, such as the matrix a. The reason is that constant matrices in the multichannel case correspond to constant scalars in the single-channel case. Since constant scalars are usually represented by lower-case letters, and because we want the multichannel notation to look as much as possible like the single-channel notation, we often use lower-case letters for constant matrices instead of the more conventional capital letters.

Let a be a matrix. Then

a^T denotes the *transpose* of a
a^* denotes the *complex conjugate* of a
a^{*T} denotes the *complex conjugate transpose* of a
a^{-1} denotes the *inverse* of a square matrix a
det a
or $|a|$ denotes the *determinant* of a square matrix a
adj a denotes the *adjugate* of a square matrix a.

Note that the adjugate of a is often also called the *adjoint* of a. The adjugate is defined as the transpose of the matrix of cofactors of a. For example, we have

$$a = \begin{bmatrix} 1 & 2 & 3 \\ 2 & 3 & 2 \\ 3 & 3 & 4 \end{bmatrix}, \quad \text{adj } a = \begin{bmatrix} 6 & 1 & -5 \\ -2 & -5 & 4 \\ -3 & 3 & -1 \end{bmatrix}.$$

The letter I denotes the *identity* (or *unit*) matrix. If we want to indicate explicitly that it is an $n \times n$ identity matrix, we write I_n. Because

$$a \,(\text{adj } a) = (\text{adj } a)\, a = (\det A)\, I \,,$$

we see that the inverse of a is equal to the adjugate of a divided by the determinant of a, that is,

$$a^{-1} = \frac{\text{adj } a}{\det a} \,.$$

A *diagonal matrix* D with diagonal terms $d_1, d_2, \ldots, d_n$ is written as

$$D = \text{diag}\,[d_1, d_2, \ldots, d_n] \,.$$

Whenever we use 0 to denote a matrix with all zero elements, we usually say so explicitly. Usually a vector will be a *column vector*, that is, an $n \times 1$ matrix, so a *row vector* would be denoted as the transpose of a column vector. However, the exception is that we make use of the letter r to denote certain row vectors, that is, $1 \times n$ matrices.

4.2 Eigenvectors and eigenvalues of a matrix

The motivation for introducing the concept of the characteristic equation of a square matrix a of order n may be described in the following way. Let $y = ax$ be a linear transformation which carries a vector x into a vector y. We want to investigate the possibility of certain vectors x being carried by the transformation into λx, where λ is a scalar. Any such vector x which is transformed into λx, that is, any vector x for which

$$ax = \lambda x \,, \tag{1}$$

is called an *invariant vector, characteristic vector,* or *eigenvector* under the transformation.

Let us now introduce the characteristic equation. From eq. (1) we may write

$$\lambda x - ax = 0 \,,$$

which may be factored as

$$(\lambda I - a)\, x = 0 \,. \tag{2}$$

The matrix $(\lambda I - a)$ is called the *characteristic matrix* of a. The system of homogenous equations (2) has nontrivial solutions if and only if

$$\det (\lambda I - a) = 0 \,. \tag{3}$$

The expansion of this determinant yields a polynomial $\phi(\lambda)$ of degree n in λ, where n is the order of the matrix a. This polynomial is known as the *characteristic polynomial* of the matrix a. Equation (3), which is

$$\phi(\lambda) = 0 ,$$

is called the characteristic equation of a, and its roots $\lambda_1, \lambda_2, \ldots, \lambda_n$ are called the *characteristic roots, eigenroots,* or *eigenvalues* of a. If $\lambda = \lambda_i$ is an eigenroot, then eq. (2) has a nontrivial solution x_i which is the eigenvector associated with the eigenroot λ_i, that is,

$$(\lambda_i I - a) x_i = 0 .$$

The following are some of the general theorems about eigenroots and eigenvectors.

Theorem 1. If $\lambda_1, \lambda_2, \ldots, \lambda_n$ are distinct eigenroots of a and if $x_1, x_2, \ldots, x_n$ are nonzero eigenvectors, respectively, associated with these eigenroots, then the $x_1, x_2, \ldots, x_n$ are linearly independent.

Theorem 2. The eigenroots of a and a^{T} are the same. (*Note:* superscript ^{T} indicates matrix transpose.)

Theorem 3. The eigenroots of a^* are the conjugates of the eigenroots of a. (*Note*: Superscript * indicates complex conjugate.)

Theorem 4. If a is nonsingular and if λ_i is an eigenroot of a, then λ_i^{-1} is an eigenroot of a^{-1} and $\lambda_i^{-1} \det a$ is an eigenroot of adj a.

Theorem 5. The characteristic equation of an orthogonal matrix p is a reciprocal equation. Proof:

$$\phi(\lambda) = \det (\lambda I - p) = \det (\lambda p I p^{\mathrm{T}} - p) = \det (-p\lambda(\lambda^{-1}I - p^{\mathrm{T}}))$$
$$= \pm\lambda^n \det (\lambda^{-1}I - p) = \pm\lambda^n \phi(\lambda^{-1}) .$$

Instead of using the variable λ in what follows, we find it more convenient to use the variable z defined as the reciprocal of λ, that is,

$$z = \lambda^{-1} .$$

Thus the characteristic eq. (2) becomes

$$(z^{-1} I - a) x = 0 ,$$

which upon multiplying through by z becomes

$$(I - az) x = 0 . \tag{4}$$

The matrix $(I - az)$ is the *characteristic matrix*. The system of homogeneous equations (4) has a nontrivial solution, provided the determinant

$$\det (I - az) = 0 .$$

The expansion of this determinant yields a polynomial $\psi(z)$ of degree n in z. This polynomial may be called the *characteristic polynomial* (in the variable

z) of the matrix a. The roots of this polynomial $z_1, z_2, \ldots, z_n$ may be called the *eigenroots* or *eigenvalues* (again in terms of the variable z). These eigenroots are related to those in terms of the variable λ by

$$z_1 = \lambda_1^{-1}, \, z_2 = \lambda_2^{-1}, \ldots, \, z_n = \lambda_n^{-1}$$

since

$$\psi(z) = z^n \phi(z^{-1}).$$

If $z = z_i$ is an eigenroot, then eq. (4) has a nontrivial solution x_i, which is the eigenvector associated with the eigenroot z_i, that is,

$$(I - az_i) x_i = 0.$$

The eigenvector x_i is the same eigenvector as the one associated with the eigenroot $\lambda_i = z_i^{-1}$.

4.3 Similar matrices

Two square matrices a and b are called *similar*, provided there exists a non-singular matrix r such that

$$b = r^{-1} \, a \, r.$$

The following two theorems hold for similar matrices a and b.

Theorem 1. If z_i is an eigenroot of a, then z_i is also an eigenroot of b.

Theorem 2. If y_i is an eigenvector of b corresponding to the eigenroot z_i of b, then $x_i = r \, y_i$ is an eigenvector of a corresponding to the same eigenroot z_i of a.

The eigenroots $z_i = \lambda_i^{-1}$ of a diagonal matrix

$$D = \text{diag} \, [d_1, d_2, \ldots, d_n]$$

are the reciprocals of its diagonal elements, that is, $z_i = d_i^{-1}$ for $i = 1, 2, \ldots, n$. A set of eigenvectors of a diagonal matrix is the set of elementary vectors e_i (where e_i is defined as the vector with all zero elements, except the ith element which is unity). As a consequence, it follows that a diagonal matrix always has n linearly independent eigenvectors. Thus a square matrix a is similar to a diagonal matrix if and only if a has n linearly independent eigenvectors.

It follows, therefore, that not every square matrix is similar to a diagonal matrix. However, every square matrix a is similar to a triangular matrix whose diagonal elements are the eigenroots λ_i of a.

4.4 Matrix polynomials

We now wish to review some of the important properties of matrix polynomials, which are also called polynomial matrices, or λ-matrices (i.e., lambda matrices). This treatment is concerned mainly with those properties to be used in our study of multichannel time series analysis. The interested reader may also want to refer to the excellent chapters on this subject given in Frazer, Duncan, and Collar,[36] Gantmacher,[37] and Wedderburn.[38]

Let z denote an abstract symbol (an indeterminate) which is assumed to be commutative with itself and with matrices. Thus if a is a matrix, then

$$zaz = z^2 a = az^2 .$$

Let $a_0, a_1, \ldots, a_{p-1}, a_p$ be square matrices of order n. Then $A(z)$ defined as

$$A(z) = a_0 + a_1 z + \cdots + a_{p-1} z^{p-1} + a_p z^p$$

is called a *polynomial matrix* or alternatively a *matrix polynomial*. A matrix polynomial $A(z)$ is called singular or nonsingular according to whether det $A(z)$ is or is not zero.

Let $A(z)$ and $B(z)$ be two matrix polynomials:

$$A(z) = a_0 + a_1 z + \cdots + a_{p-1} z^{p-1} + a_p z^p \qquad (1)$$
$$B(z) = b_0 + b_1 z + \cdots + b_{q-1} z^{q-1} + b_q z^q . \qquad (2)$$

We say that these two polynomial matrices are equal, that is, $A(z) = B(z)$, provided that $p = q$ and $a_i = b_i$ for $i = 0, 1, 2, \ldots, p$.

The sum of two polynomial matrices $A(z)$ and $B(z)$ is a polynomial matrix $C(z) = A(z) + B(z)$ whose coefficients are obtained by adding the corresponding coefficients of $A(z)$ and $B(z)$. The product of two polynomial matrices $A(z)$ and $B(z)$ is a polynomial matrix $C(z) = A(z) B(z)$ whose coefficients are obtained by convolving the coefficients of $A(z)$ with $B(z)$. In general, two polynomial matrices are not commutative, that is, $A(z) B(z)$ is not in general equal to $B(z) A(z)$. The product $A(z) B(z)$ is a polynomial matrix of degree of at most $p + q$. If either $A(z)$ or $B(z)$ is nonsingular, the degree of $A(z) B(z)$ and also of $B(z) A(z)$ is exactly $p + q$.

Subroutine BRAINY performs matrix polynomial multiplication; subroutine BRAINY is the multichannel counterpart of subrouting FOLD in the single-channel case. Because polynomial multiplication corresponds to complete transient convolution, we may alternatively say that subroutine BRAINY performs the complete transient convolution of two multichannel signals.[39] In the discussion given in this section we restrict ourselves to the

[36] Frazer, R. A., W. J. Duncan, and A. R. Collar, *Elementary Matrices*, Cambridge Univ. Press, Cambridge, England, 1963, chapter 3.

[37] Gantmacher, F. R., *The Theory of Matrices*, vol. 1, Chelsea, New York, 1959, chapter 6.

[38] Wedderburn, J. H. M., *Lectures on Matrices*, Dover, New York, 1964, chapter 2.

[39] The name BRAINY for a convolution subroutine comes from analogy with the convolutions in the brain.

case of square matrices; however, subroutine BRAINY is more general in that it allows the use of rectangular matrices. The calling statement is

CALL BRAINY(NRA,NCA,LA,A,NRB,NCB,LB,B,C),

where the subroutine inputs are

$$NRA = \text{number of rows of } A = p$$
$$NCA = \text{number of columns of } A = q$$
$$LA = \text{length of multichannel signal } A = m + 1$$
$$A = (a_0, a_1, \ldots, a_m), \text{ where each coefficient}$$
$$a_i \text{ is a } p \times q \text{ constant matrix}$$
$$NRB = \text{number of rows of } B = q$$
$$NCB = \text{number of columns of } B = r$$
$$LB = \text{length of multichannel signal } B = n + 1$$
$$B = (b_0, b_1, \ldots, b_n), \text{ where each coefficient}$$
$$b_i \text{ is a } q \times r \text{ constant matrix},$$

and the subroutine output is

$$C = (c_0, c_1, \ldots, c_{m+n}),$$

where each coefficient c_k is a $p \times r$ constant matrix given by

$$c_k = \Sigma a_i b_{k-i},$$

where the summation is over all i with $0 \leqslant i \leqslant m$ and $0 \leqslant k - i \leqslant n$. The subroutine output C is the complete transient convolution of the multichannel signals A and B. Alternatively, the subroutine output C gives the coefficients of the matrix polynomial

$$C(z) = c_0 + c_1 z + c_2 z^2 + \cdots + c_{m+n} z^{m+n},$$

which is the product of the matrix polynomials

$$A(z) = a_0 + a_1 z + \cdots + a_m z^m$$

and

$$B(z) = b_0 + b_1 z + \cdots + b_n z^n,$$

that is,

$$C(z) = A(z) B(z).$$

Subroutine BRAINY requires subroutine ZERO. The program for subroutine BRAINY is

```
SUBROUTINE BRAINY(NRA,NCA,LA,A,NRB,NCB,LB,B,C)
DIMENSION A(NRA,NCA,LA),B(NCA,NCB,LB),C(NRA,
1NCB,1)
```

```
C      DIMENSION C(NRA,NCB,LC)
C      FOR COMPLEX VERSION REMOVE THE C FROM
C      1COLUMN 1 OF NEXT CARD
C      COMPLEX A,B,C
       LC=LA+LB−1
       CALL ZERO(NRA*NCB*LC,C)
       DO 1 I=1,LA
       DO 1 J=1,LB
       K=I+J−1
       DO 1 M=1,NRA
       DO 1 N=1,NCB
       DO 1 L=1,NCA
     1 C(M,N,K)=C(M,N,K)+A(M,L,I)*B(L,N,J)
       RETURN
       END
```

(*Note.* Unlike subroutine FOLD, subroutine BRAINY does not have $LC = LA+LB-1 = m+n+1$ as a subroutine output.)

As a numerical example, let

$$NRA = 2$$
$$NCA = 2$$
$$LA = 3$$
$$A = (a_0, a_1, a_2) = \left(\begin{bmatrix} 0 & 0 \\ 1 & -1 \end{bmatrix}, \begin{bmatrix} 2 & 1 \\ 0 & 1 \end{bmatrix}, \begin{bmatrix} 1 & 0 \\ 1 & 0 \end{bmatrix} \right)$$
$$= (0, 1, 0, -1, 2, 0, 1, 1, 1, 1, 0, 0)$$
$$NRB = 2$$
$$NCB = 2$$
$$LB = 3$$
$$B = (b_0, b_1, b_2) = \left(\begin{bmatrix} 0 & 0 \\ 1 & 0 \end{bmatrix}, \begin{bmatrix} 0 & 1 \\ 1 & 1 \end{bmatrix}, \begin{bmatrix} 1 & 1 \\ 0 & 0 \end{bmatrix} \right)$$
$$= (0, 1, 0, 0, 0, 1, 1, 1, 1, 0, 1, 0) .$$

Then with the call statement

$$CALL\ BRAINY(NRA,NCA,LA,A,NRB,NCB,LB,B,C),$$

we obtain the subroutine output

$$C = (0,-1,0,0,1,0,0,0,1,2,3,2,2,0,3,1,1,1,1,1)$$
$$= (c_0, c_1, c_2, c_3, c_4)$$
$$= \left(\begin{bmatrix} 0 & 0 \\ -1 & 0 \end{bmatrix}, \begin{bmatrix} 1 & 0 \\ 0 & 0 \end{bmatrix}, \begin{bmatrix} 1 & 3 \\ 2 & 2 \end{bmatrix}, \begin{bmatrix} 2 & 3 \\ 0 & 1 \end{bmatrix}, \begin{bmatrix} 1 & 1 \\ 1 & 1 \end{bmatrix} \right)$$

corresponding to the matrix product

$$C(z) = A(z)\, B(z)\,,$$

whereas with the call statement

CALL BRAINY(NRB,NCB,LB,B,NRA,NCA,LA,A,C),

we obtain the subroutine output

$C = (0,0,0,0,1,3,-1,0,1,3,0,2,3,2,2,0,2,0,0,0)$

$= (c_0, c_1, c_2, c_3, c_4)$

$$= \left(\begin{bmatrix} 0 & 0 \\ 0 & 0 \end{bmatrix}, \begin{bmatrix} 1 & -1 \\ 3 & 0 \end{bmatrix}, \begin{bmatrix} 1 & 0 \\ 3 & 2 \end{bmatrix}, \begin{bmatrix} 3 & 2 \\ 2 & 0 \end{bmatrix}, \begin{bmatrix} 2 & 0 \\ 0 & 0 \end{bmatrix} \right)$$

corresponding to the matrix product

$$C(z) = B(z)\, A(z)\,.$$

Let us now return to our theoretical development. The equality

$$A(z) = a_0 + a_1 z + \cdots + a_{p-1} z^{p-1} + a_p z^p$$

is not disturbed when z is considered as a (scalar) complex number. In our work we generally assume that z is a (scalar) complex variable. However, when z is replaced by a square matrix C, several results can be obtained, depending upon how we distribute the C's on each side of the coefficients a_i. In particular, we define

$$A_R(C) = a_0 + a_1 C + \cdots + a_{p-1} C^{p-1} + a_p C^p$$

and

$$A_L(C) = a_0 + C a_1 + \cdots + C^{p-1} a_{p-1} + C^p a_p$$

as, respectively, the right and left functional values of $A(C)$.

Let $A(z)$ and $B(z)$ be the matrix polynomials (1) and (2) and suppose b_q is nonsingular. Then there exist unique matrix polynomials $Q_1(z)$ and $R_1(z)$, where $R_1(z)$ is either zero or of degree less than $B(z)$, such that

$$A(z) = Q_1(z)B(z) + R_1(z)\,. \tag{3}$$

If $R_1(z) = 0$, then $B(z)$ is called a *right divisor* of $A(z)$. Similarly there exist unique matrix polynomials $Q_2(z)$ and $R_2(z)$, where $R_2(z)$ is either zero or of degree less than that of $B(z)$, such that

$$A(z) = B(z)Q_2(z) + R_2(z)\,. \tag{4}$$

If $R_2(z) = 0$, then $B(z)$ is called a *left divisor* of $A(z)$.

A matrix polynomial of the form

$$\begin{aligned} S(z) &= s_0\, I + s_1 z\, I + \cdots + s_{q-1} z^{q-1}\, I + s_q z^q I \\ &= (s_0 + s_1 z + \cdots + s_{q-1} z^{q-1} + s_q z^q)\, I \end{aligned} \tag{5}$$

(where $s_0, s_1, \ldots, s_{q-1}, s_q$ are scalars and I is the identity matrix) is called a *scalar matrix polynomial*. That is, a scalar matrix polynomial S(z) is equal to a scalar polynomial times the identity matrix I. A scalar matrix polynomial S(z) commutes with every matrix polynomial, that is,

$$A(z)S(z) = S(z)A(z) .$$

If in eqs. (3) and (4), B(z) is a scalar matrix polynomial S(z), then

$$A(z) = Q_1(z)S(z) + R_1(z) = S(z)Q_1(z) + R_1(z) .$$

A matrix polynomial $A(z) = [a_{ij}(z)]$ of degree p is divisible by a scalar matrix polynomial S(z) given by eq. (5) if and only if every $a_{ij}(z)$ is divisible by the scalar polynomial $s_0 + s_1 z + \cdots + s_{q-1}z^{q-1} + s_q z^q$.

Now we can outline the remainder theorem. Let A(z) be the matrix polynomial given by eq. (1), and let $b = [b_{ij}]$ be a constant nonsingular square matrix. Since $I - bz$ is nonsingular, we may write

$$A(z) = Q_1(z) (I - bz) + R_1$$

and

$$A(z) = (I - bz)Q_2(z) + R_2 ,$$

where R_1 and R_2 are free of z. The *remainder theorem* states that the remainder R_1 is given by

$$R_1 = A_R(b^{-1}) = a_0 + a_1 b^{-1} + \cdots + a_{p-1}b^{-p+1} + a_p b^{-p} ,$$

and the remainder R_2 is given by

$$R_2 = A_L(b^{-1}) = a_0 + b^{-1}a_1 + \cdots + b^{-p+1}a_{p-1} + b^{-p}a_p .$$

In the special case when A(z) is a scalar matrix polynomial, say,

$$A(z) = S(z)I$$
$$= (s_0 + s_1 z + \cdots + s_{p-1}z^{p-1} + s_p z^p)I ,$$

where $s_0, s_1, \ldots, s_{p-1}, s_p$ are scalars, then the remainders R_1 and R_2 are identical, so that

$$R_1 = R_2 = s_0 I + s_1 b^{-1} + \cdots + s_{p-1}b^{-p+1} + s_p b^{-p} = S(b^{-1}) .$$

As a consequence, we find that a scalar matrix polynomial S(z)I is divisible by $I - bz$ if and only if $S(b^{-1}) = 0$.

From these results the Cayley–Hamilton theorem (for a nonsingular matrix) may readily be proved. Consider the nonsingular square matrix $a = [a_{ij}]$ having characteristic matrix

$$I - az$$

and characteristic equation

$$\psi(z) = \det (I - az) = 0 .$$

By definition of the adjugate, adj $(I - az)$, we have

$$(I - az) \text{ adj } (I - az) = \psi(z)I .$$

Hence the scalar polynomial $\psi(z)$ I is divisible by I $- az$, and hence $\psi(a^{-1}) = 0$. Thus we have proved the *Cayley–Hamilton theorem* for a nonsingular square matrix a, namely, the following:

The inverse a^{-1} of a nonsingular square matrix a satisfies its characteristic equation

$$\psi(a^{-1}) = 0 ,$$

where $\psi(z)$ is the characteristic polynomial in z defined by

$$\psi(z) = \det (I - az) .$$

(*Note.* Use is made of this form of the Cayley–Hamilton theorem in Sec. 5.9.)

4.5 Inverse of a matrix polynomial

The determinant, adjugate, and inverse of a matrix polynomial (or polynomial matrix) can be defined in the same way as for a matrix with scalar elements. For example, the *determinant* of the square matrix.

$$\begin{bmatrix} a_{11} & a_{12} \\ a_{21} & a_{22} \end{bmatrix}$$

is defined as

$$a_{11}a_{22} - a_{21}a_{12} ,$$

regardless of whether the elements a_{11}, a_{21}, a_{12}, a_{22} are scalars or polynomials. Thus the determinant of the polynomial matrix

$$A(z) = \begin{bmatrix} 2 & 0 \\ 1 & 6 \end{bmatrix} + \begin{bmatrix} 1 & 1 \\ 0 & 1 \end{bmatrix} z = \begin{bmatrix} 2 + z & z \\ 1 & 6 + z \end{bmatrix} \tag{1}$$

is the (minimum-delay) polynomial

$$\det A(z) = (2 + z)(6 + z) - (1)(z) = 12 + 7z + z^2 . \tag{2}$$

In particular, if $A(z)$ and $B(z)$ are matrix polynomials, we have

$$\det [A(z)B(z)] = [\det A(z)][\det B(z)] = \det [B(z)A(z)] .$$

Let $[a_{ij}]$ denote a square matrix whose element in the ith row and jth column is a_{ij}. We recall that the first minor of the determinant $\det [a_{ij}]$, corresponding to the element a_{ij}, is defined as the determinant obtained by omission of the ith row and jth column of det $[a_{ij}]$. The cofactor of the element a_{ij} is this minor multiplied by $(-1)^{i+j}$. If the matrix $[a_{ij}]$ is of order p, any first minor is of order $p - 1$. If we let cof a_{ij} denote the cofactor of the element a_{ij} in the matrix $[a_{ij}]$, then the matrix

$$\text{adj } [a_{ij}] = [\text{cof } a_{ji}]$$

is called the *adjugate*, or *adjoint*, of the matrix $[a_{ij}]$. It should be noted that the adjugate of a matrix $[a_{ij}]$ is the *transpose* of the matrix of the cofactors of $[a_{ij}]$. It follows that

$$[a_{ij}] \, (\text{adj } [a_{ij}]) = (\text{adj } [a_{ij}]) \, [a_{ij}] = (\det [a_{ij}]) I \ .$$

These definitions hold, in particular, when the elements a_{ij} are polynomials in z. Hence, given a polynomial matrix $A(z)$, we may write the last equations as

$$A(z)[\text{adj } A(z)] = [\text{adj } A(z)] \, A(z) = [\det A(z)] I \ .$$

Hence the *inverse* of $A(z)$ is given as the ratio

$$A^{-1}(z) \equiv [A(z)]^{-1} = \frac{\text{adj } A(z)}{\det A(z)} \ .$$

For example, if $A(z)$ is the polynomial matrix given by eq. (1), then its determinant is given by eq. (2), its adjugate is

$$\text{adj } A(z) = \begin{bmatrix} 6 + z & -z \\ -1 & 2 + z \end{bmatrix},$$

and its inverse is

$$A^{-1}(z) = \begin{bmatrix} \dfrac{6 + z}{12 + 7z + z^2} & \dfrac{-z}{12 + 7z + z^2} \\ \dfrac{-1}{12 + 7z + z^2} & \dfrac{2 + z}{12 + 7z + z^2} \end{bmatrix}.$$

Given a nonsingular polynomial matrix $A(z)$, two cases may occur. The first case is when det $A(z)$ is a polynomial of degree greater than zero. Then $A^{-1}(z)$ is not a polynomial matrix, but is a matrix with rational functions (i.e., ratios of polynomials) as elements. The other case is when det $A(z)$ is a constant (i.e., independent of z) and not zero. The inverse $A^{-1}(z)$ is then a polynomial matrix. In this second case, $A(z)$ is called an *elementary polynomial matrix;* that is, an elementary polynomial matrix is one with an inverse which is a polynomial matrix. An example of an elementary polynomial matrix and its inverse is

$$A(z) = \begin{bmatrix} 2 + 3z & 5 + 6z \\ z & 1 + z \end{bmatrix}, \quad A^{-1}(z) = \begin{bmatrix} 0.5 + 0.5z & -2.5 - 3z \\ -0.5z & 1 + 1.5z \end{bmatrix}.$$

4.6 Subroutine for inverting matrix polynomials[40]

A polynomial matrix is a matrix whose elements are polynomials in z. Given a polynomial matrix, subroutine POMAIN computes its determinant, its adjugate matrix, and the coefficients of its characteristic polynomial. The determinant and the coefficients are scalar polynomials in z, and the adjugate matrix is a polynomial matrix. Each of these subroutine outputs is well determined even if the polynomial matrix is singular for some or possibly all values of z. The inverse matrix is the ratio of the adjugate matrix to the determinant, and hence is a matrix of rational functions in z (i.e., ratios of polynomials in z). The reason the inverse is given only as the ratio of polynomials, and polynomial division is not performed, is that polynomial division would result in infinite series unless the determinant were a constant. If the determinant is a minimum-delay polynomial, then the rational functions should be expanded in an infinite series of non-negative powers of z. If the determinant is a maximum-delay polynomial, then the rational functions should be expanded in an infinite series of negative powers of z. If the determinant is a mixed-delay polynomial, then the rational functions should be expanded in a stable series involving both non-negative and negative powers of z.

The polynomial matrix may be denoted by

$$A(z) = \sum_{k=0}^{m} a_{ij}^{(k)} z^k .$$

Each element of the $n \times n$ polynomial matrix $A(z)$ is a polynomial of degree m in z specified by its coefficients. The variable z plays no role in this subroutine. The operations of addition, subtraction, and multiplication on the polynomials are performed by manipulation of the coefficients. Since a polynomial matrix may be thought of as either a matrix whose elements are polynomials (i.e., as a polynomial matrix) or a polynomial whose coefficients are matrices (i.e., as a matrix polynomial), it follows that multiplication of polynomial matrices can be done by either of the following:

(1) a matrix multiplication algorithm with scalar additions and multiplications changed to the appropriate polynomial coefficient manipulations, or
(2) a polynomial multiplication algorithm with the coefficients of the polynomials changed from scalars to matrices.

Hence the product of $C(z)$ of two polynomial matrices $A(z)$ with $B(z)$ is given

---

[40] This section is based on a report by Jansson, B., and J. Claerbout, *Inversion of Matrices with Polynomial Elements*, Univ. Institute of Statistics, Uppsala, Sweden, 1963.

by the following Fortran DO-loop for all relevant p, q, i, k, and j:

$$c_{pq}^{(k+j)} = c_{pq}^{(k+j)} + a_{pi}^{(k)} b_{iq}^{(j)} .$$

The coding is simplified by requiring every element of A to be a polynomial of the same degree m in z. This convention involves no loss of generality as any of the coefficients of the scalar polynomials may be taken to be zero.

The subroutine is based on an extention to polynomial matrices of a method given by Gantmacher.[41] A description of the algorithm is as follows.

If $A(z)$ denotes the given polynomial matrix, then its characteristic equation may be defined in the way analogous to scalar matrices as

$$\det (\mu I - A) = 0 ,$$

which may be written as

$$\mu^n - p_1 \mu^{n-1} - p_2 \mu^{n-2} - \cdots - p_{n-1} \mu - p_n = 0 .$$

The polynomial on the left-hand side of this equation is the characteristic polynomial; in this case its coefficients p_k are themselves polynomials in z. By the Cayley–Hamilton theorem, a matrix satisfies its characteristic equation. Hence

$$0 = A^n - p_1 A^{n-1} - p_2 A^{n-2} - \cdots - p_{n-1} A - p_n I .$$

If we multiply this equation by

$$A^{-1} = (-1)^{n-1} (\operatorname{adj} A)/p_n ,$$

we obtain

$$(-1)^{n-1} \operatorname{adj} A = A^{n-1} - p_1 A^{n-2} - \cdots - p_{n-2} A - p_{n-1} I ,$$

which may be rearranged to

$$(-1)^{n-1} \operatorname{adj} A = (\ldots ((A - p_1 I)A - p_2 I)A - \cdots - p_{n-2} I)A - p_{n-1} I .$$

The subroutine starts computing from the inner of the nested parentheses and works outward. The kth coefficient p_k is the trace of the previous nest divided by k. The first step results in the computation of

$$p_1 = \operatorname{tr} A, \quad B_1 = A - p_1 I .$$

Because p_1 is given by the trace of $A(z)$, i.e., the sum of the scalar polynomials on the diagonal of $A(z)$, it follows that p_1 and the elements of B_1 are scalar polynomials of degree m. Subsequent steps result in the computation of

---

[41] Gantmacher, F. R., *The Theory of Matrices*, Chelsea, New York, 1959, vol. 1, pp. 87–89.

$$A_2 = B_1 A, \qquad p_2 = \frac{1}{2} \operatorname{tr} A_2, \qquad B_2 = A_2 - p_2 I$$

$$\cdot \qquad\qquad \cdot \qquad\qquad \cdot$$
$$\cdot \qquad\qquad \cdot \qquad\qquad \cdot$$
$$\cdot \qquad\qquad \cdot \qquad\qquad \cdot$$

$$A_n = B_{n-1} A, \qquad p_n = \frac{1}{n} \operatorname{tr} A_n, \qquad B_n = A_n - p_n I .$$

The degree of the scalar polynomials can increase by m in each step until it finally can reach n times m in the nth step. Thus the coefficients p_k of the characteristic polynomial are themselves polynomials of at most degree k times m. A check in the computations is provided by the fact that B_n should be identically zero which follows from the Cayley–Hamilton theorem. The determinant, adjugate, and inverse are given by

$$\det A(z) = (-1)^{n-1} p_n$$
$$\operatorname{adj} A(z) = (-1)^{n-1} B_{n-1}$$
$$A^{-1}(z) = \frac{\operatorname{adj} A(z)}{\det A(z)} = \frac{B_{n-1}}{p_n} .$$

Subroutine computing time requires $n^4 m^2$ machine multiplications.

The computing algorithm is valid for polynomial matrices with complex coefficients. As a result, we have made the relevant variables complex by the use of a COMPLEX statement in the subroutine. Also the method can be extended to polynomials in more than one independent variable, which would require only a change in the polynomial addition and multiplication procedures.

The subroutine is

```
      SUBROUTINE POMAIN(N,LA,A,ADJ,P,DET,S)
      DIMENSION A(N,N,LA),ADJ(N,N,1),P(N,1),DET(1),S(N,N,1)
C     LADJ=(N-1)*(LA-1)+1
C     LDET=N*(LA-1)+1
C     DIMENSION ADJ(N,N,LADJ),P(N,LDET),DET(LDET),S(N,N,
C    1LDET)
      COMPLEX A,ADJ,P,DET,S
      CALL MOVE(N*N*LA,A,S)
      J=LA
      DO 4 L=1,N
C     CALCULATE COEFFICIENTS P(.,K) OF CHARACTERISTIC
C    1POLYNOMIAL
      DO 1 K=1,J
      P(L,K)=0.0
      DO 1 I=1,N
    1 P(L,K)=P(L,K)+S(I,I,K)/FLOAT(L)
      IF(L.EQ.N) GO TO 5
```

```
C      SUBTRACT P(.,K)*IDENTITY MATRIX
     2 CALL MOVE(N*N*J,S,ADJ)
       DO 3 I=1,N
       DO 3 K=1,J
     3 ADJ(I,I,K)=ADJ(I,I,K)-P(L,K)
C      MULTIPLY BY INPUT MATRIX
       CALL BRAINY(N,N,LA,A,N,N,J,ADJ,S)
     4 J=J+LA-1
C      GIVE DETERMINANT AND ADJUGATE CORRECT SIGN
     5 CONTINUE
C      NOW J=LDET=LA+(N-1)*(LA-1)=N*(LA-1)+1
C      HENCE J-LA+1=(N-1)*(LA-1)+1=LADJ
       CALL SCALE(FLOAT(2*MOD(N,2)-1),N*N*(J-LA+1),ADJ)
       DO 6 L=1,J
     6 DET(L)=P(N,L)*FLOAT(2*MOD(N,2)-1)
       RETURN
       END
```

The complex version of subroutine POMAIN given above requires the complex versions of subroutines MOVE, BRAINY, ZERO, and SCALE. The real version of subroutine POMAIN may be obtained by removing the COMPLEX statement from the above program; the real version needs the real versions of subroutines MOVE, BRAINY, ZERO, and SCALE. Let us denote the given $n \times n$ polynomial matrix of degree m by

$$A(z) = a_0 + a_1 z + \cdots + a_m z^m .$$

The call statement for subroutine POMAIN is

CALL POMAIN(N,LA,A,ADJ,P,DET,S),

where the subroutine inputs are

N = order of polynomial matrix = n (where $n \geqslant 2$)
LA = degree of polynomial matrix plus one = $m + 1$
A = coefficients of polynomial matrix
= $(a_0, a_1, \ldots, a_m)$,

and where the subroutine outputs are

ADJ = coefficients of adj $A(z)$
P = coefficients of characteristic polynomial
DET = coefficients of det $A(z)$
S = working space.

As a numerical example, suppose that

$$A(z) = \begin{bmatrix} 1 - 3z + 2z^2 & 21z - 6z^2 \\ 14z + 5z^2 & 1 + z + 14z^2 \end{bmatrix}$$

$$N = 2$$
$$LA = 3$$
$$A = (a_0, a_1, a_2)$$

$$= \left(\begin{bmatrix} 1 & 0 \\ 0 & 1 \end{bmatrix}, \begin{bmatrix} -3 & 21 \\ 14 & 1 \end{bmatrix}, \begin{bmatrix} 2 & -6 \\ 5 & 14 \end{bmatrix} \right)$$

$$= (1, 0, 0, 1, -3, 14, 21, 1, 2, 5, -6, 14).$$

Then the subroutine gives as output

$$ADJ = (1, 0, 0, 1, 1, -14, -21, -3, 14, -5, 6, 2)$$

$$= \left(\begin{bmatrix} 1 & 0 \\ 0 & 1 \end{bmatrix}, \begin{bmatrix} 1 & -21 \\ -14 & -3 \end{bmatrix}, \begin{bmatrix} 14 & 6 \\ -5 & 2 \end{bmatrix} \right)$$

$$DET = (1, -2, -281, -61, 58).$$

Hence the inverse matrix is

$$A^{-1}(z) = \frac{\text{adj } A(z)}{\text{det } A(z)}$$

$$= \frac{1}{1 - 2z - 281z^2 - 61z^3 + 58z^4} \begin{bmatrix} 1 + z + 14z^2 & -21z + 6z^2 \\ -14z - 5z^2 & 1 - 3z + 2z^2 \end{bmatrix}$$

4.7 Extended hermitian matrices and extended unitary matrices

A *quasi-polynomial* is an expression like a polynomial with a finite number of terms

$$A(z) = a_{-n}z^{-n} + a_{-n+1}z^{-n+1} + \cdots + a_0 + a_1 z + \cdots + a_m z^m,$$

but unlike a polynomial it can involve negative powers of z. A matrix $A(z)$ is called a *quasi-polynomial matrix*, provided each of its elements is a polynomial or quasi-polynomial in z. A matrix $A(z)$ is a *rational matrix*, provided that each of its elements is a rational function in z.

Let us now introduce the *subscript asterisk* notation. Given $A(z)$, then $A_*(z)$ is defined as

$$A_*(z) = [A(1/z^*)]^{*\mathrm{T}}.$$

It therefore follows that

$$A_{**}(z) = A(z)$$

and

$$[A(z)B(z)]_* = B_*(z)A_*(z).$$

For example, if $A(z)$ is the quasi-polynomial matrix

$$A(z) = \sum_{s=-m}^{m} a_s z^s ,$$

then $A_*(z)$ is the quasi-polynomial matrix

$$A_*(z) = \sum_{s=-m}^{m} a_s^{*T} z^{-s} .$$

That is, to convert the quasi-polynomial matrix $A(z)$ to $A_*(z)$ we replaced each coefficient a_s by its complex conjugate transpose a_s^{*T} and replaced z by z^{-1}. As a numerical example, if

$$A(z) = \begin{bmatrix} 1 & 3 \\ 2 & 4 \end{bmatrix} z^{-1} + \begin{bmatrix} 5 & 7 \\ 6 & 8 \end{bmatrix} + \begin{bmatrix} 9 & 11 \\ 10 & 12 \end{bmatrix} z ,$$

then

$$A_*(z) = \begin{bmatrix} 9 & 10 \\ 11 & 12 \end{bmatrix} z^{-1} + \begin{bmatrix} 5 & 6 \\ 7 & 8 \end{bmatrix} + \begin{bmatrix} 1 & 2 \\ 3 & 4 \end{bmatrix} z .$$

Two important types of matrices which we now want to discuss are the extended hermitian matrix and the extended unitary matrix. In case all the coefficients are real, the extended hermitian matrix may be called an extended symmetrical matrix, and the extended unitary matrix may be called an extended orthogonal matrix.

A matrix $H(z)$ is called *extended hermitian*, provided that

$$H_*(z) = H(z) .$$

On the unit circle $z = e^{-2\pi i f}$, we have

$$[H(e^{-2\pi i f})]^{*T} = H(e^{-2\pi i f}) .$$

Hence on the unit circle, an extended hermitian matrix is hermitian in the ordinary sense. In case all the coefficients of an extended hermitian matrix are real, then it may be called *extended symmetrical*. A numerical example of an extended symmetrical matrix is

$$\begin{bmatrix} -0.5 & -0.5 \\ 0.4 & -0.6 \end{bmatrix} z^{-1} + \begin{bmatrix} 1.41 & 0.01 \\ 0.01 & 1.61 \end{bmatrix} + \begin{bmatrix} -0.5 & 0.4 \\ -0.5 & -0.6 \end{bmatrix} z . \quad (1)$$

Note that the center term is an ordinary symmetrical matrix.

If $A(z)$ is a polynomial matrix, then its *autocorrelation* (or *spectral*) *matrix* $\Phi(z)$ defined as

$$\Phi(z) = A(z)A_*(z)$$

is an extended hermitian matrix since

$$\Phi_*(z) = [A(z)A_*(z)]_* = A(z)A_*(z) = \Phi(z) .$$

For example, if

$$A(z) = \begin{bmatrix} 1 & 0 \\ 0 & 1 \end{bmatrix} + \begin{bmatrix} -0.5 & 0.4 \\ -0.5 & -0.6 \end{bmatrix} z , \tag{2}$$

then $A(z)A_*(z)$ is the extended symmetrical matrix given by eq. (1) above.

A matrix $P(z)$ is called *extended unitary*, provided that

$$P(z)P_*(z) = I .$$

Hence the inverse of an extended unitary matrix is given by

$$P^{-1}(z) = P_*(z) .$$

An extended unitary matrix is also called an *all-pass matrix*. On the unit circle $z = e^{-2\pi i f}$ we have

$$[P(e^{-2\pi i f})]^{*T} = P^{-1}(e^{-2\pi i f}) .$$

Hence on the unit circle, an extended unitary matrix is unitary in the ordinary sense. In case all the coefficients of an extended unitary matrix are real, then it may be called *extended orthogonal*. A numerical example of an extended orthogonal matrix is

$$P(z) = \frac{1}{z + 4} \begin{bmatrix} 2 + 2z & -3z \\ 3 & 2 + 2z \end{bmatrix} , \tag{3}$$

which has the inverse

$$P^{-1}(z) = P_*(z) = [P(1/z^*)]^{*T} = \frac{1}{4z + 1} \begin{bmatrix} 2 + 2z & 3z \\ -3 & 2 + 2z \end{bmatrix} . \tag{4}$$

4.8 The determinantal equation and the adjugate

Let

$$A(z) = a_0 + a_1 z + \cdots + a_m z^m$$

be a $p \times p$ polynomial matrix. Then

$$\det A(z) = 0$$

is called the *determinantal equation*, and its roots are denoted by $z_1, z_2, \ldots, z_n$, where n is the degree of the polynomial $\det A(z)$ in z. Although these roots are not necessarily all distinct, it is convenient to specify them by n distinct symbols. The degree n must satisfy

$$n \leqslant mp .$$

Because we want to keep our exposition as simple as possible in order to convey the essential features of multichannel time series analysis, we assume that

$$n = mp ,$$

and that all the roots

$$z_1, z_2, \ldots, z_n$$

are distinct, finite, and nonzero.

The (constant) matrix $A(z_s)$ obtained by substitution of any root z_s for z in the polynomial matrix $A(z)$ is necessarily singular. When z_s is an unrepeated root (as we assume in our work), then the $p \times p$ matrix $A(z_s)$ has rank $p - 1$, and the *adjugate* evaluated at $z = z_s$

$$\text{adj } A(z_s)$$

is a $p \times p$ matrix with rank 1, and it is expressible as a product of the form

$$\text{adj } A(z_s) = c_s r_s ,$$

where c_s is a nonzero (constant) column vector, and r_s is a nonzero (constant) row vector appropriate to the given root z_s. The proof of this statement may be found in Frazer, Duncan, and Collar.[42]

As a numerical example, suppose that

$$A(z) = \begin{bmatrix} 1 - 3z - 4z^2 & -z + 4z^2 \\ 14z - 58z^2 & 1 - 11z + 28z^2 \end{bmatrix}.$$

Then

$$\text{adj } A(z) = \begin{bmatrix} 1 - 11z + 28z^2 & z - 4z^2 \\ -14z + 58z^2 & 1 - 3z - 4z^2 \end{bmatrix}$$

and

$$\det A(z) = 1 - 14z + 71z^2 - 154z^3 + 120z^4 .$$

The roots of the determinantal equation are

$$z_1 = \frac{1}{5}, \quad z_2 = \frac{1}{4}, \quad z_3 = \frac{1}{3}, \quad z_4 = \frac{1}{2} .$$

For $z_1 = 0.2$, we have

$$\text{adj } A(0.2) = \begin{bmatrix} -0.08 & 0.04 \\ -0.48 & 0.24 \end{bmatrix} = c_1 r_1 ,$$

and so, for example, we may write c_1 and r_1 as

$$c_1 = \begin{bmatrix} 0.08 \\ 0.48 \end{bmatrix}, \quad r_1 = [1.0 \quad -0.5] .$$

---

[42] Frazer, R. A., W. J. Duncan, and A. R. Collar, *Elementary Matrices*, Cambridge Univ. Press, Cambridge, England, 1963, pp. 61–62.

Note that c_1 and r_1 are by no means unique; for example, we could equally as well write c_1 and r_1 as

$$c_1 = \begin{bmatrix} 1 \\ 6 \end{bmatrix}, \quad r_1 = [-0.08 \quad 0.04] .$$

As another example, suppose we have the polynomial matrix

$$A(z) = \begin{bmatrix} 2 + z & z \\ 1 & 6 + z \end{bmatrix}.$$

The autocorrelation matrix is the extended hermitian matrix

$$\Phi(z) = A(z) \, A_*(z) = \begin{bmatrix} 2z^{-1} + 6 + 2z & 3 + 7z \\ 7z^{-1} + 3 & 6z^{-1} + 38 + 6z \end{bmatrix}.$$

Its adjugate is

$$\text{adj } \Phi(z) = \begin{bmatrix} 6z^{-1} + 38 + 6z & -3 - 7z \\ -7z^{-1} - 3 & 2z^{-1} + 6 + 2z \end{bmatrix},$$

and its determinant is

$$\det \Phi(z) = 12z^{-2} + 91z^{-1} + 194 + 91z + 12z^2 .$$

The zeros of the determinantal equation are

$$z_1 = -\frac{1}{4}, \quad z_2 = -\frac{1}{3}, \quad z_3 = -3, \quad z_4 = -4 .$$

For the root $z_1 = -\tfrac{1}{4}$ we have

$$\text{adj } \Phi(-0.25) = \begin{bmatrix} 12.5 & -1.25 \\ 25 & -2.50 \end{bmatrix} = c_1 \, r_1 ,$$

and so, for example, we could write c_1 and r_1 as

$$c_1 = \begin{bmatrix} 12.5 \\ 25 \end{bmatrix}, \quad r_1 = [1 \quad -0.1] ,$$

or, for example, we could write c_1 and r_1 as

$$c_1 = \begin{bmatrix} 1 \\ 2 \end{bmatrix}, \quad r_1 = [12.5 \quad -1.25] .$$

4.9 Eigenvectors and eigenvalues of a polynomial matrix

We want to consider the $p \times p$ polynomial matrix

$$U(z) = I - u_1 z - u_2 z^2 - \cdots - u_m z^m \tag{1}$$

of degree m. But first let us consider the special case when $m = 1$, that is, when

$$U(z) = I - u_1 z .\tag{2}$$

We have

$$U^{-1}(z) = \frac{adj\ U(z)}{det\ U(z)}\tag{3}$$

so that

$$U(z)\ adj\ U(z) = I\ det\ U(z) .\tag{4}$$

The determinantal equation is

$$det\ U(z) = 0,\tag{5}$$

which has p roots $z_1, z_2, \ldots, z_p$; that is,

$$det\ U(z_i) = 0 \qquad for\ i = 1, 2, \ldots, p .\tag{6}$$

Also from the last section we know that

$$adj\ U(z_i) = c_i r_i \qquad for\ i = 1, 2, \ldots, p ,\tag{7}$$

where c_i is a column vector, and r_i is a row vector, associated with the root z_i. Hence eq. (4) becomes at $z = z_i$

$$U(z_i) c_i r_i = 0 ,\tag{8}$$

where 0 in this equation denotes the $p \times p$ zero matrix. From this equation it follows that

$$U(z_i) c_i = 0$$

or

$$(I - u_1 z_i) c_i = 0 \qquad for\ i = 1, 2, \ldots, p ,\tag{9}$$

where 0 now denotes the $p \times 1$ zero column. In this equation we recognize the column vector c_i as the eigen-column-vector of the matrix u_1 associated with the eigenroot $\lambda_i = z_i^{-1}$. Hence given the matrix polynomial (2), we can compute its determinant $det\ U(z)$ and find its roots $z_1, z_2, \ldots, z_p$, as shown by eq. (6). Substituting the numerical values of these roots into adj $U(z)$, we find the eigencolumns $c_1, c_2, \ldots, c_p$, as shown by eq. (7). In other words, given the matrix polynomial (2), we can compute its eigenroots z_i and eigencolumns c_i for $i = 1, 2, \ldots, p$.

Inversely, suppose we are given the eigenroots z_i and the corresponding eigencolumns c_i for $i = 1, 2, \ldots, p$. We may then form the $p \times p$ matrix of eigencolumns

$$C = [c_1, c_2, \ldots, c_p]$$

and the $p \times p$ diagonal matrix of eigenroots

$$Z = diag\ [z_1, z_2, \ldots, z_p] .$$

Then in this notation eq. (9)

$$I c_i - u_1 c_i z_i = 0 \qquad \text{for } i = 1, 2, \ldots, p$$

becomes

$$C - u_1 CZ = 0, \tag{10}$$

where 0 in this equation denotes the $p \times p$ zero matrix. We may then solve this equation for u_1; the solution is

$$u_1 = CZ^{-1}C^{-1}.$$

Hence given the eigenroots Z and the eigencolumns C, we may solve for the matrix polynomial (2).

The procedures we have just described for the matrix polynomial (2) of degree $m = 1$ also work for the matrix polynomial (1) of arbitrary degree m. Given the matrix polynomial (1), the determinantal equation yields $n = mp$ roots $z_1, z_2, \ldots, z_n$; that is,

$$\det U(z_i) = 0 \qquad \text{for } i = 1, 2, \ldots, n. \tag{11}$$

Substituting these roots into the adjugate, we have

$$\text{adj } U(z_i) = c_i r_i \qquad \text{for } i = 1, 2, \ldots, n, \tag{12}$$

which yields the eigencolumns $c_1, c_2, \ldots, c_n$. Hence given the matrix polynomial (1), we can compute its eigenroots z_i and its eigencolumns c_i for $i = 1, 2, \ldots, n$, where $n = mp$. These numerical values satisfy

$$U(z_i)c_i = 0,$$

which is

$$(I - u_1 z_i - u_2 z_i^2 - \cdots - u_m z_i^m)c_i = 0. \tag{13}$$

Inversely, suppose that we are given the eigenroots z_i and the eigencolumns c_i for $i = 1, 2, \ldots, n$, where $n = mp$. We may then form the $p \times n$ matrix of eigencolumns

$$C = [c_1, c_2, \ldots, c_n]$$

and the $n \times n$ diagonal matrix of eigenroots

$$Z = \text{diag } [z_1, z_2, \ldots, z_n].$$

Then in matrix notation eq. (13) becomes

$$C - u_1 CZ - u_2 CZ^2 - \cdots - u_m CZ^m = 0, \tag{14}$$

where 0 in this equation denotes the $p \times n$ zero matrix. We can then solve the set of simultaneous equations represented by eq. (14) for the $p \times p$ matrices $u_1, u_2, \ldots, u_m$. Hence given the eigenroots Z and the eigencolumns C, we may solve for the matrix polynomial (1).

Let us now consider the $p \times p$ matrix polynomial

$$A(z) = a_0 + a_1 z + \cdots + a_m z^m . \tag{15}$$

We may factor this into the form

$$A(z) = a_0(I - u_1 z - \cdots - u_m z^m) = a_0 U(z) ,$$

where

$$u_i = -a_0^{-1} a_i \qquad \text{for } i = 1, 2, \ldots, m .$$

Since we assume a_0 is not a singular matrix, we see from

$$\det A(z) = (\det a_0) \det U(z)$$

that $A(z)$ and $U(z)$ have the same eigenroots $z_1, z_2, \ldots, z_n$, where $n = mp$. Also we see from

$$\text{adj } A(z_i) = \text{adj } [a_0 U(z_i)] = \text{adj } U(z_i) \text{ adj } a_0$$
$$= c_i r_i \text{ adj } a_0 \quad = c_i(r_i \text{ adj } a_0)$$

that $A(z)$ and $U(z)$ have the same eigencolumns $c_1, c_2, \ldots, c_n$, where $n = mp$. From eq. (13) we have

$$A(z_i)c_i = 0 \qquad \text{for } i = 1, 2, \ldots, n , \tag{16}$$

where 0 denotes the $p \times 1$ vector of zeros. Thus we may treat the more general matrix polynomial (15) by the same methods as we developed for the matrix polynomial (1).

As a numerical example, suppose that we are given the polynomial matrix

$$U(z) = \begin{bmatrix} 1 - 3z - 4z^2 & -z + 4z^2 \\ 14z - 58z^2 & 1 - 11z + 28z^2 \end{bmatrix} . \tag{17}$$

Either directly, or by use of subroutine **POMAIN**, we may compute that

$$\det U(z) = 1 - 14z + 71z^2 - 154z^3 + 120z^4$$
$$= (1 - 5z)(1 - 4z)(1 - 3z)(1 - 2z)$$

and

$$\text{adj } U(z) = \begin{bmatrix} 1 - 11z + 28z^2 & z - 4z^2 \\ -14z + 58z^2 & 1 - 3z - 4z^2 \end{bmatrix} .$$

Hence the eigenroots are

$$z_1 = \frac{1}{5}, \quad z_2 = \frac{1}{4}, \quad z_3 = \frac{1}{3}, \quad z_4 = \frac{1}{2},$$

and

$$\text{adj } U(z_1) = \begin{bmatrix} -0.08 & 0.04 \\ -0.48 & 0.24 \end{bmatrix} = \begin{bmatrix} -0.08 \\ -0.48 \end{bmatrix} [1 \quad -0.5] = c_1 r_1$$

$$\text{adj } U(z_2) = \begin{bmatrix} 0 \\ 0.125 \end{bmatrix} \begin{bmatrix} 0 \\ 0 \end{bmatrix} = \begin{bmatrix} 0 \\ 0.125 \end{bmatrix} \begin{bmatrix} 1 & 0 \end{bmatrix} = c_2 \, r_2$$

$$\text{adj } U(z_3) = \begin{bmatrix} 0.444 & -0.111 \\ 1.777 & -0.444 \end{bmatrix} = \begin{bmatrix} 0.444 \\ 1.777 \end{bmatrix} \begin{bmatrix} 1 & -0.25 \end{bmatrix} = c_3 \, r_3$$

$$\text{adj } U(z_4) = \begin{bmatrix} 2.5 & -0.5 \\ 7.5 & -1.5 \end{bmatrix} = \begin{bmatrix} 2.5 \\ 7.5 \end{bmatrix} \begin{bmatrix} 1 & -0.2 \end{bmatrix} = c_4 \, r_4 \ .$$

Thus we have found the eigenroots and eigencolumns of $U(z)$ given by eq. (17).

On the other hand, suppose that we are given the following information:

$$z_1 = \frac{1}{5}, \quad z_2 = \frac{1}{4}, \quad z_3 = \frac{1}{3}, \quad z_4 = \frac{1}{2}$$

$$c_1 = \begin{bmatrix} 1 \\ 6 \end{bmatrix}, \quad c_2 = \begin{bmatrix} 0 \\ 1 \end{bmatrix}, \quad c_3 = \begin{bmatrix} 1 \\ 4 \end{bmatrix}, \quad c_4 = \begin{bmatrix} 1 \\ 3 \end{bmatrix},$$

and we want to construct

$$U(z) = I - u_1 z - u_2 z^2 ,$$

where $p = 2$, $m = 2$, $n = mp = 4$. We form

$$C = \begin{bmatrix} 1 & 0 & 1 & 1 \\ 6 & 1 & 4 & 3 \end{bmatrix}$$

and

$$Z = \text{diag} \begin{bmatrix} \frac{1}{5}, & \frac{1}{4}, & \frac{1}{3}, & \frac{1}{2} \end{bmatrix}.$$

Then we set up the equation

$$u_1 CZ + u_2 CZ^2 = C ,$$

and solving for u_1 and u_2 we obtain

$$u_1 = \begin{bmatrix} 3 & 1 \\ -14 & 11 \end{bmatrix}, \quad u_2 = \begin{bmatrix} 4 & -4 \\ 58 & -28 \end{bmatrix}.$$

Hence the required polynomial matrix is

$$U(z) = \begin{bmatrix} 1 - 3z - 4z^2 & -z + 4z^2 \\ 14z - 58z^2 & 1 - 11z + 28z^2 \end{bmatrix}. \tag{18}$$

We see that the polynomial matrices (17) and (18) are the same. Indeed, this is the way it should be because each has the same eigenroots and eigencolumns, as any eigencolumn can be multiplied by an arbitrary scale factor without affecting $U(z)$.

4.10 Factoring matrix polynomials into binomial factors

One of the first things taught in high school algebra is the factorization of a polynomial into binomial factors. In this section we wish to consider the corresponding problem in the case of matrix polynomials.

Suppose that we are given the $p \times p$ matrix polynomial

$$A(z) = a_0 + a_1 z + a_2 z^2 + \cdots + a_m z^m , \tag{1}$$

where $a_0, a_1, a_2, \ldots, a_m$ are each $p \times p$ constant matrices. The problem is to find $p \times p$ constant matrices b_k such that

$$A(z) = b_0(I + z b_1)(I + z b_2) \cdots (I + z b_m) . \tag{2}$$

A solution to this problem is as follows. The adjugate adj $A(z)$ is equal to

$$\text{adj } A(z) = A^{-1}(z) \det A(z) , \tag{3}$$

where $A^{-1}(z)$ is the inverse of $A(z)$, and where $\det A(z)$ is the determinant of $A(z)$. If we postmultiply eq. (2) by adj $A(z)$, we obtain

$$I \det A(z) = b_0(I + z b_1)(I + z b_2) \cdots (I + z b_m) \text{ adj } A(z) . \tag{4}$$

Let $z_1, z_2, \ldots, z_n$, where $n = mp$ be the roots of the polynomial $\det A(z)$. From Sec. 4.8 we know that

$$\text{adj } A(z_k) = c_k r_k \qquad \text{for } k = 1, 2, \ldots, n ,$$

where c_k is a column, and r_k is a row. For $z = z_k$, we have $\det A(z_k) = 0$, so eq. (4) becomes

$$\begin{aligned} 0 &= b_0(I + z_k b_1)(I + z_k b_2) \cdots (I + z_k b_m) \text{ adj } A(z_k) \\ &= b_0(I + z_k b_1)(I + z_k b_2) \cdots (I + z_k b_m) c_k r_k . \end{aligned} \tag{5}$$

Equation (5) is satisfied, provided

$$(I + z_k b_m) c_k = 0 . \tag{6}$$

Equation (6) states that c_k is an eigenvector of b_m with eigenvalue $\lambda_k = -1/z_k$. Pick p roots, say, $z_1, z_2, \ldots, z_p$ from the $n = mp$ roots of $\det A(z)$ that are available. Then eq. (6) gives

$$b_m c_k = c_k \left(-\frac{1}{z_k} \right), \quad k = 1, 2, \ldots, p . \tag{7}$$

Let C be the $p \times p$ matrix of eigencolumns

$$C = [c_1, \quad c_2, \quad \ldots, \quad c_p]$$

and D be the $p \times p$ diagonal matrix of eigenvalues

$$D = \text{diag} \left[-z_1^{-1}, \quad -z_2^{-1}, \quad \ldots, \quad -z_p^{-1} \right].$$

Then eq. (7) becomes

$$b_m C = CD.$$

If we solve this equation, we thus determine the $p \times p$ matrix b_m as

$$b_m = CDC^{-1}.$$

The binomial $(I + zb_m)$ is a right divisor of the matrix polynomial $A(z)$. *Proof:* If we let $z = -b_m^{-1}$ in the matrix polynomial $A(z)$, then we obtain the right functional value (as defined in Sec. 4.4) given by

$$A_R(-b_m^{-1}) = a_0 - a_1 b_m^{-1} - a_2 b_m^{-2} - \cdots - a_m b_m^{-m}$$

which is equal to (since $b_m^{-1} = CD^{-1}C^{-1}$)

$$A_R(-b_m^{-1}) = a_0 - a_1 CD^{-1}C^{-1} - a_2 CD^{-2}C^{-1} - \cdots - a_m CD^{-m}C^{-1},$$

which is

$$A_R(-b_m^{-1}) = [a_0 C - a_1 CD^{-1} - a_2 CD^{-2} - \cdots - a_m CD^{-m}]C^{-1}. \qquad (8)$$

The expression in square brackets is equivalent to

$$(a_0 + a_1 z_k + a_2 z_k^2 + \cdots + a_m z_k^m)c_k \qquad \text{for } k = 1, 2, \ldots, p.$$

This expression, in turn, is

$$A(z_k)c_k \qquad \text{for } k = 1, 2, \ldots, p,$$

where $z_1, z_2, \ldots, z_p$ are eigenroots of $A(z)$ and $c_1, c_2, \ldots, c_p$ are the corresponding eigencolumns. Yet from eq. (16) in Sec. 4.9, we know that the eigenroots and eigencolumns satisfy

$$A(z_k)c_k = 0 \qquad \text{for } k = 1, 2, \ldots, p,$$

where 0 denotes the $p \times 1$ column vector. Hence the expression in square brackets in eq. (8) vanishes identically, and hence the right functional value $A_R(-b_m^{-1})$ vanishes identically. Thus if we write $A(z)$ as

$$A(z) = Q_1(z)(I + b_m z) + R_1,$$

where the remainder R_1 is free of z, we may evoke the remainder theorem (given in Sec. 4.4) which states that the remainder R_1 is given by the right functional value $A_R(-b_m^{-1})$. Since the remainder R_1 vanishes identically, it follows that the binomial $(I + b_m z)$ is a right divisor of $A(z)$, as we wanted to show. Q.E.D.

Consider now

$$I \det A(z) = b_0(I + zb_1) \cdots (I + zb_{m-1})[(I + zb_m) \text{ adj } A(z)].$$

The factor in square brackets, namely,

$$(I + zb_m) \text{ adj } A(z),$$

also becomes the product of a column and a row at the remaining zeros of det $A(z)$. If we pick p roots from the remaining $mp - p$ roots, we can therefore determine b_{m-1} by the same method. We can then continue the process until the remaining $p \times p$ matrices b_{m-2}, b_{m-3}, ..., b_2, b_1 are determined, thereby exhausting all the roots of det $A(z)$. Finally, since

$$A(z = 0) = b_0 = a_0 ,$$

we obtain b_0. Thus we have found

$$B(z) = b_0(I + b_1 z)(I + b_2 z) \cdots (I + b_m z)$$

which satisfies

$$I \det A(z) = B(z) \operatorname{adj} A(z) \tag{9}$$

for $z = z_k$ ($k = 1, \ldots, mp$) and for $z = 0$. By hypothesis we know that

$$I \det A(z) = A(z) \operatorname{adj} A(z) \tag{10}$$

for all z. Each of the elements of the matrix eqs. (9) and (10) is a polynomial of degree at most mp. From a theorem in algebra, it is known that if any two polynomials of degree mp are equal to each other at $mp + 1$ different values of the variable z, then they are equal over the entire range of z. Thus

$$I \det A(z) = B(z) \operatorname{adj} A(z)$$

for all z or

$$A(z) = B(z) .$$

Thus $B(z)$ represents a factorization of the given matrix polynomial $A(z)$ into binomial factors.

Since the choice of the p zeros for each of the m factors is arbitrary, it follows that there are $(mp)!/(p!)^m$ ways to factor $A(z)$ into binomial factors.

Subroutine FACT factors the $p \times p$ matrix polynomial (1) into binomial factors as given by (2). The call statement is

$$\text{CALL FACT(N,LA,A,ADJ,ZEROS,S,B),}$$

where the subroutine inputs are

$$N = \text{order of matrix} = p$$
$$LA = \text{number of coefficients in matrix polynomial} = m + 1$$
$$A = \text{coefficients of given matrix polynomial } A(z)$$
$$= (a_0, a_1, \ldots, a_m)$$
$$ADJ = \text{coefficients of adj } A(z)$$
$$ZEROS = \text{zeros of det } A(z) = (z_1, z_2, \ldots, z_n), \text{ where } n = mp ,$$

and where the subroutine outputs are

S = working space
B = desired matrices = $(b_0, b_1, \ldots, b_m)$.

Subroutine FACT makes use of complex arithmetic. In turn, the subroutines which FACT calls, as depicted in the tree

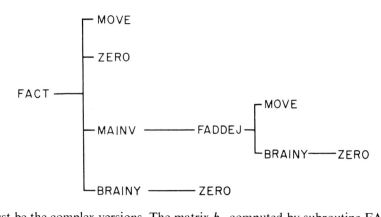

must be the complex versions. The matrix b_m computed by subroutine FACT corresponds to the first set of p zeros $z_1, z_2, \ldots, z_p$ stored in array ZEROS, the matrix b_{m-1} corresponds to the second set of p zeros $z_{p+1}, z_{p+2}, \ldots, z_{2p}$ stored in array ZEROS, ... Note that adj $A(z)$ and det $A(z)$ can be computed from $A(z)$ by subroutine POMAIN, and the roots $z_1, z_2, \ldots, z_n$ can be computed from det $A(z)$ by subroutine POLRT, thereby giving us the numbers which go in the arrays ADJ and ZEROS.

As a numerical example, suppose that

$$N = 2$$
$$LA = 2$$
$$A = (a_0, a_1) = \left(\begin{bmatrix} 2 & 0 \\ 1 & 6 \end{bmatrix}, \begin{bmatrix} 1 & 1 \\ 0 & 1 \end{bmatrix} \right)$$
$$= (2, 1, 0, 6, 1, 0, 1, 1)$$
$$ADJ = \left(\begin{bmatrix} 6 & 0 \\ -1 & 2 \end{bmatrix}, \begin{bmatrix} 1 & -1 \\ 0 & 1 \end{bmatrix} \right)$$
$$= (6, -1, 0, 2, 1, 0, -1, 1)$$
$$ZEROS = (z_1, z_2) = (-3, -4).$$

Then subroutine FACT gives as output

$$B = (2, 1, 0, 6, 0.5, -0.833, 0.5, 0.833)$$
$$= \left(\begin{bmatrix} 2 & 0 \\ 1 & 6 \end{bmatrix}, \begin{bmatrix} 0.5 & 0.5 \\ -0.0833 & 0.0833 \end{bmatrix} \right) = (b_0, b_1).$$

As a check, one may verify that

$$a_0 + a_1 z = b_0(I + b_1 z).$$

As another numerical example, suppose that

$$N = 2$$
$$LA = 3$$
$$A = (a_0, a_1, a_2) = \left(\begin{bmatrix} 1 & 0 \\ 0 & 1 \end{bmatrix}, \begin{bmatrix} -3 & 21 \\ 14 & 1 \end{bmatrix}, \begin{bmatrix} 2 & -6 \\ 5 & 14 \end{bmatrix} \right)$$
$$= (1, 0, 0, 1, -3, 14, 21, 1, 2, 5, -6, 14)$$
$$ADJ = (1, 0, 0, 1, 1, -14, -21, -3, 14, -5, 6, 2)$$
(see numerical example in Sec. 4.6)
$$ZEROS = (z_1, z_2, z_3, z_4) = (-0.06, 0.06, -1.73, 2.79) .$$

Then subroutine FACT gives as output

$$B = (1,0,0,1, -0.29, 0.66, 0.09, 0.51, -2.71, 13.34, 20.91, 0.49)$$
$$= \left(\begin{bmatrix} 1 & 0 \\ 0 & 1 \end{bmatrix}, \begin{bmatrix} -0.29 & 0.09 \\ 0.66 & 0.51 \end{bmatrix}, \begin{bmatrix} -2.71 & 20.91 \\ 13.34 & 0.49 \end{bmatrix} \right)$$
$$= (b_0, b_1, b_2) .$$

As a check, one may verify that

$$a_0 + a_1 z + a_2 z^2 = b_0(I + b_1 z)(I + b_2 z) .$$

The program for subroutine FACT is

```
      SUBROUTINE  FACT(N,LA,A,ADJ,ZEROS,S,B)
      COMPLEX  A,ADJ,ZEROS,S,B,ZI
      DIMENSION  A(N,N,LA),ADJ(N,N,1),ZEROS(N,1),S(N,N,1),
     1B(N,N,LA)
C     LADJ=(N-1)*(LA-1)+1
C     DIMENSION  ADJ(N,N,LADJ),ZEROS(N,LA-1),S(N,N,
C     15+2*LADJ)
      NP=LA-1
C     INPUTS ARE MATRIX POLYNOMIAL A,ITS ADJUGATE
C     1ADJ,ZEROS OF DET A
C     OUTPUT IS B WHERE A(Z)=B0*(I+ZB1)*(I+ZB2)*...*
C     1(I+ZBNP)
C     MOVE ADJUGATE TO S(1,1,6)
      CALL MOVE(N*N*((N-1)*NP+1),ADJ,S(1,1,6))
C     LOOP ON THE FACTORS (I+Z*Q*D*QINV)
      DO 30 IP=1,NP
      L=(N-1)*NP+IP
      CALL  RITE(2,N,N,L,S(1,1,6))
      CALL  ZERO(N*N*5,S)
      DO 20 ICOL=1,N
C     INSERT ROOTS INTO (PREVIOUS FACTORS*ADJUGATE)
C     1TO GET EIGENCOLUMNS.
```

```
      CALL ZERO(N*N,B)
      DO 10 I=1,L
      ZI=ZEROS(ICOL,IP)**(I-1)
      DO 10 K=1,N
      DO 10 J=1,N
   10 B(J,K,1)=B(J,K,1)+S(J,K,I+5)*ZI
      CALL RITE(2,N,N,1,B)
C     FORM MATRIX Q OF EIGENCOLUMNS AND STORE IN
C    1S(1,1,3).
      CALL MOVE(N,B,S(1,ICOL,3))
C     FORM DIAGONAL MATRIX D WITH -1./ZERO AND
C    1STORE IN S(1,1,4).
      S(ICOL,ICOL,4)=-1./ZEROS(ICOL,IP)
C     FORM IDENTITY MATRIX I AND STORE IN S(1,1,1).
   20 S(ICOL,ICOL,1)=1.0
C     FORM Q**-1 AND STORE IN S(1,1.5).
      CALL MAINV(N,S(1,1,3),S(1,1,5))
C     FORM Q*D*Q**-1 AND STORE IN S(1,1,2).
      CALL BRAINY(N,N,1,S(1,1,3),N,N,1,S(1,1,4),B)
      CALL BRAINY(N,N,1,B,N,N,1,S(1,1,5),S(1,1,2))
      CALL RITE(2,N,N,5,S)
C     STORE MATRIX Q*D*Q**-1 IN B ARRAY.
      I=NP-IP+2
      CALL MOVE(N*N,S(1,1,2),B(1,1,I))
C     NEW FACTOR = (I+Z*Q*D*Q**-1) = (I+Z*B)
C     FORM NEW FACTOR*(PREVIOUS FACTORS*ADJUGATE)
C    1AND STORE IN S(1,1,6).
      CALL BRAINY(N,N,2,S,N,N,L,S(1,1,6),S(1,1,L+6))
   30 CALL MOVE(N*N*(L+1),S(1,1,L+6),S(1,1,6))
      CALL MOVE(N*N,A,B)
      RETURN
      END
```

The purpose of the three CALL RITE statements in the above program is to print intermediate results; these three statements can be deleted in the final version of the program.

5

Multichannel Digital
Filtering and Spectral Analysis

5.1 Multichannel operators

Time series, or data generated sequentially in time, are observed in nearly all branches of science, arts, and commerce; time series occur in such diverse forms as weather recordings, prices on the New York Stock Exchange, the EKG recordings of the human heart, and musical recordings. Time series have been exhaustively studied over the years from many angles and by many different sorts of people. The rewards can be enormous; the penalties of careless analysis can be severe. People have sought, and continue constantly to seek, safe and sure methods of appraising the information contained in time series. There have been many failures; however, this intensive research has not been fruitless, although usually it has been inaccessible to the ultimate user of the information. But now for the first time, the digital computer makes it possible for the person who wants to use the results of time series analysis to carry out his analysis himself. The digital computer has eliminated the need for the middlemen who have always stood between the source of information as represented by the time series and the ultimate consequences of this information. The true value of this new aspect of time series analysis cannot be overestimated.

An example may be of some interest. The oil exploration geophysicist records seismic information in the form of time series and interprets this information. Until recently, this process was done by fixed analog methods, so the working geophysicist was completely dependent in his results on the analog recording equipment and the special purpose analog filtering equipment which was supplied to him. Except by an involved and expensive trial and error process in which new equipment was designed over the years, the geophysicist had very limited control over the type of filtering operation which he could apply to the data in any given instance. With the advent of digital recording, the geophysicist can now record a much broader band of seismic information; he can then digitally filter and re-filter this information on a general purpose digital computer. As a result, he can design filters himself based upon the data at hand and his present needs; he can alter the design of a filter in a matter of minutes by a programming change; he can incorporate his own ideas into the analysis and see the results immediately. The digital computer has closed the gap between data collection and the final interpretation; it has multiplied the intellectual power of the worker even as the engine multiplied his physical power.

In the course of years, two quite distinct schools of time series analysis have arisen; one of these is commonly referred to as the *fundamental*, and the other as the *technical*. In chapter 3, we examined physical models of wave propagation; this represents a fundamental approach to the problem of analyzing the time series of wave motion. However, by and large, the present volume is concerned with the interplay of the fundamental and the technical. Technical analysis refers to the processing of time series by methods which make use of the actual history of the data itself; it assumes that the information flow over the course of time is determined definitely and inexorably by various forces which are accurately reflected in the time series themselves. Of course, the worth of the information provided by the fundamentalists is freely admitted, and as much of this information should be incorporated into the technical analysis as possible. Still there are many other factors affecting the movement of the time series; in fact, there are factors which defy analysis and for which no fundamental information is obtainable, but which are nevertheless all synthesized, weighed, and finally expressed in the figures making up the values of the time series.

As an example of the use of a combined fundamental–technical approach, let us refer back to the method of prediction deconvolution given in Sec. 2.10. The recorded seismogram expresses information on the deep geological structure; however, this information is masked by reverberations. A fundamental analysis ascertains that these reverberations represent dynamic motion of the minimum-delay type. As a result, these dynamics can be evaluated and removed from the time series by a strictly technical approach; the result is a reverberation-free record which gives a much clearer picture of the desired information as to the deep structure. The constant interplay between the fundamental approach and the technical approach yields results which are inaccessible by either approach alone.

Many systems of interest have multiple inputs and multiple outputs; such systems are called *multichannel systems* where each input represents an input channel and each output represents an output channel. The analysis of a multichannel system represents a formidable task; for this reason, techniques for handling such problems have made use of matrix methods in order to deal with the large number of variables entering into the problem. In particular, the matrix approach expedites the programming of the mathematical methods on a computer; the use of a computer is almost essential for the calculation and control of the interrelated effects of a multichannel system. In addition, the matrix approach aids in the conceptual thinking about these problems and provides a unified basis for the consideration of both linear and nonlinear systems.

Certain basic problems appear in the analysis of any system, regardless of its nature, composition, and complexity. The problems are:

(1) Identification of the relevant attributes of the objects making up the system,

(2) Formation of a system of mathematical relations for these attributes.

The viewpoint of system theory is that the emphasis is placed not on the physical identity of the attributes associated with a system but on the mathematical relations among the attributes.

A multichannel system generates many time series; these time series are interrelated. A multichannel operator acts upon all these time series simultaneously, and thus it can take advantage of the structure between different time series as well as along a single time series. The theory of multichannel discrete operators (of filters) conceptually is the same as the theory of single-channel discrete operators; mathematically it represents the extension from ordinary (scalar) algebra to matrix algebra. That is, multichannel theory can be obtained from single-channel theory by the appropriate substitution of matrices for scalars. A multichannel operator is one with several input channels and several output channels. In the case where there is the same number of input channels as output channels, we need deal only with square matrices and vectors, where the order of a matrix or a vector is equal to the number of channels. If the number of input channels is different from the number of output channels, then we must deal with rectangular matrices.

We treat the case where there are the same number of output channels as input channels; we designate the number of channels by the letter p. The basic convolution formula for the action of the multichannel operator is

$$y_t = a_0 x_t + a_1 x_{t-1} + \cdots + a_m x_{t-m},$$

where t is an integer denoting the discrete time index, x_t is the input at time t, y_t is the output at time t, and

$$(a_0, a_1, \ldots, a_m)$$

denotes the set of operator coefficients. The input x_t and output y_t for a fixed t each are $p \times 1$ column vectors, and any given filter coefficient a_s is a $p \times p$ constant square matrix. Multichannel convolution can be computed by subroutine BRAINY given in Sec. 4.4.

The z-transform of a multichannel operator is formed in the same way as in the single-channel case, except that now the z-transform is a matrix polynominal (*cf.* Chapter 4). The z-transform of the multichannel operator $(a_0, a_1, \ldots, a_m)$ where each coefficient a_s is a $p \times p$ constant matrix is the $p \times p$ matrix polynomial

$$A(z) = a_0 + a_1 z + \cdots + a_m z^m .$$

As a numerical example, let us consider a discrete multichannel operator with two input channels and two output channels. In this case the input and output may be represented by the 2×1 column vectors:

$$\text{input} = x_t = \begin{bmatrix} x_{1t} \\ x_{2t} \end{bmatrix}, \quad \text{output} = y_t = \begin{bmatrix} y_{1t} \\ y_{2t} \end{bmatrix},$$

and the operator coefficients may be represented by the 2×2 square matrices:

$$a_0 = \begin{bmatrix} 2 & 1 \\ 0 & 6 \end{bmatrix}, \quad a_1 = \begin{bmatrix} 1 & 0 \\ 1 & 1 \end{bmatrix}.$$

The convolution formula relating input x_t and output y_t is in this case

$$y_t = a_0 x_t + a_1 x_{t-1}$$

or

$$\begin{bmatrix} y_{1t} \\ y_{2t} \end{bmatrix} = \begin{bmatrix} 2 & 1 \\ 0 & 6 \end{bmatrix} \begin{bmatrix} x_{1t} \\ x_{2t} \end{bmatrix} + \begin{bmatrix} 1 & 0 \\ 1 & 1 \end{bmatrix} \begin{bmatrix} x_{1,t-1} \\ x_{2,t-1} \end{bmatrix}.$$

The z-transform of the operator is

$$A(z) = \begin{bmatrix} 2 & 1 \\ 0 & 6 \end{bmatrix} + \begin{bmatrix} 1 & 0 \\ 1 & 1 \end{bmatrix} z .$$

This equation exhibits the z-transform as a polynomial with matrix coefficients. Combining terms, we may write $A(z)$ as

$$A(z) = \begin{bmatrix} 2 + z & 1 \\ z & 6 + z \end{bmatrix}.$$

This equation exhibits the *z*-transform as a matrix with polynomial entries. Both of these ways of looking at A(*z*) will prove valuable at one time or another.

The determinant, adjugate, and inverse of a matrix with polynomial entries can be defined in a way entirely analogous to scalar-valued matrices (*cf.* Sec. 4.5). Given A(*z*), we denote its determinant by det A(*z*), its adjugate by adj A(*z*), and its inverse by A^{-1}(*z*). For the above example, these quantities may be computed easily by subroutine POMAIN given in Sec. 4.6. The call statement is

$$\text{CALL POMAIN(N,LA,A,ADJ,P,DET,S)}$$

with subroutine inputs given by

$$N = 2$$
$$LA = 2$$
$$A = (2.0, 0.0, 1.0, 6.0, 1.0, 1.0, 0.0, 1.0) .$$

The resulting subroutine outputs are

$$ADJ = (6.0, 0.0, -1.0, 2.0, 1.0, -1.0, 0.0, 1.0)$$
$$P \quad \text{(not required in this example)}$$
$$DET = (12.0, 7.0, 1.0)$$
$$S \quad \text{(not required in this example)} .$$

Note that

$$LADJ = (N-1) * (LA-1) + 1 = 2$$
$$LDET = N * (LA-1) + 1 = 3 .$$

Thus we have computed

$$\det A(z) = 12 + 7z + z^2$$

and

$$\text{adj } A(z) = \begin{bmatrix} 6 + z & -1 \\ -z & 2 + z \end{bmatrix}$$

from which it follows that the inverse is

$$A^{-1}(z) = \frac{\text{adj } A(z)}{\det A(z)} = \frac{1}{12 + 7z + z^2} \begin{bmatrix} 6 + z & -1 \\ -z & 2 + z \end{bmatrix} .$$

In the classification of the delay properties of a multichannel operator, the determinant of A(*z*) plays a central role. This determinant, namely, det A(*z*), is a scalar-valued polynomial in *z*. *If* det A(*z*) *represents a single-channel minimum-delay operator, then the parent multichannel operator* A(*z*) *is also called minimum delay. On the other hand, if* det A(*z*) *represents a single-channel maximum-delay operator, then the parent multichannel operator* A(*z*) *is also called maximum delay. Finally, if* det $A(z)$ *represents a single-channel mixed-delay operator, then the parent multichannel operator* $A(z)$ *is also called mixed delay.*

In our example, we see that

$$\det A(z) = (3 + z)(4 + z)$$

which has zeros $z_1 = -3$ and $z_2 = -4$, both of which lie outside the unit circle; hence det $A(z)$ and therefore $A(z)$ are each minimum delay.

Hence the theory of multichannel discrete operators can be regarded as the matrix-valued counterpart of single-channel discrete operator theory. The essential difference in programming multichannel operations on a digital computer is that we now deal with discrete operators whose coefficients are matrices instead of scalars. Single-channel concepts, such as autocorrelation, cross correlation, and convolution are the same in the multichannel case, except that now the digital computer must be programmed to carry out matrix multiplication instead of scalar multiplication, matrix addition instead of scalar addition, matrix inversion instead of scalar division, etc., and that we must be careful to take into account the special features of matrix algebra, such as the fact that matrix multiplication is not commutative as is scalar multiplication.

5.2 Inverse of a multichannel operator

In this section we wish to establish the basic conditions for the stability of the inverse of a multichannel finite-length discrete operator. The z-transform of the inverse operator is $A^{-1}(z)$, given by

$$A^{-1}(z) = \text{adj } A(z)[1/\det A(z)] .$$

Since adj $A(z)$ is necessarily a matrix with polynomial entries, it follows that adj $A(z)$ represents a finite-length realizable discrete operator. To obtain $A^{-1}(z)$ we see that each term in adj $A(z)$ is multiplied by $1/\det A(z)$. Hence the stability of the inverse operator $A^{-1}(z)$ depends entirely on the stability of the single-channel operator $1/\det A(z)$. But the single-channel operator $1/\det A(z)$ is the inverse of the single-channel operator with z-transform det $A(z)$. Now from Sec. 2.4, we know that the inverse of a single-channel operator can be represented by a stable minimum-delay realizable function, provided the single-channel operator is minimum delay. Likewise, the inverse can be represented by a stable purely nonrealizable function, provided the single-channel operator is maximum delay; the inverse can be represented by a stable function involving both a realizable component and a purely nonrealizable component, provided the single-channel operator is mixed delay.

From this we can conclude that the inverse of a multichannel operator $A(z)$ can be represented by a stable matrix-valued minimum-delay realizable function, provided the single-channel filter det $A(z)$ is minimum delay; the inverse of $A(z)$ can be represented by a stable matrix-valued purely non-realizable function, provided det $A(z)$ is maximum delay; the inverse of $A(z)$ can be represented by a stable matrix-valued function with both a realizable component and a purely nonrealizable component, provided det $A(z)$ is mixed delay. Hence we call the multichannel filter $A(z)$ minimum delay, maximum delay, or mixed delay, provided that the single-channel filter det $A(z)$ is minimum delay, maximum delay, or mixed delay, respectively.

Thus exactly as we do in the case of single-channel theory, we can make the following statements for the multichannel case: *A minimum-delay multichannel discrete operator has a multichannel inverse that is also a minimum-delay (and hence realizable) multichannel operator. A maximum-delay multichannel discrete operator has a multichannel inverse that is a stable but purely nonrealizable function. A mixed-delay multichannel discrete operator has a stable inverse, this inverse being composed of a realizable component and a nonrealizable component.*

It is worthwhile to exhibit the general structure of the inverse of a multichannel finite-length operator $A(z)$. To do so we write the relationship among $A(z)$, adj $A(z)$, and det $A(z)$ as

$$[\text{adj } A(z)]A(z) = I \text{ det } A(z) , \tag{1}$$

where I is the $p \times p$ identity matrix. The determinantal equation of the polynomial matrix $A(z)$ is defined as

$$\text{det } A(z) = 0 .$$

Now det $A(z)$ is a polynomial of degree of at most n, where n is defined as equal to mp. For the sake of simplicity of notation and clarity of exposition, we assume that the determinantal equation has n distinct roots, which we denote by

$$z_1, z_2, \ldots, z_n \quad (\text{where } n = mp) .$$

Hence det $A(z)$ may be written in factored form as

$$\text{det } A(z) = c(z - z_1)(z - z_2) \ldots (z - z_n) , \tag{2}$$

where c is a constant. From eq. (1) we obtain

$$[\text{adj } A(z_i)]A(z_i) = 0 , \tag{3}$$

where 0 in this equation denotes a $p \times p$ matrix of zeros. Now adj $A(z_i)$ can be written as the product of a column vector c_i, and a row vector r_i as described in Sec. 4.8; that is,

$$\text{adj } A(z_i) = c_i r_i .$$

Hence eq. (3) becomes

$$c_i r_i A(z_i) = 0 \,,$$

where again 0 denotes a $p \times p$ zero matrix. From this equation it follows that

$$r_i A(z_i) = 0 \,,$$

where 0 here denotes a $1 \times p$ row vector of zeros. Because of this equation we may call r_i the eigen-row-vector of the polynomial matrix $A(z)$ corresponding to the eigenvalue z_i.

Again returning to the relationship among $A(z)$, adj $A(z)$, and det $A(z)$, we may write

$$A(z)[\text{adj } A(z)] = I \det A(z) \,, \tag{4}$$

from which it follows that

$$A(z_i)[\text{adj } A(z_i)] = 0 \,,$$

where 0 denotes a $p \times p$ zero matrix. Again writing adj $A(z_i)$ as $c_i r_i$, we obtain

$$A(z_i) c_i r_i = 0 \,,$$

where 0 denotes the $p \times p$ zero matrix. From this equation it follows as before that

$$A(z_i) c_i = 0 \,,$$

where 0 denotes a $p \times 1$ column vector of zeros. Hence we may call c_i the eigen-column-vector of the polynomial matrix $A(z)$ corresponding to the eigenvalue z_i.

Returning to our numerical example given in Sec. 5.1, let us substitute the eigenvalue $z_1 = -3$ for z in adj $A(z)$. We obtain

$$\text{adj } A(z_1) = \text{adj } A(-3) = \begin{bmatrix} 3 & -1 \\ 3 & -1 \end{bmatrix} = \begin{bmatrix} 1 \\ 1 \end{bmatrix} [3 \quad -1] \,,$$

so the eigenvectors are

$$c_1 = \begin{bmatrix} 1 \\ 1 \end{bmatrix}, \quad r_1 = [3 \quad -1] \,.$$

Likewise, for the eigenvalue $z_2 = -4$, we find that

$$\text{adj } A(z_2) = \text{adj } A(-4) = \begin{bmatrix} 2 & -1 \\ 4 & -2 \end{bmatrix} = \begin{bmatrix} 1 \\ 2 \end{bmatrix} [2 \quad -1] \,,$$

so the eigenvectors are

$$c_2 = \begin{bmatrix} 1 \\ 2 \end{bmatrix}, \quad r_2 = [2 \quad -1] \,.$$

Recalling that $A^{-1}(z) = \text{adj } A(z)/\det A(z)$ and using eq. (2), we may write the z-transform of the inverse multichannel discrete operator as

$$A^{-1}(z) = \frac{\text{adj } A(z)}{c(z - z_1)(z - z_2) \cdots (z - z_n)}.$$

This may be expanded in partial fractions as

$$A^{-1}(z) = \frac{u_1}{z - z_1} + \frac{u_2}{z - z_2} + \cdots + \frac{u_n}{z - z_n},$$

where $u_1, u_2, \ldots, u_n$ are each $p \times p$ matrices. To determine u_1, we multiply both sides of the equation by $z - z_1$, and then set $z = z_1$, thereby obtaining

$$u_1 = \frac{\text{adj } A(z_1)}{c(z_1 - z_2)(z_1 - z_3) \cdots (z_1 - z_n)}.$$

If we define α_1 as

$$\alpha_1 = \frac{1}{c(z_1 - z_2)(z_1 - z_3) \cdots (z_1 - z_n)}$$

and recall that $\text{adj } A(z_1) = c_1 r_1$, then we have

$$u_1 = \alpha_1 c_1 r_1.$$

In a similar fashion, we may define $\alpha_2, \alpha_3, \ldots, \alpha_n$. Hence the partial fraction expansion of the inverse filter is

$$A^{-1}(z) = \frac{\alpha_1 c_1 r_1}{z - z_1} + \frac{\alpha_2 c_2 r_2}{z - z_2} + \cdots + \frac{\alpha_n c_n r_n}{z - z_n},$$

where z_i, c_i, and r_i are the respective eigenvalues, eigen-column-vectors, and eigen-row-vectors of the polynomial matrix $A(z)$.

In our numerical example, we have

$$\alpha_1 = \frac{1}{z_1 - z_2} = 1, \quad \alpha_2 = \frac{1}{z_2 - z_1} = -1,$$

so the partial fraction expansion of the inverse operator is

$$A^{-1}(z) = \frac{1}{z + 3} \begin{bmatrix} 1 \\ 1 \end{bmatrix} \begin{bmatrix} 3 & -1 \end{bmatrix} - \frac{1}{z + 4} \begin{bmatrix} 1 \\ 2 \end{bmatrix} \begin{bmatrix} 2 & -1 \end{bmatrix}.$$

If $|z_i| > 1$, the fraction $1/(z - z_i)$ can be expanded in a stable series of non-negative powers of z, namely, the series

$$\frac{1}{z - z_i} = -z_i^{-1} - z_i^{-2}z - z_i^{-3}z^2 - \cdots.$$

Hence if all the eigenvalues z_i are greater than unity in magnitude, then the inverse system $A^{-1}(z)$ can be expanded in a stable series of non-negative powers of z; that is,

$$A^{-1}(z) = \sum_{i=1}^{n} \alpha_i c_i r_i (-z_i^{-1} - z_i^{-2} z - z_i^{-3} z^2 - \cdots).$$

But the eigenvalues z_i are the roots of the characteristic equation det $A(z) = 0$, and hence these eigenvalues will all be greater than unity in magnitude, provided that det $A(z)$ represents a single-channel minimum-delay operator. Thus this is precisely the case when det $A(z)$ and hence $A(z)$ represent minimum-delay operators with inverses that can be represented by stable realizable functions. In our numerical example, both eigenvalues exceed unity in magnitude, so that the operator is minimum delay. Its inverse has the representation

$$A^{-1}(z) = \begin{bmatrix} 1 \\ 1 \end{bmatrix} \begin{bmatrix} 3 & -1 \end{bmatrix} \left(\frac{1}{3} - \frac{1}{9} z + \frac{1}{27} z^2 - \cdots \right)$$
$$- \begin{bmatrix} 1 \\ 2 \end{bmatrix} \begin{bmatrix} 2 & -1 \end{bmatrix} \left(\frac{1}{4} - \frac{1}{16} z + \frac{1}{64} z^2 - \cdots \right).$$

If $|z_i| < 1$, the fraction $1/(z - z_i)$ can be expanded in a stable series of negative powers of z, namely, the series

$$\frac{1}{z - z_i} = z^{-1} + z_i z^{-2} + z_i^2 z^{-3} + \cdots.$$

If all the eigenvalues are less than unity in magnitude, then the multichannel filter is maximum delay; its inverse can be represented by a stable purely nonrealizable function; here we make use of the expansion of $1/(z - z_i)$ given above for each z_i. If some of the eigenvalues are greater than unity in magnitude, while the others are less than unity in magnitude, then we must make use of one or the other of the two expansions of $1/(z - z_i)$ for each z_i, depending on the magnitude of z_i. This is the case of $A(z)$ being mixed delay; its inverse can be expressed as a stable function involving both a realizable component and a purely nonrealizable component.

5.3 Autocorrelation of the inverse multichannel operator

In the previous section, we saw that the inverse of the p-channel operator

$$A(z) = a_0 + a_1 z + \cdots + a_m z^m$$

is

$$A^{-1}(z) = \sum_{i=1}^{n} \frac{\alpha_i c_i r_i}{z - z_i},$$

where $n = mp$. Hence the autocorrelation ϕ_t of the inverse multichannel operator has the z-transform

$$\Phi(z) = \sum_{t=-\infty}^{\infty} \phi_t z^t = A^{-1}(z) A_*^{-1}(z), \tag{1}$$

where $A_*^{-1}(z)$ is given by

$$A_*^{-1}(z) = [A^{-1}(1/z^*)]^{*\mathrm{T}} = \left[\sum_{j=1}^{n} \frac{\alpha_j c_j r_j}{(1/z^*) - z_j} \right]^{*\mathrm{T}}$$

$$= \sum_{j=1}^{n} \frac{\alpha_j^* r_j^{*\mathrm{T}} c_j^{*\mathrm{T}}}{z^{-1} - z_j^*}.$$

Thus we have

$$\Phi(z) = \sum_{i=1}^{n} \sum_{j=1}^{n} (\alpha_i \alpha_j^*) c_i (r_i r_j^{*\mathrm{T}}) c_j^{*\mathrm{T}} \frac{1}{(z - z_i)(z^{-1} - z_j^*)}, \qquad (2)$$

where $\alpha_i \alpha_j^*$ is a scalar, and $r_i r_j^{*\mathrm{T}}$, which is the product of a row with a column, is a scalar. Let us make use of the partial fraction expansion

$$\frac{1}{(z - z_i)(z^{-1} - z_j^*)} = \frac{1}{z_i z_j^* - 1} \left[\frac{1}{1 - (z/z_i)} + \frac{(z^{-1}/z_j^*)}{1 - (z^{-1}/z_j^*)} \right],$$

which in the case when the multichannel operator is minimum delay (i.e., when all the roots $z_1, z_2, \ldots, z_n$ have magnitude greater than unity) gives the convergent expansion

$$\frac{1}{(z - z_i)(z^{-1} - z_j^*)} = \frac{1}{z_i z_j^* - 1} \left[\sum_{s=1}^{\infty} \left(\frac{z^{-1}}{z_j^*} \right)^s + \sum_{t=0}^{\infty} \left(\frac{z}{z_i} \right)^t \right]. \qquad (3)$$

Substituting eq. (3) into eq. (2) and comparing the result with eq. (1), we see that the autocorrelation coefficient ϕ_t is given by

$$\phi_t = \sum_{i=1}^{n} \sum_{j=1}^{n} \frac{\alpha_i \alpha_j^* c_i (r_i r_j^{*\mathrm{T}}) c_j^{*\mathrm{T}}}{(z_i z_j^* - 1)} \frac{1}{z_i^t} = \sum_{i=1}^{n} \frac{c_i}{z_i^t} \left[\sum_{j=1}^{n} \frac{(\alpha_i \alpha_j^*)(r_i r_j^{*\mathrm{T}})}{z_i z_j^* - 1} c_j^{*\mathrm{T}} \right]$$

for $t = 0, 1, 2, \ldots$. The quantity in square brackets in the above equation is a row vector; if we call this row vector $\gamma_i^{*\mathrm{T}}$, then we have

$$\phi_t = \sum_{i=1}^{n} \frac{c_i \gamma_i^{*\mathrm{T}}}{z_i^t}$$

for $t = 0, 1, 2, \ldots$. Likewise, we find that

$$\phi_{-s} = \sum_{j=1}^{n} \frac{\gamma_j c_i^{*\mathrm{T}}}{z_j^s}$$

for $s = 1, 2, 3, \ldots$, from which we can verify

$$\phi_{-s} = \phi_s^{*\mathrm{T}}$$

for $s = 1, 2, 3, \ldots$. In matrix form, the autocorrelation coefficient ϕ_t may be written as

$$\phi_t = CZ^{-t}\Gamma^{*T} \qquad \text{for } t = 0, 1, 2, \ldots,$$

where

$$C = [c_1, c_2, \ldots, c_n]$$

is the $p \times n$ matrix made up of the columns vectors c_i for $i = 1, 2, \ldots, n$, where

$$Z = \text{diag} [z_1, z_2, \ldots, z_n]$$

is the $n \times n$ diagonal matrix of the roots $z_1, z_2, \ldots, z_n$, and where

$$\Gamma = [\gamma_1, \gamma_2, \ldots, \gamma_n]$$

is the $p \times n$ matrix made up of the column vectors γ_i. Likewise, we have

$$\phi_{-s} = \Gamma Z^{-s} C^{*T} \qquad \text{for } s = 1, 2, 3, \ldots.$$

5.4 Minimum-delay factorization of the multichannel spectrum

Given the p-channel spectral (or autocorrelation) matrix

$$\Psi(z) = \sum_{s=-m}^{m} r_s z^s,$$

where the $p \times p$ matrices r_s are the autocorrelation coefficients, we wish to determine the p-channel minimum-delay operator

$$A(z) = a_0 + a_1 z + \cdots + a_m z^m,$$

such that

$$\Psi(z) = A(z)A_*(z).$$

This problem is the multichannel counterpart of the single-channel spectral factorization given in Sec. 2.9. From Sec. 4.7 we recall that $A_*(z)$ is defined as

$$A_*(z) = [A(1/z^*)]^{*T}$$
$$= a_0^{*T} + a_1^{*T}z^{-1} + \cdots + a_m^{*T}z^{-m}.$$

From the extended hermitian property of $\Psi(z)$, we have

$$\sum_{s=-m}^{m} r_s z^s = \left[\sum_{s=-m}^{m} r_s(1/z^*)^s \right]^{*T}$$
$$= \sum_{s=-m}^{m} r_s^{*T} z^{-s},$$

which gives

$$r_{-s} = r_s^{*T} .$$

In the special case when the r_s are real matrices, this reduces simply to

$$r_{-s} = r_s^{T} .$$

Before discussing the general case of factoring the multichannel power transfer function in order to obtain its corresponding multichannel minimum-delay operator, let us consider a numerical example. Let us suppose $\Psi(z)$ is given as

$$\Psi(z) = \begin{bmatrix} 2z^{-1} + 6 + 2z & 3 + 7z \\ 7z^{-1} + 3 & 6z^{-1} + 38 + 6z \end{bmatrix}.$$

We wish to find a minimum-delay operator (a_0, a_1) such that

$$\Psi(z) = (a_0 + a_1 z)(a_0^{*T} + a_1^{*T} z^{-1}) .$$

From $\Psi(z)$ we may readily compute the adjugate and determinant as

$$\text{adj } \Psi(z) = \begin{bmatrix} 6z^{-1} + 38 + 6z & -3 - 7z \\ -7z^{-1} - 3 & 2z^{-1} + 6 + 2z \end{bmatrix}$$
$$\det \Psi(z) = 12z^{-2} + 91z^{-1} + 194 + 91z + 12z^2 .$$

Next we wish to factor $\det \Psi(z)$ into binomial factors. (*Note.* The quasi-polynomial $\det \Psi(z)$ can be reduced to a polynomial of one-half the degree by the substitution $z + z^{-1} = u$, thereby reducing the computation required for the factorization.) The result of the factorization is

$$\det \Psi(z) = (z + 3)(z + 4)(3 + z^{-1})(4 + z^{-1}) ,$$

so that the roots of $\det \Psi(z) = 0$ are

$$z_1 = -3, \; z_2 = -4, \; z_3 = -\frac{1}{3}, \; z_4 = -\frac{1}{4} .$$

In order to obtain the minimum-delay factorization we are required to choose those roots which lie outside the unit circle, namely, $z_1 = -3$ and $z_2 = -4$. Substituting, one by one, these roots into $\text{adj } \Psi(z)$, we obtain the equations

$$\text{adj } \Psi(-3) = \begin{bmatrix} 18 & 18 \\ -\frac{2}{3} & -\frac{2}{3} \end{bmatrix} = \begin{bmatrix} 1 \\ -\frac{1}{27} \end{bmatrix} [18 \qquad 18] = c_1 r_1$$

$$\text{adj } \Psi(-4) = \begin{bmatrix} 12.50 & 25.00 \\ -1.25 & -2.50 \end{bmatrix} = \begin{bmatrix} 1 \\ -0.1 \end{bmatrix} [12.5 \qquad 25] = c_2 r_2$$

which define the column vectors c_1 and c_2 and the row vectors r_1 and r_2. We then form the matrix

$$R = \begin{bmatrix} r_1 \\ r_2 \end{bmatrix} = \begin{bmatrix} 18 & 18 \\ 12.5 & 25 \end{bmatrix}$$

and the diagonal matrix

$$D = \begin{bmatrix} 1/z_1 & 0 \\ 0 & 1/z_2 \end{bmatrix} = \begin{bmatrix} -\frac{1}{3} & 0 \\ 0 & -\frac{1}{4} \end{bmatrix}$$

from which we compute

$$u = R^{-1} DR = \begin{bmatrix} -\frac{5}{12} & -\frac{1}{6} \\ \frac{1}{12} & -\frac{1}{6} \end{bmatrix}.$$

By construction the matrix u satisfies

$$\Psi(z) = (I - uz) \, a_0 a_0^{*T} (I - u^{*T} z^{-1}).$$

(Since u is real, we may drop the superscript $*$ on the u.) Next we want to determine $a_0 a_0^{*T}$. By letting $z = 1$, we have

$$\Psi(1) = (I - u) a_0 a_0^{*T} (I - u^T)$$

which gives

$$a_0 a_0^{*T} = (I - u)^{-1} \Psi(1)(I - u^T)^{-1} = \begin{bmatrix} 4 & 2 \\ 2 & 37 \end{bmatrix}.$$

If c is any arbitrary unitary matrix (i.e., $cc^{*T} = I$), then we see that

$$(a_0 c)(a_0 c)^{*T} = \begin{bmatrix} 4 & 2 \\ 2 & 37 \end{bmatrix},$$

and hence the matrix a_0 is determined, except for the arbitrary unitary post-multiplier c. In particular, therefore, the matrix a_0 can be chosen to be a triangular matrix, thereby leading to a causal-chain system.[43] Such a choice gives

$$a_0 = \begin{bmatrix} 2 & 0 \\ 1 & 6 \end{bmatrix}.$$

Hence we may compute

$$a_0 + a_1 z = (I - uz) a_0$$

so that the required minimum-delay causal-chain operator is

$$a_0 = \begin{bmatrix} 2 & 0 \\ 1 & 6 \end{bmatrix}, \quad a_1 = -u a_0 = \begin{bmatrix} 1 & 1 \\ 0 & 1 \end{bmatrix}.$$

In summary, then, the multichannel factorization method is as follows. Given $\Psi(z)$, we wish to find a minimum-delay $A(z)$ such that

$$\Psi(z) = A(z) A_*(z).$$

Write $A(z)$ in the factored form as

$$A(z) = (I - u_1 z)(I - u_2 z) \cdots (I - u_m z) a_0.$$

---

[43] Wold, H., and L. Juréen, *Demand Analysis*, Wiley, New York, 1953.

Hence

$$\Psi(z) = (I - u_1 z) \cdots (I - u_m z) a_0 a_0^{*T} (I - u_m^{*T} z^{-1}) \ldots (I - u_1^{*T} z^{-1}).$$

Next premultiply by $\Psi^{-1}(z)$ det $\Psi(z) = $ adj $\Psi(z)$; this yields

$$I \text{ det } \Psi(z) = \text{adj } \Psi(z)(I - u_1 z) \cdots (I - u_m z) a_0 a_0^{*T} (I - u_m^{*T} z^{-1}) \ldots (I - u_1^{*T} z^{-1}).$$

Now the number of zeros of the quasi-polynomial det $\Psi(z)$ is 2 mp. Moreover, because

$$\text{det } \Psi(z) = \text{det } A(z) \text{ det } A_*(z)$$

we see that if z_i is a zero of det $\Psi(z)$, then $1/z_i^*$ is also a zero. As in the single-channel case discussed in Sec. 2.9, one of this pair of zeros goes into the construction of $A(z)$ and the other into the construction of $A_*(z)$, and the choice is arbitrary for each of the mp pairs of zeros of det $\Psi(z)$. As a result, there will be 2^{mp} multichannel factorizations if we exclude the case of zeros on the unit circle and other multiple zeros. In order to obtain the minimum-delay factorization we choose those zeros which are greater than unity in magnitude. At a zero z_i the adjugate factors into the product of a column c_i and a row r_i, that is

$$\text{adj } \Psi(z_i) = c_i r_i ,$$

which gives

$$0 = c_i r_i (I - u_1 z_i) \cdots (I - u_m z_i) a_0 a_0^{*T} (I - u_m^{*T} z_i^{-1}) \ldots (I - u_1^{*T} z_i^{-1}).$$

Thus we have

$$r_i (I - u_1 z_i) = 0 ,$$

and using this equation for the first p zeros (i.e., $i = 1, 2, \ldots, p$), we may determine u_1, as we did in the numerical example. At the remaining zeros $z = z_i$, the factor adj $\Psi(z)(I - u_1 z)$ also becomes the product of a column and a row, and hence we may use the same procedure with the next p zeros (i.e., $i = p + 1, p + 2, \ldots, 2p$) and thus determine u_2. Likewise, we can then consecutively determine $u_3, \ldots, u_m$, thereby exhausting the mp zeros which have magnitude greater than one. Finally we determine a_0 as we did in the numerical example, and hence we obtain the required causal-chain minimum-delay operator:

$$A(z) = (I - u_1 z)(I - u_2 z) \cdots (I - u_m z) a_0$$
$$= a_0 + a_1 z + a_2 z^2 + \cdots + a_m z^m .$$

Given the multichannel operator $(b_0, b_1, \ldots, b_m)$ where each coefficient is a $p \times p$ matrix, subroutine FACTOR finds the causal-chain minimum-delay multichannel operator $(a_0, a_1, \ldots, a_m)$ which has the same autocorrelation as

$(b_0, b_1, \ldots, b_m)$. Let $(r_{-m}, r_{-m+1}, \ldots, r_{m-1}, r_m)$ denote the autocorrelation of the given operator, that is, let

$$\Psi(z) = B(z)B_*(z) = \sum_{s=-m}^{m} r_s z^s ,$$

where

$$B(z) = b_0 + b_1 z + \cdots + b_m z^m .$$

Then the required operator $(a_0, a_1, \ldots, a_m)$ is the causal-chain minimum-delay operator which satisfies

$$A(z)A_*(z) = \Psi(z) ,$$

where

$$A(z) = a_0 + a_1 z + \cdots + a_m z^m .$$

Subroutine FACTOR makes use of complex arithmetic. As a result, the subroutines which FACTOR calls, as depicted in the tree

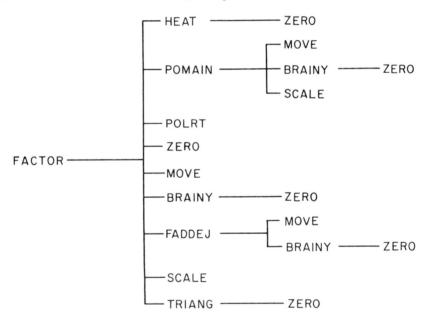

must be the complex versions, except subroutine POLRT, for which special provision is made within subroutine FACTOR. The call statement is

CALL FACTOR(M,N,LR,R,LAJ,AJ,LDETR,DETR,NZR,ZR,
1ZB,LRR,RR,FACT,DIAG,CR,P,PINV,V,TEMP,B,BS,BZ1,RZ1,
2W,BZINV)

As seen, all of the call statement cannot fit onto one card; the three lines represent three cards. The 1 in column 6 of the second card indicates that it is a continuation card, so that the characters in columns 7 through 72 on the second card are considered by the Fortran compiler as being logically adjacent to column 72 of the first card. Likewise, the 2 in column 6 of the third card indicates that it is a continuation card. The subroutine inputs are

$$M = p = \text{number of channels} \qquad (\text{where } p \geqslant 2)$$
$$N = m + 1 = \text{length of given multichannel operator}$$
$$BS = \text{given multichannel operator}$$
$$= (b_0, b_1, \ldots, b_m).$$

The subroutine outputs are

$$LR = \text{length of two-sided autocorrelation} = 2m + 1$$
$$R = \text{two-sided autocorrelation of given multichannel operator}$$
$$= (r_{-m}, r_{-m+1}, \ldots, r_{m-1}, r_m)$$
$$= \text{coefficients of quasi-polynomial matrix } \Psi(z)$$
$$LAJ = 2m(p-1) + 1 = \text{number of coefficients in adj } \Psi(z)$$
$$AJ = \text{coefficients of adj } \Psi(z)$$
$$LDETR = 2mp + 1 = \text{number of coefficients in det } \Psi(z)$$
$$DETR = \text{coefficients of det } \Psi(z)$$
$$NZR = 2mp = \text{number of zeros of det } \Psi(z)$$
$$ZR = \text{zeros of det } \Psi(z)$$
$$= (z_1, z_2, \ldots, z_{2mp})$$
$$ZB = \text{zeros of causal-chain minimum-delay operator}$$
$$(a_0, a_1, \ldots, a_m)$$
$$LRR = 2m(p-1) + m$$
$$RR = \text{working space}$$
$$FACT = \text{working space}$$
$$DIAG = \text{working space}$$
$$CR = \text{working space}$$
$$P = \text{working space}$$
$$PINV = \text{working space}$$
$$V = \text{working space}$$
$$TEMP = \text{working space}$$
$$B = \text{required causal-chain minimum-delay operator}$$
$$= (a_0, a_1, \ldots, a_m)$$
$$BZ1 = \text{working space}$$
$$RZ1 = \text{working space}$$
$$W = \text{working space}$$
$$BZINV = \text{working space}.$$

Let us give two numerical examples of the usage of subroutine **FACTOR**. For the first example, let the subroutine inputs be

$$M = p = 2$$
$$N = m + 1 = 3$$

$$BS = (b_0, b_1, b_2) = \left(\begin{bmatrix} 1 & 0 \\ 0 & 1 \end{bmatrix}, \begin{bmatrix} -3 & 21 \\ 14 & 1 \end{bmatrix}, \begin{bmatrix} 2 & -6 \\ 5 & 14 \end{bmatrix} \right)$$
$$= (1, 0, 0, 1, -3, 14, 21, 1, 2, 5, -6, 14).$$

Then the causal-chain minimum-delay operator which has the same autocorrelation as the given operator (b_0, b_1, b_2) is given as the subroutine output

$$B = (21.05, -1.23, 0, 13.32, -6.33, 13.85, 2.77, 6.87,$$
$$0.10, 0.24, -0.44, 1.07)$$

$$= \left(\begin{bmatrix} 21.05 & 0 \\ -1.23 & 13.32 \end{bmatrix}, \begin{bmatrix} -6.33 & 2.77 \\ 13.85 & 6.87 \end{bmatrix}, \begin{bmatrix} 0.10 & -0.44 \\ 0.24 & 1.07 \end{bmatrix} \right)$$
$$= (a_0, a_1, a_2).$$

For the second example, let the subroutine inputs be

$$M = p = 3$$
$$N = m + 1 = 2$$

$$BS = (b_0, b_1) = \left(\begin{bmatrix} 1 & 0 & 0 \\ 0 & 1 & 0 \\ 0 & 0 & 1 \end{bmatrix}, \begin{bmatrix} 2 & 0 & 0 \\ 3 & 5 & 1 \\ 1 & 2 & 6 \end{bmatrix} \right)$$
$$= (1, 0, 0, 0, 1, 0, 0, 0, 1, 2, 3, 1, 0, 5, 2, 0, 1, 6).$$

Then the required causal-chain minimum-delay multichannel operator is given as the subroutine output

$$B = (1.92, 2.35, 0.73, 0.00, 5.29, 3.14, 0.00, 0.00, 5.52,$$
$$1.04, 1.56, 0.52, -0.46, 0.25, 0.15, 0.12, -0.17, 0.93)$$

$$= \left(\begin{bmatrix} 1.92 & 0.00 & 0.00 \\ 2.35 & 5.29 & 0.00 \\ 0.73 & 3.14 & 5.52 \end{bmatrix}, \begin{bmatrix} 1.04 & -0.46 & 0.12 \\ 1.56 & 0.25 & -0.17 \\ 0.52 & 0.15 & 0.93 \end{bmatrix} \right).$$

Subroutine FACTOR may be modified in several useful ways. For example, if instead of selecting the mp zeros with magnitude greater than unity, one could select the mp zeros with magnitude less than unity and thereby obtain the causal-chain maximum-delay multichannel operator. By other selections of the mp zeros, one could obtain various causal-chain mixed-delay operators. If the given information is not the wavelet $(b_0, b_1, \ldots, b_m)$, but instead the autocorrelation $(r_{-m}, r_{-m+1}, \ldots, r_{m-1}, r_m)$, only a slight modification of FACTOR is necessary in order to obtain the various causal-chain operators with the given autocorrelation. This is a case often met in practice. The program for subroutine FACTOR is given on pp. 197–200.

```
      SUBROUTINE FACTOR(M,N,LR,R,LAJ,AJ,LDETR,DETR,NZR,ZR,ZB,
     1LRR,RR,FACT,DIAG,CR,P,PINV,V,TEMP,B,BS,BZ1,RZ1,W,BZINV)
C     NX= LARGEST VALUE OF NZR TO BE PROCESSED
C     NONDUMMY DIMENSION XCOF(NX+1),COF(NX+1),RZR(NX),CZR(NX)
C     FOR EXAMPLE, IF NX=49 THEN
      DIMENSION XCOF(50),COF(50),RZR(49),CZR(49)
      DIMENSION R(M,M,LR),AJ(M,M,LAJ),DETR(LDETR),ZR(NZR),ZB(M,N-1),
     1RR(M,M,LRR),FACT(M,M,2),DIAG(M,M),CR(M,M),P(M,M),PINV(M,M),V(M,M),
     2TEMP(M,M,LDETR),B(M,M,N),BS(M,M,N),BZ1(M,M),RZ1(M,M),W(M,M),BZINV(M,M)
      DIMENSION R(M,M,1),AJ(M,M,1),DETR(1),ZR(1),ZB(M,1),
     1RR(M,M,1),FACT(M,M,2),DIAG(M,M),CR(M,M),P(M,M),PINV(M,M),V(M,M),
     2TEMP(M,M,1),B(M,M,N),BS(M,M,N),BZ1(M,M),RZ1(M,M),W(M,M),BZINV(M,M)
      COMPLEX R,AJ,DETR,ZR,ZB,RR,FACT,DIAG,CR,P,PINV,V,TEMP,B,BS,BZ1,
     1RZ1,W,BZINV,DETP,DET,ZER,ZI
      N1=N-1
      NZB=N1*M
      LR=N+N1
      LAJ=(M-1)*(LR-1)+1
      LDETR=(LR-1)*M+1
      NZR=2*NZB
      LRR=LAJ+N1
C     COMPUTE ONE SIDE OF AUTOCORRELATION
      CALL HEAT(M,M,N,BS,M,M,N,BS,N,R(1,1,N))
C     GENERATE OTHER SIDE OF AUTOCORRELATION
      DO 10 I=2,N
      JP=N+I-1
      JM=N-I+1
```

```
      DO 10 J=1,M
      DO 10 K=1,M
   10 R(J,K,JM)=R(K,J,JP)
C     FIND ADJUGATE AND DETERMINANT OF R
      CALL POMAIN(M,LR,R,AJ,RR,DETR,TEMP))
C     FIND ZEROS OF DETERMINANT
      DO 14 I=1,LDETR
   14 XCOF(I)=REAL(DETR(I))
      CALL POLRT(XCOF,COF,LDETR-1,RZR,CZR,IER)
      DO 15 I=1,NZR
   15 ZR(I)=CMPLX(RZR(I),CZR(I))
      J=1
      DO 20 I=1,NZR
C     IT IS ASSUMED THAT NO ZERO HAS MAGNITUDE UNITY
      IF(CABS(ZR(I)).LT.1.0) GO TO 20
C     CHOOSE THE ZEROS WITH MAGNITUDE GREATER THAN UNITY TO FORM B.
      DETR(J)=ZR(I)
      J=J+1
   20 CONTINUE
      CALL MOVE(NZB,DETR,ZB)
C     SET B=I ,FACT(J,K,1)=I
      CALL ZERO(M*M,FACT)
      CALL ZERO(M*M,B)
      DO 29 J=1,M
   29 FACT(J,J,1)=1.
      B(J,J,1)=1.0
      LBT=1
```

```
C     SET RR=AJ
      CALL MOVE(LAJ*M*M,AJ,RR)
      LRRT=LAJ
C     LOOP ON THE FACTORS (1−Z*PINV*DIAG*P)
      DO 60 IFACTS=1,N1
C     FORM DIAGONAL MATRIX
      CALL ZERO(M*M,DIAG)
      DO 30 I=1,M
   30 DIAG(I,I)=1./ZB(I,IFACTS)
C     INSERT ZEROS IN RR TO GET EIGENVECTORS
      DO 50 IVECT=1,M
      CALL ZERO(M*M,CR)
      ZER=ZB(IVECT,IFACTS)
      DO 40 I=1,LRRT
      ZI=ZER**(I−1−LAJ/2)
      DO 40 K=1,M
      DO 40 J=1,M
   40 CR(J,K)=CR(J,K)+RR(J,K,I)*ZI
      DO 50 I=1,M
   50 P(IVECT,I)=CR(1,I)
C     FORM PINV*DIAG*P
      CALL BRAINY(M,M,1,DIAG,M,M,1,P,FACT(1,1,2))
      CALL FADDEJ(M,P,PINV,DETP,DIAG,TEMP)
      CALL MOVE(M*M,FACT(1,1,2),P)
      CALL BRAINY(M,M,1,PINV,M,M,1,P,FACT(1,1,2))
      CALL SCALE(−1. , M*M,FACT(1,1,2))
C     SET  RR=RR*(1−Z*PINV*DIAG*P)
```

```
      CALL BRAINY(M,M,LRRT,RR,M,M,2,FACT,TEMP)
      LRRT=LRRT+1
      CALL MOVE(LRRT*M*M,TEMP,RR)
C     SET B=B*(I-FACT)
      CALL BRAINY(M,M,LBT,B,M,M,2,FACT,TEMP)
      LBT=LBT+1
      CALL MOVE(M*M*LBT,TEMP,B)
 60   CONTINUE
      CALL HEAT(M,M,N,B,M,M,N,B,N,TEMP)
C     FORM B(Z=1) AND R(Z=1)
      CALL ZERO (M*M,RZ1)
      CALL ZERO(M*M,BZ1)
      DO 120 J=1,M
      DO 120 K=1,M
      DO 110 I=1,N
 110  BZ1(J,K)=BZ1(J,K)+B(J,K,I)
      DO 120 I=1,LR
 120  RZ1(J,K)=RZ1(J,K)+R(J,K,I)
C     FORM BINV(Z=1)*R(Z=1)*BINVTRANSP(Z=1) = W
      CALL FADDEJ(M,BZ1,BZINV,DET,TEMP,W)
      CALL BRAINY(M,M,1,BZINV,M,M,1,RZ1,TEMP)
      CALL HEAT(M,M,1,TEMP,M,M,1,BZINV,1,W)
C     TRIANGULARIZE W
      CALL TRIANG(M,W,V,TEMP)
C     PUT B IN CAUSAL-CHAIN FORM
      CALL HEAT(M,M,N,B,M,M,1,V,N,TEMP)
      CALL MOVE(M*M*N,TEMP,B)
      CALL HEAT(M,M,N,B,M,N,B,N,TEMP)
      RETURN
      END
```

5.5 *Autocorrelation and cross correlation of multichannel time series*

A *p*-channel stochastic process may be represented by the column vector

$$x_t = \begin{bmatrix} x_1(t) \\ x_2(t) \\ \cdot \\ \cdot \\ \cdot \\ x_p(t) \end{bmatrix},$$

where t denotes the integer-valued time index, and where the element $x_i(t)$ denotes the single-channel process observed on channel number i. The multichannel autocorrelation coefficient for time-shift s is given by the $p \times p$ matrix

$$\phi_s = E\{x_{t+s}\, x_t^T\} = \begin{bmatrix} \phi_{11}(s) & \phi_{12}(s) & \cdots & \phi_{1p}(s) \\ \phi_{21}(s) & \phi_{22}(s) & \cdots & \phi_{2p}(s) \\ \cdots & \cdots & & \cdots \\ \phi_{p1}(s) & \phi_{p2}(s) & \cdots & \phi_{pp}(s) \end{bmatrix},$$

where $\phi_{ij}(s) = E\{x_i(t + s)x_j(t)\}$ is the single-channel autocorrelation when $i = j$ and the single-channel cross correlation when $i \neq j$. The symbol E denotes mathematical expectation. The process is called (covariance) stationary, provided that this autocorrelation matrix depends only upon s, and not upon absolute time t; for this reason we have written only the single subscript s denoting the time shift on the symbol ϕ_s. To indicate explicitly that ϕ_s is the multichannel autocorrelation of x_t we could write $\phi_{xx}(s)$, instead of just ϕ_s.

The cross correlation for time-shift s of two mutually stationary p-channel processes

$$x_t = \begin{bmatrix} x_1(t) \\ \cdot \\ \cdot \\ x_p(t) \end{bmatrix}, \quad y_t = \begin{bmatrix} y_1(t) \\ \cdot \\ \cdot \\ y_p(t) \end{bmatrix}$$

is defined as the $p \times p$ matrix

$$\phi_{xy}(s) = E\{x_{t+s} y_t^T\}.$$

If we let

$$\phi_{x_i y_j}(s) = E\{x_i(t + s)y_j(t)\}$$

denote the single-channel cross-correlation coefficient between the single-channel time series $x_i(t)$ and $y_j(t)$, then the multichannel cross-correlation coefficient is seen to be

$$\phi_{xy}(s) = \begin{bmatrix} \phi_{x_1 y_1}(s) & \cdots & \phi_{x_1 y_p}(s) \\ & & \\ \vdots & & \vdots \\ & & \\ \phi_{x_p y_1}(s) & \cdots & \phi_{x_p y_p}(s) \end{bmatrix}.$$

When $y_t = x_t$, then this coefficient reduces to the multichannel autocorrelation coefficient $\phi_{xx}(s)$.

Subroutine MACRO computes the empirical multichannel cross correlation of the sample p-channel time series

$$x_1, x_2, x_3, \ldots, x_m$$

with the sample p-channel time series

$$y_1, y_2, y_3, \ldots, y_n .$$

Each observation x_t and y_t is a $p \times 1$ vector. The empirical cross correlation is given by the $p \times p$ matrix

$$g_{xy}(s) = \Sigma x_{t+s} y_t^T .$$

Here the summation is over all integers t, where it is assumed that x_t and y_t are zero outside their respective time intervals $1 \leqslant t \leqslant m$ and $1 \leqslant t \leqslant n$. The call statement is

CALL MACRO(N,LX,X,LY,Y,LG,G)

where the subroutine inputs are

$\quad$ N = number of channels = p
$\quad$ LX = length of x_t = m
$\quad$ X = $(x_1, x_2, \ldots, x_m)$ stored in the trace mode
$\quad\quad$ = $[x_1(1), x_1(2), \ldots, x_1(m), x_2(1), x_2(2), \ldots, x_p(m)]$
$\quad$ LY = length of y_t = n
$\quad$ Y = $(y_1, y_2, \ldots, y_m)$ stored in the trace mode
$\quad\quad$ = $[y_1(1), y_1(2), \ldots, y_1(n), y_2(1), y_2(2),$
$\quad\quad\quad \ldots, y_p(n)]$
$\quad$ LG = desired length of cross correlation = $k + 1$,

and the subroutine output is

$\quad$ G = $[g_{xy}(0), g_{xy}(1), \ldots, g_{xy}(k)]$ stored in the trace mode
$\quad\quad$ = $[g_{x_1 y_1}(0), g_{x_1 y_1}(1), \ldots, g_{x_1 y_1}(k), g_{x_2 y_1}(0), g_{x_2 y_1}(1),$
$\quad\quad\quad \ldots, g_{x_p y_p}(k)].$

Subroutine MACRO needs subroutines CROSS and DOT. The program is

```
      SUBROUTINE  MACRO(N,LX,X,LY,Y,LG,G)
C     DIMENSION  X(LX*N),Y(LY*N),G(LG*N*N)
      DIMENSION  X(2),Y(2),G(2)
      DO 1 I=1,N
      I1=1+(I−1)*LX
      DO 1 J=1,N
      J1=1+(J−1)*LY
      IJ=1+LG*(I−1)+LG*N*(J−1)
    1 CALL  CROSS(LX,X(I1),LY,Y(J1),LG,G(IJ))
      RETURN
      END
```

As a numerical example, let us consider the three-channel time series x_t whose components

$$x_1(t) = \text{Wolfer's sunspot numbers}$$
$$x_2(t) = \text{northern light activity index}$$
$$x_3(t) = \text{earthquake activity index}$$

consist of yearly observations over the 100-year period from 1770 to 1869. These observations, which may be found in Quenouille,[44] are shown in Table 3. Each of the three component time series are read into storage, their respective averages, namely,

$$\bar{x}_1 = 46.94$$
$$\bar{x}_2 = 63.43$$
$$\bar{x}_3 = 97.97 ,$$

are removed by subroutine REMAV, and the resulting zero-average component time series are stored in array X in trace mode. Hence as subroutine inputs to MACRO, let

N = 3
LX = 100
X = (54.06, 35.06, 19.06, −11.94, −15.94, ... , −9.94, 27.06,
91.57, 49.57, −60.43, −53.43, −63.43, ... , 38.57, 46.57,
−31.97, −35.97, −31.97, 99.03, −34.97, ... , 64.03, 39.03),
where the ... in each case indicate the omission of 93 observations,
L = 10 .

---

[44] Quenouille, M. H., *Associated Measurements*, Butterworths, London, 1952, pp. 165, 169.

TABLE 3. Time series of sunspot numbers $x_1(t)$, northern light activity $x_2(t)$, and earthquake activity $x_3(t)$

t	$x_1(t)$	$x_2(t)$	$x_3(t)$	t	$x_1(t)$	$x_2(t)$	$x_3(t)$
1770	101	155	66	1820	16	71	90
1771	82	113	62	1821	7	24	86
1772	66	3	66	1822	4	20	119
1773	35	10	197	1823	2	22	82
1774	31	0	63	1824	8	13	79
1775	7	0	0	1825	17	35	111
1776	20	12	121	1826	36	84	60
1777	92	86	0	1827	50	119	118
1778	154	102	113	1828	62	86	206
1779	126	20	27	1829	67	71	122
1780	85	98	107	1830	71	115	134
1781	68	116	50	1831	48	91	131
1782	38	87	122	1832	28	43	84
1783	23	131	127	1833	8	67	100
1784	10	168	152	1834	13	60	99
1785	24	173	216	1835	57	49	99
1786	83	238	171	1836	122	100	69
1787	132	146	70	1837	138	150	67
1788	131	0	141	1838	103	178	26
1789	118	0	69	1839	86	187	106
1790	90	0	160	1840	63	76	108
1791	67	0	92	1841	37	75	155
1792	60	12	70	1842	24	100	40
1793	47	0	46	1843	11	68	75
1794	41	37	96	1844	15	93	99
1795	21	14	78	1845	40	20	86
1796	16	11	110	1846	62	51	127
1797	6	28	79	1847	98	72	201
1798	4	19	85	1848	124	118	76
1799	7	30	113	1849	96	146	64
1800	14	11	59	1850	66	101	31
1801	34	26	86	1851	64	61	138
1802	45	0	199	1852	54	87	163
1803	43	29	53	1853	39	53	98
1804	48	47	81	1854	21	69	70
1805	42	36	81	1855	7	46	155
1806	28	35	156	1856	4	47	97
1807	10	17	27	1857	23	35	82
1808	8	0	81	1858	55	74	90
1809	2	3	107	1859	94	104	122
1810	0	6	152	1860	96	97	70
1811	1	18	99	1861	77	106	96
1812	5	15	177	1862	59	113	111
1813	12	0	48	1863	44	103	42
1814	14	3	70	1864	47	68	97
1815	35	9	158	1865	30	67	91
1816	46	64	22	1866	16	82	64
1817	41	126	43	1867	7	89	81
1818	30	38	102	1868	37	102	162
1819	24	33	111	1869	74	110	137

The call statement

$$\text{CALL MACRO(N,LX,X,LX,X,L,R)}$$

yields the subroutine output

R = (138376,	111584,	59239,	...,	45820,
82163,	57386,	34870,	...,	5917,
−10475,	−21082,	−14960,	...,	−3891,
82163,	80203,	61582,	...,	84172,
264369,	185153,	109748,	...,	19194,
13704,	20338,	49482,	...,	−16274,
−10475,	5461,	8308,	...,	−7236,
13704,	23665,	27971,	...,	−11933,
197843,	−3031,	−4835,	...,	−34044),

where the ... in each case indicate the omission of 6 values. The first 10 values in array R, namely, 138376, 111584, 59239, ..., 45820, give the (unnormalized) estimates of $\phi_{11}(t)$ for $t = 0, 1, \ldots, 9$; the next 10, namely, 82163, 57386, 34870, ..., 5917, give the (unnormalized) estimates of $\phi_{21}(t)$ for $t = 0, 1, \ldots, 9$; the next 10, $\phi_{31}(t)$; the next 10, $\phi_{12}(t)$; the next 10, $\phi_{22}(t)$; the next 10, $\phi_{32}(t)$; the next 10, $\phi_{13}(t)$; the next 10, $\phi_{23}(t)$; and the last 10, namely, 197843, −3031, −4835, ..., −34044, give the (unnormalized) estimates of $\phi_{33}(t)$ for $t = 0, 1, \ldots, 9$.

Subroutine HEAT is more general than subroutine MACRO. Given the sample time series

$$x_1, x_2, x_3, \ldots, x_m,$$

where each observation x_t is a $p \times q$ matrix, and given the sample time series

$$y_1, y_2, y_3, \ldots, y_n,$$

where each observation y_t is a $r \times q$ matrix, the real version of subroutine HEAT computes the empirical cross correlation

$$g_{xy}(s) = \sum x_{t+s} y_t^T \qquad \text{for } s = 0, 1, 2, \ldots, k,$$

whereas the complex version of subroutine HEAT computes the empirical cross correlation

$$g_{xy}(s) = \sum x_{t+s} y_t^{*T} \qquad \text{for } s = 0, 1, 2, \ldots, k.$$

The summations are over all integers t, where it is assumed that x_t and y_t are zero outside of their respective time intervals $1 \leqslant t \leqslant m$ and $1 \leqslant t \leqslant n$. Subroutine HEAT requires subroutine ZERO. The call statement is

$$\text{CALL HEAT(NRX,NCX,LX,X,NRY,NCY,LY,Y,LG,G)}$$

where the subroutine inputs are

$$\text{NRX} = \text{number of rows of } x_t = p$$
$$\text{NCX} = \text{number of columns of } x_t = q$$
$$\text{LX} = \text{length of } x_t = m$$
$$\text{X} = (x_1, x_2, \ldots, x_m) \text{ stored in the multiplexed mode}$$
$$\text{NRY} = \text{number of rows of } y_t = r$$
$$\text{NCY} = \text{number of columns of } y_t = q$$
$$\text{LY} = \text{length of } y_t = n$$
$$\text{Y} = (y_1, y_2, \ldots, y_n) \text{ stored in the multiplexed mode}$$
$$\text{LG} = \text{desired length of cross correlation} = k + 1,$$

and the subroutine output is

$$\text{G} = [g_{xy}(0), g_{xy}(1), \ldots, g_{xy}(k)] \text{ stored in the}$$
multiplexed mode.

As a numerical example let the subroutine inputs be

$$\text{NRX} = \text{NRY} = 2$$
$$\text{NCX} = \text{NCY} = 2$$
$$\text{LX} = \text{LY} = 2$$

$$\text{X} = \text{Y} = \left(\begin{bmatrix} 1 & 0 \\ 0 & 1 \end{bmatrix}, \begin{bmatrix} -2 & 6 \\ 0 & -4 \end{bmatrix} \right)$$
$$= (1, 0, 0, 1, -2, 0, 6, -4)$$

$$\text{LG} = 3 .$$

Then the subroutine output is

$$\text{G} = (41, -24, -24, 17, -2, 0, 6, -4, 0, 0, 0, 0)$$
$$= \left(\begin{bmatrix} 41 & -24 \\ -24 & 17 \end{bmatrix}, \begin{bmatrix} -2 & 6 \\ 0 & -4 \end{bmatrix}, \begin{bmatrix} 0 & 0 \\ 0 & 0 \end{bmatrix} \right) .$$

As we have seen, subroutine HEAT computes the center point and as much of the right-hand side of the cross-correlation function $g_{xy}(s)$ as desired; that is, the statement

CALL HEAT(NRX,NCX,LX,X,NRY,NCY,LY,Y,LG,G)   (1)

yields

$$\text{G} = [g_{xy}(0), g_{xy}(1), \ldots, g_{xy}(k)] .$$

However, suppose that one wants the left-hand side. Then one should compute the center point and right-hand side of $g_{yx}(s)$; that is, one should use the call statement

CALL HEAT(NRY,NCY,LY,Y,NRX,NCX,LX,X,LG,G) .   (2)

In call statement (2), the roles of X and Y are interchanged from the previous call statement (1). For call statement (2) the subroutine output is

$$G = [g_{yx}(0), g_{yx}(1), \ldots, g_{yx}(k)] .$$

But from the definition of cross correlation, we know that

$$g_{yx}(s) = [g_{xy}(-s)]^{*\mathrm{T}} .$$

Hence call statement (2) results in the complex conjugate transpose of the center point and left-hand side of $g_{xy}(s)$; that is, the subroutine output for call statement (2) may be written as

$$G = [g_{xy}^{*\mathrm{T}}(0), g_{xy}^{*\mathrm{T}}(-1), \ldots, g_{xy}^{*\mathrm{T}}(-k)] .$$

(*Note.* By the same procedure we can compute the transpose of the center point and left-hand side of a cross-correlation function with subroutine MACRO.) The real version of subroutine HEAT, which requires the real version of subroutine ZERO, is

```
SUBROUTINE HEAT(NRX,NCX,LX,X,NRY,NCY,LY,Y,LG,G)
DIMENSION X(NRX,NCX,LX),Y(NRY,NCY,LY),G(NRX,
1NRY,LG)
CALL ZERO(NRX*NRY*LG,G)
MIN=MIN0(LG,LX)
DO 1 M=1,NRX
DO 1 N=1,NRY
DO 1 L=1,NCX
DO 1 J=1,MIN
LDOT=MIN0(LY,LX−J+1)
DO 1 I=1,LDOT
K=I+J−1
1 G(M,N,J)=G(M,N,J)+X(M,L,K)*Y(N,L,I)
RETURN
END
```

The complex version of subroutine HEAT, which requires the complex version of subroutine ZERO, is

```
SUBROUTINE HEAT(NRX,NCX,LX,X,NRY,NCY,LY,Y,LG,G)
COMPLEX X,Y,G
DIMENSION X(NRX,NCX,LX),Y(NRY,NCY,LY),G(NRX,
1NRY,LG)
CALL ZERO(NRX*NRY*LG,G)
MIN=MIN0(LG,LX)
DO 1 M=1,NRX
DO 1 N=1,NRY
DO 1 L=1,NCX
```

```
      DO 1 J=1,MIN
      LDOT=MIN0(LY,LX−J+1)
      DO 1 I=1,LDOT
      K=I+J−1
    1 G(M,N,J)=G(M,N,J)+X(M,L,K)*CONJG(Y(N,L,I))
      RETURN
      END
```

As another numerical example, let us consider the three-channel time series x_t of sunspot numbers, northern light activity, and earthquake activity given above. Again the averages are removed, but this time we store the zero-average component time series in array X in multiplied mode. Hence as subroutine inputs to HEAT, we have

$$NRX = 3$$
$$NCX = 1$$
$$LX = 100$$
$$X = (54.06, 91.57, -31.97, 35.06, 49.57, -35.97,$$
$$\dots, 27.06, 46.57, 39.03)$$

(where the . . . indicates the omission of 291 observations). The call statement

CALL HEAT(NRX,NCX,LX,X,NRX,NCX,LX,X,10,R)

yields the subroutine output

$$
\begin{array}{llllll}
R = (138376, & 82163, & -10475, & 82163, & \dots, & 197843, \\
111548, & 57386, & -21082, & 80203, & \dots, & -3031, \\
59239, & 34870, & -14960, & 61582, & \dots, & -4835, & \dots, \\
45820, & 5917, & -3891, & 84172, & \dots, & -34044)
\end{array}
$$

(where the first, second, third, and fifth sets of . . . each indicates the omission of 4 values, and the fourth set of . . . indicates the omission of 54 values).

5.6 Spectral analysis of multichannel time series

The multichannel autocorrelation coefficient

$$
\phi_s = \begin{bmatrix}
\phi_{11}(s) & \phi_{12}(s) & \cdots & \phi_{1p}(s) \\
\phi_{21}(s) & \phi_{22}(s) & \cdots & \phi_{2p}(s) \\
\cdots & \cdots & & \cdots \\
\phi_{p1}(s) & \phi_{p2}(s) & \cdots & \phi_{pp}(s)
\end{bmatrix}
$$

is a $p \times p$ matrix whose on-diagonal elements are the single-channel autocorrelation coefficients $\phi_{jj}(s)$ and whose off-diagonal elements are the single-channel cross-correlation coefficients $\phi_{jk}(s)$. The spectral density matrix $\Phi(f)$ is the discrete Fourier transform of the autocorrelation function ϕ_s; that is,

$$\Phi(f) = \sum_{s=-\infty}^{\infty} \phi_s e^{-2\pi i f s} .$$

Thus the spectral density matrix

$$\Phi(f) = \begin{bmatrix} \Phi_{11}(f) & \Phi_{12}(f) & \cdots & \Phi_{1p}(f) \\ \Phi_{21}(f) & \Phi_{22}(f) & \cdots & \Phi_{2p}(f) \\ \cdots & \cdots & & \cdots \\ \Phi_{p1}(f) & \Phi_{p2}(f) & \cdots & \Phi_{pp}(f) \end{bmatrix} = \Phi^{*\mathrm{T}}(f)$$

is a $p \times p$ matrix whose on-diagonal elements are the single-channel auto-spectral densities $\Phi_{jj}(f)$ and whose off-diagonal elements are the single-channel cross-spectral densities $\Phi_{jk}(f)$.

Let us now make the assumption that the time series in question are real. The *auto-spectral density* $\Phi_{jj}(f)$ is a real even function of the frequency f. The *cross-spectral density*

$$\Phi_{jk}(f) = \sum_{s=-\infty}^{\infty} \phi_{jk}(s)\, e^{-2\pi i f s} \quad (\text{where } j \neq k)$$

is complex-valued. Its real part

$$C_{jk}(f) = \mathrm{Re}[\Phi_{jk}(f)]$$

is called the *co-spectral density*. The negative of its imaginary part

$$Q_{jk}(f) = -\mathrm{Im}[\Phi_{jk}(f)]$$

is called the *quadrature spectral density*. Hence the cross-spectral density may be written as

$$\Phi_{jk}(f) = C_{jk}(f) - iQ_{jk}(f) .$$

In terms of the cross correlation $\phi_{jk}(s)$, the co-spectral density may be written as the discrete cosine transform

$$C_{jk}(f) = \sum_{s=-\infty}^{\infty} \phi_{jk}(s) \cos 2\pi f s$$

$$= \phi_{jk}(0) + \sum_{s=1}^{\infty} [\phi_{jk}(s) + \phi_{kj}(s)] \cos 2\pi f s$$

where we have used the fact that $\phi_{jk}(-s) = \phi_{kj}(s)$. Likewise, the quadrature spectral density may be written as the discrete sine transform

$$Q_{jk}(f) = \sum_{s=-\infty}^{\infty} \phi_{jk}(s) \sin 2\pi f s$$

$$= \sum_{s=1}^{\infty} [\phi_{jk}(s) - \phi_{kj}(s)] \sin 2\pi f s .$$

If we write the cross-correlation function $\phi_{jk}(s)$ as the sum of its even part $e_{jk}(s)$ and its odd part $o_{jk}(s)$, we obtain

$$\phi_{jk}(s) = e_{jk}(s) + o_{jk}(s),$$

where

$$e_{jk}(s) = \frac{1}{2}[\phi_{jk}(s) + \phi_{kj}(s)] = e_{jk}(-s)$$

$$o_{jk}(s) = \frac{1}{2}[\phi_{jk}(s) - \phi_{kj}(s)] = -o_{jk}(-s).$$

Hence the co-spectral density is the even function of f given by

$$C_{jk}(f) = e_{jk}(0) + 2 \sum_{s=1}^{\infty} e_{jk}(s) \cos 2\pi f s,$$

and the quadrature spectral density is the odd function of f given by

$$Q_{jk}(f) = 2 \sum_{s=1}^{\infty} o_{jk}(s) \sin 2\pi f s.$$

Subroutine QUADCO computes the matrix of empirical autospectra, co-spectra, and quadrature spectra from the multichannel autocorrelation function. That is, QUADCO computes the empirical quantities in the matrix

$$M(f) = \begin{bmatrix} \hat{\Phi}_{11}(f) & \hat{C}_{12}(f) & \cdots & \hat{C}_{1p}(f) \\ \hat{Q}_{12}(f) & \hat{\Phi}_{22}(f) & \cdots & \hat{C}_{2p}(f) \\ \cdots & \cdots & & \cdots \\ \hat{Q}_{1p}(f) & \hat{Q}_{2p}(f) & \cdots & \hat{\Phi}_{pp}(f) \end{bmatrix}$$

for the discrete set of frequencies

$$f = 0, \Delta f, 2\Delta f, 3\Delta f, \ldots, m\Delta f,$$

where

$$\Delta f = \frac{1}{2m} \quad \text{cycles per time unit}$$

$$= \frac{\pi}{m} \quad \text{radians per time unit}$$

$$= \frac{180}{m} \quad \text{degrees per time unit}.$$

The empirical autospectra are computed by the formula

$$\hat{\Phi}_{jj}(f) = \phi_{jj}(0) + 2 \sum_{s=1}^{m} \phi_{jj}(s) \, w_s \cos 2\pi f s,$$

where w_s is the triangular weighting function given by

$$w_s = 1 - \frac{s}{m+1} \quad \text{for } s = 0, 1, 2, \ldots, m.$$

The empirical co-spectra are computed by the formula

$$\hat{C}_{jk}(f) = e_{jk}(0) + 2 \sum_{s=1}^{m} e_{jk}(s) \, w_s \, \cos 2\pi f s \,,$$

and the empirical quadrature spectra are computed by the formula

$$\hat{Q}_{jk}(f) = 2 \sum_{s=1}^{m} o_{jk}(s) \, w_s \, \sin 2\pi f s \,,$$

where again w_s is the triangular weighting function. (*Note.* Some other weighting function, such as the Parzen weighting function, could be used by making a slight modification in the program for QUADCO.) The call statement is

CALL QUADCO(L,N,R,S,SP)

where the subroutine inputs are

$$L = \text{time length of correlation} = m + 1$$
$$N = \text{number of channels} = p$$
$$R = \text{multichannel autocorrelation}$$
$$\quad = (\phi_0, \phi_1, \phi_2, \ldots, \phi_m) \text{ stored in the trace mode,}$$

and the subroutine outputs are

$$S = [M(0), M(\Delta f), M(2\Delta f), M(3\Delta f), \ldots, M(m\Delta f)]$$
$$\quad \text{stored in the trace mode, where } \Delta f = (1/2m)$$
$$\quad \text{cycles per time unit}$$
$$SP = \text{working space of } 2*L-1 \text{ cells required for the}$$
$$\quad \text{computations.}$$

The subroutine input R to QUADCO may be directly computed by subroutine MACRO from a multichannel time series stored in array X in trace mode by the call statement

CALL MACRO(N,LX,X,LX,X,LR,R) .

As a numerical example of the use of QUADCO, let the subroutine inputs to QUADCO be

$$L = 2$$
$$N = 2$$
$$R = \left(\begin{bmatrix} 7 & -1 \\ -1 & 3 \end{bmatrix}, \begin{bmatrix} -2 & -2 \\ 1 & 1 \end{bmatrix} \right)$$
$$= (7, -2, -1, 1, -1, -2, 3, 1).$$

Then the subroutine output from QUADCO is

$$S = (5, 9, 0, -0, -1.5, -0.5, 4, 2)$$

$$= \left(\begin{bmatrix} 5 & -1.5 \\ 0 & 4 \end{bmatrix}, \begin{bmatrix} 9 & -0.5 \\ -0 & 2 \end{bmatrix} \right)$$

$$= [M(0), M(0.5)] \qquad (f \text{ in cycles per time unit})$$

$$= \left(\begin{bmatrix} \hat{\Phi}_{11}(0) & \hat{C}_{12}(0) \\ \hat{Q}_{12}(0) & \hat{\Phi}_{22}(0) \end{bmatrix}, \begin{bmatrix} \hat{\Phi}_{11}(0.5) & \hat{C}_{12}(0.5) \\ \hat{Q}_{12}(0.5) & \hat{\Phi}_{22}(0.5) \end{bmatrix} \right).$$

In the matrix $M(f)$ we note that the autospectra are on the main diagonal, the co-spectra $\hat{C}_{jk}(f)$ for $k > j$ are above the diagonal, and the respective quadrature spectra $\hat{Q}_{jk}(f)$ for $k > j$ are below the diagonal. The cross-spectra $\hat{\Phi}_{jk}(f)$ for $k > j$ are then given by $\hat{C}_{jk}(f) - i\hat{Q}_{jk}(f)$. At first glance, it might appear that we have neglected the cross-spectra

$$\hat{\Phi}_{kj}(f) = \hat{C}_{kj}(f) - i\hat{Q}_{kj}(f) \qquad \text{for } k > j.$$

However, since $\phi_{kj}(s) = \phi_{jk}(-s)$, it follows that

$$\hat{\Phi}_{kj}(f) = \hat{\Phi}_{jk}^*(f) = \hat{C}_{jk}(f) + i\hat{Q}_{jk}(f),$$

so that the matrix $M(f)$ also provides the necessary information about $\hat{\Phi}_{kj}(f)$ for $k > j$.

Subroutine QUADCO needs subroutines COSTAB, SINTAB, and COSP. The program is

```
      SUBROUTINE QUADCO(L,N,R,S,SP)
      DIMENSION  R(L,N,N),S(L,N,N),SP(1)
C     DIMENSION  SP(2*L-1)
      DO 20 J=1,N
      DO 20 K=J,N
      DO 10 I=1,L
      WEIGHT=FLOAT(L-I+1)/FLOAT(L)
      EVEN=R(I,J,K)+R(I,K,J)
      ODD=R(I,J,K)-R(I,K,J)
      R(I,K,J)=WEIGHT*ODD
   10 R(I,J,K)=WEIGHT*EVEN
   20 R(1,J,K)=R(1,J,K)/2.0
      DO 40 J=1,N
      DO 40 K=1,N
      IF(K.GE.J) CALL  COSTAB(L,SP)
      IF(K.LT.J) CALL  SINTAB(L,SP)
      DO 30 I=1,L
   30 CALL  COSP(L,R(1,J,K),SP,L,I,S(I,J,K))
   40 R(1,J,K)=R(1,J,K)*2.
      RETURN
      END
```

As another numerical example, let us consider the three-channel time series x_t of sunspot numbers, northern light activity, and earthquake activity given in the foregoing section as an example of the usage of subroutine MACRO. Let the subroutine inputs be

$$L = 10$$
$$N = 3$$
$$R = \text{output of subroutine MACRO in cited example in Sec. 5.5.}$$

Then the call statement

$$\text{CALL QUADCO(L,N,R,S,SP)}$$

yields the subroutine output

S = (373642,	404695,	. . . ,	7630,
0,	58471,	. . . ,	0,
0,	58562,	. . . ,	0,
416328,	233183,	. . . ,	2563,
964217,	749841,	. . . ,	27193,
0,	-105651,	. . . ,	0,
22819,	-42734,	. . . ,	3015,
113218,	129095,	. . . ,	-7311,
157336,	213071,	. . . ,	236331),

where each of the . . . indicates the omission of 7 values. The first 10 values in array S, namely, 373642, 404695, . . . , 7630, give $\hat{\Phi}_{11}(f)$ for $f = 0, 20, 40, \ldots,$ 160, 180 degrees per year; the next 10 values, $\hat{Q}_{12}(f)$; the next 10 values, $\hat{Q}_{13}(f)$; the next 10 values, $\hat{C}_{12}(f)$; the next 10 values, $\hat{\Phi}_{22}(f)$; the next 10 values, $\hat{Q}_{23}(f)$; the next 10 values, $\hat{C}_{13}(f)$; the next 10 values, $\hat{C}_{23}(f)$; and the last 10 values, namely, 157336, 213071, . . . , 236331, $\hat{\Phi}_{33}(f)$.

5.7 *Coherency and phase*

The geometric mean of two autospectra is

$$M_{jk}(f) = \sqrt{\Phi_{jj}(f)\Phi_{kk}(f)} \,.$$

The geometric mean serves as a measure of the theoretical *top limit* of the *common power* at any given frequency f in the two single-channel time series. In order to attain this top limit, the power at that frequency must have a fixed phase relationship for the two single-channel time series in question. If this top limit is indeed attained at a given frequency, we say that the two time series are *coherent* at that frequency. However, it is usually the case that the phase relationships at a given frequency are changing in a random fashion. If the change were completely random, then the theoretical bottom limit, namely, zero, of the common power would be reached, and the two time series would be *completely incoherent*. In most cases observed in time series analysis, the coherency is somewhere between these two theoretical extremes.

The *coefficient of coherency* is defined as

$$K_{jk}(f) = |K_{jk}(f)|e^{-i\theta_{jk}(f)} = \frac{\Phi_{jk}(f)}{M_{jk}(f)} = \frac{C_{jk}(f) - iQ_{jk}(f)}{M_{jk}(f)}.$$

The *magnitude of the coherency* is

$$|K_{jk}(f)| = \frac{\sqrt{C_{jk}^2(f) + Q_{jk}^2(f)}}{M_{jk}(f)} = |K_{kj}(f)|,$$

and the *phase-lag of the coherency* is

$$\theta_{jk}(f) = \arctan\frac{Q_{jk}(f)}{C_{jk}(f)} = -\theta_{kj}(f).$$

The magnitude of the coherency lies between the limits 0 corresponding to the completely incoherent case and 1 corresponding to the coherent case; that is,

$$0 \leqslant |K_{jk}(f)| \leqslant 1.$$

Subroutine COHERE computes the magnitude and phase-lag of the coherency for $f = 0, \Delta f, 2\Delta f, \ldots, m\Delta f$, where $\Delta f = 1/2m$ cycles per time unit. The call statement is

$$\text{CALL COHERE(L,N,S,C)}$$

where the subroutine inputs are

L = $m + 1$
N = number of channels = p
S = $[M(0), M(\Delta f), M(2\Delta f), \ldots, M(m\Delta f)]$ stored in the trace
    mode, where $\Delta f = (1/2m)$ cycles per time unit,

and the subroutine outputs are

C = $[H(0), H(\Delta f), H(2\Delta f), \ldots, H(m\Delta f)]$ stored in the trace
    mode, where $\Delta f = (1/2m)$ cycles per time unit,

where the $p \times p$ matrix $H(f)$ is defined as

$$H(f) = \begin{bmatrix} \Phi_{11}(f) & |K_{12}(f)| & \cdots & |K_{1p}(f)| \\ \theta_{12}(f) & \Phi_{22}(f) & \cdots & |K_{2p}(f)| \\ \cdots & \cdots & & \cdots \\ \theta_{1p}(f) & \theta_{2p}(f) & \cdots & \Phi_{pp}(f) \end{bmatrix}.$$

The phase-lags are expressed in degrees. The elements above the diagonal are the magnitudes of the coherencies; the elements below the diagonal are the phase-lags in degrees; the elements on the diagonal are the autospectra each scaled to have its largest value unity. The subroutine input S to COHERE is the same as the subroutine output S from QUADCO, so COHERE can be called directly after QUADCO. As an illustration, let us continue the first numerical example given in the last section. We recall that

$$N = 2$$
$$L = 2$$
$$S = (5, -9, 0, -0, -1.5, -0.5, 4, 2).$$

With these values as subroutine inputs to COHERE, we obtain the subroutine output

$$C = (0.555, 1, 180, -180, 0.335, 0.118, 1, 0.5)$$

$$= \left(\begin{bmatrix} 0.555 & 0.335 \\ 180 & 1 \end{bmatrix}, \begin{bmatrix} 1 & 0.118 \\ -180 & 0.5 \end{bmatrix} \right)$$

$$= [H(0), H(0.5)] \quad (f \text{ in cycles per time unit})$$

$$= \left(\begin{bmatrix} \Phi_{11}(0) & |K_{12}(0)| \\ \theta_{12}(0) & \Phi_{22}(0) \end{bmatrix}, \begin{bmatrix} \Phi_{11}(0.5) & |K_{12}(0.5)| \\ \theta_{12}(0.5) & \Phi_{22}(0.5) \end{bmatrix} \right).$$

Subroutine COHERE needs subroutine MOVE and NORMAG. The program is

```
      SUBROUTINE COHERE(L,N,S,C)
      DIMENSION S(L,N,N),C(L,N,N)
C     EQUIVALENCE(S,C) IS ALLOWED
      DO 10 JP=2,N
      J=JP-1
      DO 10 K=JP,N
      DO 10 I=1,L
      CO=SQRT(ABS((S(I,J,K)**2+S(I,K,J)**2)/(S(I,J,J)*S(I,K,K))))
      PH=ATAN2(S(I,K,J),S(I,J,K))
      C(I,J,K)=CO
   10 C(I,K,J)=180.0*(PH/3.14159265)
      DO 20 J=1,N
      CALL MOVE (L,S(1,J,J),C(1,J,J))
   20 CALL NORMAG(L,C(1,J,J))
      RETURN
      END
```

As another illustration, let us continue the second numerical example given in the last section, namely, the example of the three-channel time series of sunspot numbers, northern lights activity, and earthquake activity. Let the subroutine inputs be

L = 10
N = 3
S = output of subroutine QUADCO in the cited example in
     Sec. 5.6.

The call statement

$$\text{CALL COHERE(L,N,S,S)}$$

yields the subroutine output

S = (0.92,	1.00,	...,	0.02,
0.00,	14.08,	...,	0.00,
0.00,	126.12,	...,	0.00,
0.69,	0.44,	...,	0.18,
1.00,	0.78,	...,	0.03,
0.00,	−39.30,	...,	180.00,
0.09,	0.25,	...,	0.07,
0.29,	0.42,	...,	0.09,
0.67,	0.90,	...,	1.00),

where each of the . . . indicates the omission of 7 values. The first 10 values in array S, namely, 0.92, 1.00, . . . , 0.02, give the normalized $\hat{\Phi}_{11}(f)$ for $f = 0$, 20, 40, . . . , 160, 180 degrees per year; the next 10 values, $\theta_{12}(f)$; the next 10 values, $\theta_{13}(f)$; the next 10 values, $|K_{12}(f)|$; the next 10 values, the normalized $\hat{\Phi}_{22}(f)$; the next 10 values, $\theta_{23}(f)$; the next 10 values, $|K_{13}(f)|$; the next 10 values, $|K_{23}(f)|$; and the last 10 values, the normalized $\hat{\Phi}_{33}(f)$.

5.8 Stationary Markov processes

Let the $p \times 1$ vector x_t denote a p-channel stationary[45] stochastic process with zero mean and with autocorrelation

$$\phi_s = E\{x_{t+s}x_t^T\} .$$

Such a process is a stationary[45] Markov process, provided that the linear least-squares prediction of the value x_t based upon all the preceding values x_{t-1}, $x_{t-2}, x_{t-3}, \ldots$ is the same as the linear least-squares prediction based upon only the first preceding value x_{t-1}. Let the linear least-squares prediction of x_t in terms of x_{t-1} be given by

$$\text{pred}\ \{x_t\} = ux_{t-1},$$

---

[45] When we use the term "stationary," we mean stationary in the sense that the second moments depend only on time differences and not upon absolute time, that is, second-order (or covariance) stationary.

where u is a constant $p \times p$ matrix. By the orthogonality principle, the constant u is given as the solution of the normal equations

$$E\{(x_t - ux_{t-1})x_{t-1}^T\} = 0 .$$

The normal equations may be written as

$$u\phi_0 = \phi_1 ,$$

so the solution is

$$u = \phi_1\phi_0^{-1} .$$

For a stationary Markov process, ux_{t-1} is by definition the prediction of x_t in terms of $x_{t-1}, x_{t-2}, x_{t-3}, \ldots$, and hence the error $x_t - ux_{t-1}$ must be orthogonal to all the preceding values, that is,

$$E\{(x_t - ux_{t-1})x_{t-s}^T\} = 0 \qquad \text{for } s = 1,2,3,\ldots$$

or

$$\phi_s - u\phi_{s-1} = 0 \qquad \text{for } s = 1,2,3,\ldots.$$

In particular, this equation shows that the autocorrelation coefficients ϕ_s (for positive time-shifts s) may be expressed in terms of ϕ_0 as a geometric progression

$$\phi_s = u\phi_{s-1} = u^2\phi_{s-2} = \cdots = u^s\phi_0 .$$

Let x_t be a stationary Markov process, and let us define the $p \times 1$ innovation (or prediction error) ϵ_t as

$$\epsilon_t = x_t - ux_{t-1} ,$$

where $u = \phi_1\phi_0^{-1}$ is the operator coefficient determined by the solution of the normal equations. As a result, ϵ_t is orthogonal to x_s and x_{s-1} for every s less than t; hence ϵ_t is orthogonal to $\epsilon_s = x_s - ux_{s-1}$, that is,

$$E\{\epsilon_t \epsilon_s^T\} = 0 \qquad \text{for } t > s, \text{ and hence for } t \neq s .$$

Thus the prediction-error series ϵ_t represents an orthogonal (or white noise) process.

At this point, let us note that the operator coefficient $u = \phi_1\phi_0^{-1}$ is a $p \times p$ matrix all of whose eigenvalues are less than or equal to unity in magnitude. By successive use of the difference equation

$$x_s = ux_{s-1} + \epsilon_s ,$$

we obtain

$$x_t = \epsilon_t + u(\epsilon_{t-1} + ux_{t-2})$$
$$= \epsilon_t + u\,\epsilon_{t-1} + u^2(\epsilon_{t-2} + ux_{t-3})$$

and so on, until in the limit we have

$$x_t = \epsilon_t + u\,\epsilon_{t-1} + u^2\,\epsilon_{t-2} + \cdots = \sum_{s=0}^{\infty} u^s\,\epsilon_{t-s}\;.$$

This infinite series converges in the cases when all the eigenvalues of the matrix u are less than unity in magnitude. Let us now consider the correlation between the prediction error ϵ_t and the present ($s = 0$) and future ($s = 1, 2, 3, \ldots$) values x_{t+s}. This correlation is

$$\mathrm{E}\{\epsilon_t x_{t+s}^{\mathrm{T}}\} = \mathrm{E}\{\epsilon_t(\epsilon_{t+s} + u\,\epsilon_{t+s-1} + u^2\,\epsilon_{t+s-2} + \cdots)^{\mathrm{T}}\}$$

which by the orthogonality of the prediction errors is

$$\mathrm{E}\{\epsilon_t x_{t+s}^{\mathrm{T}}\} = \mathrm{E}\{\epsilon_t(u^s\,\epsilon_t)^{\mathrm{T}}\}\;.$$

If we let $\sigma_\epsilon^2 = \mathrm{E}\{\epsilon_t\,\epsilon_t^{\mathrm{T}}\}$ denote the variance matrix of the prediction error, then we have

$$\mathrm{E}\{\epsilon_t x_{t+s}^{\mathrm{T}}\} = \sigma_\epsilon^2(u^{\mathrm{T}})^s \qquad \text{for } s = 0, 1, 2, \ldots\;.$$

However, we also have

$$\begin{aligned}\mathrm{E}\{\epsilon_t x_{t+s}^{\mathrm{T}}\} &= \mathrm{E}\{(x_t - ux_{t-1})x_{t+s}^{\mathrm{T}}\}\\ &= \phi_{-s} - u\phi_{-s-1}\;.\end{aligned}$$

Therefore, we have

$$\phi_{-s} - u\phi_{-s-1} = \sigma_\epsilon^2(u^{\mathrm{T}})^s \qquad \text{for } s = 0, 1, 2, \ldots\;.$$

In summary, the autocorrelation coefficients ϕ_t of a stationary Markov process obey the following relationship:

$$\phi_t - u\phi_{t-1} = \begin{cases} 0 & \text{for } t = 1,2,3,\ldots \\ \sigma_\epsilon^2 & \text{for } t = 0 \\ \sigma_\epsilon^2(u^{\mathrm{T}})^{-t} & \text{for } t = -1, -2, -3, \ldots\;. \end{cases}$$

Taking the z-transforms, we obtain the equation

$$\sum_{t=-\infty}^{\infty} \phi_t z^t - u\sum_{t=-\infty}^{\infty} \phi_{t-1} z^t = \sigma_\epsilon^2 \sum_{t=-\infty}^{0} (u^{\mathrm{T}})^{-t} z^t\;. \tag{1}$$

According to our usual convention, let the corresponding capital letter denote the z-transform of a time function denoted by a lower-case letter. The z-transform of the autocorrelation is then denoted by

$$\Phi(z) = \sum_{t=-\infty}^{\infty} \phi_t z^t\;.$$

Hence we have

$$z\Phi(z) = \sum_{t=-\infty}^{\infty} \phi_{t-1} z^t\;.$$

Also we see that the geometric series on the right-hand side of eq. (1) may be summed (assuming that all the eigenvalues of u are less than unity in magnitude) to give

$$\sum_{t=-\infty}^{0} (u^T)^{-t} z^t = \sum_{s=0}^{\infty} (u^T z^{-1})^s$$

$$= (I - u^T z^{-1})^{-1} .$$

Thus eq. (1) may be written as

$$\Phi(z) - uz\Phi(z) = \sigma_\epsilon^2 (I - u^T z^{-1})^{-1} .$$

Solving for the z-transform $\Phi(z)$ of the autocorrelation function, we obtain

$$\Phi(z) = (I - uz)^{-1} \sigma_\epsilon^2 (I - u^T z^{-1})^{-1} .$$

The power spectrum of the process is obtained by letting $z = e^{-2\pi i f}$ in $\Phi(z)$; hence the power spectrum is

$$\Phi(e^{-2\pi i f}) = (I - ue^{-2\pi i f})^{-1} \sigma_\epsilon^2 (I - u^T e^{2\pi i f})^{-1} .$$

The variance matrix of the process x_t is

$$\phi_0 = E\{x_t x_t^T\}$$
$$= E\{(\epsilon_t + u\,\epsilon_{t-1} + u^2\,\epsilon_{t-2} + \cdots)(\epsilon_t + u\,\epsilon_{t-1} + u^2\,\epsilon_{t-2} + \cdots)^T\}$$

which because of the orthogonality of the prediction errors becomes

$$\phi_0 = \sum_{s=0}^{\infty} u^s\, E\{\epsilon_{t-s}\,\epsilon_{t-s}^T\}(u^T)^s$$

or

$$\phi_0 = \sum_{s=0}^{\infty} u^s \sigma_\epsilon^2 (u^T)^s .$$

5.9 *Autoregressive processes*

A stationary Markov process may also be called an autoregressive process of first order. A *multichannel $(p \times 1)$ autoregressive process of second order* is a stationary process y_t for which the linear least-squares prediction of the value y_t based upon all the preceding values $y_{t-1}, y_{t-2}, y_{t-3}, \ldots$ is the same as the linear least-squares prediction based upon only the first *two* preceding values y_{t-1}, y_{t-2}. Let us briefly state some of the properties of such processes. The linear least-squares prediction of y_t in terms of the past values $y_{t-1}, y_{t-2}, \ldots$ is given by

$$\text{pred } \{y_t\} = u_1 y_{t-1} + u_2 y_{t-2},$$

where u_1 and u_2 are constant $p \times p$ matrices. The $p \times 1$ prediction error

$$\eta_t = y_t - u_1 y_{t-1} - u_2 y_{t-2}$$

is orthogonal to all the past values y_{t-s} (where $s = 1, 2, 3, \ldots$); that is, we have the normal equations

$$E\{(y_t - u_1 y_{t-1} - u_2 y_{t-2})y_{t-s}^T\} = 0 \qquad \text{for } s = 1, 2, 3, \ldots .$$

These normal equations become

$$\psi_s - u_1 \psi_{s-1} - u_2 \psi_{s-2} = 0 \qquad \text{for } s = 1, 2, 3, \ldots$$

in terms of the $p \times p$ autocorrelation coefficients $\psi_s = E\{y_{t+s} y_t^T\}$ of the process. Furthermore, we conclude that the prediction errors η_t are orthogonal; that is,

$$E\{\eta_t \eta_s^T\} = 0 \qquad \text{for } t \neq s .$$

Now let us make use of an important fact, namely, a p-channel autoregressive process of second order may be transformed into a $2p$-channel Markov process (i.e., a $2p$-channel autoregressive process of first order). Hence let us define the $2p$-channel Markov process x_t in terms of the p-channel second-order autoregressive process y_t as

$$x_t = \begin{bmatrix} y_t \\ y_{t-1} \end{bmatrix}.$$

Likewise, let us define the $2p$-channel prediction error ϵ_t of the Markov process in terms of the p-channel prediction error of the second-order autoregressive process as

$$\epsilon_t = \begin{bmatrix} \eta_t \\ 0 \end{bmatrix}.$$

Then the second-order difference equation for the second-order autoregressive process

$$y_t = u_1 y_{t-1} + u_2 y_{t-2} + \eta_t \tag{1}$$

may be transformed into the first-order difference equation for the Markov process

$$x_t = u x_{t-1} + \epsilon_t , \tag{2}$$

where the $2p \times 2p$ matrix u is defined in terms of the $p \times p$ matrices u_1 and u_2 as

$$u = \begin{bmatrix} u_1 & u_2 \\ I_p & 0 \end{bmatrix}.$$

(Here I_p is the $p \times p$ identity matrix.) To see that this is indeed so, we write the first-order difference equation as

$$\begin{bmatrix} y_t \\ y_{t-1} \end{bmatrix} = \begin{bmatrix} u_1 & u_2 \\ I & 0 \end{bmatrix} \begin{bmatrix} y_{t-1} \\ y_{t-2} \end{bmatrix} + \begin{bmatrix} \eta_t \\ 0 \end{bmatrix}.$$

This contains two equations: the first is the second-order difference equation (1), and the second is the identity $y_{t-1} = Iy_{t-1}$.

Let the $2p \times 2p$ matrix ϕ_s denote the autocorrelation coefficient of the $2p$-channel Markov process x_t. From the last section we know that ϕ_s satisfies $\phi_s = u^s \phi_0$ for all $s \geq 0$.

The operator $(I_p, -u_1, -u_2)$ transforms y_t into η_t; that is,

$$\eta_t = (I_p, -u_1, -u_2) * y_t = y_t - u_1 y_{t-1} - u_2 y_{t-2}.$$

The z-transform of this operator is the $p \times p$ matrix polynomial

$$I_p - u_1 z - u_2 z^2.$$

The determinant of this z-transform (in the absence of degeneracies) is a polynomial of degree $2p$; that is,

$$\det (I_p - u_1 z - u_2 z^2) = 1 - \alpha_1 z - \alpha_2 z^2 - \cdots - \alpha_{2p} z^{2p},$$

where the polynomial coefficients $1, -\alpha_1, -\alpha_2, \ldots, -\alpha_{2p}$ are scalars. Likewise, the operator $(I_{2p}, -u)$ transforms x_t into ϵ_t; that is,

$$\epsilon_t = (I_{2p}, u) * x_t = x_t - u x_{t-1}.$$

The z-transform of this operator is the $2p \times 2p$ matrix polynomial

$$I_{2p} - uz.$$

The determinant of this z-transform is a polynomial of degree $2p$, and indeed it is identical to $\det (I_p - u_1 z - u_2 z^2)$; that is,

$$\det (I_{2p} - uz) = 1 - \alpha_1 z - \alpha_2 z^2 - \cdots - \alpha_{2p} z^{2p}.$$

Now let us appeal to the Cayley–Hamilton theorem (see Sec. 4.4). The characteristic matrix of the matrix u is the z-transform

$$I_{2p} - uz$$

of the operator $(I_{2p}, -u)$. The characteristic equation is

$$\det (I_{2p} - uz) = 0,$$

which is

$$1 - \alpha_1 z - \alpha_2 z^2 - \cdots - \alpha_{2p} z^{2p} = 0.$$

The Cayley–Hamilton theorem states that the inverse u^{-1} satisfies the characteristic equation; that is,

$$I_{2p} - \alpha_1 u^{-1} - \alpha_2 u^{-2} - \cdots - \alpha_{2p} u^{-2p} = 0 \,,$$

where the 0 on the right-hand side stands for the $2p \times 2p$ matrix of zeros. If we multiply (on the right) this equation by $u^{2p}\phi_{t-2p}$ (where $t \geqslant 2p$), we obtain

$$u^{2p}\phi_{t-2p} - \alpha_1 u^{2p-1}\phi_{t-2p} - \alpha_2 u^{2p-2}\phi_{t-2p} - \cdots - \alpha_{2p}\phi_{t-2p} = 0$$

which is (since $u^{2p-k}\phi_{t-2p} = \phi_{t-k}$)

$$\phi_t - \alpha_1\phi_{t-1} - \alpha_2\phi_{t-2} - \cdots - \alpha_{2p}\phi_{t-2p} = 0 \qquad \text{for } t \geqslant 2p \,. \qquad (3)$$

Now let us express the autocorrelation coefficient ϕ_t of the Markov process in terms of the autocorrelation coefficients ψ_t of the second-order autoregressive process. The required relationship is

$$\phi_t = \mathbf{E}\{x_{s+t}x_s^{\mathrm{T}}\} = \mathbf{E}\left\{\begin{bmatrix} y_{s+t} \\ y_{s+t-1} \end{bmatrix} \begin{bmatrix} y_s^{\mathrm{T}} & y_{s-1}^{\mathrm{T}} \end{bmatrix}\right\}$$

$$= \begin{bmatrix} \psi_t & \psi_{t+1} \\ \psi_{t-1} & \psi_t \end{bmatrix}.$$

Using this relationship in equation (3), we obtain in particular that

$$\psi_{t-1} - \alpha_1\psi_{t-2} - \alpha_2\psi_{t-3} - \cdots - \alpha_{2p}\psi_{t-2p-1} = 0 \qquad \text{for } t \geqslant 2p \,,$$

which is (by letting $s = t - 1$)

$$\psi_s - \alpha_1\psi_{s-1} - \alpha_2\psi_{s-2} - \cdots - \alpha_{2p}\psi_{s-2p} = 0 \qquad \text{for } s > 2p - 2 \,.$$

In this section we have seen how a p-channel autoregressive process of order 2 may be transformed into a $2p$-channel Markov process. By the same method, a p-channel autoregressive process of order q may be transformed into a qp-channel Markov process. More generally, every *second-order process*[46] whose covariance possesses a proper rational spectrum has a *Markovian realization*.

In systems engineering, two types of problems are encountered, namely, those dealing with the external and those with the internal behavior of a system. The Wiener formulation of filter design calls for the solution of the Wiener–Hopf integral equation, in which the unknown is the impulse response function of the optimum filter. (In the discrete time case, the Wiener–Hopf equation becomes the set of normal equations, in which the unknowns are the coefficients of the impulse response function of the optimum discrete filter.) The impulse response function specifies the external behavior of the filter, that is, the performance specifications of the filter. In conventional engineering practice, the engineer would regard these performance specifications as his

---

[46] The theory of *second-order processes* takes into account only those properties of stochastic processes determined by their first and second moments.

input; that is, he would have to produce the wiring diagram of an electrical network which would realize this optimum impulse response function. However, in digital filtering practice, the word "filter" is no longer synonymous with "electric RLC network"; some of the more conventional problems of network synthesis can be bypassed to a large extent by the use of digital computer programs such as WIENER. Subroutine WIENER makes use of the numerical coefficients representing the impulse response function as determined from the normal equations in order to digitally simulate the action of the required optimum filter. Moreover, these coefficients can be re-computed (either continually or at intervals with interpolation) from the most recent or most pertinent data so that the resulting filter is responsive or self-adaptive to the desired information in a time-varying manner. Such time-varying adaptive digital filters are in general use as deconvolution filters in seismic exploration for oil (*cf.* Sec. 2.10). Although it is true that a tremendous amount of computation is required relative to prior standards, the increased performance record of these digital filters justifies their usage on an economic basis. In fact, with the rapid development of digital computer technology, more and more ambitious digital filtering methods become economically attractive each year.

Physical information should be included in statistical procedures; for example, the physical fact that a wavelet is minimum delay makes possible statistical methods for processing the received data in order to detect the wavelet. As a result, the question of the internal behavior of a system is more than one of purely engineering interest. The stability and delay properties of a system are intimately associated with its internal behavior, and these matters cannot be disregarded. Hence the network synthesis procedures of the engineers take on a new and deeper meaning in this connection, and are very important indeed. In many practical cases, Markovian models of the physical situation are known, whereas the necessary correlation functions are difficult to measure. In these cases, the state variable techniques of digital filtering become relevant, such as those incorporated in the Kalman–Bucy filter.[47, 48] Its program specifications are given as a set of first-order difference equations, which are the so-called state variable equations, without the intermediate step of computing the input/output relations of the filter. Kalman[49] shows that the principal difference between the Wiener filter and the Kalman–Bucy filter lies in the initial specifications (correlation functions vs Markov processes) of the stochastic process to be filtered, as well as in the format of the final result,

---

[47] Kalman, R. E., and R. S. Bucy, "New results in linear filtering and prediction theory," *J. Basic Eng.* **83D**, 95–108 (1961).

[48] Kalman, R. E., "Linear stochastic filtering theory, Reappraisal and outlook," in *Symposium on System Theory*, Polytech. Inst. of Brooklyn, Brooklyn, N.Y., pp. 197–205 (1965).

[49] Kalman, R. E., *op. cit.*, p. 200.

namely, the optimum filter (impulse response vs first-order difference equations). The relationship between these two approaches has been indicated in this section. From the fact that every second-order process whose covariance possesses a proper rational spectrum has a Markov realization, Kalman[50] shows that the starting assumptions for the Wiener filter and the Kalman–Bucy filter are equivalent in the finite dimensional case. As a result, Kalman[51] establishes that there is a complete parallelism between the two approaches, and the two theories yield equivalent results.

5.10 Nonlinear filtering theory[52]

Better digital computer methods to enhance the correlation properties of seismic events can be attained through the development of time-varying and space-varying filters which optimally adjust to the dynamics of multichannel seismic data. These filters would be used to enhance and follow events which are correlated from trace to trace, as well as to follow the changes in character of events along a given trace. Because of the complexity of such a nonlinear problem its final solution rests in our ability to partition it into parts that are amenable to solution.

The basic idea is to break down this highly nonlinear problem into two parts, namely, (1) the development of an integrated scheme of digital *linear* filters classified into a finite number of groups and (2) the development of a set of rules for *switching* between the various groups. Once we have made this division we see that each part is amenable to solution. Part (1) falls under the theory of *linear filtering* which can be handled by well-known methods; part (2) falls under the category of *finite state machines* for which a theory is rapidly being developed in algebra.

Hence the basic idea of this nonlinear filtering theory is to combine the algebraic theory of finite state machines with classical linear filtering theory. In other words, the nonlinear filters are made up of locally linear (Wiener) filters which move from state to state under the action of a finite state machine. That is, at each state a linear filter is given, but these filters change in time and space according to the action of the finite state machine.

The algebraic theory of finite state machines is based on certain fundamental principles which govern the transformations from state to state. A finite state machine can always be decomposed into a set of irreducible or *indecomposable machines*. These indecomposable machines can be found, and

[50] Kalman, R. E., *op. cit.*, p. 204.

[51] Kalman, R. E., *op. cit.*, p. 200.

[52] This section is based on the work of Krohn, K., and J. Rhodes, *Development of New Mathematical Techniques for Biosignal Analysis* (Annual Report to N.A.S.A., Contract NAS 12–122), Krohn-Rhodes Research Institute, Berkeley, Calif., 1967.

explicit expressions can be given for the minimal circuits corresponding to each of them. The theory uses standard engineering methods, such as combining irreducible machines into series-parallel networks, to built up arbitrary finite state machines.

The indecomposable machines fall into two categories. The first class contains the unit-delay machine, the delay-blank machine, and four submachines. The second class is made up of those machines which stand in a one-to-one correspondence with the finite indecomposable groups occurring in group theory. These two classes exhaust all irreducible machines.

The irreducible machines of the first class are called *units*, whereas those of the second class are called *primes*, as an analogy with the positive integers $(1 = \text{unit}; 2, 3, 5, 7, 11, \ldots = \text{primes})$. As we know, any integer can be represented as the product of unity and prime numbers (e.g., $12 = 1 \cdot 2 \cdot 2 \cdot 3$); likewise, any finite state machine can be constructed from units and primes.

Let us consider a given finite state machine. The primes associated with this machine are those which can be obtained by deleting some states, inputs, and outputs of the machine. We say that these primes divide the machine. Thus in any decomposition of the machine every member of the set of primes associated with the machine must occur. It follows that the machine can be constructed from this set of primes and the units.

At one extreme, there are the machines which just perform combinatorial operations. For such a machine the set of primes associated with it is empty. Therefore, a combinatorial machine can be constructed from the set of unit irreducible machines. That is, a *combinatorial machine* can be constructed as a series-parallel network from the unit-delay and delay-blank machines.

At the other extreme, there are those machines for which every input permutes the states. These machines can be constructed as a series-parallel network from just the primes, not allowing the units. Such machines are called *arithmetic machines*.

Now let us consider any finite state machine which we will call M. Suppose that n is the smallest integer such that our given machine M can be constructed as a *series network* by cascading the n machines $M_1, M_2, \ldots, M_n$, where $M_1, M_3, M_5, \ldots$ are combinatorial machines, and $M_2, M_4, M_6, \ldots$ are arithmetic machines, or vice versa. This smallest such integer n is called the *complexity* of the finite state machine M. That is, the complexity of a finite state machine is the number of times one must do combinatorial operations followed by arithmetic operations, followed by combinatorial operations, followed by arithmetic operations, etc., in order to finally perform the operation of the machine.

The seismic correlation problem involves seismic data from which we would like to infer the geologic structure. Inferring the geologic structure may be described roughly as follows. Look at the collections of all inferences over past, present, and future which have characteristics in agreement with the given past data, and which can be performed by the machines at hand. Then choose the simplest member of this class of machines.

For example, suppose we are given some sequences of seismic data (the inputs) and the resulting geologic inferences (the outputs), as well as the true geologic structures (the desired outputs). Then we would consider the collection of all finite state machines which agree with the given data. From this collection we could choose the one with the smallest complexity. This machine would then be the one into which we would feed fresh seismic data in order to make the geologic inferences.

Briefly, then, the geologic inferences would be made by using linear digital filters *locally* (i.e., each such linear filter is valid only in a particular section of space-time), and by varying these filters *globally* (i.e., over a widespread area of space-time). The particular filters to be used locally would be designed according to the standard Wiener methods for linear filters; the switching between such filters on a global basis would be done by the action of the finite state machine. At each local state a linear filter is used, but these change in time and space on a global pattern under the control of a finite state machine.

As a simple example, suppose we wish to estimate some statistical function y as a product of two unknown statistical functions α and β; that is, we seek α and β such that the product $\alpha\beta$ is the best possible approximation to y (under some criterion which defines "best"). Now this is a nonlinear problem because it involves the multiplication of two unknown statistical functions. However, by using the algebraic theory of machines, we can convert it into local linear problems as follows. Assume an initial value for α, say, $\alpha^{(0)}$; then estimate β, which yields the estimate $\beta^{(1)}$. This is a linear estimation problem because, with α given, we no longer have a product $\alpha\beta$ of unknown functions, but simply one unknown function $\alpha^{(0)}\beta$, and so the estimate $\beta^{(1)}$ can be found by strictly linear means. Hence at this local level, we have a linear estimation problem. Now on the global level, our finite state machine would instruct us to switch to the other state, namely, the state when β is known (i.e., the value $\beta^{(1)}$ computed in the previous state) and α is unknown. Again we have a linear estimation problem; we estimate α as $\alpha^{(1)}$ by the linear estimation technique. Then we switch back to the first state and with α given as $\alpha^{(1)}$ re-estimate β as $\beta^{(2)}$; then we switch back to the second state and with β given as $\beta^{(2)}$ re-estimate α as $\alpha^{(2)}$, etc. Because such a scheme can be devised as a contraction mapping, these successive estimates will converge to limiting values which represent the final estimates of α and β.

The theory of linear filtering represents a well-known body of information. However, the theory of finite state machines is not so well known. Let us now look at some examples from algebraic machine theory. An *asynchronous sequential machine* is one whose outputs are functions of both the present and past inputs but does not require a clock pulse to originate transitions between states. That is, a transition can occur following any change in inputs. A *synchronous sequential machine* is one that requires a clock pulse to originate transitions. The synthesis procedure for a sequential machine involves the following steps:

(1) A complete description of its terminal behavior by means of a transition table (or graph)

(2) Reduction of the transition table (or graph) to its shortest possible form

(3) Synthesis of the resultant network.

In order to fix these ideas we consider a sequential machine with a finite number of states $S_1, S_2, \ldots, S_N$, a finite number of possible inputs $X_1, X_2, \ldots, X_M$, and a finite number of possible outputs $Y_1, Y_2, \ldots, Y_P$. Let us represent time by the discrete (integer) variable n, so the machine may be thought of as a synchronous device. The state, input, and output at time n are denoted by $s(n)$, $x(n)$, and $y(n)$, respectively. The present output $y(n)$ and the present state $s(n)$ are functions of the present input $x(n)$ and the previous state $s(n - 1)$.

For example, suppose a machine has two states S_1, S_2, two input symbols X_1, X_2, and two output symbols Y_1, Y_2. The action of such a machine may be described by a *transition graph*, such as:

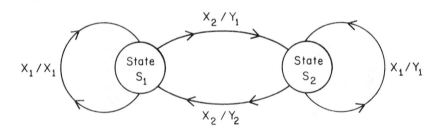

The nodes of the graph represent the states, and the branches represent the transitions between the states as shown by the arrows. The numerator of the fraction labeling a branch denotes the input causing the transition, and the denominator denotes the output. Thus the branch from state S_1 to S_2 indicates that when $s(n - 1) = S_1$ and $x(n) = X_2$, then $s(n) = S_2$ and $y(n) = Y_1$. Similarly, the branch from state S_2 to state S_2 indicates that when $s(n - 1) = S_2$ and $x(n) = X_1$, then $s(n) = S_2$ and $y(n) = Y_1$.

This same information can be expressed by a *transition table*. Thus for our example the transition table is as follows.

TABLE 4. Transition table for a sequential machine with two states, two input symbols, and two output symbols

s(n − 1)	x(n)			
	X_1		X_2	
	s(n)	y(n)	s(n)	y(n)
S_1	S_1	Y_1	S_2	Y_1
S_2	S_2	Y_1	S_1	Y_2

If we let $S_1 = 0$, $S_2 = 1$, $X_1 = 0$, $X_2 = 1$, $Y_1 = 0$, and $Y_2 = 1$, then this table becomes the following.

TABLE 5. Table 4 with specific numerical values inserted

s(n − 1)	x(n)			
	0		1	
	s(n)	y(n)	s(n)	y(n)
0	0	0	1	0
1	1	0	0	1

One possible realization of this table is shown in the block diagram of Fig. 17.

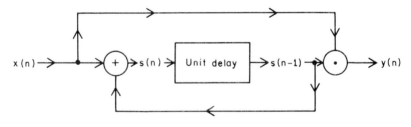

Fig. 17. A machine realization of Table 5.

   The general problem of synthesis is the problem of determining from an arbitrary transition graph or table how many feedback loops are necessary and what specific logic should be incorporated into the function generator. A generalized block diagram where each line may represent many channels is shown in Fig. 18.

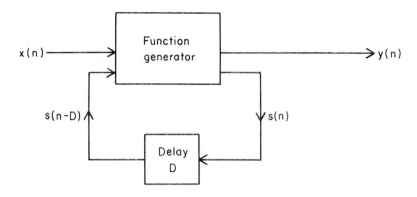

Fig. 18. Generalized block diagram for a sequential machine.

Here

$x(n)$ = present input
$y(n)$ = present output = function of $x(n)$ and $s(n - D)$
$s(n)$ = present state = function of $x(n)$ and $s(n - D)$
$s(n - D)$ = previous state
D = delay in changing from one internal state to another. (D may be a set of different delays corresponding to the multichannel nature of the variables.)
$s(n - D)$ = $s(n)$, except when a transition from one internal state to another has been initiated. Once the transition is complete, the equality sign again holds.

The transition time corresponds to the delay time D, for the function generator is assumed instantaneous in behavior.

The operation of the generalized circuit is as follows:

(1) A change in $x(n)$ produces a change in $s(n)$. [The new $s(n)$ corresponds to the next internal state of the system.]
(2) The new $s(n)$ produces a change in $s(n - D)$ after a delay of D.
(3) The new $s(n - D)$ produces a change in $y(n)$. [The system enters the new internal state simultaneously with the change in $s(n - D)$.]
(4) The change in the $s(n - D)$ may cause another change in the $s(n)$ in the same manner as did the change in $x(n)$.

In this section the problem of designing near-optimum nonlinear filters has been reduced to two separate subproblems, namely, the design of *linear* filters on local criteria and the design of *finite* state machines to control these linear filters on global criteria. The key word for the first subproblem is "linear"; for the second, "finite." There are methods for handling each of these subproblems.

5.11 Reduction of a multichannel process to uncorrelated single-channel processes

As an example, let us consider the two-channel symmetric autoregressive process x_t given by

$$\sigma\begin{bmatrix} A(z) & B(z) \\ B(z) & A(z) \end{bmatrix}\begin{bmatrix} x_{1t} \\ x_{2t} \end{bmatrix} = \begin{bmatrix} \epsilon_{1t} \\ \epsilon_{2t} \end{bmatrix},$$

where $A(z) = a_0 + a_1 z + \cdots + a_m z^m$ and $B(z) = b_0 + b_1 z + \cdots + b_n z^n$ represent single-channel operators. The spectral matrix of x_t is the extended hermitian matrix

$$\Phi(z) = \left(\begin{bmatrix} A(z) & B(z) \\ B(z) & A(z) \end{bmatrix}\begin{bmatrix} A(z^{-1}) & B(z^{-1}) \\ B(z^{-1}) & A(z^{-1}) \end{bmatrix}\right)^{-1}.$$

We see that

$$\Phi(z)\begin{bmatrix} 1/\sqrt{2} \\ 1/\sqrt{2} \end{bmatrix} = [A(z) + B(z)]^{-1}\,[A(z^{-1}) + B(z^{-1})]^{-1}\begin{bmatrix} 1/\sqrt{2} \\ 1/\sqrt{2} \end{bmatrix},$$

so that $C_1 = [1/\sqrt{2}, 1/\sqrt{2}]^T$ is the eigen-column-vector of $\Phi(z)$ corresponding to the eigenvalue

$$\lambda_1(z) = [A(z) + B(z)]^{-1}[A(z^{-1}) + B(z^{-1})]^{-1}.$$

Likewise, we see that $C_2 = [1/\sqrt{2}, -1/\sqrt{2}]^T$ is the eigen-column-vector of $\Phi(z)$ corresponding to the eigenvalue

$$\lambda_2(z) = [A(z) - B(z)]^{-1}[A(z^{-1}) - B(z^{-1})]^{-1}.$$

Hence $\Phi(z)$ may be written as

$$\Phi(z) = C_1\lambda_1(z)C_1^T + C_2\lambda_2(z)C_2^T$$

$$= [C_1 \quad C_2]\begin{bmatrix} \lambda_1(z) & 0 \\ 0 & \lambda_2(z) \end{bmatrix}\begin{bmatrix} C_1^T \\ C_2^T \end{bmatrix}.$$

In this case, the matrix

$$U = [C_1 \quad C_2] = \begin{bmatrix} 1/\sqrt{2} & 1/\sqrt{2} \\ 1/\sqrt{2} & -1/\sqrt{2} \end{bmatrix}$$

is an orthogonal matrix (so $U\,U^T = I$); more generally, U will be an extended unitary matrix

$$U(z) = [C_1(z) \quad C_2(z)]$$

(so $U(z) U_*(z) = U(z)[U(1/z^*)]^{*T} = I$). Hence the spectral matrix of x_t may be written as

$$\Phi(z) = U(z)\Lambda(z)U_*(z),$$

where $\Lambda(z)$ is the diagonal matrix with the elements $\lambda_1(z)$ and $\lambda_2(z)$ on its diagonal. If we define the two-channel process y_t by the unitary transformation

$$y_t = U_*(z)x_t$$

which, in our example, gives

$$y_{1t} = (x_{1t} + x_{2t})/\sqrt{2}$$
$$y_{2t} = (x_{1t} - x_{2t})/\sqrt{2},$$

then we see that the component single-channel processes y_{1t} and y_{2t} are mutually uncorrelated with spectral functions $\lambda_1(z)$ and $\lambda_2(z)$, respectively, because

$$\Phi_{yy}(z) = U_*(z)\Phi(z)U(z)$$
$$= U_*(z)U(z)\Lambda(z)U_*(z)U(z)$$
$$= \Lambda(z),$$

which shows that the diagonal matrix $\Lambda(z)$ is the spectral matrix of the process y_t.

Although we have dealt with two-channel processes in this section, it is clear that this treatment applies to an arbitrary number of channels.

6

Multichannel Prediction and Signal Enhancement

6.1 Multichannel Wiener filtering

The many present-day theories for prediction and signal enhancement in time series analysis are to a large measure the outgrowth of the original work of Norbert Wiener.[53] The papers and books which have interpreted, modified, and extended the methods of Wiener represent a large and significant contribution to science and engineering. Although the mathematical level of Wiener's book was quite advanced, engineers were willing to study and make use of his results because his work represented the first analytical techniques for the systematic design of filters to be used for the separation of desired signals from unwanted noise.

Let us briefly review some of the problems involved in preserving or enhancing the waveshape of a signal immersed in noise, and in predicting the future values of the signal. A filter which performs the operation of signal enhancement is called an *enhancement filter*, or a *data-smoothing filter*. The reason for the use of the word "smoothing" is that such a filter generally produces the effect of "smoothing the data" in performing its task of removing the unwanted random roughness caused by the noise. A filter which performs the operation of signal prediction or forecasting is called a *prediction filter*. A filter may combine both operations; a *smoothing and predicting* filter separates

---

[53] Wiener, N., *The Extrapolation, Interpolation, and Smoothing of Stationary Time Series with Engineering Applications*, M.I.T. Press, Cambridge, Mass., 1942.

the wanted signal from a signal-plus-noise complex and yields future values of the signal.

The simplest case of *prediction* is that in which the pure signal s_t is processed. That is, we suppose that the signal time series s_t is available without any noise. We know the signal s_t for past values of time, and we require a device to yield, as well as possible, the value at a future, or advanced, time. In other words, the signal s_t is the input to a realizable filter. The filter is designed so that its actual output y_t is the best approximation to the desired output $s_{t+\alpha}$, namely, the signal advanced by the positive time advance (or prediction distance) α.

Signal enhancement may be described as the problem of separating as well as possible a signal time series from an unwanted noise time series. The time series x_t which we have available is a noisy time series. It is assumed that the noisy time series x_t consists of a pure component s_t, called the signal, and an impure component n_t, called the noise, that is, $x_t = s_t + n_t$. We are only interested in the signal s_t, the noise n_t being unwanted. We therefore want to design a realizable filter which will filter out, as well as possible, the noise contaminating the signal, thereby enhancing the signal in relation to the noise. The filter should be designed so that its actual output y_t is as close as possible to the desired output s_t, namely, the signal.

The signal enhancement operation may be modified in several ways. For example, the desired output may be the signal delayed by a certain time constant β. This is the case of *signal enhancement with delay*. The noisy time series x_t is fed into a realizable filter. The filter is designed so that its actual output y_t is the best approximation to the desired output $s_{t-\beta}$, namely, the signal delayed by the positive time delay (or time lag) β.

Another example is the case in which the desired output is the signal advanced by a certain time constant α. The introduction of this time advance (or prediction distance) means that the filter is required to predict future values of the signal. This case which incorporates both signal enhancement and prediction is called *signal enhancement with advance*. Here we feed the noisy time series x_t into a realizable filter. The filter is designed so that its actual output y_t is the best approximation to the desired output $s_{t+\alpha}$, namely, the signal advanced by the positive time advance α.

Finally, let us formulate the general case, which includes each of the above cases as a special case. The desired output may be any time series z_t. We wish to feed a time series x_t into a realizable filter. The filter is designed so that its actual output y_t is the best approximation to the desired output z_t.

After the publication of Wiener's book in 1942, there appeared over the years many simplified and more easily assimilated versions of his theory. In keeping with Wiener's original treatment which was formulated primarily in terms of continuous time, most of these papers, being written for engineers, were restricted to continuous time functions rather than discrete time series.

A notable exception, however, was an important paper of N. Levinson.[54] Levinson's paper, which was written a few months after Wiener's work appeared in 1942, adapted the Wiener methods to the case of discrete time series and finite-length discrete operators. Levinson's work made it possible for several war-time scientific projects at M.I.T. engaged in the statistical analysis of time series data to make use of Wiener's results. One such project was the M.I.T. long-range weather forecasting project (W30–053–ac–1065) directed by Professor G. P. Wadsworth,[55] which performed statistical analyses on meteorological and climatological data. Levinson's treatment was concerned with the single-channel case; the extension to the multichannel case is given in the next two sections: Sec. 6.2 gives the derivation of the multichannel finite-length discrete Wiener filter, and Sec. 6.3 gives the multichannel counterpart[56] of the Levinson recursive method of solving the normal equations for the filter coefficients.

Various criticisms have been directed at the Wiener theory of signal enhancement and prediction. Some of these criticisms are directed at the underlying assumptions used in the theory; these assumptions are discussed in the next section. Other criticisms have resulted from the almost insurmountable practical problems encountered in actually synthesizing the optimal filters in the form of physical networks (hardware). Except in a relatively few special and simple applications, the synthesis of a Wiener filter by analog methods is an extremely laborious and difficult task. As a result, the designer must often resort to approximations and compromises. In the continuous time formulation of Wiener theory, the optimum filter is given as the solution of the Wiener—Hopf integral equation. The solution rests on the factorization of the spectrum, and the difficulties encountered in solving the Wiener–Hopf integral equation for arbitrary spectral kernels are severe at best. This has motivated investigators to search for appropriate approximation solutions. In the multichannel case, these problems of synthesizing the theoretically optimum filter responses become so difficult that virtually no analog realizations of multichannel Wiener filters exist in practice.

However, when one turns from analog to digital, the difficult problems of synthesizing the theoretically optimum filter responses disappear. In Sec. 6.4 we give subroutine WIENER, which is a software realization that designs and computes the optimum multichannel Wiener filter from the given data.

[54] Levinson, N., "The Wiener RMS (root-mean-square) error criterion in filter design and prediction"; Appendix in Wiener, N., *op. cit.*

[55] Wadsworth, G. P., "Short range and extended forecasting by statistical methods," *Tech. Rept.* 105–37, Air Weather Service, Washington, D.C., 1948.

[56] Robinson, E. A., "Mathematical development of discrete filters for the detection of nuclear explosions," *J. Geophys. Research* **68**, 5559–5567 (1963). The recursive method for finding the prediction error operator and hindsight error operator, but not the filter coefficients, was independently given by Whittle, P., *Prediction and Regulation*, English Univ. Press, London, 1963, p. 102.

The general purpose digital computer replaces the need for specialized analog equipment and makes possible the widespread use of multichannel Wiener filters on a practical and economically attractive basis. Moreover, one can use subroutine WIENER in data-processing applications even though he does not wish to follow all of the mathematical derivations given in Secs. 6.2 and 6.3, just as one can drive a car without knowing about all of the principles involved in its manufacture. However, one should always have in mind the basic assumptions and limitations; much of this knowledge will come from practice, that is, from the use of Wiener filters under various conditions on actual data. Here as elsewhere there is no substitute for experience.

6.2 Design of multichannel Wiener digital filters

The basic problem in the design of multichannel Wiener digital filters is that of determining the numerical values of the filter coefficients $(f_0, f_1, f_2, \ldots)$. The solution of this problem rests on three main assumptions which determine the range of application of the results. The three assumptions are:

(1) The time series representing the input x_t and the desired output z_t are stationary, which means essentially that the statistical properties of the input and desired output do not change with time.

(2) The approximation criterion is taken to be the mean-square-error between the desired output and the actual output. This means that we determine the operator $(f_0, f_1, f_2, \ldots)$ in such a way as to minimize the trace of the mean-square-error matrix between the desired output z_t and the actual output y_t. This trace is given by

$$I = \operatorname{tr} E\{(z_t - y_t)(z_t - y_t)^{\mathrm{T}}\} .$$

The average is the ensemble average E, which is taken over all possible inputs and desired outputs with each weighted according to its probability of occurrence. In case the time series are ergodic, the ensemble averages can be replaced by the corresponding time averages.

(3) The operation to be used for signal enhancement and prediction is assumed to be a linear operation on the available information, or in engineering terms, a time-invariant linear filter is used. The available information consists of the past history of the perturbed signal, i.e., the time series x_s with $-\infty < s \leq t$, where t is the present time. A physically realizable filter [i.e., one with a memory function $(f_0, f_1, f_2, \ldots)$ but no anticipation function] performs a linear operation on x_s over just this range. For digital computer applications, we want to further restrict ourselves to the case when the operator is of finite length, say, $(f_0, f_1, \ldots, f_m)$.

The Wiener theory may therefore be described as linear least-square prediction and enhancement of stationary time series by means of a realizable, time-invariant linear operator. It is recognized that the theory applies only when the above three assumptions are fulfilled, or at least are approximately satisfied. If any one of the conditions is eliminated or changed, then the change must be taken into account.

The theory of linear least-square prediction and enhancement is based on statistical regularity. It is on this basis that it is possible to predict, albeit not perfectly, the future behavior of a time series when all that is known is a perturbed version of its past history. In general, prediction and enhancement depend fundamentally on the assumption that regularities that have occurred in the past will recur in the future. Such an assumption, of course, can never be proved, but should be regarded as a postulate. The basic assumption that statistical regularities of the past will hold in the future appears in the mathematical treatment as the assumption that the various time series are stationary. This implies that a value of a parameter obtained by averaging the time series over the past will be the same as the value obtained by averaging over the future. More specifically, prediction and enhancement depend essentially on the existence of correlations between the desired output z_t and the input x_t. The assumption that the prediction and/or enhancement is to be done by a linear operation implies that the only type of correlation that can be used is linear correlation, namely, the autocorrelation function

$$\phi_{xx}(\tau) = E\{x_t x_{t-\tau}^T\}, \qquad \tau = 0, 1, 2, \ldots$$

of the input, and the cross-correlation function

$$\phi_{zx}(\tau) = E\{z_t x_{t-\tau}^T\}, \qquad \tau = 0, 1, 2, \ldots$$

between desired output and input. If the cross-correlation function between desired output and input (which in the case of pure prediction reduces to the displaced autocorrelation function of the input) were zero, then no significant linear estimation would be possible, and so the best mean-square estimate of the desired output would be its mean value.

With the proper use of vectors and matrices, the case of multichannel filtering is only a simple extension of the case of single-channel filtering.

Let the *filter* be represented by the $M \times N$ matrix-valued coefficients

$$f_s \equiv f(s) = \begin{bmatrix} f_{11}(s) & f_{12}(s) & \cdots & f_{N1}(s) \\ & \cdots & & \\ f_{M1}(s) & f_{21}(s) & \cdots & f_{MN}(s) \end{bmatrix}.$$

Let the input time series be given by the $N \times 1$ vector-valued time series

$$x_t \equiv x(t) = \begin{bmatrix} x_1(t) \\ x_2(t) \\ \cdot \\ \cdot \\ \cdot \\ x_N(t) \end{bmatrix},$$

and let the desired output time series be given by the $M \times 1$ vector-valued time series

$$z_t \equiv z(t) = \begin{bmatrix} z_1(t) \\ z_2(t) \\ \cdot \\ \cdot \\ \cdot \\ z_M(t) \end{bmatrix}.$$

Let us now derive the optimum finite-length operator for prediction and/or enhancement. Without loss of generality, we may assume that the mean values have been removed from the input and desired output, so $E\{x_t\} = 0$ and $E\{z_t\} = 0$. The actual output, which is the convolution of the input with the operator, is given by the matrix equation

$$y_t = f_0 x_t + f_1 x_{t-1} + \cdots + f_m x_{t-m}.$$

The structure of these mathematical operations is shown schematically by Fig. 19.

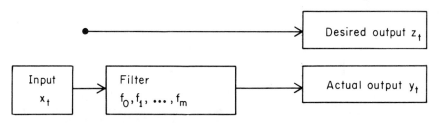

Fig. 19. Block diagram of multichannel Wiener filtering.

We note that the actual output is given by the $M \times 1$ vector-valued time series

$$y_t \equiv y(t) = \begin{bmatrix} y_1(t) \\ y_2(t) \\ \cdot \\ \cdot \\ \cdot \\ y_M(t) \end{bmatrix}.$$

The error e_t between desired output and actual output is then

$$e_t = z_t - y_t = z_t - (f_0 x_t + f_1 x_{t-1} + \cdots + f_m x_{t-m}).$$

This error is, in fact, the $M \times 1$ vector-valued time series

$$e_t = z_t - y_t = \begin{bmatrix} z_1(t) - y_1(t) \\ \cdots \\ z_M(t) - y_M(t) \end{bmatrix} \equiv \begin{bmatrix} e_1(t) \\ \cdots \\ e_M(t) \end{bmatrix}.$$

Now we consider the *mean-square-error matrix* defined by

$$E\{e_t\, e_t^T\} = \begin{bmatrix} E\{e_1^2(t)\} & E\{e_1(t)\, e_2(t)\} & \cdots & E\{e_1(t)\, e_M(t)\} \\ & \cdots & & \\ E\{e_M(t)\, e_1(t)\} & E\{e_M(t)\, e_2(t)\} & \cdots & E\{e_M^2(t)\} \end{bmatrix}$$

The trace (abbreviated tr) of a square matrix is defined as the sum of its diagonal entries. Hence the trace of the mean-square-error matrix is

$$I \equiv \mathrm{tr}\, E\{e_t\, e_t^T\} = E\{e_1^2(t)\} + E\{e_2^2(t)\} + \cdots + E\{e_M^2(t)\} .$$

We wish to determine the values of the filter coefficients f_s such that the trace I of the mean-square-error matrix is a minimum. Now the error e_t may be written as

$$e_t = z_t - y_t = z_t - \sum_{s=0}^{m} f_s x_{t-s} .$$

Hence

$$\begin{aligned} e_t\, e_t^T &= (z_t - \Sigma f_s x_{t-s})(z_t - \Sigma f_r x_{t-r})^T \\ &= z_t z_t^T - z_t(\Sigma f_r x_{t-r})^T - \Sigma f_s x_{t-s} z_t^T + (\Sigma f_s x_{t-s})(\Sigma f_r x_{t-r})^T \\ &= z_t z_t^T - z_t \Sigma x_{t-r}^T f_r^T - \Sigma f_s x_{t-s} z_t^T + \Sigma\, \Sigma f_s x_{t-s} x_{t-r}^T f_r^T . \end{aligned}$$

Thus, taking the ensemble average, we have

$$E(e_t e_t^T) = E(z_t z_t^T) - \Sigma E(z_t x_{t-r}^T) f_r^T - \Sigma f_s\, E(x_{t-s} z_t^T) + \Sigma\, \Sigma f_s\, E(x_{t-s} x_{t-r}^T) f_r .$$

Define the cross-correlation matrix between desired output and input as

$$E(z_t x_{t-r}^T) = E(z_{t+r} x_t^T) = \phi_{zx}(r) \qquad (M \times N \text{ matrix}) ,$$

where the first equal sign in this equation follows because of stationarity. Also define the cross-correlation matrix between input and desired output as

$$E(x_{t-s} z_t^T) = \phi_{xz}(-s) \qquad (N \times M \text{ matrix}) .$$

At this point, let us note that these two cross-correlation functions are related by

$$\phi_{xz}^T(-s) = E(z_t x_{t-s}^T) = \phi_{zx}(s) .$$

Finally define the autocorrelation function of the input as

$$E(x_{t-s} x_{t-r}^T) = \phi_{xx}(r - s) \qquad (N \times N \text{ matrix}) .$$

Hence we see that $E(e_t e_t^T)$ may be written in terms of these correlation functions as

$$E(e_t e_t^T) = E(z_t z_t^T) - \Sigma \phi_{zx}(r) f_r^T - \Sigma f_s \phi_{xz}(-s) + \Sigma\, \Sigma f_s \phi_{xx}(r - s) f_r^T .$$

Setting the partial derivative of

$$I = \mathrm{tr}\, E(e_t e_t^T)$$

with respect to each filter coefficient equal to zero, we obtain the set of simultaneous equations given by

$$f_0\phi_{xx}(0) + f_1\phi_{xx}(-1) + \cdots + f_m\phi_{xx}(-m) = \phi_{zx}(0)$$
$$f_0\phi_{xx}(1) + f_1\phi_{xx}(0) + \cdots + f_m\phi_{xx}(1-m) = \phi_{zx}(1)$$
$$\cdots$$
$$f_0\phi_{xx}(m) + f_1\phi_{xx}(m-1) + \cdots + f_m\phi_{xx}(0) = \phi_{zx}(m) .$$

The solution of these equations yields the optimum $(m+1)$-length operator. These equations are called the *normal equations*. The known quantities are the autocorrelation coefficients $\phi_{xx}(\tau)$ of the input x_t and the cross-correlation coefficients $\phi_{zx}(\tau)$ of the desired output z_t with the input x_t. The unknown quantities are the operator coefficients $(f_0, f_1, \ldots, f_m)$. Because the matrix of this set of equations is an autocorrelation matrix, the solution may be obtained by making use of the computationally efficient recursion given in the next section. In practice, one usually assumes that the time series are ergodic, and estimates the required autocorrelation and cross-correlation coefficients as time averages rather than as ensemble averages.

Let us now investigate the structure of the normal equations with respect to the minimization problem. If we make the following definitions

$$\text{term } 1 = E(z_t z_t^T) = \phi_{zz}(0)$$
$$\text{term } 2 = \Sigma \phi_{zx}(r) f_r^T$$
$$\text{term } 3 = \Sigma f_s \phi_{xz}(-s) = \Sigma f_s \phi_{zx}^T(s)$$
$$\text{term } 4 = \Sigma \Sigma f_s \phi_{xx}(r-s) f_r^T ,$$

then we see that

$$E(e_t e_t^T) = \text{term } 1 - \text{term } 2 - \text{term } 3 + \text{term } 4 .$$

When we minimize $I = \text{tr } E(e_t e_t^T)$, the result is that

$$\text{term } 4 = \text{term } 2 = \text{term } 3 .$$

Hence from

$$\text{term } 4 = \text{term } 2 ,$$

we have

$$\sum_r \sum_s f_s \phi_{xx}(r-s) f_r^T = \sum_r \phi_{zx}(r) f_r^T .$$

Cancelling the $\sum_r$ and f_r^T, we have

$$\sum_{s=0}^{m} f_s \phi_{xx}(r-s) = \phi_{zx}(r) \qquad \text{for } r = 0, 1, 2, \ldots, m ,$$

which are the normal equations. As a verification, let us consider the equation

$$\text{term } 4 = \text{term } 3 .$$

This equation gives

$$\Sigma \, \Sigma f_s \phi_{xx}(r - s) f_r^{\mathrm{T}} = \Sigma f_s \phi_{xz}(-s)$$

or

$$\Sigma \phi_{xx}(r - s) f_r^{\mathrm{T}} = \phi_{xz}(-s) .$$

Since

$$\phi_{xz}^{\mathrm{T}}(-s) = \phi_{zx}(s) ,$$

it follows that

$$\phi_{xz}(-s) = \phi_{zx}^{\mathrm{T}}(s) .$$

Thus

$$\Sigma \phi_{xx}(r - s) f_r^{\mathrm{T}} = \phi_{zx}^{\mathrm{T}}(s) .$$

Taking transposes, we have [since $\phi_{xx}^{\mathrm{T}}(r - s) = \phi_{xx}(s - r)$]

$$\sum_{r=0}^{m} f_r \phi_{xx}(s - r) = \phi_{zx}(s) \qquad \text{for } s = 0, 1, 2, \ldots, m ,$$

which again are the same normal equations, but in this case the role of s and r is reversed from that of the foregoing case.

The minimum value of the trace of the mean-square-error matrix is

$$I_{\min} = \text{tr (term 1} - \text{term 2)} = \text{tr } \phi_{zz}(0) - \text{tr } \sum_{r=0}^{m} \phi_{zx}(r) f_r^{\mathrm{T}} .$$

The value of the minimum trace $I_{\min}$ of the mean-square-error matrix depends upon the parameter m (i.e., depends upon the filter length). If m is increased (i.e., if we use a longer filter), the value of $I_{\min}$ must either remain stationary or decrease. In practice one usually computes filters of successively increasing lengths, making use of the recursion given in the next section. The values of minimum mean-square-error traces $I_{\min}$ diminish as the length of the filter increases. The recursion from n to $n + 1$ can be stopped when one of a set of pre-set conditions is first met, such as:

(1) the filter reaches some maximum pre-set length
(2) the normalized mean-square-error $I_{\min}/\text{tr } \phi_{zz}(0)$ reaches some minimum pre-set value
(3) the normalized mean-square-error sequence levels out and shows little likelihood of further appreciable decrease.

These questions are intimately connected to the problem of fitting autoregressive schemes of successively increasing order to time series data, for which effective procedures and statistical tests exist.[57,58] In summary, we may say that these are statistical issues for which there is an extensive statistical literature.[59]

6.3 *Recursive solution of the multichannel normal equations*

In the last section we saw how to design multichannel least-squares (Wiener) filters. The numerical coefficients of such filters are found by the solution of a set of linear equations called the normal equations. Whenever a filter with a large number of coefficients is required, this solution requires a great deal of computation if one of the conventional computational techniques for solving a set of linear equations is used. However, because the matrix of this set of equations is in the form of a block Töplitz matrix (i.e., a matrix with equal submatrices, or blocks, on any block diagonal) a recursive technique may be used which greatly decreases the amount of computation necessary.

For simplicity of notation, let r_t designate the multichannel autocorrelation coefficient $\phi_{xx}(t)$, and let g_t designate the multichannel cross-correlation coefficient $\phi_{zx}(t)$. Then the normal equations given in the last section may be written as

$$f_0 r_0 + f_1 r_{-1} + \cdots + f_m r_{-m} = g_0$$
$$f_0 r_1 + f_1 r_0 + \cdots + f_m r_{-m+1} = g_1$$
$$\cdots$$
$$f_0 r_m + f_1 r_{m-1} + \cdots + f_m r_0 = g_m .$$

In matrix notation, the normal equations become

$$[f_0, f_1, \ldots, f_m] \begin{bmatrix} r_0 & r_1 & \ldots & r_m \\ r_{-1} & r_0 & \ldots & r_{m-1} \\ & & \ldots & \\ r_{-m} & r_{-m+1} & \ldots & r_0 \end{bmatrix} = [g_0, g_1, \ldots, g_m] .$$

In this set of normal equations the M × N matrix elements $f_0, f_1, \ldots, f_m$ are the filter coefficients and represent the unknowns. The symmetric square matrix, which is the multichannel autocorrelation matrix, is in the form of a block Töplitz matrix; that is, the N × N matrix elements r_{i-j} along any (block) diagonal are the same. These N × N matrix elements, namely, $r_{-m}, r_{-m+1}, \ldots, r_m$, are the autocorrelation coefficients of the input x_t. These autocorrelation coefficients satisfy

$$r_{-t} = r_t^T$$

[57] Bartlett, M. S., "On the theoretical specification and sampling properties of auto-correlated time series" (with discussion), *J. Roy. Stat. Soc. Suppl.* **8**, 27–41 (1946).

[58] Quenouille, M. H., "A large sample test for the goodness of fit of autoregressive schemes," *J. Roy. Stat. Soc., Ser.* **A**, **110**, 123–129 (1947).

[59] See Wold, H., ed., *Bibliography on Time Series and Stochastic Processes*, Oliver and Boyd, Edinburgh, 1965.

and represent known quantities in the normal equations. The M × N matrix elements on the right-hand side, namely, $g_0, g_1, \ldots, g_m$, are the cross-correlation coefficients between the desired output z_t and the input x_t. These cross-correlation coefficients also represent known quantities in the normal equations.

Our purpose in this section is to provide an efficient computational solution to these normal equations.

Corresponding to each autocorrelation matrix (for $n = 0, 1, 2, 3, \ldots$)

$$R_{n+1} = \begin{bmatrix} r_0 & r_1 & \cdots & r_{n+1} \\ r_{-1} & r_0 & \cdots & r_n \\ & & \cdots & \\ r_{-n-1} & r_{-n} & \cdots & r_0 \end{bmatrix},$$

there are two auxiliary sequences, one called the *prediction-error operator* and the other the *hindsight-error operator*. The prediction-error operator

$$[a_0(n), a_1(n), \ldots, a_n(n)]$$

is that operator which satisfies

$$[a_0(n), a_1(n), \ldots, a_n(n), 0]R_{n+1} = [v_a(n), 0, \ldots, 0, u_a(n)] ,$$

where $a_0(n)$ is equal to the identity matrix I. In particular, $u_a(n)$ is computed by the formula

$$u_a(n) = a_0(n)r_{n+1} + a_1(n)r_n + \cdots + a_n(n)r_1 .$$

The hindsight-error operator

$$[0, b_n(n), \ldots, b_1(n), b_0(n)]$$

is that operator which satisfies

$$[0, b_n(n), \ldots, b_1(n), b_0(n)]R_{n+1} = [u_b(n), 0, \ldots, 0, v_b(n)] ,$$

where $b_0(n)$ is equal to the identity matrix. Although $u_b(n)$ may be computed by the formula

$$u_b(n) = b_n(n)r_{-1} + \cdots + b_1(n)r_{-n} + b_0(n)r_{-n-1} ,$$

we do not need to do so, for $u_b(n)$ is the transpose of $u_a(n)$, that is,

$$u_b(n) = u_a(n)^{\mathrm{T}} .$$

It is convenient to write these two auxiliary sequences as the coefficients of matrix polynomials

$$A_n(z) = a_0(n) + a_1(n)z + \cdots + a_n(n)z^n$$
$$B_n(z) = b_n(n)z^n + \cdots + b_1(n)z + b_0(n) .$$

In the single-channel case (i.e., when N = 1) it is true that $A_n(z) = B_n(z)$; however, this is not generally so in the multichannel case (i.e., when N > 1).

To extend the length of these auxiliary sequences, we form the linear combination $A_n(z) - c_a(n + 1)z^{n+1}B_n(z^{-1})$ to find

$$[a_0(n), a_1(n) - c_a(n + 1)b_n(n), \ldots, a_n(n) - c_a(n + 1)b_1(n), -c_a(n + 1)b_0(n)]R_{n+1}$$
$$= [v_a(n) - c_a(n + 1)u_b(n), 0, \ldots, 0, u_a(n) - c_a(n + 1)v_b(n)]$$

and the linear combination $B_n(z) - c_b(n + 1)z^{n+1}A_n(z^{-1})$ to find

$$[-c_b(n + 1)a_0(n), b_n(n) - c_b(n + 1)a_1(n), \ldots, b_1(n) - c_b(n + 1)a_n(n), b_0(n)]R_n$$
$$= [u_b(n) - c_b(n + 1)v_a(n), 0, \ldots, 0, v_b(n) - c_b(n + 1)u_a(n)].$$

We want to choose $c_a(n + 1)$ and $c_b(n + 1)$ so that

$$u_a(n) - c_a(n + 1)v_b(n) = 0$$
$$u_b(n) - c_b(n + 1)v_a(n) = 0 .$$

That is, we compute $c_a(n + 1)$ and $c_b(n + 1)$ by the formulas

$$c_a(n + 1) = u_a(n)v_b(n)^{-1}$$
$$c_b(n + 1) = u_b(n)v_a(n)^{-1} .$$

The new prediction-error operator (i.e., the one for $n + 1$) is then

$$[a_0(n + 1), a_1(n + 1), \ldots, a_n(n + 1), a_{n+1}(n + 1)] = [a_0(n),$$
$$a_1(n) - c_a(n + 1)b_n(n), \ldots, a_n(n) - c_a(n + 1)b_1(n), -c_a(n + 1)b_0(n)] ,$$

and the new hindsight-error operator (i.e., the one for $n + 1$) is

$$[b_{n+1}(n + 1), b_n(n + 1), \ldots, b_1(n + 1), b_0(n + 1)] = [-c_b(n + 1)a_0(n),$$
$$b_n(n) - c_b(n + 1)a_1(n), \ldots, b_1(n) - c_b(n + 1)a_n(n), b_0(n)] .$$

Thus the polynomials satisfy the following recursion formulas:

$$A_{n+1}(z) = A_n(z) - c_a(n + 1)z^{n+1}B_n(z^{-1})$$
$$B_{n+1}(z) = B_n(z) - c_b(n + 1)z^{n+1}A_n(z^{-1}) .$$

The new variances (i.e., the ones for $n + 1$) are given by

$$v_a(n + 1) = v_a(n) - c_a(n + 1)u_b(n)$$
$$v_b(n + 1) = v_b(n) - c_b(n + 1)u_a(n) .$$

We now make use of the hindsight-error operator $B_{n+1}(z)$ to extend the length of the filter. The filter polynomial (for n) is

$$F_n(z) = f_0(n) + f_1(n)z + \cdots + f_n(n)z^n ,$$

where the filter coefficients satisfy

$$[f_0(n), f_1(n), \ldots, f_n(n), 0]R_{n+1} = [g_0, g_1, \ldots, g_n, \gamma(n + 1)] ,$$

where, in particular, $\gamma(n + 1)$ is computed by the formula

$$\gamma(n + 1) = f_0(n)r_{n+1} + f_1(n)r_n + \cdots + f_n(n)r_1 .$$

The linear combination $F_n(z) - c_f(n + 1)z^{n+1}B_{n+1}(z^{-1})$ gives

$$[f_0(n) - c_f(n + 1)b_{n+1}(n + 1), \ldots, f_n(n) - c_f(n + 1)b_1(n + 1),$$
$$- c_f(n + 1)b_0(n + 1)]R_{n+1} = [g_0, \ldots, g_n, \gamma(n + 1) - c_f(n + 1)v_b(n + 1)].$$

Thus we set

$$g_{n+1} = \gamma(n + 1) - c_f(n + 1)v_b(n + 1)$$

so $c_f(n + 1)$ may be computed by

$$c_f(n + 1) = [\gamma(n + 1) - g_{n+1}]v_b(n + 1)^{-1}.$$

Hence the new filter (i.e., the one for $n + 1$) is given by

$$f_0(n + 1), \ldots, f_n(n + 1), f_{n+1}(n + 1)] = [f_0(n) - c_f(n + 1)b_{n+1}(n + 1),$$
$$\ldots, f_n(n) - c_f(n + 1)b_1(n + 1), - c_f(n + 1)b_0(n + 1)].$$

In terms of the polynomials, this gives the recursion formula

$$F_{n+1}(z) = F_n(z) - c_f(n + 1)z^{n+1}B_{n+1}(z^{-1}).$$

Let us now consider a numerical example. Suppose that the number N of input channels is $N = 2$ and that the number M of output channels is $M = 1$. Let the first two autocorrelation coefficients be

$$r_0 = \begin{bmatrix} 7 & -1 \\ -1 & 3 \end{bmatrix}, \quad r_1 = \begin{bmatrix} -2 & -2 \\ 1 & 1 \end{bmatrix},$$

and the first two cross-correlation coefficients be

$$g_0 = \begin{bmatrix} 1 & 0 \end{bmatrix}, \quad g_1 = \begin{bmatrix} 0 & 1 \end{bmatrix}.$$

The first step in the recursion is to set the initial values

$$a_0(0) = b_0(0) = \begin{bmatrix} 1 & 0 \\ 0 & 1 \end{bmatrix}$$

$$v_a(0) = a_0(0)r_0 = \begin{bmatrix} 7 & -1 \\ -1 & 3 \end{bmatrix}$$

$$v_b(0) = b_0(0)r_0 = \begin{bmatrix} 7 & -1 \\ -1 & 3 \end{bmatrix}$$

$$f_0(0) = g_0 r_0^{-1} = \begin{bmatrix} 1 & 0 \end{bmatrix} \begin{bmatrix} 0.15 & 0.05 \\ 0.05 & 0.35 \end{bmatrix} = \begin{bmatrix} 0.15 & 0.05 \end{bmatrix}.$$

We also have

$$u_a(0) = a_0(0)r_1 = \begin{bmatrix} -2 & -2 \\ 1 & 1 \end{bmatrix}$$

$$u_b(0) = u_a(0)^{\mathrm{T}} = \begin{bmatrix} -2 & 1 \\ -2 & 1 \end{bmatrix}.$$

We now wish to extend our filter from the initial case 0 to case 1. To do so, we compute

$$c_a(1) = u_a(0)v_b(0)^{-1} = \begin{bmatrix} -2 & -2 \\ 1 & 1 \end{bmatrix} \begin{bmatrix} 0.15 & 0.05 \\ 0.05 & 0.35 \end{bmatrix} = \begin{bmatrix} -0.4 & -0.8 \\ 0.2 & 0.4 \end{bmatrix}$$

$$c_b(1) = u_b(0)v_a(0)^{-1} = \begin{bmatrix} -2 & 1 \\ -2 & 1 \end{bmatrix} \begin{bmatrix} 0.15 & 0.05 \\ 0.05 & 0.35 \end{bmatrix} = \begin{bmatrix} -0.25 & 0.25 \\ -0.25 & 0.25 \end{bmatrix}.$$

Hence the new auxiliary sequences are

$$[a_0(1), a_1(1)] = [a_0(0), -c_a(1)b_0(0)]$$
$$[b_1(1), b_0(1)] = [-c_b(1)a_0(0), b_0(0)],$$

which gives

$$a_0(1) = a_0(0) = \begin{bmatrix} 1 & 0 \\ 0 & 1 \end{bmatrix}$$

$$a_1(1) = -c_a(1)b_0(0) = \begin{bmatrix} 0.4 & 0.8 \\ -0.2 & -0.4 \end{bmatrix}$$

$$b_1(1) = -c_b(1)a_0(0) = \begin{bmatrix} 0.25 & -0.25 \\ 0.25 & -0.25 \end{bmatrix}$$

$$b_0(1) = b_0(0) = \begin{bmatrix} 1 & 0 \\ 0 & 1 \end{bmatrix}.$$

The new variances are

$$v_a(1) = v_a(0) - c_a(1)u_b(0)$$
$$= \begin{bmatrix} 7 & -1 \\ -1 & 3 \end{bmatrix} - \begin{bmatrix} -0.4 & -0.8 \\ 0.2 & 0.4 \end{bmatrix} \begin{bmatrix} -2 & 1 \\ -2 & 1 \end{bmatrix} = \begin{bmatrix} 4.6 & 0.2 \\ 0.2 & 2.4 \end{bmatrix}$$

$$v_b(1) = v_b(0) - c_b(1)u_a(0)$$
$$= \begin{bmatrix} 7 & -1 \\ -1 & 3 \end{bmatrix} - \begin{bmatrix} -0.25 & 0.25 \\ -0.25 & 0.25 \end{bmatrix} \begin{bmatrix} -2 & -2 \\ 1 & 1 \end{bmatrix} = \begin{bmatrix} 6.25 & -1.75 \\ -1.75 & 2.25 \end{bmatrix}.$$

We next compute

$$\gamma(1) = f_0(0)r_1 = [0.15 \quad 0.05] \begin{bmatrix} -2 & -2 \\ 1 & 1 \end{bmatrix} = [-0.25 \quad -0.25],$$

and then compute

$$c_f(1) = [\gamma(1) - g_1]v_b(1)^{-1}$$
$$= \left[[-0.25 \quad -0.25] - [0 \quad 1] \right] \begin{bmatrix} 0.20455 & 0.15909 \\ 0.15909 & 0.56818 \end{bmatrix}$$
$$= [-0.25 \quad -0.75].$$

Thus we finally have

$$[f_0(1), f_1(1)] = [f_0(0) - c_f(1)b_1(1), -c_f(1)b_0(1)],$$

which gives

$$f_0(1) = f_0(0) - c_f(1)b_1(1)$$

$$= [0.15 \quad 0.05] - [-0.25 \quad -0.75] \begin{bmatrix} 0.25 & -0.25 \\ 0.25 & -0.25 \end{bmatrix}$$

$$= [0.40 \quad -0.20]$$

$$f_1(1) = -c_f(1)b_0(1)$$

$$= -[-0.25 \quad -0.75] = [0.25 \quad 0.75].$$

This process can be continued utilizing further coefficients of the autocorrelation and cross correlation to obtain a filter of greater length.

Subroutine NORMEQ solves the multichannel normal equations by the recursive process just described. The calling statement is

CALL NORMEQ (N,M,LF,F,R,G,A,AP,B,BP,VA,VB,DA,DB,CA,CB,
CF,GAM)

where the subroutine inputs are

N = number of input channels
M = number of output channels
$LF = m + 1$ = length of filter (with restriction that $LF \geqslant 1$)
R = multichannel autocorrelation coefficients (multiplexed)
$= (r_0, r_1, \ldots, r_m)$
G = multichannel cross-correlation coefficients (multiplexed)
$= (g_0, g_1, \ldots, g_m)$,

and where the subroutine outputs are

F = multichannel filter coefficients (multiplexed)
$= (f_0, f_1, \ldots, f_m)$
A = prediction-error operator coefficients (multiplexed) for step m
$= [a_0(m), a_1(m), \ldots, a_m(m)]$
AP = prediction-error operator coefficients (multiplexed) for step $m - 1$
$= [a_0(m - 1), a_1(m - 1), \ldots, a_{m-1}(m - 1), 0]$ (provided $m \geqslant 1$)
B = hindsight-error operator coefficients (multiplexed) for step m
$= [b_0(m), b_1(m), \ldots, b_m(m)]$
BP = hindsight-error operator coefficients (multiplexed) for step $m - 1$
$= [b_0(m - 1), b_1(m - 1), \ldots, b_{m-1}(m - 1), 0]$ (provided $m \geqslant 1$)
$VA = v_a(m)$
$VB = v_b(m)$
$DA = -u_a(m - 1)$ (provided $m \geqslant 1$)
$DB = -u_b(m - 1)$ (provided $m \geqslant 1$)
$CA = -c_a(m)$ (provided $m \geqslant 1$)
$CB = -c_b(m)$ (provided $m \geqslant 1$)
$CF = -c_f(m)$ (provided $m \geqslant 1$)
$GAM = -[\gamma(m) - g_m]$ (provided $m \geqslant 1$).

As a check, let us re-compute our numerical example by means of subroutine NORMEQ. As subroutine inputs we place

$$N = 2$$
$$M = 1$$
$$LF = 1$$
$$R = (7.0, -1.0, -1.0, 3.0)$$
$$G = (1.0, 0.0),$$

which yields the subroutine outputs

$$F = (0.15, 0.05)$$
$$A = (1.0, 0.0, 0.0, 1.0)$$
$$B = (1.0, 0.0, 0.0, 1.0)$$
$$VA = (7.0, -1.0, -1.0, 3.0)$$
$$VB = (7.0, -1.0, -1.0, 3.0),$$

which checks with our numerical example for $m = LF - 1 = 0$. Now if we
place as subroutine inputs the quantities

$$N = 2$$
$$M = 1$$
$$LF = 2$$
$$R = (7.0, -1.0, -1.0, 3.0, -2.0, 1.0, -2.0, 1.0)$$
$$G = (1.0, 0.0, 0.0, 1.0),$$

then the subroutine yields as outputs the quantities

$$F = (0.40, -0.20, 0.25, 0.75)$$
$$A = (1.00, 0.00, 0.00, 1.00, 0.40, -0.20, 0.80, -0.40)$$
$$AP = (1.00, 0.00, 0.00, 1.00, 0.00, 0.00, 0.00, 0.00)$$
$$B = (1.00, 0.00, 0.00, 1.00, 0.25, 0.25, -0.25, -0.25)$$
$$BP = (1.00, 0.00, 0.00, 1.00, 0.00, 0.00, 0.00, 0.00)$$
$$VA = (4.60, 0.20, 0.20, 2.40)$$
$$VB = (6.25, -1.75, -1.75, 2.25)$$
$$DA = (2.00, -1.00, 2.00, -1.00)$$
$$DB = (2.00, 2.00, -1.00, -1.00)$$
$$CA = (0.40, -0.20, 0.80, -0.40)$$
$$CB = (0.25, 0.25, -0.25, -0.25)$$
$$CF = (0.25, 0.75)$$
$$GAM = (0.25, 1.25),$$

which checks with our numerical example for $m = LF - 1 = 1$.

Subroutine NORMEQ requires subroutines ZERO, MOVE, SIMEQ1,
and MAINE. The program is

```
SUBROUTINE NORMEQ(N,M,LF,F,R,G,A,AP,B,BP,VA,VB,
1DA,DB,CA,CB,CF,GAM)
```

```
      DIMENSION  F(M,N,LF),R(N,N,LF),G(M,N,LF)
      DIMENSION  A(N,N,LF),AP(N,N,LF),B(N,N,LF),BP(N,N,LF)
      DIMENSION  VA(N,N),VB(N,N),DA(N,N),DB(N,N)
      DIMENSION  CA(N,N),CB(N,N),CF(M,N),GAM(M,N)
      CALL ZERO(N*N*LF,A)
      CALL ZERO(N*N*LF,B)
      CALL ZERO(M*N*LF,F)
      DO 2 I=1,N
      DO 1 J=1,N
      VA(I,J)=R(I,J,1)
    1 VB(I,J)=R(I,J,1)
      A(I,I,1)=1.
    2 B(I,I,1)=1.
      CALL SIMEQ1(M,N,F,R,G)
      IF(LF.EQ.1) RETURN
      DO 8 L=2,LF
      CALL ZERO(N*N,DA)
      CALL MOVE(M*N,G(1,1,L),GAM)
      DO 5 I=1,N
      DO 4 LI=1,L
      LD=L-LI+1
      DO 4 K=1,N
      DO 3 J=1,N
    3 DA(I,J)=DA(I,J)-A(I,K,LI)*R(K,J,LD)
      DO 4 J=1,M
    4 GAM(J,I)=GAM(J,I)-F(J,K,LI)*R(K,I,LD)
      DO 5 J=1,N
    5 DB(J,I)=DA(I,J)
      CALL SIMEQ1(N,N,CA,VB,DA)
      CALL SIMEQ1(N,N,CB,VA,DB)
      CALL MOVE(N*N*L,A,AP)
      CALL MOVE(N*N*L,B,BP)
      DO 7 J=1,N
      DO 7 K=1,N
      DO 6 LI=1,L
      LD=L-LI+1
      DO 6 I=1,N
      A(I,J,LI)=A(I,J,LI)+CA(I,K)*BP(K,J,LD)
    6 B(I,J,LI)=B(I,J,LI)+CB(I,K)*AP(K,J,LD)
      DO 7 I=1,N
      VA(I,J)=VA(I,J)-CA(I,K)*DB(K,J)
    7 VB(I,J)=VB(I,J)-CB(I,K)*DA(K,J)
      CALL SIMEQ1(M,N,CF,VB,GAM)
```

```
      DO 8 LI=1,L
      LD=L-LI+1
      DO 8 J=1,N
      DO 8 K=1,N
      DO 8 I=1,M
    8 F(I,J,LI)=F(I,J,LI)+CF(I,K)*B(K,J,LD)
      RETURN
      END
```

6.4 Subroutine for multichannel Wiener filtering

Given an input multichannel time series and a desired output multichannel time series, subroutine WIENER computes the multichannel Wiener digital filter and the resulting actual output multichannel time series. The call statement is

CALL WIENER(N,LX,X,M,LZ,Z,LR,LW,FLOOR,LF,F,E,LY,Y,S)

The subroutine inputs are

N = number of input channels to filter, where $N \geqslant 1$
LX = length of input time series = ν
X = N-channel input time series
$\quad$ = $(x_1, x_2, \ldots, x_\nu)$ in multiplexed mode
M = number of output channels from filter, where $M \geqslant 1$
LZ = length of desired output time series = μ
Z = M-channel desired output time series
$\quad$ = $(z_1, z_2, \ldots, z_\mu)$
LR = $m + 1$
$\quad$ = maximum possible length of filter in the sense that the recursion to a longer filter is stopped once the filter reaches this maximum pre-set length
LW = $q + 1$
$\quad$ = length of one side of triangular window

$$w_t = \begin{cases} 1 - \dfrac{|t|}{q} & \text{for } |t| = 0, 1, 2, \ldots, q \\ 0 & \text{for } |t| > q \end{cases}$$

$\quad$ used to weight correlation functions (both the autocorrelation and the cross correlation). (*Note*. If $LW \leqslant 1$, then no weighting is used; that is, if $LW \leqslant 1$, the program makes $w_t = 1$ for all t.)
$FLOOR$ = non-negative number between 0 and 1 which represents a lower bound on the normalized mean-square-error

$$\frac{I_{min}}{\text{tr } \phi_{zz}(0)}$$

in the sense that the recursion to a longer filter is stopped once the normalized mean-square-error falls to or below this lower bound.

The subroutine outputs are

$\mathbf{LF}$ = length of filter = $k + 1$, where $k \leqslant m$
$\mathbf{F}$ = computed multichannel Wiener filter of length $k + 1$
   = $(f_0, f_1, \ldots, f_k)$ in multiplexed mode
$\mathbf{E}$ = normalized mean-square-error sequence for filters
   of length 1, length 2, ..., length $k + 1$
   = $[I_{min}(0)/\text{tr}\ \phi_{zz}(0),\ I_{min}(1)/\text{tr}\ \phi_{zz}(0), \ldots,$
   $I_{min}(k)/\text{tr}\ \phi_{zz}(0)]$,
   where $I_{min}(n)$ is the trace of the mean-square-error
   matrix for the optimum filter of length $n + 1$.
   [*Note.* $E(LF) = I_{min}(k)/\text{tr}\ \phi_{zz}(0)$ is the normalized
   mean-square-error for the computed filter
   $(f_0, f_1, \ldots, f_k)$.]
$\mathbf{LY}$ = length of actual output = $\nu + k$
$\mathbf{Y}$ = actual output
   = $(y_1, y_2, \ldots, y_{\nu+k})$ in multiplexed mode
$\mathbf{S}$ = working space (contains correlations, etc.).

As a numerical example, let us consider the three-channel time series x_t with components

$$x_1(t) = \text{Wolfer's sunspot numbers}$$
$$x_2(t) = \text{northern light activity index}$$
$$x_3(t) = \text{earthquake activity index}$$

consisting of yearly observations over the 100-year period from 1770 through 1869. These observations are shown in Table 3 in Sec. 5.5. Each of these three component time series are read into storage, their respective averages, namely,

$$\bar{x}_1 = 46.94$$
$$\bar{x}_2 = 63.43$$
$$\bar{x}_3 = 97.97,$$

are removed by subroutine REMAV, and the resulting zero-average time series are multiplexed by subroutine MATRAN. Let the zero-average time series be designated by η_t; that is, let

$$\eta_t = \begin{bmatrix} \eta_1(t) \\ \eta_2(t) \\ \eta_3(t) \end{bmatrix} = \begin{bmatrix} x_1(t) - \bar{x}_1 \\ x_2(t) - \bar{x}_2 \\ x_3(t) - \bar{x}_3 \end{bmatrix}.$$

As subroutine inputs, let

$$N = 3$$
$$LX = 99$$
$$X = (\eta_1, \eta_2, \ldots, \eta_{98}, \eta_{99}) \text{ in multiplexed mode}$$
$$= (54.06, 91.57, -31.97, 35.06, 49.57, -35.97, \ldots,$$
$$-39.94, 25.57, -16.97, -9.94, 38.57, 64.03)$$
$$M = 3$$
$$LZ = 99$$
$$Z = (z_1, z_2, \ldots, z_{98}, z_{99}) \text{ in multiplexed mode}$$
$$= (\eta_2, \eta_3, \ldots, \eta_{99}, \eta_{100}) \text{ in multiplexed mode}$$
$$= (35.06, 49.57, -35.97, 19.06, -60.43, -31.97, \ldots,$$
$$-9.94, 38.57, 64.03, 27.06, 46.57, 39.03)$$
$$LR = 3$$
$$LW = 0$$
$$FLOOR = 0.0 .$$

Then as subroutine outputs we obtain

$LF = 3$
$F = (1.38, 0.06, -0.17, 0.04, 0.83, -0.03, 0.02, 0.06, -0.12,$
$\quad -0.77, -0.00, -0.22, -0.02, -0.23, 0.19, -0.03, 0.05,$
$\quad -0.07, 0.05, -0.06, 0.00, 0.06, 0.11, 0.22, -0.01,$
$\quad -0.17, -0.02)$

$$= \left(\begin{bmatrix} 1.38 & 0.04 & 0.02 \\ 0.06 & 0.83 & 0.06 \\ -0.17 & -0.03 & -0.12 \end{bmatrix}, \begin{bmatrix} -0.77 & -0.02 & -0.03 \\ -0.00 & -0.23 & 0.05 \\ -0.22 & 0.19 & -0.07 \end{bmatrix}, \right.$$
$$\left. \begin{bmatrix} 0.05 & 0.06 & -0.01 \\ -0.06 & 0.11 & -0.17 \\ 0.00 & 0.22 & -0.02 \end{bmatrix}\right) = (f_0, f_1, f_2) = \text{computed filter}$$

$E = (0.604, 0.539, 0.517),$
$\quad$ where $E(3) = 0.517$ is the normalized mean-square-error
$\quad$ for the computed filter
$LY = 101$
$Y = (77.52, 76.90, -8.43, 7.23, 17.79, 4.61, \ldots,$
$\quad 19.43, 38.34, 11.93, 4.53, 2.18, 11.05, 0.79, -6.32, 7.40)$
$\quad = (y_1, y_2, \ldots, y_{99}, y_{100}, y_{101}) \text{ in multiplexed mode.}$

Now

$$y_{99} = f_0 \eta_{99} + f_1 \eta_{98} + f_2 \eta_{97}$$
$$= \begin{bmatrix} y_1(99) \\ y_2(99) \\ y_3(99) \end{bmatrix} = \begin{bmatrix} Y(295) \\ Y(296) \\ Y(297) \end{bmatrix} = \begin{bmatrix} 19.43 \\ 38.34 \\ 11.93 \end{bmatrix}$$

is the actual output corresponding to the desired output

$$z_{99} = \eta_{100} = \begin{bmatrix} \eta_1(100) \\ \eta_2(100) \\ \eta_3(100) \end{bmatrix} = \begin{bmatrix} Z(295) \\ Z(296) \\ Z(297) \end{bmatrix} = \begin{bmatrix} 27.06 \\ 46.57 \\ 39.03 \end{bmatrix}.$$

Let us now recompute y_{99} for the same subroutine inputs, except for LR and LW, which we vary in order to see how the values of y_{99} and E(LF) are affected by these two parameters. We therefore obtain the following table:

TABLE 6. Actual outputs and normalized mean-square-errors for various values of
        LW and LF

Desired output	$\eta_1(100)$ 27.06	$\eta_2(100)$ 46.57	$\eta_3(100)$ 39.03	
Actual output	$y_1(99)$	$y_2(99)$	$y_3(99)$	Normalized mean-square-error E(LF)
LW = 10, LF = 1	−0.89	31.87	5.95	0.604
LF = 2	11.39	30.36	10.20	0.564
LF = 3	11.98	35.80	11.97	0.552
LF = 4	11.58	36.26	11.90	0.548
LF = 5	12.11	37.88	12.71	0.541
LW = 20, LF = 1	−0.89	31.87	5.95	0.604
LF = 2	14.11	30.72	9.95	0.553
LF = 3	14.61	36.91	11.85	0.537
LF = 4	14.10	37.83	11.94	0.528
LF = 5	15.07	40.85	13.61	0.513
LW = 0, LF = 1	−0.89	31.87	5.95	0.604
LF = 2	17.74	31.28	9.46	0.539
LF = 3	19.43	38.34	11.93	0.517
LF = 4	18.94	40.88	12.65	0.503
LF = 5	20.59	47.08	15.56	0.467

The value LW = 10 represents the most drastic weighting of the correlation, the value LW = 20 a less drastic weighting, and LW = 0 represents the least drastic weighting (i.e., no weighting at all[60]). We see that the weighting of the correlation yields a filter which gives a poorer fit over the given data, as shown by the normalized mean-square-errors in the table. However, because the weighting of the empirical correlation should yield a better estimate of the true correlation, it is expected that the resulting filter will better represent the true

---

[60] That is, if LW $\leq$ 1, the program in effect makes LW $= \infty$, or, in other words, the triangular weighting function becomes $w_t = 1$ for all t.

dynamics and hence perform better on fresh data. This problem has received extensive treatment in the statistical literature.[61]

Our purpose for introducing the numerical data for sunspot numbers, northern light activity, and earthquake activity was to provide a numerical illustration of subroutine WIENER. However, the interested reader may want to refer to Quenouille[62] who gives various statistical procedures and tests which he performs on this data, as well as on other data.

Two programs exist for subroutine WIENER: version 1 and version 2. Version 1 of subroutine WIENER requires subroutines RECUR, ZERO, MOVE, SCALE, BRAINY, HEAT, MAINE, and SIMEQ1, as well as function SPUR. The programs for subroutine WIENER (version 1) and subroutine RECUR are

```
      SUBROUTINE WIENER(N,LX,X,M,LZ,Z,LR,LW,FLOOR,
     1LF,F,E,LY,Y,S)
C     VERSION 1 OF SUBROUTINE WIENER
C     DIMENSION X(N,LX),Z(M,LZ),F(M,N,LR)
C     DIMENSION E(LR),Y(M,LY),S(NN*(5*LR+6)+MN*(LR+2)
C     1+2*M*M)
      DIMENSION X(1),Z(1),F(1),E(1),Y(1),S(1)
      NN=N*N
      NNLR=NN*LR
      MN=M*N
      IR=1
      IA=1+NNLR
      IB=IA+NNLR
      IAP=IB+NNLR
      IBP=IAP+NNLR
      IVA=IBP+NNLR
      IVB=IVA+NN
      IDA=IVB+NN
      IDB=IDA+NN
      ICA=IDB+NN
      ICB=ICA+NN
      IG=ICB+NN
      ICF=IG+MN*LR
      IGAM=ICF+MN
      IH=IGAM+MN
```

[61] See Wold, H., ed., *Bibliography on Time Series and Stochastic Processes*, Oliver and Boyd, Edinburgh, 1965.

[62] Quenouille, M. H., *Associated Measurements*, Butterworths, London, 1952.

```
      IFGT=IH+M*M
      CALL HEAT(M,1,LZ,Z,M,1,LZ,Z,1,S(IH))
      IF(LW.LE.1) L=LR
      IGZ=IG+MN*LW
      IRZ=IR+NN*LW
      IF(LW.GT.1.AND.LW.LT.LR) L=LW
      IF(LW.GT.1.AND.LW.LT.LR) CALL ZERO(MN*(LR-LW),
     1S(IGZ))
      IF(LW.GT.1.AND.LW.LT.LR) CALL ZERO(NN*(LR-LW),
     1S(IRZ))
      IF(LW.GT.1.AND.LW.GE.LR) L=LR
      CALL HEAT(M,1,LZ,Z,N,1,LX,X,L,S(IG))
      CALL HEAT(N,1,LX,X,N,1,LX,X,L,S(IR))
      IF(LW.LE.1.OR.L.LE.1) GO TO 2
      DO 1 K=2,L
      IGK=IG+MN*(K-1)
      IRK=IR+NN*(K-1)
      WINDOW=1.0-FLOAT(K-1)/FLOAT(LW-1)
      CALL SCALE(WINDOW,MN,S(IGK))
    1 CALL SCALE(WINDOW,NN,S(IRK))
    2 CALL RECUR(N,M,LR,S,S(IH),S(IG),FLOOR,LF,F,E,S(IA),
     1S(IB),S(IAP),S(IBP),S(IVA),S(IVB),S(IDA),S(IDB),S(ICA),S(ICB),
     2S(ICF),S(IGAM),S(IFGT))
      LY=LX+LF-1
      CALL BRAINY(M,N,LF,F,N,1,LX,X,Y)
      RETURN
      END

      SUBROUTINE RECUR(N,M,LR,R,H,G,FLOOR,LF,F,E,
     1A,B,AP,BP,VA,VB,DA,DB,CA,CB,CF,GAM,FGT)
      DIMENSION F(M,N,LR),R(N,N,LR),G(M,N,LR),H(M,M)
      DIMENSION A(N,N,LR),AP(N,N,LR),B(N,N,LR),BP(N,N,LR)
      DIMENSION VA(N,N),VB(N,N),DA(N,N),DB(N,N)
      DIMENSION CA(N,N),CB(N,N),CF(M,N),GAM(M,N)
      DIMENSION FGT(M,M),E(LR)
      CALL ZERO(N*N*LR,A)
      CALL ZERO(N*N*LR,B)
      CALL ZERO(M*N*LR,F)
      DO 2 I=1,N
      DO 1 J=1,N
      VA(I,J)=R(I,J,1)
    1 VB(I,J)=R(I,J,1)
      A(I,I,1)=1.
    2 B(I,I,1)=1.
```

```
      CALL  SIMEQ1(M,N,F,R,G)
      LF=1
      CALL  HEAT(M,N,1,F,M,N,1,G,1,FGT)
      E(1)=1.0−SPUR(M,FGT)/SPUR(M,H)
      IF(E(1).LE.FLOOR) RETURN
      IF(LR.EQ.1) RETURN
      DO 9 L=2,LR
      CALL  ZERO(N*N,DA)
      CALL  MOVE(M*N,G(1,1,L),GAM)
      DO 5 I=1,N
      DO 4 LI=1,L
      LD=L−LI+1
      DO 4 K=1,N
      DO 3 J=1,N
    3 DA(I,J)=DA(I,J)−A(I,K,LI)*R(K,J,LD)
      DO 4 J=1,M
    4 GAM(J,I)=GAM(J,I)−F(J,K,LI)*R(K,I,LD)
      DO 5 J=1,N
    5 DB(J,I)=DA(I,J)
      CALL  SIMEQ1(N,N,CA,VB,DA)
      CALL  SIMEQ1(N,N,CB,VA,DB)
      CALL  MOVE(N*N*L,A,AP)
      CALL  MOVE(N*N*L,B,BP)
      DO 7 J=1,N
      DO 7 K=1,N
      DO 6 LI=1,L
      LD=L−LI+1
      DO 6 I=1,N
      A(I,J,LI)=A(I,J,LI)+CA(I,K)*BP(K,J,LD)
    6 B(I,J,LI)=B(I,J,LI)+CB(I,K)*AP(K,J,LD)
      DO 7 I=1,N
      VA(I,J)=VA(I,J)−CA(I,K)*DB(K,J)
    7 VB(I,J)=VB(I,J)−CB(I,K)*DA(K,J)
      CALL  SIMEQ1(M,N,CF,VB,GAM)
      DO 8 LI=1,L
      LD=L−LI+1
      DO 8 J=1,N
      DO 8 K=1,N
      DO 8 I=1,M
    8 F(I,J,LI)=F(I,J,LI)+CF(I,K)*B(K,J,LD)
      CALL  HEAT(M,N,L,F,M,N,L,G,1,FGT)
      E(L)=1.0−SPUR(M,FGT)/SPUR(M,H)
      LF=L
```

```
        IF(E(L).LE.FLOOR) RETURN
      9 CONTINUE
        RETURN
        END
```

Version 2 of subroutine WIENER requires subroutines RECUR2, ZERO, MOVE, SCALE, BRAINY, HEAT, MAINE, SPIRIT, ORACLE, and FORM, as well as function SPUR. The programs for WIENER (version 2), RECUR2, SPIRIT, and ORACLE are

```
        SUBROUTINE WIENER(N,LX,X,M,LZ,Z,LR,LW,FLOOR,LF,
       1F,E,LY,Y,S)
C       VERSION 2 OF SUBROUTINE WIENER
C       DIMENSION X(N,LX),Z(M,LZ),F(M,N,LR)
C       DIMENSION E(LR),Y(M,LY),S(NN*5*LR+MN*LR+M*M)
        DIMENSION X(1),Z(1),F(1),E(1),Y(1),S(1)
        MN=M*N
        NN=N*N
        IR=NN*(LR-1)+1
        IG=5*NN*LR+1
        IH=IG+MN*LR
        CALL HEAT(M,1,LZ,Z,M,1,LZ,Z,1,S(IH))
        IF(LW.LE.1) L=LR
        IGZ=IG+MN*LW
        IRZ=IR+NN*LW
        IF(LW.GT.1.AND.LW.LT.LR) CALL ZERO(MN*(LR-LW),
       1S(IGZ))
        IF(LW.GT.1.AND.LW.LT.LR) CALL ZERO(NN*(LR-LW),
       1S(IRZ))
        IF(LW.GT.1.AND.LW.LT.LR) L=LW
        IF(LW.GT.1.AND.LW.GE.LR) L=LR
        CALL HEAT(M,1,LZ,Z,N,1,LX,X,L,S(IG))
        CALL HEAT(N,1,LX,X,N,1,LX,X,L,S(IR))
        IF(LW.LE.1.OR.L.LE.1) GO TO 2
        DO 1 K=2,L
        IGK=IG+MN*(K-1)
        IRK=IR+NN*(K-1)
        WINDOW=1.0-FLOAT(K-1)/FLOAT(LW-1)
        CALL SCALE(WINDOW,MN,S(IGK))
      1 CALL SCALE(WINDOW,NN,S(IRK))
      2 CALL RECUR2(N,M,LR,S,S(IH),S(IG),FLOOR,LF,F,E)
        LY=LX+LF-1
        CALL BRAINY(M,N,LF,F,N,1,LX,X,Y)
        RETURN
        END
```

```
      SUBROUTINE RECUR2(N,M,LR,R,H,G,FLOOR,LF,F,E)
C     NMAX=LARGEST VALUE OF N TO BE PROCESSED
C     NNMAX=NMAX*NMAX
C     NONDUMMY DIMENSION VF(NNMAX),VB(NNMAX),
C    1FGT(NNMAX)
C     FOR EXAMPLE, IF NMAX=5 THEN
      DIMENSION VF(25),VB(25),FGT(25)
      DIMENSION R(N,N,LR),H(M,M),G(M,N,LR),F(M,N,LR),E(LR)
      NN=N*N
      NNLR=NN*LR
      ISP=2*LR+1
      IAF=ISP+LR
      IAB=IAF+LR
      DO 1 L=2,LR
      JP=LR+L-1
      JM=LR-L+1
      DO 1 J=1,M
      DO 1 K=1,M
    1 R(J,K,JM)=R(K,J,JP)
      DO 2 L=1,LR
      JM=LR-L+1
      CALL SPIRIT(N,L,R(1,1,JM),R(1,1,IAF),R(1,1,IAB),VF,VB,R
     1(1,1,ISP))
      CALL ORACLE(M,N,L,R(1,1,JM),R(1,1,IAB),VB,G(1,1,L),F)
      CALL HEAT(M,N,L,F,M,N,L,G,1,FGT)
      E(L)=1.0-SPUR(M,FGT)/SPUR(M,H)
      LF=L
      IF(E(L).LE.FLOOR) RETURN
    2 CONTINUE
      RETURN
      END

      SUBROUTINE SPIRIT(N,L,R,AF,AB,VF,VB,SP)
C     NMAX=LARGEST VALUE OF N TO BE PROCESSED
C     NNMAX=NMAX*NMAX
C     NONDUMMY DIMENSION DF(NNMAX),DB(NNMAX),CF
C    1(NNMAX),CB(NNMAX)
C     FOR EXAMPLE, IF NMAX=5 THEN
      DIMENSION DF(25),DB(25),CF(25),CB(25)
C     DIMENSION R(N,N,2*L-1)
      DIMENSION AF(N,N,L),AB(N,N,L),VF(N,N),VB(N,N),R(N,N,1),
     1SP(N,N,L)
      IF(L.NE.1) GO TO 20
    1 CALL MOVE(N*N,R,VF)
```

```
          CALL  MOVE(N*N,R,VB)
          CALL  ZERO(N*N,AF)
          DO  10  I=1,N
    10   AF(I,I,1)=1.
          CALL  MOVE(N*N,AF,AB)
          RETURN
    20   CALL  HEAT(N,N,L-1,AB,N,N,L-1,R(1,1,L+1),1,DB)
          DO  30  I=1,N
          DO  30  J=1,N
          IJ=(I-1)*N+J
          JI=(J-1)*N+I
    30   DF(IJ)=DB(JI)
          CALL  MAINE(N,VB,SP)
          CALL  BRAINY(N,N,1,DF,N,N,1,SP,CF)
          CALL  MAINE(N,VF,SP)
          CALL  BRAINY(N,N,1,DB,N,N,1,SP,CB)
          CALL  MOVE(N*N*(L-1),AB,SP(1,1,2))
          CALL  ZERO(N*N,SP)
          CALL  MOVE(N*N*L,SP,AB)
          CALL  ZERO(N*N,AF(1,1,L))
          CALL  FORM(N,N,L,AB,CB,AF)
          CALL  FORM(N,N,L,AF,CF,SP)
          CALL  FORM(N,N,1,VF,CF,DB)
          CALL  FORM(N,N,1,VB,CB,DF)
          RETURN
          END

          SUBROUTINE  ORACLE(M,N,L,R,AB,VB,G,A)
C         NMAX=LARGEST VALUE OF N TO BE PROCESSED
C         NNMAX=NMAX*NMAX
C         NONDUMMY DIMENSION VBI(NNMAX),C(NNMAX)
C         FOR EXAMPLE,IF NMAX=5 THEN
          DIMENSION  VBI(25),C(25)
C         DIMENSION  R(N,N,2*L-1)
          DIMENSION  R(N,N,1),AB(N,N,L),VB(N,N),G(M,N),A(M,N,L)
          IF(L.EQ.1)CALL ZERO(M*N,A)
          IF(L.NE.1)CALL HEAT(M,N,L-1,A,N,N,L-1,R,1,A(1,1,L))
          DO  10  I=1,M
          DO  10  J=1,N
    10   A(I,J,L)=A(I,J,L)-G(I,J)
          CALL  MAINE(N,VB,VBI)
          CALL  BRAINY(M,N,1,A(1,1,L),N,N,1,VBI,C)
          CALL  ZERO(M*N,A(1,1,L))
```

        CALL FORM(M,N,L,A,C,AB)
        RETURN
        END

6.5 Prediction of commodity futures

As a practical application of subroutine AUGURY given in Sec. 2.8, the commodity futures on the Chicago grain market were investigated. Table 7 gives

TABLE 7. Two time series of weekly prices in cents. Each time series has 50 observations from June 1965 to May 1966

May oats	May corn	May oats (cont.)	May corn (cont.)
72.5	124.6	70.0	122.7
72.5	125.0	70.0	123.0
72.1	126.0	70.7	126.0
72.3	128.0	70.6	128.0
72.3	127.0	70.1	128.0
71.5	127.2	69.6	127.2
70.8	125.8	69.1	127.7
70.7	125.1	70.5	130.0
70.6	125.2	72.7	131.9
70.5	126.5	72.2	131.9
71.5	124.9	71.2	131.2
70.0	124.2	71.3	131.0
68.5	123.9	72.0	131.0
68.5	125.0	71.5	128.9
68.5	125.7	71.0	127.0
68.0	124.0	70.0	125.0
67.9	125.0	70.0	125.0
67.9	124.2	70.2	125.0
67.9	123.0	70.0	125.0
68.1	122.1	68.5	125.2
68.2	121.5	69.6	126.0
68.3	121.2	70.6	127.0
68.6	121.3	70.6	127.7
69.2	122.0	68.6	127.2
69.5	123.2	67.9	125.9

the weekly prices of May oats and May corn from June 1965 to May 1966. Each time series is made up of 50 observations spaced one week apart.

The mean value of the oats time series is 70.098, and that of the corn time series is 125.922. These means were removed from the time series before the computations for the predictions were made and then added back into the final predicted values, so as to make the predicted values compatible with the original time series.

In each case we predicted one observation ahead, that is, we used a prediction distance of one time unit, i.e., one week. The necessary correlations were computed over the entire known 50 observations of each time series.

The predicted values of interest are the next (unavailable) observations, namely, the 51st observation of each of the two time series. That is, the 50th observation represents the latest available observation of each time series, and the 51st observation is the future unavailable observation which we desire to predict.

Tables 8 and 9 give the results of predicting the 51st observation of each time series. "Single-channel prediction" refers to predicting the given time

TABLE 8. Prediction of the 51st observation of the oats time series

Single-channel prediction			Double-channel prediction		
Operator length	Percent error	Predicted value	Operator length	Percent error	Predicted value
1	34	68.3	1	21	68.4
2	32	68.2	2	18	68.2
3	29	68.7	3	17	68.6

TABLE 9. Prediction of the 51st observation of the corn time series

Single-channel prediction			Double-channel prediction		
Operator length	Percent error	Predicted value	Operator length	Percent error	Predicted value
1	18	125.9	1	21	125.7
2	15	125.4	2	18	125.2
3	15	125.4	3	17	125.4

series from only its own past, whereas "double-channel prediction" refers to predicting the given time series from its own past as well as from the past of the other time series. In the notation of Sec. 6.2, the operator length is the parameter $LF = m + 1$, the percent error is the parameter $I_{min}/\text{tr } \phi_{zz}(0)$ (multiplied by 100 in order to convert it to percent), and the predicted value is y_{51}. The desired output z_t, of course, is the given input x_t (the oats and corn time series) advanced by one time unit.

From Tables 8 and 9 we see that the oats time series is less predictable than the corn time series (as evidenced by the single-channel prediction error range of 34% to 29% for oats versus 18% to 15% for corn).

The latest observed value for oats (i.e., the 50th value in Table 7) is 67.9.

The predictions of the 51st value (given in Table 8) range from 68.2 to 68.7, and hence our predictions indicate that the price of oats will rise. Moreover, acting on the basis of the longer operator (LF = 3), the predicted rise would be to the value of 68.7 or 68.6.

Likewise, the latest observed value for corn (i.e., the 50th value in Table 7) is 125.9. The predictions of the 51st value (given in Table 9) range from 125.2 to 125.9, and hence our predictions indicate that the price of corn will fall. Moreover, acting on the basis of the longer operator (LF = 3), the predicted fall would be to the value of 125.4.

6.6 Output energy filters with linear constraints

Let $x_0, x_1, x_2, \ldots, x_n$ be a sample of $n + 1$ observations from a p-channel stationary stochastic process given by the $p \times 1$ column vector

$$
x_t = \begin{bmatrix} x_1(t) \\ x_2(t) \\ \cdot \\ \cdot \\ \cdot \\ x_p(t) \end{bmatrix}.
$$

From this sample let us form the $[p(m + 1)] \times [m + n + 1]$ matrix

$$
X = \begin{bmatrix} x_0 & x_1 & x_2 & \ldots & x_n & 0 & \ldots & 0 & 0 \\ 0 & x_0 & x_1 & \ldots & x_{n-1} & x_n & \ldots & 0 & 0 \\ & & & & \ldots & & & & \\ 0 & 0 & 0 & & & & \ldots & x_{n-1} & x_n \end{bmatrix}.
$$

Let $a_0, a_1, \ldots, a_m$ be a multichannel filter with p input channels and 1 output channel. Thus the filter coefficients are the $p \times 1$ row vectors

$$
a_s = [a_1(s), a_2(s), \ldots, a_p(s)] \qquad \text{for } s = 0, 1, 2, \ldots, m.
$$

We assume that $m < n$; for example, m might be equal to about 5 or 10% of the value of n. With these coefficients we form the $1 \times [p(m + 1)]$ row vector

$$
A = [a_0, a_1, a_2, \ldots, a_m].
$$

Let the single-channel output (i.e., 1×1 matrix) y_t be given by the convolution

$$
y_t = \sum_{s=0}^{m} a_s x_{t-s} \qquad \text{for } s = 0, 1, 2, \ldots, m + n. \tag{1}
$$

If we form the $1 \times (m + n + 1)$ row vector

$$
Y = [y_0, y_1, y_2, \ldots, y_{m+n}],
$$

then this convolution may be written simply as

$$Y = AX.$$

The energy in the output is given by the sum of squares

$$E = y_0^2 + y_1^2 + \cdots + y_{m+n}^2 = YY^T = AXX^TA^T.$$

We recognize XX^T as being the $[p(m+1)] \times [p(m+1)]$ autocorrelation matrix

$$R = XX^T = \begin{bmatrix} r_0 & r_1 & \cdots & r_m \\ r_{-1} & r_0 & \cdots & r_{m-1} \\ & \cdots & & \cdots \\ r_{-m} & r_{-m+1} & \cdots & r_0 \end{bmatrix},$$

where the autocorrelation coefficients are the $p \times p$ matrices

$$r_s = \sum_t x_{t+s} x_t^T.$$

The matrix R is a block Töplitz matrix. The output energy can be written as the quadratic form

$$E = ARA^T.$$

If we wish to minimize the output energy E, we may do so by letting the filter coefficients be zero, that is, $A = 0$. This represents a trivial case, so in order to obtain nontrivial (minimum) output energy filters one must introduce various constraints. In this section we want to consider some different types of output energy filters.

The first type of output energy filter which we want to consider is that of the prediction-error operator for unit prediction distance. The prediction operator for predicting one unit ahead on, say, channel 1, may be computed by subroutine WIENER with subroutine inputs

$$\begin{aligned} N &= p \\ LX &= n + 1 \\ X &= (x_0, x_1, x_2, \ldots, x_n) \text{ in multiplexed mode} \\ M &= 1 \\ LZ &= n \\ Z &= [x_1(1), x_1(2), x_1(3), \ldots, x_1(n)] \\ LR &= m \\ LW &= 0 \\ FLOOR &= 0. \end{aligned}$$

The required prediction operator is given by the subroutine outputs

$$\text{LF} = m$$
$$\text{F} = (f_0, f_1, \ldots, f_{m-1}) \text{ in multiplexed mode}$$
$$= [f_1(0), f_2(0), \ldots, f_p(0), f_1(1), f_2(1), \ldots, f_p(1),$$
$$\ldots, f_1(m-1), f_2(m-1), \ldots, f_p(m-1)] .$$

The required prediction-error filter (*cf.* Sec. 2.8) is given by

$$a_0 = [1, 0, \ldots, 0]$$
$$a_1 = -f_0 = [-f_1(0), -f_2(0), \ldots, -f_p(0)]$$
$$a_2 = -f_1 = [-f_1(1), -f_2(1), \ldots, -f_p(1)]$$
$$\cdots$$
$$a_m = -f_{m-1} = [-f_1(m-1), -f_2(m-1), \ldots, -f_p(m-1)] .$$

Using this operator in eq. (1), we obtain the prediction-error series y_t.

Alternatively, the above prediction-error filter can be derived as the output energy filter with the linear constraint

$$a_0 = [1, 0, \ldots, 0] ,$$

that is,

$$a_1(0) = 1, \; a_2(0) = 0, \ldots, \; a_p(0) = 0 . \tag{2}$$

Hence we want to minimize the output energy ARA^T subject to this linear constraint. According to the method of Lagrange multipliers, we minimize the expression

$$\text{ARA}^T - \lambda_1[a_1(0) - 1] - \lambda_2 a_2(0) - \cdots - \lambda_p a_p(0) ,$$

where $\lambda_1, \lambda_2, \ldots, \lambda_p$ are the undetermined multipliers. We set the derivative of this expression with respect to each filter coefficient equal to zero. We obtain the equation

$$[a_0, a_1, \ldots, a_m] \, \text{R} = [\Lambda, 0, \ldots, 0] , \tag{3}$$

where Λ is the $1 \times p$ row vector

$$\cdot \Lambda = [\lambda_1, \lambda_2, \ldots, \lambda_p] ,$$

and each 0 is the $1 \times p$ zero vector. If we let C be the $1 \times p$ row vector

$$\text{C} = [1, 0, \ldots, 0] ,$$

and let H be the $p \times [p(m+1)]$ matrix

$$\text{H} = [\text{I}, 0, \ldots, 0] ,$$

where I is the $p \times p$ identity matrix, and each 0 is the $p \times p$ zero matrix, then the constraint eqs. (2) can be written as

$$\text{C} = \text{AH}^T . \tag{4}$$

Also eq. (3) can be written as

$$AR = \Lambda H . \tag{5}$$

Let us now solve eqs. (4) and (5) for the undetermined multipliers Λ and the filter coefficients A. Multiply eq. (5) by $R^{-1}H^T$ to obtain

$$AH^T = \Lambda HR^{-1}H^T . \tag{6}$$

By eq. (4) we see that the left-hand side of eq. (6) is equal to C, that is,

$$C = \Lambda HR^{-1}H^T . \tag{7}$$

Solving eq. (7) for Λ, we obtain

$$\Lambda = C(HR^{-1}H^T)^{-1} . \tag{8}$$

Inserting eq. (8) into eq. (5), we obtain

$$AR = C(HR^{-1}H^T)^{-1}H . \tag{9}$$

Solving eq. (9) for A, we obtain

$$A = C(HR^{-1}H^T)^{-1}HR^{-1} . \tag{10}$$

This equation gives the required filter coefficients. The quantity HR^{-1} can be efficiently computed by subroutine NORMEQ. Taking the transpose of eq. (4), we obtain

$$C^T = HA^T . \tag{11}$$

Multiplying eq. (11) by Λ, we have

$$\Lambda C^T = \Lambda HA^T . \tag{12}$$

Substituting eq. (5) into eq. (12), we obtain the expression for the minimum output energy

$$ARA^T = \Lambda C^T . \tag{13}$$

In the case considered here, we have

$$ARA^T = [\lambda_1, \lambda_2, \ldots, \lambda_p][1, 0, \ldots, 0]^T = \lambda_1 ,$$

so the minimum output energy for the prediction-error filter for unit prediction distance is λ_1.

The next type of output energy filter which we want to consider is the prediction-error operator for prediction distance two. The prediction operator for two-unit prediction on, say, channel 1 may be computed by subroutine WIENER with the same subroutine inputs as before, except that we now let

$$LZ = n - 1$$
$$Z = [x_1(2), x_1(3), x_1(4), \ldots, x_1(n)]$$
$$LR = m - 1.$$

The required prediction operator is given by the subroutine outputs

$$\text{LF} = m - 1$$
$$\text{F} = (f_0, f_1, \ldots, f_{m-2}) \text{ in multiplexed mode.}$$

The required prediction-error filter (*cf.* Sec. 2.8) is given by

$$a_0 = [1, 0, \ldots, 0]$$
$$a_1 = [0, 0, \ldots, 0]$$
$$a_2 = -f_0$$
$$a_3 = -f_1$$
$$\cdots$$
$$a_m = -f_{m-2}.$$

Alternatively, this prediction-error filter can be derived as the output energy filter subject to the linear constraint

$$a_0 = [1, 0, \ldots, 0]$$
$$a_1 = [0, 0, \ldots, 0].$$

This constraint may be written as

$$C = AH^T, \tag{14}$$

where C is defined as the $1 \times 2p$ row vector

$$C = [1, 0, \ldots, 0, 0, 0, \ldots, 0],$$

and H is defined as the $2p \times [p(m + 1)]$ matrix

$$H = \begin{bmatrix} I & 0 & 0 & \cdots & 0 \\ 0 & I & 0 & \cdots & 0 \end{bmatrix},$$

where I is the $p \times p$ identity matrix, and each 0 is the $p \times p$ zero matrix. If we minimize the expression

$$ARA^T - \lambda_1[a_1(0) - 1] - \lambda_2 a_2(0) - \cdots - \lambda_{2p} a_p(1),$$

we obtain

$$AR = \Lambda H, \tag{15}$$

where Λ is defined as the $1 \times 2p$ row vector

$$\Lambda = [\lambda_1, \lambda_2, \ldots, \lambda_{2p}].$$

Equations (14) and (15) may be solved as before to yield

$$\Lambda = C(HR^{-1}H^T)^{-1}$$
$$A = C(HR^{-1}H^T)^{-1}HR^{-1}.$$

The minimum output energy is

$$ARA^T = \Lambda C^T = \lambda_1.$$

The prediction-error filter was developed as a method for the detection of reflection signals on exploration seismic records.[63] The noise in a signal-free time interval was represented as a multichannel stationary random process, but so little was known about the signals that they could not be realistically modeled except as waves of unspecified form propagating across the array of sensors (geophones). Under these assumptions, the multichannel prediction-error filter was computed on the basis of the noise sample preceding a possible reflection event. Because the prediction-error filter is designed so as to minimize the output energy due to noise, the amplitudes of the filter output due to noise alone as input are small (in a mean-square sense). However, if at some time instant a signal arrives, it cannot be predicted by the filter from the past values of the noise, and hence a large output (prediction error) occurs. The fact that the output of the prediction-error filter suddenly attains large amplitudes at the arrival of a signal provides the basis for the detection of the event. In recent years there has been wide interest in the detection of signals from underground nuclear explosions and earthquakes on seismic records. The same general principle of computing the filter coefficients on the basis of a noise sample preceding the event can be used, and so prediction-error filters have been applied with excellent results to the problem of the detection of earthquake and nuclear explosion signals.[64,65] Moreover, in many cases it is reasonable to assume that a signal from a nuclear explosion or earthquake has the same shape at each sensor, except for a time delay. As a result, the prediction-error filter can be advantageously modified by a slight change in the constraints. In order to simplify the discussion, let us assume that the necessary time delays have been introduced so that the signal is in-phase on each channel. As is well known, a delta function passes a signal without distortion. As a result, if the filter coefficients across the input channels add up to a delta function, then the common signal which has the same shape on each input channel will be passed without distortion to the output channel. Hence the required linear constraint on this type of output energy filter is that the filter coefficients add up to a delta function, that is,

$$a_1(0) + a_2(0) + \cdots + a_p(0) = 1$$
$$a_1(1) + a_2(1) + \cdots + a_p(1) = 0$$
$$a_1(2) + a_2(2) + \cdots + a_p(2) = 0$$
$$\cdots$$
$$a_1(m) + a_2(m) + \cdots + a_p(m) = 0 \, .$$

---

[63] Wadsworth, G. P., E. A. Robinson, J. G. Bryan, and P. M. Hurley, "Detection of reflections on seismic records by linear operators," *Geophys.* **18**, 539–586 (1953).

[64] Galbraith, J. N., *Computer studies of microseismic statistics with applications to prediction and detection*, Ph.D. thesis, M.I.T., Cambridge, Mass., 1963, 260 pp.

[65] Claerbout, J. F., "Detection of P-waves from weak sources at great distances," *Geophys.* **29**, 197–211 (1964).

This set of constraints may be written as

$$C = AH^T, \qquad (16)$$

where C is the $1 \times (m + 1)$ row vector

$$C = [1, 0, 0, \ldots, 0],$$

and H is the $[m + 1] \times [p(m + 1)]$ matrix

$$H = \begin{bmatrix} 1 & 1 & \ldots & 1 & 0 & 0 & \ldots & 0 & \ldots & 0 & 0 & \ldots & 0 \\ 0 & 0 & \ldots & 0 & 1 & 1 & \ldots & 1 & \ldots & 0 & 0 & \ldots & 0 \\ & & & & & \ldots & & & & & & \\ 0 & 0 & \ldots & 0 & 0 & 0 & \ldots & 0 & \ldots & 1 & 1 & \ldots & 1 \end{bmatrix}.$$

Using the method of Lagrange multipliers, we minimize the expression

$$ARA^T - \lambda_0[a_1(0) + \cdots + a_p(0) - 1] - \lambda_1[a_1(1) + \cdots + a_p(1)]$$
$$- \cdots - \lambda_m[a_1(m) + \cdots + a_p(m)].$$

We set the derivative with respect to each filter coefficient equal to zero; we obtain

$$AR = \Lambda H, \qquad (17)$$

where Λ is defined as the $1 \times (m + 1)$ row vector

$$\Lambda = [\lambda_0, \lambda_1, \lambda_2, \ldots, \lambda_m].$$

Solving eqs. (16) and (17) as before for Λ and A, we obtain

$$\Lambda = C(HR^{-1}H^T)^{-1}$$
$$A = C(HR^{-1}H^T)^{-1}HR^{-1}.$$

The minimum output energy is

$$ARA^T = \Lambda C^T = \lambda_1.$$

As a numerical example of this type of output energy filter, namely, one which passes a common signal on each input channel without distortion to the output channel, suppose that the multichannel autocorrelation coefficients are

$$r_0 = \begin{bmatrix} 22.5097 & 1.4816 & 5.4150 \\ 1.4816 & 21.2192 & 2.2276 \\ 5.4150 & 2.2276 & 5.2926 \end{bmatrix}$$

$$r_1 = \begin{bmatrix} 11.9200 & 12.8252 & 5.9307 \\ 1.8887 & 8.6105 & 0.4026 \\ 1.4676 & 5.4628 & 1.2396 \end{bmatrix}$$

$$r_2 = \begin{bmatrix} 4.7561 & 15.0747 & 3.0360 \\ 4.6381 & -0.5430 & 2.5272 \\ -0.8854 & 3.8220 & 0.4568 \end{bmatrix}$$

$$r_3 = \begin{bmatrix} 2.6824 & 5.8707 & 1.3049 \\ 7.2501 & -2.0538 & 2.4228 \\ -0.0486 & 0.1298 & -0.0032 \end{bmatrix}.$$

Then the required filter has coefficients

$$\begin{aligned}
a_0 &= [\; 0.1553, & 0.2490, & 0.5957] \\
a_1 &= [-0.2856, & 0.0079, & 0.2778] \\
a_2 &= [-0.1980, & -0.0284, & 0.2264] \\
a_3 &= [-0.0376, & -0.0303, & 0.6777]\,.
\end{aligned}$$

We note that the elements of a_0 add up to unity, whereas the elements of any other coefficient add up to zero.

In this section we have discussed three types of output energy filters with linear constraints, namely, the prediction-error filter for unit prediction distance, the prediction-error filter for prediction distance two, and the output energy filter which passes a common signal without distortion. Other useful types[66] of output energy filters may be obtained by varying the linear constraints.

6.7 Output energy filters with quadratic constraints

There are various kinds of quadratic constraints that may be imposed on the coefficients of an output energy filter. One such constraint is that the sum given by

energy due to $[a_1(0), \ldots, a_1(m)]$ acting on $x_1(t)$
+ energy due to $[a_2(0), \ldots, a_2(m)]$ acting on $x_2(t)$
+ $\cdots$
+ energy due to $[a_p(0), \ldots, a_p(m)]$ acting on $x_p(t)$

be fixed, say, equal to unity. Thus we want to minimize the expression

$$ARA^T - \lambda \left[\sum_{j=1}^{p} \alpha_j R_j \alpha_j^T - 1 \right], \tag{1}$$

where

$$\alpha_j = [a_j(0), a_j(1), \ldots, a_j(m)]$$

---

[66] Claerbout, J. F., "A summary by illustrations of least squares filters with constraints," M.I.T. Lincoln Lab. Tech. Note, No. 1966–7, 1966.

and

$$R_j = \begin{bmatrix} r_{jj}(0) & r_{jj}(1) & \cdots & r_{jj}(m) \\ r_{jj}(-1) & r_{jj}(0) & \cdots & r_{jj}(m-1) \\ & & \cdots & \\ r_{jj}(-m) & r_{jj}(-m+1) & \cdots & r_{jj}(0) \end{bmatrix}.$$

Setting the derivatives of eq. (1) with respect to the $a_j(s)$ equal to zero, we obtain

$$A(R - \lambda Q) = 0,\tag{2}$$

where Q is the $p(m+1) \times p(m+1)$ matrix

$$Q = \begin{bmatrix} q_0 & q_1 & \cdots & q_m \\ q_{-1} & q_0 & \cdots & q_{m-1} \\ & & \cdots & \\ q_{-m} & q_{-m+1} & \cdots & q_0 \end{bmatrix},$$

and where q_s is the $p \times p$ matrix

$$q_s = \begin{bmatrix} r_{11}(s) & 0 & \cdots & 0 \\ 0 & r_{22}(s) & \cdots & 0 \\ & & \cdots & \\ 0 & 0 & \cdots & r_{pp}(s) \end{bmatrix}.$$

Equation (2) represents a generalized eigenvalue problem for which standard methods of solution exist.[67]

---

[67] M.I.T. Geophysical Analysis Group, *Further Research on Linear Operators in Seismic Analysis*, Rept. No. 6, M.I.T., Cambridge, Mass., 1954.

Appendix 1

Relationship to Mathematical Operator Theory

1.1 Single-channel theory

Material in this book on statistical prediction theory is also related to scattering theory in physics, to theory of non-self-adjoint differential equations,[2] and to operator theory in mathematics.[3] In this appendix, we want to point out some of the connections with mathematical operator theory.

Fundamental in this context are the *Banach spaces* $\mathbf{L}^p$ (where $1 \leq p \leq \infty$) consisting of functions $F(e^{-i\omega})$ defined on the unit circle and based on the measure $d\omega/2\pi$. Because the spaces $\mathbf{L}^p$ shrink as p increases, the space $\mathbf{L}^1$ contains all the others. Each function F in $\mathbf{L}^1$ has the Fourier series defined by

$$F(e^{-i\omega}) \sim \sum_{-\infty}^{\infty} f_n e^{-i\omega n} \, d\omega \, ,$$

where the Fourier coefficients are

$$f_n = \frac{1}{2\pi} \int_{-\pi}^{\pi} F(e^{-i\omega}) \, e^{i\omega n} \, d\omega \, .$$

The sequence f_n (where $-\infty < n < \infty$) may be regarded as a *discrete time function*, where the integer n represents the time index. Then the function $F(e^{-i\omega})$ is called the *amplitude and phase spectrum* of f_n, where the real variable ω represents angular frequency in radians per time unit (*cf.* Secs. 2.1 and 2.2). In particular, $\mathbf{L}^2$ is a Hilbert space with inner product:

$$(F,G) = \frac{1}{2\pi} \int_{-\pi}^{\pi} FG^* \, d\omega = \sum_{-\infty}^{\infty} f_n g_n^* \, ,$$

where g_n represents the Fourier coefficients of $G(e^{-i\omega})$.

---

[1] Lax, P. D., and R. S. Phillips, "Scattering theory," *Bull. Am. Math. Soc.* **70**, 130–142 (1964).

[2] Potapov, V. P., "The multiplicative structure of J-contractive matrix functions," (in Russian), *Trudy Moskov. Mat. Obsc.* **4**, 125–236 (1955); English translation, *Am. Math Soc. Transl.* **15**, 131–243 (1960).

[3] Helson, H., *Lectures on Invariant Spaces*, Academic Press, New York, 1964.

For each p, the *Hardy space* H^p is defined as the subset of L^p consisting of the functions $F(e^{-i\omega})$ whose Fourier coefficients f_n all vanish for $n < 0$. That is, the Hardy space is that subset of the Banach space consisting of the spectra of realizable (i.e., one-sided) time functions. If we delay a one-sided time function by one time unit, we still obtain a one-sided time function. Since a unit time delay in the time-domain corresponds to multiplication by $e^{-i\omega}$ in the frequency domain, it follows that H^p is carried into itself by the *shift operator* S defined by

$$(SF)(e^{-i\omega}) = e^{-i\omega}F(e^{-i\omega}).$$

This property of the space H^p is important. An alternative definition of Hardy space is that H^p consists of the functions $F(z)$ analytic inside the unit circle such that

$$\frac{1}{2\pi} \int_{-\pi}^{\pi} \left| F(re^{-i\omega}) \right|^p \, d\omega$$

is bounded as r tends to unity. The connection between the two definitions is provided by the correspondence of the Fourier series

$$F(e^{-i\omega}) \sim \sum_{0}^{\infty} f_n e^{-i\omega n}$$

resulting from the first definition and the power series

$$F(z) = \sum_{0}^{\infty} f_n z^n$$

resulting from the second definition. The function $F(e^{-i\omega})$ of the first definition is almost everywhere the radial limit of the function $F(z)$ of the second definition, and conversely, the function $F(z)$ of the second definition can be obtained from the function $F(e^{-i\omega})$ of the first definition by the Cauchy formula. Thus, the connection is complete. The function $F(z)$ is called the *z-transform* of f_n.

A function $P(e^{-i\omega})$ of L^2 with modulus unity, that is, with

$$|P(e^{-i\omega})| = 1,$$

is called a *phase-shift function*. Thus, a phase-shift function can be written in polar form as

$$P(e^{-i\omega}) = e^{i\theta(\omega)}$$

where the function $\theta(\omega)$ represents the phase shift. A realizable phase-shift function is called an *all-pass function*. In other words, an all-pass function is defined as a function which is contained in Hardy space H^2 and which has modulus unity. All-pass functions are also called *inner functions*. The structure of all-pass functions is known. More precisely, each all-pass function $P(z)$ is a product of the form

$$P(z) = cB(z)S(z),$$

where c is a complex constant of modulus unity, $B(z)$ is a *Blaschke function*, and $S(z)$ is a *singular function*. Blaschke functions are products of the form

$$B(z) = z^k \prod_{j=1}^{\infty} \frac{a_j - z}{1 - a_j^* z} \frac{|a_j|}{a_j},$$

where k is zero or a positive integer, and the a_j are complex numbers (not necessarily distinct) satisfying

$$0 < |a_j| < 1, \sum_{j=1}^{\infty} (1 - |a_j|) < \infty.$$

The factor z^k in $B(z)$ is called the *pure-delay component*, whereas the remaining factor (i.e., the product) is called the *dispersive component*. The dispersive component has all of its zeros a_j within the unit circle; for each zero there is a pole $1/a_j^*$ outside the unit circle. Each zero and its corresponding pole are symmetrical with respect to the unit circle. In the dispersive component, the denominator polynomials $1 - a_j^* z$ are minimum-delay polynomials, and the numerator polynomials $a_j - z$ are the corresponding maximum-delay polynomials. The singular function $S(z)$ has no known physical significance and is invariably omitted in engineering discussions. The simplest singular function is

$$S(z) = \exp\left(-\frac{1 + z}{1 - z}\right).$$

There are many equivalent ways of defining minimum delay.[4] One definition is: A function $A(e^{-i\omega})$ of H^2 is called *minimum delay* if the partial energy,

$$\sum_{n=0}^{N} |a_n|^2,$$

is a maximum (for $N = 0, 1, 2, \ldots$) in the class of all functions of H^2 with the same modulus as $A(e^{-i\omega})$. In this definition, the coefficients a_n are the Fourier coefficients of $A(e^{-i\omega})$; that is, $(a_0, a_1, a_2, \ldots)$ represents the realizable stable time function with phase and amplitude spectrum $A(e^{-i\omega})$. An equivalent definition is: A function $A(e^{-i\omega})$ of H^2 is called *minimum delay* if the functions

$$A, e^{-i\omega}A, e^{-i\omega2}A, e^{-i\omega3}A, \ldots$$

span H^2. Another term for minimum-delay function is *outer function*. The cannonical representation theorem states that each function F of H^2 has the representation

$$F = AP,$$

---

[4] Robinson, E. A., *Random Wavelets and Cybernetic Systems*, Griffin & Co., London, 1962.

where P is all-pass (i.e., inner) and A is minimum delay (i.e., outer). The factors P and A are unique, except for constant factors of modulus unity.

A minimum-delay function is determined by its modulus, except for a constant of magnitude unity. Since there is a one-to-one correspondence between the modulus of a frequency function and the autocorrelation of a time function, we can equivalently say that a minimum-delay time function is determined by its autocorrelation, except for a constant of magnitude unity. We gave a numerical method for this determination in Sec. 2.9.

Beurling[5] investigated the structure of Hardy space H^2 by the use of the concept of invariant subspaces. A closed subspace M of Hilbert space L^2 is called invariant if

$$e^{-i\omega}F(e^{-i\omega})$$

belongs to M for every $F(e^{-i\omega})$ that belongs to M. The subspace M is called doubly invariant if both

$$e^{-i\omega}F(e^{-i\omega}) \quad \text{and} \quad e^{i\omega}F(e^{-i\omega})$$

belong to M for every $F(e^{-i\omega})$ that belongs to M. The subspace M is called simply invariant if it is invariant but not doubly invariant.

Beurling's theorem is: The simply invariant subspaces of Hilbert space L^2 are precisely the subspaces of the form

$$P(e^{-i\omega})H^2,$$

where $P(e^{-i\omega})$ is an arbitrary phase-shift function (i.e., $|P(e^{-i\omega})| = 1$). The phase-shift function $P(e^{-i\omega})$ is determined by the subspace, except for a constant factor. When the subspace is contained in H^2, then the phase-shift function $P(e^{-i\omega})$ belongs to H^2, and hence $P(e^{-i\omega})$ is an all-pass (i.e., inner) function.

There is a natural partial ordering of the family of all-pass functions. We say that the all-pass function Q has *more delay* (or is *stronger*) than the all-pass function P if there is an all-pass function R such that

$$Q = PR.$$

From Beurling's theorem, we have an equivalent formulation, namely, the all-pass function Q has more delay (or is stronger) than the all-pass function P if and only if

$$QH^2 \subset PH^2.$$

1.2 Multichannel theory

In the single-channel case, we are concerned with scalar functions $F(e^{-i\omega})$ defined on the unit circle $z = e^{-i\omega}$. In the multichannel case, we are concerned

    [5] Beurling, A., "On two problems concerning linear transformations in Hilbert space," *Acta. Math.* **81**, 239–255 (1949).

with matrix-valued functions $F(e^{-i\omega})$ defined on the unit circle. The Banach and Hardy spaces of matrix-valued functions are defined in an analogous way to the Banach and Hardy spaces of scalar functions. A fundamental result in the multichannel theory is the analog[6] of Beurling's theorem characterizing the invariant subspaces. The characterization is essentially the same as for scalar functions. Likewise, multichannel minimum-delay and all-pass functions can be defined and have properties similar to their single-channel counterparts.[7] In particular, a partial ordering among multichannel all-pass functions can be introduced in a way similar to that for scalar all-pass functions. Multichannel all-pass functions can be factored into the product of a multichannel Blaschke function, a multichannel singular function, and a constant unitary matrix. The multichannel all-pass function is what we have termed an *extended-unitary matrix* in Sec. 4.7. A p-channel Blaschke function has the general form

$$\prod_{j=1}^{\infty} V_j \begin{bmatrix} B_j(z)I_q & 0_{q,r} \\ 0_{r,q} & I_r \end{bmatrix} V_j^{-1},$$

where

$$p = q + r$$
$$I_q = q \times q \text{ identity matrix}$$
$$I_r = r \times r \text{ identity matrix}$$
$$0_{q,r} = q \times r \text{ zero matrix}$$
$$0_{r,q} = r \times q \text{ zero matrix}$$
$$V_j = p \times p \text{ (constant) unitary matrix},$$

and where

$$B_j(z) = \frac{a_j - z}{1 - a_j^* z} \frac{|a_j|}{a_j}$$

is an elementary single-channel Blaschke function.

In Sec. 5.4, we gave a numerical method for the determination of a multichannel minimum-delay time function from its autocorrelation. However, in applications the following approximate method is usually better. The least-squares multichannel prediction-error operator computed as in Sec. 6.3 is necessarily minimum delay. The required multichannel minimum-delay operator for the given autocorrelation can then be computed as the inverse of the multichannel prediction-error operator.[8]

---

[6] Lax, P. D., "Translation invariant spaces," in *Proc. Internat. Symp. Linear Spaces*, Macmillan, New York, 1961, pp. 299–306.

[7] Robinson, E. A., 1962, *op. cit.*

[8] Robinson, E. A., *Statistical Communication and Detection with Special Reference to Digital Data Processing of Radar and Seismic Signals*, Griffin, London, and Hafner, New York, 1967.

Appendix 2

Glossary of Subroutines

Name of Subroutine	Description	Subroutines Required	Pages
MAINE (version 1)	Inverse of a symmetrical matrix	—	11
MAINE (version 2)	Inverse of a symmetrical matrix	—	12
ZERO (real or complex)	Stores zeros in an array	—	16
MOVE (real or complex) (version 1)	Moves an array	—	17
MOVE (real or complex) (version 2)	Moves an array	—	18
SCALE (real or complex)	Scales an array	—	19
DOT	Dot, or inner, product	—	20
DOTR	Dot product reverse	—	20
MINSN	Finds minimum element of array	—	21
MAXSN	Finds maximum element of array	—	21
REMAV	Removes arithmetic average	—	22
REVERS	Reverses order of elements of an array	—	22
NORMEN	Normalizes by energy	—	23
NORM1	Normalizes by first element	—	23
NORMAG	Normalizes by largest magnitude	—	23
IMPULS	Stores impulse function	—	26
CROSS	Autocorrelation and cross correlation	DOT	27, 20
FOLD	Polynomial multiplication, or convolution	ZERO	29, 16
POLYDV (real or complex)	Polynomial division, or deconvolution	ZERO, MOVE (both real or both complex)	31, 16, 17
PSQRT	Polynomial square root	—	32
POLYEV (partially complex)	Polynomial evaluation	—	33
POLRT	Polynomial roots	—	35

Name of Subroutine	Description	Subroutines Required	Pages
SIMEQ1	Solves simultaneous linear equations	MOVE, MAINE	39, 17, 11
FADDEJ (real)	Inverse, determinant, and adjugate of a matrix	MOVE, BRAINY, ZERO, SCALE (all real)	40, 17,154, 16, 19
FADDEJ (complex)	Inverse, determinant, and adjugate of a matrix	MOVE, BRAINY, ZERO (all complex)	41, 17,154, 16
MAINV (real)	Inverse of a matrix	FADDEJ, MOVE, BRAINY, ZERO, SCALE (all real)	42, 40, 17, 154, 16, 19
MAINV (complex)	Inverse of a matrix	FADDEJ, MOVE, BRAINY, ZERO (all complex)	42, 41, 17, 154, 16
EUREKA	Solves single-channel normal equations by recursion	—	44
INVTOP	Inverse of a Töplitz matrix	EUREKA, IMPULS	46, 44, 26
TRIANG (real)	Triangular factorization of positive definite matrix	ZERO (real)	47, 16
TRIANG (complex)	Triangular factorization of positive definite matrix	ZERO (complex)	48, 16
SPUR (Fortran function)	Spur, or trace, of a matrix	—	49
MATRAN (machine-dependent)	Transpose of a rectangular matrix on itself	—	52
INDATA (machine-dependent)	Reads data into machine	—	53
OUTDAT	Writes data out of machine	—	54
RITE	Writes a sequence of matrices	—	55
COSTAB	Generates full wave-length cosine table	—	60
SINTAB	Generates full wave-length sine table	—	60
COSP	One value of either cosine or sine transform	—	61
NLOGN (complex)	Fast Fourier transform	—	63
TRIG	One value of Fourier transform	—	65
DRUM	Makes phase curve continuous	—	65
POLAR	Computes polar coordinates	—	66

Name of Subroutine	Description	Subroutines Required	Pages
CAST	Cosine and sine transforms	POLYEV, POLAR, DRUM	67, 33, 66, 65
SHAPE	Waveshaping filter	CROSS, EUREKA, DOT, FOLD, ZERO	75, 27, 44, 20, 29, 16
SPIKE	Spiking filter for optimum spike position	IMPULS, SHAPE, CROSS, EUREKA, DOT, FOLD, ZERO, MINSN	79, 26, 75, 27, 44, 20, 29, 16, 21
SIDE	Simpson sideways recursion		80
SPIKER	Spiking filter for optimum spike position	IMPULS, SHAPE, CROSS, EUREKA, DOT, FOLD, ZERO, MINSN, SIDE	82, 26, 75, 27, 44, 20, 29, 16, 21, 80
SHAPER	Waveshaping filter for optimum position	CROSS, DOT, EUREKA, FOLD, MINSN, SHAPE, SIDE, ZERO	84, 27, 20, 44, 29, 21, 75, 80, 16
COSTR	One value of cosine transform of two-sided function	—	90
SMOOTH	Hamming–Tukey spectral smoothing	—	91
AUGURY	Multichannel Wiener prediction	OMEN, FORM, MAINE, MOVE, ZERO, BRAINY, HEAT	99, 99,100, 11, 17, 16,154, 207
OMEN	Called by AUGURY	FORM, MAINE, MOVE, ZERO, BRAINY, HEAT	99,100, 11, 17, 16, 154,207
FORM	Called by OMEN, SPIRIT, and ORACLE	—	100
Main program	Synthetic seismogram	INDATA, FOLD, ZERO	137, 53, 29, 16
BRAINY (real or complex)	Matrix polynomial multiplication (or convolution of multichannel signals)	ZERO (real or complex)	154, 16
POMAIN (real or complex)	Inversion of matrix polynomial	MOVE, BRAINY, ZERO, SCALE (all real or all complex)	162, 17,154, 16, 19
FACT (complex)	Factors matrix polynomial into binomial factors	ZERO, MOVE, MAINV, FADDEJ, BRAINY (all complex)	177, 16, 17, 42, 41, 154

Name of Subroutine	Description	Subroutines Required	Pages
FACTOR (complex)	Minimum-delay factorization of multichannel spectrum	ZERO, MOVE, SCALE, BRAINY, POMAIN, TRIANG, FADDEJ, HEAT (all complex), POLRT (real)	197, 16, 17, 19, 154, 162, 48, 41,207, 35
MACRO	Multichannel autocorrelation or cross correlation	CROSS, DOT	203, 27, 20
HEAT (real)	Multichannel autocorrelation or cross correlation	ZERO (real)	207, 16
HEAT (complex)	Multichannel autocorrelation or cross correlation	ZERO (complex)	207, 16
QUADCO	Quadrature spectra and co-spectra	COSTAB, SINTAB, COSP	212, 60, 60, 61
COHERE	Magnitude and phase-lag of coherency	MOVE, NORMAG	215, 17, 23
NORMEQ	Solves multichannel normal equations by recursion	ZERO, MOVE, SIMEQ1, MAINE	247, 16, 17, 39, 11
WIENER (version 1)	Multichannel Wiener filtering	RECUR, ZERO, MOVE, SCALE, BRAINY, HEAT, MAINE, SIMEQ1, SPUR	253,254, 16, 17, 19, 154,207, 11, 39, 49
RECUR	Called by WIENER (version 1)	ZERO, SIMEQ1, HEAT, MOVE, SPUR, MAINE	254, 16, 39, 207, 17, 49, 11
WIENER (version 2)		RECUR2, ZERO, MOVE, SCALE, BRAINY, HEAT, MAINE, SPIRIT, ORACLE, FORM, SPUR	256,257, 16, 17, 19, 154,207, 11,257, 258, 100, 49
RECUR2	Called by WIENER (version 2)	SPIRIT, ORACLE, HEAT, SPUR	257,257,258, 207, 49
SPIRIT	Called by RECUR2	MOVE, ZERO, HEAT, MAINE, BRAINY, FORM	257, 17, 16, 207, 11, 154,100
ORACLE	Called by RECUR2	ZERO, HEAT, MAINE, BRAINY, FORM	258, 16,207, 11, 154,100

Appendix 3

Program Revisions

Many of the programs in the book were written for clarity rather than efficiency. Hence, a user processing large amounts of data can reduce machine time by revising some of the programs. For example, in COSTAB and SINTAB in Sec. 2.2, machine time can be reduced by a factor of 4 by computing trigonometric functions only in the first quadrant since

$$\cos (2m - j)\theta = \cos j\theta$$

and

$$\cos (m \pm j)\theta = -\cos j\theta$$

for $j = 0, 1, 2, \ldots, [m/2]$, where $\theta = \pi/m$, and similarly for the sine function.

As another example, COSP in Sec. 2.2, TRIG in Sec. 2.2, and COSTR in Sec. 2.6 can all be speeded up considerably by use of Goertzel's algorithm,[9] or, if the complete transform is wanted, by use of the fast Fourier transform algorithm for the mixed radix case.[10] The following revised versions of subroutines TRIG and COSTR written by R. C. Singleton illustrate the possibility of improving efficiency without significantly complicating the method of computing. Professor Singleton's program for TRIG is:

```
SUBROUTINE TRIG(LX,X,W,S,C)
DIMENSION X(LX)
SINW = SIN(W)
COSW = COS(W)
S = 0.0
C = X(LX)
KK = LX − 1
DO 10 I = KK,1,−1
T = C
C = T*COSW − S*SINW + X(I)
10 S = T*SINW + S*COSW
RETURN
END
```

---

[9] Goertzel, G., *Amer. Math. Monthly* **65**, 34–35 (1958).
[10] Good, I. J., "The interaction algorithm and practical Fourier series," *J. Roy. Stat. Soc., Ser. B*, **20**, 361–372 (1958). Addendum, *J. Roy. Stat. Soc., Ser. B*, **22**, 372–375 (1960).

This version saves two multiplications, one addition, and several fetches and stores each time through the inner loop. Computing time is reduced by about one-third. The method is based on the equations:

$$F_{LX} = X(LX)$$
$$F_I = F_{I+1} e^{iW} + X(I) \quad \text{for } I = LX - 1, \ldots, 2, 1$$

and

$$C = \text{Real} (F_1)$$
$$S = \text{Imag} (F_1) .$$

Professor Singleton's program for COSTR is:

```
SUBROUTINE  COSTR(LR,R,W,S)
DIMENSION  R(LR)
CD = SIN(0.5*W)
CD = 2*CD*CD
CR = -(CD+CD)
COSW = 1.0
S = 0.0
DO  1  I = 2,LR
CD = CR*COSW+CD
COSW = COSW+CD
1  S = R(I)*COSW+S
S = R(1)+S+S
RETURN
END
```

This version saves four multiplications and several fetches and stores each time through the inner loop. Computing time is reduced by about fifty percent. The method is based upon the use of second difference relations for cosine calculations.[11]

In Sec. 2.2, we gave subroutine NLOGN which uses the fast Fourier transform algorithm for the radix 2 case. This algorithm may be described as follows. Given $q = 2^n$ data points $(x_0, x_1, x_2, \ldots, x_{q-1})$, the finite Fourier transform $(y_0, y_1, y_2, \ldots, y_{q-1})$ is defined as

$$y_j = \sum_{k=0}^{q-1} x_k e^{-2\pi i jk/q}, \quad j = 0, 1, \ldots, q - 1 . \tag{1}$$

The given data points may be recovered by the inverse transform,

---

[11] Singleton, R. C., "A method for computing the fast Fourier transform with auxiliary memory and limited high-speed storage," *IEEE Trans. on Audio and Electroacoustics*, **AU–15**, 91–98 (1967).

$$x_m = \frac{1}{q} \sum_{j=0}^{q-1} y_j \, e^{2\pi i jm/q}, \quad m = 0, 1, \ldots, q-1. \tag{2}$$

Equations (1) and (2) become in matrix notation, respectively,

$$\mathbf{Y} = \mathbf{X}\mathbf{W} \tag{3}$$
$$\mathbf{X} = \mathbf{Y}\mathbf{W}^{-1}, \tag{4}$$

where $\mathbf{X}$ is the $1 \times q$ row vector

$$\mathbf{X} = [x_0, x_1, \ldots, x_{q-1}], \tag{5}$$

$\mathbf{Y}$ is the $1 \times q$ row vector

$$\mathbf{Y} = [y_0, y_1, \ldots, y_{q-1}], \tag{6}$$

and $\mathbf{W}$ is the $q \times q$ matrix

$$\mathbf{W} = [e^{-2\pi i k j/q}]; \quad k, j = 0, 1, 2, \ldots, q-1. \tag{7}$$

By direct multiplication, computation of eq. (3) requires q^2 multiply-and-add operations. As we shall see, the same computation requires only $q \log q$ multiply-and-add operations by the fast Fourier transform algorithm.

If we define w as

$$w = e^{-2\pi i/q}, \tag{8}$$

then the matrix $\mathbf{W}$ can be written as

$$\mathbf{W} = [w^{kj}]; \quad k, j = 0, 1, 2, \ldots, q-1. \tag{9}$$

For example, when $q = 2^2 = 4$, we have

$$\mathbf{W} = \begin{bmatrix} w^0 & w^0 & w^0 & w^0 \\ w^0 & w^1 & w^2 & w^3 \\ w^0 & w^2 & w^4 & w^6 \\ w^0 & w^3 & w^6 & w^9 \end{bmatrix} = \begin{bmatrix} 1 & 1 & 1 & 1 \\ 1 & w & w^2 & w^3 \\ 1 & w^2 & 1 & w^2 \\ 1 & w^3 & w^2 & w \end{bmatrix}$$

because $w^4 = w^0 = 1$, $w^6 = w^2$, $w^9 = w^5 = w$. As another example, in the case when $q = 2^3 = 8$, we have

$$\mathbf{W} = \begin{bmatrix} w^0 & w^0 & w^0 & w^0 & w^0 & w^0 & w^0 & w^0 \\ w^0 & w^1 & w^2 & w^3 & w^4 & w^5 & w^6 & w^7 \\ w^0 & w^2 & w^4 & w^6 & w^8 & w^{10} & w^{12} & w^{14} \\ w^0 & w^3 & w^6 & w^9 & w^{12} & w^{15} & w^{18} & w^{21} \\ w^0 & w^4 & w^8 & w^{12} & w^{16} & w^{20} & w^{24} & w^{28} \\ w^0 & w^5 & w^{10} & w^{15} & w^{20} & w^{25} & w^{30} & w^{35} \\ w^0 & w^6 & w^{12} & w^{18} & w^{24} & w^{30} & w^{36} & w^{42} \\ w^0 & w^7 & w^{14} & w^{21} & w^{28} & w^{35} & w^{42} & w^{49} \end{bmatrix}$$

$$\begin{bmatrix} 1 & 1 & 1 & 1 & 1 & 1 & 1 & 1 \\ 1 & w^1 & w^2 & w^3 & w^4 & w^5 & w^6 & w^7 \\ 1 & w^2 & w^4 & w^6 & 1 & w^2 & w^4 & w^6 \\ 1 & w^3 & w^6 & w & w^4 & w^7 & w^2 & w^5 \\ 1 & w^4 & 1 & w^4 & 1 & w^4 & 1 & w^4 \\ 1 & w^5 & w^2 & w^7 & w^4 & w & w^6 & w^3 \\ 1 & w^6 & w^4 & w^2 & 1 & w^6 & w^4 & w^2 \\ 1 & w^7 & w^6 & w^5 & w^4 & w^3 & w^2 & w \end{bmatrix}.$$

The matrix **W** is symmetric. Furthermore, the matrix **W** has the property that

$$\mathbf{WW^{*T}} = qI, \tag{10}$$

which means that, except for the scale factor $1/\sqrt{q}$, the matrix **W** is a unitary matrix. Hence, the inverse of **W** is

$$\mathbf{W}^{-1} = \frac{1}{q}\,\mathbf{W^{*T}}, \tag{11}$$

and thus eq. (2) may be written as

$$\mathbf{X} = \frac{1}{q}\,\mathbf{YW^{*T}}. \tag{12}$$

If we let k denote the time t, and j/q denote frequency f, then the time increment Δt is 1, and the frequency increment Δf is $1/q$. Parseval's equality states that

$$\sum_{k=0}^{q-1} x_k x_k^* \,\Delta t = \sum_{j=0}^{q-1} y_j y_j^* \,\Delta f,$$

which in matrix notation is

$$\mathbf{XX^{*T}} = \mathbf{YY^{*T}}\frac{1}{q}.$$

This same equality can be directly found from eqs. (3) and (10) by

$$\mathbf{YY^{*T}} = (\mathbf{XW})(\mathbf{XW})^{*T} = \mathbf{XWW^{*T}X^{*T}} = q\mathbf{XX^{*T}}.$$

The fast Fourier transform algorithm is based on the factorization of the matrix **W** into n sparse matrices and a permutation matrix. The integer n is defined as

$$n = \log_2 q.$$

(The algorithm requires that the number q of data points be a power of 2, that is, $q = 2^n$.) The factorization may be written as

$$\mathbf{W} = \mathbf{S_1 S_2 \cdots S_n P}.$$

Let us now discuss the matrices appearing in the factorization. The matrices $S_1, S_2, \ldots, S_n$ are the sparse matrices, and the matrix P is the permutation matrix. Let us give two examples as to how the factorization is formed.

Our *first example* is the case when $n = 2$, so $q = 4$. We write the numbers 0, 1, 2, 3 in their binary form, and then define the permutation as that transformation which takes a given binary number into its reverse binary number. Thus, the permutation is shown by

Decimal		Binary		Reverse binary		Corresponding decimal
0	=	00	$\rightarrow$	00	=	0
1	=	01	$\rightarrow$	10	=	2
2	=	10	$\rightarrow$	01	=	1
3	=	11	$\rightarrow$	11	=	3

That is, the permutation is the product of disjoint cycles given by

$$(0)(1, 2)(3) .$$

The corresponding permutation matrix is

$$P = \begin{bmatrix} 1 & 0 & 0 & 0 \\ 0 & 0 & 1 & 0 \\ 0 & 1 & 0 & 0 \\ 0 & 0 & 0 & 1 \end{bmatrix}.$$

The matrix P satisfies the equation

$$(y_0, y_2, y_1, y_3)P = (y_0, y_1, y_2, y_3) .$$

Our *second example* is the case when $n = 3$, so $q = 8$. We have

Decimal		Binary		Reverse binary		Corresponding decimal
0	=	000	$\rightarrow$	000	=	0
1	=	001	$\rightarrow$	100	=	4
2	=	010	$\rightarrow$	010	=	2
3	=	011	$\rightarrow$	110	=	6
4	=	100	$\rightarrow$	001	=	1
5	=	101	$\rightarrow$	101	=	5
6	=	110	$\rightarrow$	011	=	3
7	=	111	$\rightarrow$	111	=	7

so the permutation is the product of distinct cycles given by

$$(0)(1, 4)(2)(3, 6)(5)(7) .$$

The permutation matrix in this case is

$$P = \begin{bmatrix} 1 & 0 & 0 & 0 & 0 & 0 & 0 & 0 \\ 0 & 0 & 0 & 0 & 1 & 0 & 0 & 0 \\ 0 & 0 & 1 & 0 & 0 & 0 & 0 & 0 \\ 0 & 0 & 0 & 0 & 0 & 0 & 1 & 0 \\ 0 & 1 & 0 & 0 & 0 & 0 & 0 & 0 \\ 0 & 0 & 0 & 0 & 0 & 1 & 0 & 0 \\ 0 & 0 & 0 & 1 & 0 & 0 & 0 & 0 \\ 0 & 0 & 0 & 0 & 0 & 0 & 0 & 1 \end{bmatrix}.$$

This matrix satisfies

$$(y_0, y_4, y_2, y_6, y_1, y_5, y_3, y_7)P = (y_0, y_1, y_2, y_3, y_4, y_5, y_6, y_7).$$

Because $P^2 = I$ and $P = P^T$, the permutation matrix is an orthogonal matrix.

Now let us define the matrices S_1 and S_2 in the *first example*, namely, the case when $n = 2$. We define S_1 as

$$S_1 = \begin{bmatrix} 1 & 0 & 1 & 0 \\ 0 & 1 & 0 & 1 \\ w^0 & 0 & w^2 & 0 \\ 0 & w^0 & 0 & w^2 \end{bmatrix}$$

and S_2 as

$$S_2 = \begin{bmatrix} 1 & 1 & 0 & 0 \\ w^0 & w^2 & 0 & 0 \\ 0 & 0 & 1 & 1 \\ 0 & 0 & w^1 & w^3 \end{bmatrix}.$$

Note that the sequence of the powers of w is 0, 2, 1, 3, which is the sequence produced by the reverse binary numbers demonstrated above. Because any column of the matrix S_1 has only two nonzero elements, one of which is unity, the product

$$(x_0, x_1, x_2, x_3)S_1 = T_1$$

requires four multiply-and-add operations, that is, q multiply-and-add operations. Likewise, the product

$$T_1 S_2$$

requires four multiply-and-add operations. Hence, the combined operation, namely,

$$(x_0, x_1, x_2, x_3)S_1 S_2,$$

requires 4·2, that is, qn, multiply-and-add operations. However, it can be shown[12] that

$$(x_0, x_1, x_2, x_3)S_1 S_2 = (y_0, y_2, y_1, y_3).$$

---

[12] Good, I. J., *op. cit.*

If we multiply this result by the permutation matrix P, it follows that we obtain the desired Fourier transform (y_0, y_1, y_2, y_3). In summary, we have

$$(x_0, x_1, x_2, x_3)S_1 S_2 P = (y_0, y_1, y_2, y_3) ,$$

where the total number of multiply-and-add operations is

$$qn = q \log_2 q .$$

(*Note.* In keeping with our mathematical notation, it would have been more logical to name the fast Fourier transform subroutine QLOGQ instead of NLOGN.)

It can be readily verified by matrix multiplication that

$$W = S_1 S_2 P .$$

In our *second example*, namely the case when $n = 3$ and $q = 2^3 = 8$, we define the following:

$$S_1 = \begin{bmatrix} 1 & 0 & 0 & 0 & 1 & 0 & 0 & 0 \\ 0 & 1 & 0 & 0 & 0 & 1 & 0 & 0 \\ 0 & 0 & 1 & 0 & 0 & 0 & 1 & 0 \\ 0 & 0 & 0 & 1 & 0 & 0 & 0 & 1 \\ w^0 & 0 & 0 & 0 & w^4 & 0 & 0 & 0 \\ 0 & w^0 & 0 & 0 & 0 & w^4 & 0 & 0 \\ 0 & 0 & w^0 & 0 & 0 & 0 & w^4 & 0 \\ 0 & 0 & 0 & w^0 & 0 & 0 & 0 & w^4 \end{bmatrix}$$

$$S_2 = \begin{bmatrix} 1 & 0 & 1 & 0 & 0 & 0 & 0 & 0 \\ 0 & 1 & 0 & 1 & 0 & 0 & 0 & 0 \\ w^0 & 0 & w^4 & 0 & 0 & 0 & 0 & 0 \\ 0 & w^0 & 0 & w^4 & 0 & 0 & 0 & 0 \\ 0 & 0 & 0 & 0 & 1 & 0 & 1 & 0 \\ 0 & 0 & 0 & 0 & 0 & 1 & 0 & 1 \\ 0 & 0 & 0 & 0 & w^2 & 0 & w^6 & 0 \\ 0 & 0 & 0 & 0 & 0 & w^2 & 0 & w^6 \end{bmatrix}$$

$$S_3 = \begin{bmatrix} 1 & 1 & 0 & 0 & 0 & 0 & 0 & 0 \\ w^0 & w^4 & 0 & 0 & 0 & 0 & 0 & 0 \\ 0 & 0 & 1 & 1 & 0 & 0 & 0 & 0 \\ 0 & 0 & w^2 & w^6 & 0 & 0 & 0 & 0 \\ 0 & 0 & 0 & 0 & 1 & 1 & 0 & 0 \\ 0 & 0 & 0 & 0 & w^1 & w^5 & 0 & 0 \\ 0 & 0 & 0 & 0 & 0 & 0 & 1 & 1 \\ 0 & 0 & 0 & 0 & 0 & 0 & w^3 & w^7 \end{bmatrix}$$

Note that the sequence of powers of w appearing in these matrices is

$$0, 4, 2, 6, 1, 5, 3, 7 .$$

This is the sequence produced by the reverse binary numbers demonstrated above. The matrices S_1, S_2, S_3 have the property that

$$(x_0, x_1, x_2, x_3, x_4, x_5, x_6, x_7)S_1S_2S_3 = (y_0, y_4, y_2, y_6, y_1, y_5, y_3, y_7) .$$

Hence, it follows that the Fourier transform is

$$(x_0, x_1, x_2, x_3, x_4, x_5, x_6, x_7)S_1S_2S_3P = (y_0, y_1, y_2, y_3, y_4, y_5, y_6, y_7),$$

where the total number of multiply-and-add operations is

$$8 \cdot 3 = qn = q \log_2 q .$$

All these intermediate results are stored in the same (complex) array.

In subroutine NLOGN, the powers of w are recomputed for each matrix $S_1, S_2, \ldots, S_n$. Some gain in efficiency can be achieved by storing the powers of w in a table instead of computing them.

Suppose that the given data represents a *real-valued* time series, say,

$$(x_0, x_1, x_2, \ldots, x_{q-1}) ,$$

where $q = 2^n$. Here x_k represents the value of the time series at discrete (integer) time $t = k$, so the time spacing $\Delta t = 1$ time unit. The finite Fourier transform, as given by eq. (1), represents the spectrum

$$(y_0, y_1, y_2, \ldots, y_{q-1})$$

of the given time series. The frequency spacing is $\Delta f = 1/q$ cycles per time unit, and hence y_j represents the spectral value at frequency $f = j \Delta f = j/q$. The Nyquist frequency f_N is defined as

$$f_N = \frac{1}{2\Delta t} .$$

Hence, the Nyquist frequency may be written as

$$f_N = \frac{1}{2} = \frac{q}{2}\frac{1}{q} = \frac{q}{2}\Delta f .$$

Therefore, the spectral value at the Nyquist frequency is the value for index $j = q/2$, that is, it is $y_{q/2}$. For example, if $q = 2^3 = 8$, then the spectral value at the Nyquist frequency is y_4. The real part of the spectral value at the Nyquist frequency is

$$\text{Re}[y_{q/2}] = \sum_{k=0}^{q-1} x_k \cos \pi k ,$$

and the imaginary part is

$$\text{Im}[y_{q/2}] = 0 .$$

The real part of the spectral value at zero frequency is

$$\text{Re}[y_0] = \sum_{k=0}^{q-1} x_k \,,$$

and the imaginary part is

$$\text{Im}[y_0] = 0 \,.$$

Moreover, the real part of the spectrum is symmetric about the Nyquist frequency, that is,

$$\text{Re}[y_{\frac{q}{2}-r}] = \text{Re}[y_{\frac{q}{2}+r}] \qquad \text{for } r = 1, 2, \ldots, \frac{q}{2} - 1 \,,$$

and the imaginary part is anti-symmetric about the Nyquist frequency, that is,

$$\text{Im}[y_{\frac{q}{2}-r}] = -\text{Im}[y_{\frac{q}{2}+r}] \qquad \text{for } r = 1, 2, \ldots, \frac{q}{2} - 1 \,.$$

These symmetry relations are a direct consequence of the assumption that the given time series $(x_0, x_1, \ldots, x_{q-1})$ is real.

The FFT is based upon a doubling procedure. A sequence of length q $= 2^n$ is subdivided into q/2 subsequences each of length two. A two-point transform requires two multiply-add operations. We have q/2 of these for a total of q operations. To go from two-point to four-point transforms requires four operations repeated q/4 times for a total of q operations. We continue this procedure until we arrive at the q-point transform. Altogether we have performed q operations n times for a total of qn operations.

In Sec. 2.6, we gave a brief discussion on the use of subroutine NLOGN in computing convolutions and correlations. This approach gives a dramatic improvement in efficiency over the use of direct methods in a wide range of cases.[13,14] For example, in digital filtering applications, we often want to compute the complete transient convolution of two signals of unequal length, say,

$$(a_0, a_1, a_2, \ldots, a_\alpha) \tag{13}$$

and

$$(b_0, b_1, b_2, \ldots, b_\beta) \,. \tag{14}$$

13 McCowan, D. W., *Finite Fourier Transform Theory and Its Application to the Computation of Convolutions, Correlations, and Spectra*, Tech. Mem. No. 8–66, Teledyne Industries, Alexandria, Va., 1966.

14 Stockham, T. G., "High-Speed Convolution and Correlation," *AFIPS Conf. Proc.* **28**, 229–233 (1966).

The complete transient convolution is the signal

$$(c_0, c_1, c_2, \ldots, c_\gamma) \tag{15}$$

of length

$$\gamma + 1 = \alpha + \beta + 1$$

and with elements

$$c_k = \begin{cases} a_0 b_k + a_1 b_{k-1} + \cdots + a_k b_0 & \text{for } 0 \leq k \leq \gamma \\ 0 & \text{otherwise.} \end{cases}$$

The direct method forms the convolution by the polynomial multiplication algorithm. This method is performed by subroutine FOLD, described in Sec. 1.8. The indirect (or fast Fourier transform) method forms the convolution as described in Sec. 2.6. Briefly, the indirect method first finds the Fourier transforms of the two signals, multiplies the Fourier transforms together, and finally takes the inverse transform of the product. The result is the desired convolution. In order to make the Fourier transforms compatible with each other, all the signals must be stored in arrays of the same length $q = 2^n$. Moreover, q must be greater than or equal to the length of the longest signal. Since the longest signal is necessarily the convolution (15), we must choose q such that

$$q \geq \gamma + 1 = \alpha + \beta + 1$$

or

$$q > \alpha + \beta.$$

If we let KEW $= q$, M1 $= \alpha$, M2 $= \beta$, then the integer N $= n$ can be found by the DO-loop:

```
    M=M1+M2
    DO 1 I=1,20
    N=I
    KEW=2**N
    IF (KEW.GT.M) GO TO 2
  1 CONTINUE
    GO TO 3
```

Statement 2 would be the next operational statement in the program, whereas statement 3 would be a storage limitation return, which in this example indicates that $\alpha + \beta$ is greater than or equal to 2^{20}.

The array containing the signal (13) must have length q, with the signal values $a_0, a_1, \ldots, a_\alpha$ occupying the first $\alpha + 1$ cells, and with zeros in the remaining $q - \alpha - 1$ cells. Likewise, the array containing the signal (14) must have length q, with the signal values $b_0, b_1, \ldots, b_\beta$ in the first $\beta + 1$ cells, and zeros in the remaining $q - \beta - 1$ cells. If we name these two arrays ASIG (read A-signal) and BSIG (read B-signal), respectively, then we have the following:

$$ASIG = (a_0, a_1, \ldots, a_\alpha, 0, 0, \ldots, 0)$$
$$BSIG = (b_0, b_1, \ldots, b_\beta, 0, 0, \ldots, 0),$$

where each array has q cells, where q is the smallest number of the form 2^n such that $q > \alpha + \beta$. If $N = n = \log_2 q$, then the statements

$$CALL\ NLOGN(N, ASIG, -1.0)$$
$$CALL\ NLOGN(N, BSIG, -1.0)$$

yield the finite Fourier transforms A_j and B_j stored as

$$ASIG = (A_0, A_1, A_2, \ldots, A_{q-1})$$
$$BSIG = (B_0, B_1, B_2, \ldots, B_{q-1}),$$

where

$$A_j = \sum_{k=0}^{q-1} a_k w^{kj} \qquad \text{for } j = 0, 1, 2, \ldots, q - 1,$$

and

$$B_j = \sum_{k=0}^{q-1} b_k w^{kj} \qquad \text{for } j = 0, 1, 2, \ldots, q - 1,$$

with w defined as

$$w = e^{-2\pi i / q}.$$

A DO-loop computes C_j defined as

$$C_j = A_j B_j \qquad \text{for } j = 0, 1, 2, \ldots, q - 1$$

and stores the results in the array CSIG (read C-signal), that is,

$$CSIG = (C_1, C_2, C_3, \ldots, C_{q-1}).$$

The statement

$$CALL\ NLOGN(N, CSIG, 1.0)$$

yields the desired convolution (15) stored in the first $\gamma + 1$ cells of array CSIG, that is,

$$CSIG = (c_0, c_1, c_2, \ldots, c_\gamma, 0, 0, \ldots, 0).$$

In the above description of the fast Fourier transform method of convolution, we assumed that all the signals are complex-valued. For real-valued signals, some savings in computing time can be made because we can compute the Fourier transform of the two real-valued signals simultaneously with one call of subroutine NLOGN. For example, if the signals (13) and (14) are real, then we may define the complex signal x_k as

$$x_k = a_k + ib_k \quad \text{for } k = 0, 1, 2, \ldots, q - 1$$

(where, of course, $a_k = 0$ for $k > \alpha$ and $b_k = 0$ for $k > \beta$). If X is the array

$$X = (x_0, x_1, x_2, \ldots, x_{q-1}),$$

then the statement

$$\text{CALL NLOGN(N,X,}-1.0)$$

yields

$$X = (X_0, X_1, X_2, \ldots, X_{q-1}),$$

where

$$X_j = A_j + iB_j \quad \text{for } j = 0, 1, 2, \ldots, q - 1.$$

Since A_j and B_j are, respectively, the Fourier transforms of the real signals a_k and b_k, they satisfy:

$$\text{Im}[A_0] = \text{Im}[B_0] = 0$$
$$\text{Re}[A_j] = \text{Re}[A_{q-j}]$$
$$\text{Re}[B_j] = \text{Re}[B_{q-j}]$$
$$\text{Im}[A_j] = -\text{Im}[A_{q-j}]$$
$$\text{Im}[B_j] = -\text{Im}[B_{q-j}],$$

where $j = 1, 2, \ldots, q - 1$. Hence, the desired Fourier transforms A_j and B_j may be computed by the formulas:

$$A_0 = 0.5(X_0 + X_0^*)$$
$$B_0 = 0.5i(X_0 - X_0^*)$$
$$A_j = 0.5(X_j + X_{q-j}^*) \quad \text{for } j = 1, 2, \ldots, q - 1$$
$$B_j = 0.5i(X_j - X_{q-j}^*) \quad \text{for } j = 1, 2, \ldots, q - 1.$$

The last two formulas can be coded as a DO-loop.

The cross correlation of the signal (13) with the signal (14) may also be computed by the fast Fourier transform method. The cross correlation is defined by

$$g_k = \sum_t a_t b_{t-k}^*,$$

which states that the cross correlation is equal to the convolution of the first signal with the time-reverse of the complex conjugate of the second signal. Hence, we may use the indirect (i.e., fast Fourier transform) convolution program to convolve the q-element array

$$(a_0, a_1, \ldots, a_\alpha, 0, 0, \ldots, 0)$$

with the q-element array

$$(b_\beta^*, b_{\beta-1}^*, \ldots, b_0^*, 0, 0, \ldots, 0).$$

The result is the required cross correlation given in the q-element array

$$(g_{-\beta}, g_{-\beta+1}, \ldots, g_\alpha, 0, 0, \ldots, 0).$$

Appendix 4

Solution of
Normal Equations

As we have seen, we are often encountered in time-series analysis with the solution of normal equations which have the general form

$$f_1 r_0 + f_2 r_{-1} + \ldots + f_m r_{1-m} = g_0$$
$$f_1 r_1 + f_2 r_0 + \ldots + f_m r_{2-m} = g_1$$
$$\ldots$$
$$f_1 r_{m-1} + f_2 r_{m-2} + \ldots + f_m r_0 = g_{m-1}$$

where r_j is any arbitrary autocorrelation function. Here the r_j and the g_j are known, and the f_j are unknown *filter coefficients*. At first sight it might appear that we have the familar task of solving m linear equations for m unknowns. Nevertheless, it turns out that the computational work is much lighter than usual because of the fact that on the left hand side all the r_j along any diagonal are the same. In this section we wish to give a method which takes account of this diagonal symmetry. This method works, in addition, for the cases of complex- and/or matrix-valued f_j, r_j, and g_j, as long as the usual complex and/or matrix mathematical conventions are followed.

First of all, it is convenient to introduce a special notation for simultaneous linear equations. In this notation, the above normal equations are written as

f_1	f_2		f_m	
r_0	r_1		r_{1-m}	g_0
r_1	r_0		r_{2-m}	g_1
		$\ldots$		
r_{m-1}	r_{m-2}		r_0	g_{m-1}

293

Our method is one in which we solve the equations for the case $m=1$, then for case $m=2$, then for case $m=3$, and so on until we arrive at the desired value of m.

The procedure for the case $m=1$ is as follows. We compute α, β, λ, μ by the equations

$$
\left.\begin{array}{cc}
1 & 0 \\
r_0 & r_{-1} \\
r_1 & r_0
\end{array}\right|\begin{array}{c}
\\
\alpha \\
\lambda
\end{array}
\qquad
\left.\begin{array}{cc}
0 & 1 \\
r_0 & r_{-1} \\
r_1 & r_0
\end{array}\right|\begin{array}{c}
\\
\mu \\
\beta
\end{array}.
$$

Next we compute ε by

$$
\left.\begin{array}{c}
0 \\
r_0
\end{array}\right|\begin{array}{c}
\\
\varepsilon
\end{array}.
$$

(Hence, for this case, $\varepsilon=0$.) Then we multiply the equation for β, which is,

$$
\left.\begin{array}{c}
1 \\
r_0
\end{array}\right|\begin{array}{c}
\\
\beta
\end{array}
$$

by the unknown θ to obtain

$$
\left.\begin{array}{c}
\theta \\
r_0
\end{array}\right|\begin{array}{c}
\\
\theta\beta
\end{array}.
$$

Now we add the two equations

$$
\left.\begin{array}{c}
0 \\
r_0
\end{array}\right|\begin{array}{c}
\\
\varepsilon
\end{array}
+
\left.\begin{array}{c}
\theta \\
r_0
\end{array}\right|\begin{array}{c}
\\
\theta\beta
\end{array}
$$

and hence obtain the equation

$$
\left.\begin{array}{c}
\theta \\
r_0
\end{array}\right|\begin{array}{c}
\\
\varepsilon+\theta\beta
\end{array}.
$$

We now require that the identity

$$
\left.\begin{array}{c}
\theta \\
r_0
\end{array}\right|\begin{array}{c}
\\
\varepsilon+\theta\beta
\end{array}
=
\left.\begin{array}{c}
f_1' \\
r_0
\end{array}\right|\begin{array}{c}
\\
g_0
\end{array}
$$

be true. This identity yields the two equations

$$
\varepsilon+\phi\beta=g_0
$$
$$
\theta=f_1'.
$$

Thus we compute θ by

$$
\varepsilon+\theta\beta=g_0 \quad \text{or} \quad \theta=\frac{g_0-\varepsilon}{\beta}
$$

and then compute f_1' by

$$f_1' = 0 .$$

Let us now drop the prime on f_1', so it becomes the new f_1. Because this new f_1 (i.e. the old f_1') satisfies the equation

$$\begin{array}{c|c} f_1 & \\ \hline r_0 & g_0 \end{array},$$

it is the desired filter coefficient for the case $m=1$.

The procedure for the case $m=2$ is as follows. From the procedure for the case $m=1$, we have the two equations

$$\begin{array}{cc|c} 1 & 0 & \\ \hline r_1 & r_0 & \lambda \end{array} \quad \text{and} \quad \begin{array}{cc|c} 0 & 1 & \\ \hline r_1 & r_0 & \beta \end{array}.$$

Multiply the second equation by the unknown u, and add the result to the first equation to obtain:

$$\begin{array}{cc|c} 1 & 0 & \\ \hline r_1 & r_0 & \lambda \end{array} + \begin{array}{cc|c} 0 & u & \\ \hline r_1 & r_0 & u\beta \end{array} = \begin{array}{cc|c} 1 & u & \\ \hline r_1 & r_0 & \lambda+u\beta \end{array}.$$

We set up the identity

$$\begin{array}{cc|c} 1 & u & \\ \hline r_1 & r_0 & \lambda+u\beta \end{array} = \begin{array}{cc|c} 1 & a_1' & \\ \hline r_1 & r_0 & 0 \end{array}.$$

Thus we compute u by

$$\lambda+u\beta=0 \quad \text{or} \quad u=-\lambda/\beta$$

and then compute a_1' by

$$a_1' = u .$$

From the procedure for the case $m=1$, we also have the two equations

$$\begin{array}{cc|c} 0 & 1 & \\ \hline r_0 & r_{-1} & \mu \end{array} \quad \text{and} \quad \begin{array}{cc|c} 1 & 0 & \\ \hline r_0 & r_{-1} & \alpha \end{array}.$$

Let us form

$$\begin{array}{cc|c} 0 & 1 & \\ \hline r_0 & r_{-1} & \mu \end{array} + \begin{array}{cc|c} v & 0 & \\ \hline r_0 & r_{-1} & v\alpha \end{array} = \begin{array}{cc|c} v & 1 & \\ \hline r_0 & r_{-1} & \mu+v\alpha \end{array}$$

$$= \begin{array}{cc|c} b_1' & 1 & \\ \hline r_0 & r_{-1} & 0 \end{array}.$$

Thus we compute v by

$$\mu + v\alpha = 0 \quad \text{or} \quad v = -\mu/\alpha$$

and then compute b_1' by

$$b_1' = v \ .$$

Let us now drop the primes on a_1', b_1', so they become the new a_1, b_1, respectively. By construction, these new a_1, b_1, (i.e. the old a_1', b_1',) satisfy the equations

$$\frac{\begin{vmatrix} 1 & a_1 \\ r_1 & r_0 \end{vmatrix}}{} \ 0 \quad \text{and} \quad \frac{\begin{vmatrix} b_1 & 1 \\ r_0 & r_{-1} \end{vmatrix}}{} \ 0 \ .$$

Now let us compute the new α, β, λ, μ as follows

$$\frac{\begin{vmatrix} 1 & a_1 & 0 \\ r_0 & r_{-1} & r_{-2} \\ r_1 & r_0 & r_{-1} \\ r_2 & r_1 & r_0 \end{vmatrix}}{} \begin{matrix} \\ \alpha \\ 0 \\ \lambda \end{matrix} \quad \text{and} \quad \frac{\begin{vmatrix} 0 & b_1 & 1 \\ r_0 & r_{-1} & r_{-2} \\ r_1 & r_0 & r_{-1} \\ r_2 & r_1 & r_0 \end{vmatrix}}{} \begin{matrix} \\ \mu \\ 0 \\ \beta \end{matrix} \ .$$

Next we compute the new ε by

$$\frac{\begin{vmatrix} f_1 & 0 \\ r_1 & r_0 \end{vmatrix}}{} \ \varepsilon \ .$$

Let us form

$$\frac{\begin{vmatrix} f_1 & 0 \\ r_0 & r_{-1} \\ r_1 & r_0 \end{vmatrix}}{} \begin{matrix} \\ g_0 \\ \varepsilon \end{matrix} + \frac{\begin{vmatrix} \theta b_1 & \theta \\ r_0 & r_{-1} \\ r_1 & r_0 \end{vmatrix}}{} \begin{matrix} \\ 0 \\ \theta\beta \end{matrix}$$

$$= \frac{\begin{vmatrix} f_1 + \theta b_1 & \theta \\ r_0 & r_{-1} \\ r_1 & r_0 \end{vmatrix}}{} \begin{matrix} \\ g_0 \\ \varepsilon + \theta\beta \end{matrix} = \frac{\begin{vmatrix} f_1' & f_2' \\ r_0 & r_{-1} \\ r_1 & r_0 \end{vmatrix}}{} \begin{matrix} \\ g_0 \\ g_1 \end{matrix} \ .$$

Thus we compute the new θ by

$$\varepsilon + \theta\beta = g_1 \quad \text{or} \quad \theta = \frac{g_1 - \varepsilon}{\beta}$$

and then compute f_1', f_2' by

$$f_1' = f_1 + \theta b_1$$
$$f_2' = 0 \ .$$

Let us drop the primes on f_1', f_2', so they become the new f_1, f_2 respectively. Because these new f_1, f_2 (i.e. the old f_1', f_2') satisfy the equations

$$
\begin{array}{cc|c}
f_1 & f_2 & \\
\hline
r_0 & r_{-1} & g_0 \\
r_1 & r_0 & g_1
\end{array}
$$

they are the desired filter coefficients for the case $m=2$.

The procedure for the case $m=3$ is as follows. From the procedure for the case $m=2$, we have the equations

$$
\begin{array}{ccc|c}
1 & a_1 & 0 & \\
\hline
r_1 & r_0 & r_{-1} & 0 \\
r_2 & r_1 & r_0 & \lambda
\end{array}
\qquad
\begin{array}{ccc|c}
0 & b_1 & 1 & \\
\hline
r_1 & r_0 & r_{-1} & 0 \\
r_2 & r_1 & r_0 & \beta
\end{array}
$$

Let us form

$$
\begin{array}{ccc|c}
1 & a_1 & 0 & \\
\hline
r_1 & r_0 & r_{-1} & 0 \\
r_2 & r_1 & r_0 & \lambda
\end{array}
\;+\;
\begin{array}{ccc|c}
0 & ub_1 & u & \\
\hline
r_1 & r_0 & r_{-1} & 0 \\
r_2 & r_1 & r_0 & u\beta
\end{array}
$$

$$
=
\begin{array}{ccc|c}
1 & a_1+ub_1 & 1 & \\
\hline
r_1 & r_0 & r_{-1} & 0 \\
r_2 & r_1 & r_0 & \lambda+u\beta
\end{array}
\;\equiv\;
\begin{array}{ccc|c}
1 & a_1' & a_2' & \\
\hline
r_1 & r_0 & r_{-1} & 0 \\
r_2 & r_1 & r_0 & 0
\end{array}
$$

Thus we compute u by

$$
\lambda+u\beta=0 \quad \text{or} \quad u=-\lambda/\beta
$$

and then compute a_1', a_2' by

$$
a_1'=a_1+ub_1
$$
$$
a_2'=u .
$$

From the procedure for the case $m=2$, we also have the equations

$$
\begin{array}{ccc|c}
0 & b_1 & 1 & \\
\hline
r_0 & r_{-1} & r_{-2} & \mu \\
r_1 & r_0 & r_{-1} & 0
\end{array}
\qquad \text{and} \qquad
\begin{array}{ccc|c}
1 & a_1 & 0 & \\
\hline
r_0 & r_{-1} & r_{-2} & \alpha \\
r_1 & r_0 & r_{-1} & 0
\end{array}
$$

Let us form

$$\begin{vmatrix} 0 & b_1 & 1 \\ r_0 & r_{-1} & r_{-2} \\ r_1 & r_0 & r_{-1} \end{vmatrix} \begin{matrix} \\ \mu \\ 0 \end{matrix} \quad + \quad \begin{vmatrix} v & va_1 & 0 \\ r_0 & r_{-1} & r_{-2} \\ r_1 & r_0 & r_{-1} \end{vmatrix} \begin{matrix} \\ v\alpha \\ 0 \end{matrix}$$

$$= \begin{vmatrix} v & b_1+va_1 & 1 \\ r_0 & r_{-1} & r_{-2} \\ r_1 & r_0 & r_{-1} \end{vmatrix} \begin{matrix} \\ \mu+v\alpha \\ 0 \end{matrix} \quad \equiv \quad \begin{vmatrix} b_2' & b_1' & 1 \\ r_0 & r_{-1} & r_{-2} \\ r_1 & r_0 & r_{-1} \end{vmatrix} \begin{matrix} \\ 0 \\ 0 \end{matrix} \, .$$

Thus we compute v by

$$\mu + v\alpha = 0 \quad or \quad v = -\mu/\alpha$$

and then compute b_1', b_2' by

$$b_1' = b_1 + va_1$$
$$b_2' = v \, .$$

Let us now drop the primes on a_1', a_2', b_1', b_2', so they become the new a_1, a_2, b_1, b_2, respectiveiy. By construction these new a_1, a_2, b_1, b_2 (i.e. the old a_1', a_2', b_1', b_2') satisfy the equations

$$\begin{vmatrix} 1 & a_1 & a_2 \\ r_1 & r_0 & r_{-1} \\ r_2 & r_1 & r_0 \end{vmatrix} \begin{matrix} \\ 0 \\ 0 \end{matrix} \quad \text{and} \quad \begin{vmatrix} b_2 & b_1 & 1 \\ r_0 & r_{-1} & r_{-2} \\ r_1 & r_0 & r_{-1} \end{vmatrix} \begin{matrix} \\ 0 \\ 0 \end{matrix} \, .$$

Now let us compute the new α, β, λ, μ as follows.

$$\begin{vmatrix} 1 & a_1 & a_2 & 0 \\ r_0 & r_{-1} & r_{-2} & r_{-3} \\ r_1 & r_0 & r_{-1} & r_{-2} \\ r_2 & r_1 & r_0 & r_{-1} \\ r_3 & r_2 & r_1 & r_0 \end{vmatrix} \begin{matrix} \\ \alpha \\ 0 \\ 0 \\ \lambda \end{matrix} \quad \text{and} \quad \begin{vmatrix} 0 & b_2 & b_1 & 1 \\ r_0 & r_{-1} & r_{-2} & r_{-3} \\ r_1 & r_0 & r_{-1} & r_{-2} \\ r_2 & r_1 & r_0 & r_{-1} \\ r_3 & r_2 & r_1 & r_0 \end{vmatrix} \begin{matrix} \\ \mu \\ 0 \\ 0 \\ \beta \end{matrix} \, .$$

Next we compute the new ε by

$$\begin{vmatrix} f_1 & f_2 & 0 \\ r_2 & r_1 & r_0 \end{vmatrix} \begin{matrix} \\ \varepsilon \end{matrix} \, .$$

Let us form

$$
\begin{array}{ccc|c}
f_1 & f_2 & 0 & \\
\hline
r_0 & r_{-1} & r_{-2} & g_0 \\
r_1 & r_0 & r_{-1} & g_1 \\
r_2 & r_1 & r_0 & \varepsilon
\end{array}
\;+\;
\begin{array}{ccc|c}
\theta b_2 & \theta b_1 & \theta & \\
\hline
r_0 & r_{-1} & r_{-2} & 0 \\
r_1 & r_0 & r_{-1} & 0 \\
r_2 & r_1 & r_0 & \theta\beta
\end{array}
$$

$$
=\;
\begin{array}{ccc|c}
f_1+\theta b_2 & f_2+\theta b_1 & 0 & \\
\hline
r_0 & r_{-1} & r_{-2} & g_0 \\
r_1 & r_0 & r_{-1} & g_1 \\
r_2 & r_1 & r_0 & \varepsilon+\theta\beta
\end{array}
\;\equiv\;
\begin{array}{ccc|c}
f_1' & f_2' & f_3' & \\
\hline
r_0 & r_{-1} & r_{-2} & g_0 \\
r_1 & r_0 & r_{-1} & g_1 \\
r_2 & r_1 & r_0 & g_2
\end{array}\;.
$$

Thus we compute the new θ by

$$\varepsilon+\theta\beta=g_2 \quad \text{or} \quad \theta = \frac{g_2-\varepsilon}{\beta}$$

and then compute f_1', f_2', f_3' by

$$f_1'=f_1+\theta b_2$$
$$f_2'=f_2+\theta b_1$$
$$f_3'=0 .$$

Let us now drop the primes on f_1', f_2', f_3', so they become the new f_1, f_2, f_3 respectively. Because these new f_1, f_2, f_3 (i.e. the old f_1', f_2', f_3') satisfy the equations

$$
\begin{array}{ccc|c}
f_1 & f_2 & f_3 & \\
\hline
r_0 & r_{-1} & r_{-2} & g_0 \\
r_1 & r_0 & r_{-1} & g_1 \\
r_2 & r_1 & r_0 & g_2
\end{array}
$$

they are the desired filter coefficients for the case $m=3$.

It now is apparent that the general procedure may be repeated for the case $m=4$, for the case $m=5$, and so on until the desired value of m is reached.

If we are dealing with real-valued, scalar time-series then $r_{-j}=r_j$. Then, from this symmetry, the coefficient set

$$(1, a_1, a_2, \ldots, a_{m-1})$$

is identical to the coefficient set

$$(1, b_1, b_2, \ldots, b_{m-1})$$

for any given value of m. (Also $\alpha = \beta$ and $\lambda = \mu$.) Thus one of these two coefficients sets does not need to be computed in the real-valued scalar case, thereby allowing some gain in efficiency.

In this section we have given a highly efficient method of solving normal equations whose left hand side involves an autocorrelation function.

References

BODE, H. W. (1945). *Network Analysis and Feedback Amplifier Design*. Van Nostrand, Princeton, N.J.

BODE, H. W. and SHANNON, C. E. (1950). A simplified derivation of linear least square smoothing and prediction theory. *Proc. Inst. Rad. Eng.*, **38**, 417–425.

CLAERBOUT, J. (1963). *Digital Filters and Applications to Seismic Detection and Discrimination*. MIT M.S. thesis, Cambridge, Mass.

CRAMÉR, H. (1940). On the theory of stationary random processes. *Ann. Math.*, **41**, 215–230.

DOOB, J. L. (1953). *Stochastic Processes*. John Wiley, New York.

DAVENPORT, W. B. and ROOT, W. L. (1958). *An Introduction to the Theory of Random Signals and Noise*. McGraw-Hill, New York.

HANNAN, E. J. (1960). *Time Series Analysis*. Methuen, London.

KARHUNEN, K. (1949). Über die Struktur stationärer zufälliger Funktionen. *Ark. Mat.*, **1**, 141–160.

KENDALL, M. G. and STUART, A. (1958). *The Advanced Theory of Statistics* (three volumes). Charles Griffin and Co., London.

LANING, J. H. and BATTIN, R. H. (1956). *Random Processes in Automatic Control*. McGraw-Hill, New York.

LEVIN, M. J. (1960). Optimum estimation of impulse response in the presence of noise. *IRE Trans. Circuit Theory*.

RICE, R. B. (1962). Inverse convolution filters. *Geophysics*, **27**, 4–18.

ROBINSON, E. A. (1959). A stochastic diffusion theory of price. *Econometrica*, **27**, 679–684.

— (1960). Sums of stationary random variables. *Proceedings of the American Mathematical Society*, **11**, 77–79.

— (1961). Extremal representation of stationary stochastic processes. *Arkiv för Matematik* (Swedish Academy of Science), **4**, 379–384.

— (1962). *Random Wavelets and Cybernetic Systems*. Charles Griffin and Co., London, and Stechert-Hafner, New York.

— (1963). Extremal properties of the Wold decomposition. *Journal of Mathematical Analysis and Applications*, **6**, 75–85.

— (1963). Structural properties of stationary stochastic processes with applications. *Brown University Symposium on Time Series Analysis*, 170–192, John Wiley, New York.

SIMPSON, S. M. (1956). *Properties, Origin and Treatment of Certain Types of Seismic Noise*. MIT GAG Report **10**, Cambridge, Mass.

Appendix 5

Fast Fourier Transform

The discrete Fourier transform (DFT) of the signal x_k is defined by:

$$X_n = \sum_{k=0}^{N-1} x_k e^{-i2\pi kn/N} \quad \text{for } n = 0, 1, 2, \ldots N - 1$$

where both x_k and X_n may be complex quantities.

The inverse discrete Fourier transform (IDFT) of X_n is x_k where:

$$x_k = \frac{1}{N} \sum_{n=0}^{N-1} X_n e^{i2\pi kn/N} \quad \text{for } k = 0, 1, 2, \ldots N - 1$$

We note that the above expressions for the DFT and IDFT differ only in the sign of the exponent of the phasor $\exp(i2\pi kn/N)$ and in a scale factor $1/N$. Hence, computational procedures for the DFT can be easily modified to compute the IDFT.

The most straightforward method of calculating an N-point discrete Fourier transform, using the definition directly, requires N^2 multiplications; N multiplications for each of the N frequency points, $X_0, X_1, \ldots X_{N-1}$. However, since the amount of computation (and thus computation time) is proportional to N^2, the number of computations (and computation time) required to compute the DFT by such a direct method becomes very large for large values of N. Subroutine FFT is an algorithm which reduces the number of computations required for the DFT from N^2 to $N \log_2 N$ when N is a power of two. Thus, the letters FFT stand for fast Fourier transform.

The fundamental principle behind subroutine FFT is to decompose the computation of the DFT of a sequence $x_0, x_1, \ldots x_{N-1}$ of length N into successively smaller discrete Fourier transforms. For example, we can compute an N-point DFT by combining two $N/2$-point DFTs. The $N/2$-point DFTs can be evaluated by combining two $N/4$-point DFTs and so on. The FFT is then naturally computed by adding sums pair-wise, then adding the pairs of sums pair-wise, and so on. This would appear to be a very unnatural way of computing the DFT from the defining expression, but it is the most natural way to compute the FFT.

There are many suitable ways of understanding what is actually going on in the FFT computation, i.e. in terms of Fourier series, matrix theory, number theory, multidimensional transforms, flow graphs, and others. A physical description of the FFT is as follows. Consider a line array of equally spaced radar receivers and a plane wave signal is approaching the array at an angle. The phasor measured by each sensor will be out of phase with the phasor at each other sensor, in general, and the sum of all the phasors will be approximately zero (or small) because of the different phases. However, if each sensor output is subjected to an appropriate phase shift, they can all be added together to produce a relatively large output. A radar beam-forming network is a collection of phase shifters and adders which produce outputs which are maximum when the wave-front is impinging on the array from a given direction. This beam-forming operation turns out to be a Fourier transform.

The conventional method of forming beams is the so-called Blass array—a collection of N^2 phase shifters and adders, which is analogous to the direct method of computing the DFT. A phase shifter operating on a sinusoidal waveform is equivalent to multiplying a complex number by a root of unity. J. Butler and, independently J. P. Shelton, had figured out a way of connecting together phase shifters and adders to the sensors so as to require only $N\log_2 N$ elements to generate N beams for N antennas. The device is called a Butler matrix, and is completely analogous to the fast Fourier transform.

In the process of decomposing an N-point DFT into successively smaller-point DFTs, the FFT algorithm ''shuffles'' the input data x_0, x_1, . . . x_{N-1}. The FFT then combines the data by adding sums pair-wise, then adding pairs of sums pair-wise, and so on. This merging procedure involves the use of the quarter-length cosine table and repeatedly involves the so-called butterfly operation. Because the data have been shuffled, we must reshuffle the data by a procedure usually referred to as a bit reversal operation. An important feature of the FFT algorithm is that the merging and bit reversal can be done ''in place,'' without redefining the whole array during each butterfly operation.

If we wish to calculate the FFT repeatedly, we can compute the quarter-length cosine table once and store these values in a permanent array. Also, it is sometimes desirable to perform interpolation in the frequency or time domain. This is usually done by appending a sequence of zeroes to the actual data sequence. Thus, if 2^L points are to be interpo-lated in the transform domain (resulting in $N = 2^M$ points, for example, where $M > L$) this can be easily done by applying a 2^M-point FFT to the input data where $2^M - 2^L$ zeroes are appended to the first 2^L points. To avoid the added computation introduced by appending zeroes to our input data record, we can eliminate the operations involving zeroes by the process of pruning. With the particular FFT algorithm developed by Sande (see Gentleman and Sande, 1966), the pruning procedure due to Markel (1971) is straightforward.

The calling statement for subroutine FFT is:

CALL FFT (X, Y, TABLE, M, LL, ISN)

where the subroutine inputs are:

X = array of length N used to hold the real part of complex input
Y = array of length N used to hold the imaginary part of complex input
TABLE = array of length $N/4 + 1$ used to hold the quarter-length cosine table
M = integer = M. This integer determines the size $N = 2^M$ of the FFT to be performed.
LL = number of stages in which no pruning is allowable = L. The number of actual data points is 2^L.
ISN = DFT or IDFT indicator; set
ISN = -1 for DFT (forward FFT) and set
ISN = $+1$ for IDFT (inverse FFT)

and the subroutine outputs are:

X = array of length N used to store real part of complex output
Y = array of length N used to store imaginary part of complex output

The program is:

```
      SUBROUTINE FFT (X,Y,TABLE,M,LL,ISN)
C     FFT IS IN-PLACE DFT COMPUTATION USING SANDE
C         ALGORITHM AND MARKEL PRUNING MODIFICATION.
C     X IS ARRAY OF LENGTH 2**M USED TO HOLD REAL
C         PART OF COMPLEX INPUT.
C     Y IS ARRAY OF LENGTH 2**M USED TO HOLD
C         IMAGINARY PART OF COMPLEX INPUT.
C     TABLE IS ARRAY OF LENGTH N/4+1, WHERE N=2**M.
C     TABLE CONTAINS QUARTER-LENGTH COSINE TABLE.
C     M = INTEGER. SIZE OF FFT TO BE PERFORMED
C         IS GIVEN BY N = 2**M.
C         (NOTED THAT THE BIT REVERSE TABLE IS SET
C         FOR A MAXIMUM OF N=2**12=4096.)
C     LL = INTEGER. THERE ARE 2**LL ACTUAL DATA POINTS.
C     ISN IS EITHER -1 OR 1. SET ISN TO -1 FOR DFT
C         AND SET ISN TO 1 FOR IDFT.
      DIMENSION X(1096),Y(1096),TABLE(1025),L(12)
      EQUIVALENCE (L12,L(1)),(L11,L(2)),(L10,L(3)),
     1(L9,L(4)),(L8,L(5)),(L7,L(6)),(L6,L(7)),
     2(L5,L(8)),(L4,L(9)),(L3,L(10)),(L2,L(11)),
     3(L1,L(12))
```

```
          N=2**M
          ND4=N/4
          ND4P1=ND4+1
          ND4P2=ND4P1+1
          ND2P2=ND4+ND4P2
          LLL=2**LL
          DO 8 LO=1,M
          LMX=2**(M-LO)
          LMM=LMX
          LIX=2*LMX
          ISCL=N/LIX
C         TEST FOR PRUNING
          IF(LO-M+LL) 1,2,2
        1 LMM=LLL
        2 DO 8 LM=1,LMM
          IARG=(LM-1)*ISCL+1
          IF(IARG.LE.ND4P1) GO TO 4
          K1=ND2P2-IARG
          C=-TABLE(K1)
          K3=IARG-ND4
          S=ISN*TABLE(K3)
          GO TO 6
        4 C=TABLE(IARG)
          K2=ND4P2-IARG
          S=ISN*TABLE(K2)
        6 CONTINUE
          DO 8 LI=LIX,N,LIX
          J1=LI-LIX+LM
          J2=J1+LMX
          T1=X(J1)-X(J2)
          T2=Y(J1)-Y(J2)
          X(J1)=X(J1)+X(J2)
          Y(J1)=Y(J1)+Y(J2)
          X(J2)=C*T1-S*T2
          Y(J2)=C*T2+S*T1
        8 CONTINUE
C
C         PERFORM BIT REVERSAL
C
          DO 40 J=1,12
          L(J)=1
          IF(J-M) 31,31,40
       31 L(J)=2**(M+1-J)
       40 CONTINUE
```

```
      JN=1
      DO 60 J1=1,L1
      DO 60 J2=J1,L2,L1
      DO 60 J3=J2,L3,L2
      DO 60 J4=J3,L4,L3
      DO 60 J5=J4,L5,L4
      DO 60 J6=J5,L6,L5
      DO 60 J7=J6,L7,L6
      DO 60 J8=J7,L8,L7
      DO 60 J9=J8,L9,L8
      DO 60 J10=J9,L10,L9
      DO 60 J11=J10,L11,L10
      DO 60 JR=J11,L12,L11
      IF(JN-JR) 51,51,54
   51 R=X(JN)
      X(JN)=X(JR)
      X(JR)=R
      FI=Y(JN)
      Y(JN)=Y(JR)
      Y(JR)=FI
   54 IF(ISN)53,53,52
   52 X(JR)=X(JR)/FLOAT(N)
      Y(JR)=Y(JR)/FLOAT(N)
   53 JN=JN+1
   60 CONTINUE
      RETURN
      END
```

The quarter-length cosine table used in subroutine FFT may be generated by subroutine COSQT. The program is:

```
      SUBROUTINE COSQT(M,TABLE)
C     COSQT GENERATES QUARTER-LENGTH COSINE TABLE
      DIMENSION TABLE(2)
      N=2**M
      ND4P1=N/4+1
      SCL=6.283185307/FLOAT(N)
      DO 10 I=1,ND4P1
      ARG=FLOAT(I-1)*SCL
   10 TABLE(I)=COS(ARG)
      RETURN
      END
```

where the subroutine input is:

M = integer = M. This integer determines the size $N = 2^M$ of the FFT to be performed and the subroutine output is:

TABLE = quarter-length cosine table of length $N/4 + 1$.

Thus, we see that subroutine FFT provides an efficient computation of both the DFT and IDFT. It is important to note that only one complex array of N storage registers is physically necessary to implement the above FFT. This is because the computations are done "in place"; that is, as a new array is computed, the results can be stored in the same storage locations as the original array. In order that the above FFT computation may be done in place, the input data must be stored in nonsequential order. We say that this order is in bit-reversed order. Note that subroutine FFT requires that N be a power of 2, i.e., $N = 2^M$, so this is a radix-2 FFT. In general, there are other types of FFT algorithms called radix-r algorithms, where N is allowed to be a power of $r > 2$. For example, to compute the FFT of a complex-valued sequence of length $N = 1024$ by a radix-32 FFT algorithm, we require that $N = 32^2$.

References

Gentleman, W. M. and Sande, G., 1966. Fast Fourier transforms for fun and profit. 1966 Fall Joint Computer Conference. *AFIPS Conf. Proc.*, vol. 29, pp. 563–578.

Markel, J. D., 1971. FFT Pruning. *IEEE Trans. Audio Electroacoust.*, vol. 19, pp. 305–311.

Silvia, M. T., and Robinson, E. A., 1978. *Deconvolution of Geophysical Time Series in the Exploration for Oil and Natural Gas*, Elsevier, Amsterdam, 250 pp.

Appendix 6

Burg Algorithm and Maximum Entropy Spectrum

An alternate approach to linear prediction for the case of finite-data records and unknown autocorrelation is the method of utilizing both forward and backward predictions in a symmetric manner in the Toeplitz recursion given in Chapter 3. The key to this symmetric Toeplitz algorithm, given by J. P. Burg (1968), lies in estimating the variance as the arithmetic mean of the forward prediction-error variance and the backward prediction-error variance. In the following paragraphs we give a brief account of this method.

The *forward* prediction of the value x_k based on n "past" values x_{k-n}, . . . x_{k-2}, x_{k-1} is denoted by $\hat{x}_k^{(f)}$ and defined by:

$$\hat{x}_k^{(f)} \equiv \sum_{m=1}^{n} h_m^{(n)} x_{k-m}$$

The *backward* prediction* of the value x_{k-n} based on n "future" values x_{k-n+1}, x_{k-n+2}, . . . x_k is denoted by $\hat{x}_{k-n}^{(b)}$ and defined by:

$$\hat{x}_{k-n}^{(b)} \equiv \sum_{m=1}^{n} h_m^{(n)} x_{k-n+m}$$

Fig. 20 depicts the forward and backward prediction process.

Now the nth-order forward residual $f_k^{(n)}$ and nth-order backward residual $b_k^{(n)}$ for $n \geq 1$ are defined according to:

$$\left. \begin{array}{l} f_k^{(n)} \equiv f_k^{(n-1)} - g_n b_{k-1}^{(n-1)} \\ b_k^{(n)} \equiv b_{k-1}^{(n-1)} - g_n f_k^{(n-1)} \end{array} \right\} \quad \text{for } n + 1 \leq k \leq L \qquad (1)$$

with the initialization $f_k^{(0)} \equiv x_k$, $b_k^{(0)} \equiv x_k$ for $1 \leq k \leq L$, where L is the total number of available data points.

A schematic diagram of equation (1) is provided in Fig. 21. But the forward residual sequence $f_k^{(n)}$ and backward residual sequence $b_k^{(n)}$ can be interpreted as one-step forward and backward prediction errors respectively. That is, if we define:

$$f_k^{(n)} \equiv x_k - \sum_{m=1}^{n} h_m^{(n)} x_{k-m} = \text{forward prediction error}$$

---

* The term "hindsight" as well as the term "retrospection" are sometimes used instead of the term "backward prediction."

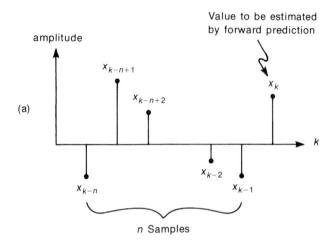

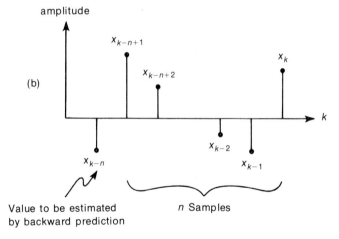

Fig. 20. (a) Forward prediction based on n past samples. (b) Backward prediction based on n future samples

$$b_k^{(n)} \equiv x_{k-n} - \sum_{m=1}^{n} h_m^{(n)} x_{k-n+m} = \text{backward prediction error}$$

we find that Fig. 21 results, with g_n replaced by $h_n^{(n)}$. In this context, we can define the forward prediction-error sample variance by:

$$Y_0^{(f)} \equiv \frac{1}{L-n} \sum_{k=n+1}^{L} [f_k^{(n)}]^2$$

and the backward prediction-error sample variance by:

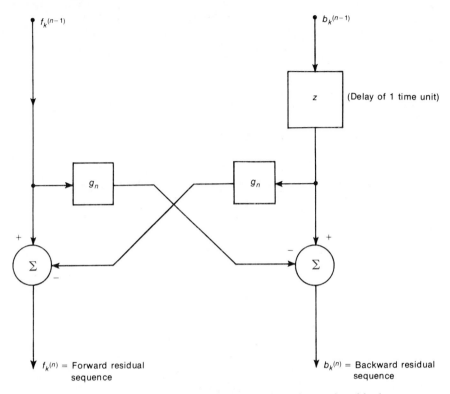

$f_k^{(n)}$ = Forward residual sequence

$b_k^{(n)}$ = Backward residual sequence

Fig. 21.   Schematic diagram of the generation of the forward residual sequence and backward residual sequence.

$$Y_0^{(b)} \equiv \frac{1}{L-n} \sum_{k=n+1}^{L} [b_k^{(n)}]^2$$

Under the assumption of stationarity of the process $\{x_k\}$, the theoretical forward prediction- and backward prediction-error variances are equal. Thus, we may combine the two sample variances by the standard statistical technique of forming their arithmetic mean, as given by:

$$Y_0^{(n)} \equiv \frac{Y_0^{(f)} + Y_0^{(b)}}{2}$$

or:

$$Y_0^{(n)} = \frac{1}{2(L-n)} \sum_{k=n+1}^{L} \{[f_k^{(n)}]^2 + [b_k^{(n)}]^2\} \tag{2}$$

Substitution of equation (1) in equation (2) gives:

$$Y_0^{(n)} = \frac{1}{2(L-n)} \sum_{k=n+1}^{L} \{[f_k^{(n-1)} - g_n b_{k-1}^{(n-1)}]^2 + [b_{k-1}^{(n-1)} - g_n f_k^{(n-1)}]^2\},$$
$$\text{for } n \geq 1$$

Now the coefficient g_n that minimizes the average sample variance $Y_0^{(n)}$ at the nth stage is the sample partial autocorrelation coefficient given by:

$$g_n = h_n^{(n)} = \frac{2 \sum\limits_{k=n+1}^{L} f_k^{(n-1)} b_{k-1}^{(n-1)}}{\sum\limits_{k=n+1}^{L} \{[f_k^{(n-1)}]^2 + [b_{k-1}^{(n-1)}]^2\}}, \quad n \geq 1 \tag{3}$$

The usual definition of a sample partial autocorrelation is the ratio of the sample covariance to the geometric mean of the sample variances. However, in the case here, the two variances have the same theoretical value, so their arithmetic mean is used instead of their geometric mean. After we compute $h_n^{(n)}$ from equation (3), we may use the computed $g_n = h_n^{(n)}$ in equation (1) in order to obtain the residuals $f_k^{(n)}$ and $b_k^{(n)}$ from the previous residuals.

At this point we have only calculated the last linear predictive filter coefficient $h_n^{(n)}$. However, the key feature of the Toeplitz recursion (see Robinson, 1967) is the recognition that if the last nth-order coefficient $h_n^{(n)}$ can be evaluated, the remaining nth-order linear predictive filter coefficients $h_m^{(n)}$, $1 \leq m \leq n - 1$, can be evaluated from $(n - 1)$th-order filter coefficients.

The Toeplitz polynomial recursion, given by equation (3) on page 125 of this book, is

$$A_n(z) = A_{n-1}(z) - c_n z A_{n-1}^R(z) \tag{4}$$

where c_n is the reflection coefficient of interface n. The coefficients of the polynomial $A_n(z)$ are the coefficients of the prediction error operator

$$(1, a_1^{(n)}, \ldots, a_n^{(n)})$$

Thus the polynomial recursion (4) gives the Levinson recursion for the coefficients of the prediction error operator, namely

$$\begin{aligned}
a_0^{(n)} &= a_0^{(n-1)} = 1 \\
a_m^{(n)} &= a_m^{(n-1)} - c_n a_{n-m}^{(n-1)}, \quad m = 1, 2, \ldots, n - 1 \\
a_n^{(n)} &= -c_n
\end{aligned} \tag{5}$$

This last equation shows that the final coefficient in the prediction error operator is the negative of the reflection coefficient.

The prediction operator $(h_1^{(n)}, h_2^{(n)}, \ldots, h_n^{(n)})$ for both forward and backward prediction is simply related to the prediction error operator. The relationship is

$$h_1^{(n)} = -a_1^{(n)}, \; h_2^{(n)} = -a_2^{(n)}, \ldots, h_n^{(n)} = -a_n^{(n)} \tag{6}$$

We know from equation (3) that the final prediction operator coefficient is equal to the partial autocorrelation g_n. Also we know from equation (5) that the reflection coefficient c_n is the negative of the final prediction error operator coefficient. Thus the last equation in (6) gives

$$h_n^{(n)} = g_n = -a_n^{(n)} = c_n$$

This equation says that the partial autocorrelation g_n is equal to the reflection coefficient c_n. We can compute this partial autocorrelation by means of equation (3). This computed value gives the final prediction operator coefficient $h_n^{(n)}$. Given $h_n^{(n)}$, we can the find the remaining coefficients of the prediction operator of order n by means of the Levinson recursion (5), which we can write as

$$h_m^{(n)} = h_m^{(n-1)} - h_n^{(n)} h_{n-m}^{(n-1)}, \qquad m = 1, 2, \ldots n - 1,$$
$$\text{(no terms if } n = 1) \quad (7)$$

Hence, given a finite data record of a zero mean stationary process $\{x_k\}$ with unknown autocorrelation, we can find a linear predictive filter by the Burg method. The procedure is summarized below:

(1) *Initialization:*

$$f_k^{(0)} = x_k, \qquad b_k^{(0)} = x_k, \qquad 1 \leq k \leq L$$

where L is the total number of available data points.

(2) Calculation of the sample partial autocorrelation coefficient $h_n = a_n^{(n)}$ (equation (3)), via the forward and backward sequences (residuals) defined in equation (1), at the nth stage.

(3) Utilization of the recursion relations (equation (7)) at the nth stage.

Further, if the lattice structure of Fig. 21 is carried to the stage where further values of the coefficient g_n are very close to zero, then the forward and backward prediction errors are approximately uncorrelated.

Subroutine BURG computes the coefficients $(1, a_1, a_2, \ldots, a_n)$ of the prediction error filter. The key feature of this technique is that it does not explicitly use the autocorrelation of the available data. The method utilizes both forward and backward predictions in a symmetric manner in the Toeplitz recursion. This subroutine also generates the *maximum entropy spectrum*. The call statement is

CALL BURG(LX,X,F,B,LA,A,M,S)

where the subroutine inputs are

LX = length of input time series
X = input time series
LA = length of prediction filter = n
M = integer exponent which controls spectral resolution

and the subroutine outputs are

A = prediction error filter = $(1, a_1, a_2, \ldots, a_n)$
S = maximum entropy spectrum at equally spaced frequencies.

The program is

```
      SUBROUTINE BURG(LX,X,F,B,LA,A,M,S)
C     NP=2**M CONTROLS SPECTRAL RESOLUTION.
C     DIMENSION A(2**M),Y(2**M),S(2**(M-1)+1)
      DIMENSION X(LX),F(LX),B(LX),A(64),S(33),Y(64),TABLE(17)
      NP=2**M
      V=0.
      DO 1 I=1,LX
      V=V+X(I)**2
      F(I)=X(I)
    1 B(I)=X(I)
      V=V/FLOAT(LX)
      DO 5 N=1,LA
      SN=0.
      SD=0.
      L=N+1
      DO 2 J=L,LX
      SN=SN+F(J)*B(J-1)
    2 SD=SD+F(J)*F(J)+B(J-1)*B(J-1)
      G=2.*SN/SD
      V=V*(1.-G*G)
      A(N)=G
      IF(N.EQ.1) GO TO 4
      NH=N/2
      DO 3 K=1,NH
      KK=N-K
      AA=A(KK)-G*A(K)
      A(K)=A(K)-G*A(KK)
    3 A(KK)=AA
    4 M1=N+1
      BS=B(N)
      DO 5 K=M1,LX
      FF=F(K)
      BB=BS
      BS=B(K)
      F(K)=FF-G*BB
    5 B(K)=BB-G*FF
      DO 6 I=1,LA
      K=LA-I+1
```

```
 6  A(K+1)=-A(K)
    A(1)=1.
    DO 7 I=1,NP
 7  Y(I)=0.
    LP=LA+2
    DO 8 I=LP,NP
 8  A(I)=0.
    CALL COSQT(M,TABLE)
    XX=1.442695*ALOG(FLOAT(LA+1))
    LL=IFIX(XX)
    IF(XX/FLOAT(LL).GT.1.) LL=LL+1
    CALL FFT(A,Y,TABLE,M,LL,-1)
    NF=NP/2+1
    DO 9 I=1,NF
 9  S(I)=V/(A(I)*A(I)+Y(I)*Y(I))
    RETURN
    END
```

References

Burg, J.P., 1968. A new analysis technique for time series data. *NATO Advanced Study Institute on Signal Processing,* Enschede.

Robinson, Enders A., 1967. *Statistical Communication and Detection with special reference to Digital Data Processing of Radar and Seismic Signals,* Charles Griffin and Co., High Wycombe, Bucks HP1 6LE, England. Reprinted in 1980 with new title, *Physical Applications of Stationary Time Series,* Charles Griffin and Co., High Wycombe, and also Macmillan, New York, 314 pp.

Silvia, M.T., and Robinson, E.A., 1978. *Deconvolution of Geophysical Time Series in the Exploration for Oil and Natural Gas,* Elsevier, Amsterdam, 250 pp.

Appendix 7

Iterative Identification

ABSTRACT

Robinson, E.A., 1978. Iterative identification of non-invertible autoregressive moving-average systems with seismic applications. In: C.H. Chen (Editor), Computer-Aided Seismic Analysis and Discrimination. Geoexploration, 16: 1—19.

Let A be an invertible (i.e. minimum-delay) polynomial of degree m and let E be any polynomial of degree n. Then $S = E/A$ represents the transfer function of an autoregressive moving-average (ARMA) system. The numerator E may also be invertible, in which case the ARMA system S is invertible. In seismic exploration the sequence with z-transform given by S represents a model of an observable seismogram, where E is the z-transform of the reflection coefficient sequence of the unknown (and desired) deep reflecting interfaces and where A represents the (invertible) z-transform of the unknown inverse reverberation filter due to the surface layers. Because there is no physical reason for the reflection coefficient sequence to be invertible, the seismic model $S = E/A$ will in general be a non-invertible ARMA system. Given such a non-invertible sequence with z-transform S, the problem is to estimate E and A under the restriction that A is invertible. We give an iterative identification scheme based on the following algorithm. Initially we let the initial estimate $E^{(0)}$ be unity. We then apply an iterative algorithm which for the kth step has inputs S and $E^{(k-1)}$ and outputs $A^{(k)}$ and $E^{(k)}$, where $A^{(k)}$ is required to be invertible. Iteration is terminated when S and $E^{(k)}/A^{(k)}$ are approximately the same, and then $E^{(k)}$ and $A^{(k)}$ are the required estimates of E and A, respectively.

INVERTIBILITY AND MINIMUM-DELAY

In most physical applications time is a continuous parameter. However, observations are often made at discrete time intervals, and even when continuous observations are made, they are often digitized for computer processing. As a result, the mathematical principles of discrete-time processes are important. Also, certain concepts that are mathematically quite difficult in continuous time have counterparts in discrete time that are much easier to handle.

One such concept is that of invertibility. In discrete time the general principle of invertibility may be grasped with use of time sequences of very short time duration. We want to give some simple examples before presenting the general theory. We denote a time sequence as b_k where the subscript k is the time parameter. Time is given by $t = k \, \Delta t$ where Δt is the digitization interval. When the time sequence has finite time duration, we may write it as a vector; for example, $b = (b_0, b_1, \ldots, b_n)$. A time sequence may represent the impulse response function of a filter. A filter is said to be stable provided that its impulse response function b has finite energy; that is, provided that:

$$\sum_{-\infty}^{\infty} b_k^2 < \infty$$

A filter is said to be *causal* provided that its impulse response function is one-sided; that is, provided that $b_k = 0$ for $k < 0$. The z-transform (according to the Laplace definition) of a stable causal time sequence b_k is defined as:

$$B(z) = \sum_{k=0}^{\infty} b_k z^k$$

Let us now give some introductory examples. Suppose that we have an input sequence $b = (b_0, b_1)$ of length two, a filter $f = (f_0, f_1)$ of length two, and the resulting output $c = (c_0, c_1, c_2)$ of length necessarily three. The output is determined from the input and filter by convolution:

$$c = (c_0, c_1, c_2) = (b_0 f_0, \, b_0 f_1 + b_1 f_0, \, b_1 f_1)$$

In order to lead into the concept of invertibility we first want to consider the design of spiking filters. A spiking filter is a filter designed so that the output c is as close as possible to a spike; for example, the zero-delay spike $(1,0,0)$, or the unit-delay spike $(0,0,1)$. or the two-delay spike $(0,0,1)$. We say that the two-term filter condenses or compresses the two-term input into a spike output. Actually a spiking filter is a special case of a wave-shaper, in which one chooses (f_0, f_1) so that c comes out as closely as possible to some desired output (d_0, d_1, d_2) which is prescribed. We use the least-squares criterion in making c as close as possible to d, so we minimize the sum of squares of the difference between them; namely:

$$J = (d_0 - c_0)^2 + (d_1 - c_1)^2 + (d_2 - c_2)^2$$
$$= (d_0 - f_0 b_0)^2 + (d_1 - f_0 b_1 - f_1 b_0)^2 + (d_2 - f_1 b_1)^2$$

If we set the partial derivative of J with respect to f_0 and the partial derivative with respect to f_1 each equal to zero, we get the set of simultaneous equations:

$$(b_0^2 + b_1^2) f_0 + (b_1 b_0) f_1 = b_0 d_0 + b_1 d_1$$
$$(b_1 b_0) f_0 + (b_0^2 + b_1^2) f_1 = b_0 d_1 + b_1 d_2$$

which we may solve in order to determine the filter coefficients f_0 and f_1. In the particular case when the desired output is a zero-delay spike $(d_0, d_1, d_2) = (1,0,0)$, the corresponding filter is called the zero-delay spiking filter for the input (b_0, b_1, b_2). The normal equations for the zero-delay spiking filter (f_0, f_1) are:

$$(b_0^2 + b_1^2) f_0 + b_1 b_0 f_1 = b_0$$
$$b_1 b_0 f_0 + (b_0^2 + b_1^2) f_1 = 0$$

with solution (f_0, f_1), except for a constant factor, given by:

$$(b_0^2 + b_1^2, -b_0 b_1)$$

We see that the z-transform (Laplace definition):

$$(b_0^2 + b_1^2) - b_0 b_1 z$$

has a zero $z = (b_0^2 + b_1^2)/b_0 b_1$ outside the unit circle, and has no zeros inside the unit circle. In fact, we will show that all zero-delay spiking filters have z-transforms (Laplace definition) with no zeros inside the unit circle: that is, we will show that all zero-delay spiking filters are minimum-phase.

Let us now give a numerical example. Suppose that the input sequence is $b = (1, 0.5)$. The zero-delay spiking filter is then $f = (0.95, -0.38)$. The actual output is $c = (0.95, 0.10, -0.19)$ which we compare to the desired output $d = (1, 0, 0)$. This result shows how well a two-term filter can condense the two-term input $(1, 0.5)$ into a spike.

Now we would like to find the equations to determine an $(m + 1)$-term filter that shapes an $(n + 1)$-term input into a prescribed desired output. This problem represents the case of a *wave-shaping filter*, which can be specialized to the case of a spiking filter by letting the desired output be a spike. Let the input sequence be $b = (b_0, b_1, \ldots, b_n)$. We want to construct the shaping filter $f = (f_0, f_1, \ldots, f_m)$. When the input goes into the filter the output is produced according to the convolution equation:

$$c_k = \sum_j f_j b_{k-j}$$

In this summation we can consider the limits of summation as minus infinity to plus infinity provided that we consider any terms off-the-ends of the finite sequences as zero. We now introduce the desired output sequence d which has the same number of terms $(m + n + 1)$ as the output sequence c. The shaping filter f is chosen so that c and d are alike (in the least-squares sense). That is, we minimize the sum of squared errors given by:

$$J = \sum_k (d_k - c_k)^2 = \sum_k \left(d_k - \sum_j f_j b_{k-j}\right)^2$$

Setting $\partial J/\partial f_i = 0$ for $i = 0, 1, 2 \ldots, m$ we obtain the set of equations, called the *normal equations*, given by:

$$\sum_{j=0}^{m} f_j r_{i-j} = g_i \qquad (i = 0, 1, 2, \ldots, m)$$

where:

$$r_{i-j} = \sum_k b_{k-j} b_{k-i}, \quad g_i = \sum_k d_k b_{k-i}$$

are the transient autocorrelation of b and the transient cross-correlation of d and b, respectively.

The minimum value of J (i.e., the minimum sum of squared errors) reduces to:

$$J = \sum_k (d_k - c_k)^2 = \sum d_k^2 - \sum f_j g_j$$

We will have occasion to use this formula for the minimum value of J shortly.

Let us now examine the normal equations given above. We notice that the left-hand side of the normal equations depends only upon the autocorrelation of the input b and not on b itself. If the desired output is the zero-delay spike $d = (1,0,0, \ldots ,0)$, then the right-hand side becomes:

$$g_0 = b_0, \, g_1 = 0, \, g_2 = 0, \ldots, g_m = 0$$

Thus, in the case of a zero-delay spiking filter, the wave-shape of the input sequence b itself does not enter into the normal equations, except for the initial value b_0, which affects the filter as only a scale factor. Therefore, the normal equations in the case of a zero-delay spiking filter depend upon the input sequence only through its autocorrelation. Any two input sequences with the same autocorrelation would have the same zero-delay spiking filter (except for a constant factor). Because autocorrelations contain no phase information, it is an interesting problem as to what the phase spectrum of the filter is.

Let us now show that the phase spectrum of the zero-delay spiking filter is minimum-negative-phase (i.e., minimum-phase-lag). Using the above formula for the minimum value of J, we see that the minimum value of J for the zero-delay spiking filter is:

$$J = \sum_k d_k^2 - \sum_j f_j g_j = 1 - f_0 g_0 = 1 - f_0 b_0$$

In order for $1 - f_0 b_0$ to indeed be a minimum, we see that f_0 must have the same sign as b_0. Moreover, f_0 must be as large as possible in magnitude. This requirement means that the filter must have as much of its energy concentrated in its leading coefficient as possible, or in other words, the filter must be minimum-delay. Thus, we have come to the important conclusion that a zero-delay spiking filter is minimum-delay. Because the concepts of minimum-phase and minimum-delay are identical, the zero-delay spiking filter has a minimum-phase-lag spectrum.

Now let us look at the other side of the coin. In order for $1 - f_0 b_0$ to be small when we consider all input sequences b with the same transient auto-correlation, the leading coefficient b_0 should be large in magnitude. In other words, the smallest mean-square spiking error occurs when the input sequence

b is minimum-delay. In summary, all zero-delay spiking filters f are necessarily minimum-delay, and the best case of spiking occurs when the input sequence b is also minimum-delay. In fact, for a minimum-delay input sequence $b = (b_0, b_1', \ldots, b_n)$ the mean-square spiking error $J = 1 - f_0 b_0$ tends to zero as the number of coefficients in the zero-delay spiking filter $(f_0, f_1, \ldots, f_m)$ tends to infinity $(m \to \infty)$. On the other hand, for a non-minimum-delay input sequence, the mean-square spiking error does not tend to zero as the number of coefficients in the zero-delay spiking filter tends to infinity. We, therefore, conclude that perfect spiking can be achieved by a stable causal spiking filter if and only if the input sequence is minimum-delay. In other words, given the sequence b we can find a stable causal filter f such that:

$$f \star b = (1, 0, 0, \ldots)$$

if and only if b is minimum-delay. Any stable causal sequence b that can be converted into a zero-delay spike by a stable causal filter f is said to be invertible. We have thus established that a stable causal sequence is invertible if and only if it is minimum-delay. For that reason, we can use the terms "invertible sequence" and "minimum-delay sequence" interchangeably, even as we use the terms "minimum-phase sequence" and "minimum-delay sequence" interchangeably.

In summary, the zero-delay spiking filter for a stable causal sequence b as input may be described as the *least-squares inverse* of b. In case b is minimum-delay, then if the number of terms in the least-squares inverse is allowed to increase, the least-squares inverse tends to the exact stable causal inverse of b.

CONVERSION TO INVERTIBILITY

In many applications we know from the physics of the situation that a certain finite-length causal sequence must be invertible. However, suppose that the estimation method used does not necessarily give an invertible sequence. Thus we must have a method for converting a sequence which is not necessarily invertible into an invertible sequence. Let us describe one such method. This method consists of the following two steps:

(1) Compute the zero-delay spiking filter a^{-1} of the given filter a. As we have seen in the preceding section, the filter a^{-1} is necessarily invertible.

(2) Now take this approach one step further; namely, compute the zero-delay spiking filter of the filter a^{-1}. This second zero-delay spiking filter is necessarily invertible, and in fact it is the required invertible counterpart of the given filter a.

In summary, the invertible counterpart of the finite-length causal sequence a is the least-squares inverse of the least-squares inverse of a.

SEISMIC APPLICATIONS

Let us consider the problem of the elimination of water reverberations from seismic records. The water reverberation problem in marine seismic operations may be described as follows. The water-air interface is a strong reflector, with reflection coefficient neariy −1. If the water-bottom interface is also a strong reflector, then the water layer represents a non-attenuating medium bounded by two strong reflecting interfaces and hence represents an energy trap. A seismic pulse generated in this energy trap will be successively reflected between the two interfaces. Consequently, reflections from deep horizons below the water layer will be obscured by the water reverberations (Fig.1).

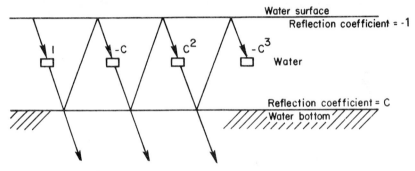

Fig.1. Water-confined reverberation. For clarity the raypaths have been drawn as slanting lines, although in our model they are perpendicular to the two interfaces.

Let us consider a down-traveling impulsive plane wave (i.e., we assume that the source wavelet is a unit spike) and let us suppose that we have a transducer which measures only down-traveling motion in the water layer. The signal received by the transducer represents the successive reflections from the air/water interface. We let T represent the two-way traveltime in the water; for example, if the water depth is 100 ft. and the water velocity is 5,000 ft./sec, then the two-way traveltime would be $T = 40$ millisec.

Referring to Fig.1, we see that the coefficient 1 occurs at time 0 and represents the initial downgoing spike. The coefficient $-c$ occurs at time T and represents the second downgoing spike, which has suffered a reflection at the bottom (reflection coefficient c) and a reflection at the surface (reflection coefficient -1). The coefficient c^2 occurs at discrete time $2T$ and represents the third downgoing spike, which has suffered two reflections at the bottom (c^2) and two reflections at the surface ($-1)^2$. The coefficient $-c^3$ occurs at discrete time $3T$ and represents the fourth downgoing spike, which has suffered three reflections at the bottom (c^3) and three reflections at the surface ($-1)^3$, etc. Thus the *water-confined reverberation spike-train* is of the form:

$$1 \quad -c \quad c^2 \quad -c^3 \quad c^4 \quad \ldots \tag{1}$$

time: $0 \quad T \quad 2T \quad 3T \quad 4T \ldots$

The reflection coefficient c cannot exceed unity in magnitude; generally c will be less than unity in magnitude for otherwise the water layer would represent a perfect energy trap and no energy would penetrate to the deeper layers. Thus in the case where $|c| < 1$, the water-confined reverberation spike-train (1) represents a convergent sequence. The z-transform (Laplace definition) of the water-confined reverberation spike-train is:

$$1 - cz^T + c^2 z^2{}^T - c^3 z^3{}^T + \ldots$$

which is in the form of a geometric series, which can be summed to give:

$$\frac{1}{1 + cz^T}$$

The z-transform of the water-confined reverberation elimination filter would therefore have the form:

$$1 + cz^T$$

so that the impulse response function would be:

$$1 \quad c \tag{2}$$

time: $0 \quad T$

To verify that the water-confined reverberation elimination filter (2) does indeed convert the water-confined reverberation spike-train (1) into a spike (and thereby eliminates the reverberation) we may convolve (1) with (2) and thereby obtain the spike $(1,0,0,0,\ldots)$ which represents the impulsive plane wave without the water reverberation.

In our analysis so far we have only considered the water reverberation. effect itself, and have not considered the effect of the water layer on deep subsurface reflections. To do so, we must take into account that the water layer acts as a filter, and the seismic energy passes through this filter once as it goes down to the deep reflecting horizon and again as it returns to the surface. That is, the water layer acts on the deep reflection data twice, once going down to the deep strata and once again coming back to the surface. Hence we have, in effect, a situation where the deep reflection data pass through two cascaded sections of the water layer, so that the overall z-transform of the filtering introduced by the water layer is the square of the z-transform due to a single pass, as given in the foregoing paragraph (Fig.2).

The z-transform of the reverberation spike-train resulting from a deep reflecting horizon is:

$$(1 - cz^T + c^2 z^2{}^T - c^3 z^3{}^T + \ldots)^2$$

or:

$$\frac{1}{(1+cz^T)^2}$$

In the time domain, we see that the *deep-reflection reverberation spike-train* is given by:

$$
\begin{array}{llllll}
& 1 & -2c & 3c^2 & -4c^3 & 5c^4 & \ldots \\
\text{time:} & 0 & T & 2T & 3T & 4T & \ldots
\end{array}
\tag{4}
$$

Expression (4) may be obtained by convolving the water-confined reverberation spike-train (1) with itself. The reverberation spike-train (4) may be interpreted as being made up of the deep reflection spike at time 0, and the

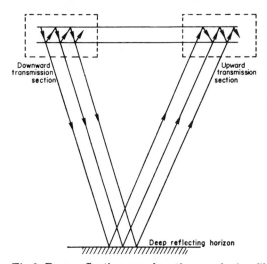

Fig.2. Deep-reflection reverberation-producing filter as two cascaded sections.

attached reverberation spikes at times $T, 2T, 3T, 4T, \ldots$ To eliminate the reverberation part of spike-train (4) we must pass spike-train (4) through the inverse filter whose z-transform is given by:

$$(1 + cz^T)^2$$

or:

$$1 + 2cz^T + c^2 z^{2T}.$$

The impulse response function of this inverse filter is:

$$
\begin{array}{llll}
& 1 & 2c & c^2 \\
\text{time:} & 0 & T & 2T
\end{array}
\tag{5}
$$

Convolving spike-train (4) with spike-train (5) we see that the output is indeed a spike $(1,0,0,0, \ldots)$ which represents the direct deep reflection spike (at time 0) with the attached reverberation spikes eliminated.

A primary reflection on the seismic record is an event resulting from the transmission of the source pulse directly down to a deep reflecting interface and then directly back up to the receiver. Neglecting everything except the reflection coefficient ϵ of the deep reflecting horizon, the primary reflection due to a unit spike source would appear as a spike ϵ at time t on the seismogram, where t is the two-way travel time from the surface to the deep reflecting interface. The z-transform of this primary event would be ϵz^t. Suppose now that there are $n+1$ deep interfaces; the z-transform of the resulting primary events would be:

$$\epsilon_0 z^{t_0} + \epsilon_1 z^{t_1} + \ldots + \epsilon_n z^{t_n} \tag{6}$$

where $\epsilon_0, \epsilon_1, \ldots, \epsilon_n$ are the reflection coefficients and $t_0, t_1, \ldots, t_n$ are the two-way times of the interfaces, respectively.

As we have seen, the water layer acts on the deep reflection data twice, once in going down and once again in coming back up; so the overall z-transform of the filtering introduced by the water layer is given by expression (3). The z-transform of the seismogram resulting from the $n+1$ deep interfaces is the product of expressions (3) and (6); namely, the rational function:

$$S(z) = \frac{\epsilon_0 z^{t_0} + \epsilon_1 z^{t_1} + \ldots + \epsilon_n z^{t_n}}{(1 + cz^T)^2} \tag{7}$$

Because of the physical nature of reverberations, the denominator of this rational function is necessarily invertible. However, there is no physical reason for the numerator to be invertible, except in special cases.

Eq. 7 represents the model for a seismogram in the case of a single surface layer. In the case of more complicated surface-layering, the seismogram model would take the form of:

$$S(z) = \frac{E(z)}{A(z)} \tag{8}$$

where $E(z) = \epsilon_0 z^{t_0} + \epsilon_1 z^{t_1} + \ldots + \epsilon_n z^{t_n}$

represents the (generally non-invertible) sequence $\epsilon_0, \epsilon_1, \ldots, \epsilon_n$ of reflection coefficients of the deep layers, and:

$A(z) = a_0 + a_1 z + \ldots + a_m z^m$

represents the (necessarily invertible) sequence $a_0, a_1, \ldots, a_m$ of the inverse reverberation filter.

Let us now briefly review ARMA systems (Box and Jenkins, 1970). The acronym ARMA stands for autoregressive moving average. The z-transform of such a system is a rational function, where the denominator polynomial (which represents the autoregressive component) must be invertible and where the numerator polynomial (which represents the moving-average component) may or may not be invertible. If the numerator polynomial is invertible, then the ARMA process is invertible. If the numerator is not invertible, then the ARMA process is not invertible.

In summary, eq. 8 represents a model of a marine seismogram as a non-invertible ARMA system. Let s_k be the values of the seismogram, i.e., s_k is the causal stable sequence with Laplace z-transform $S(z)$. We find it sometimes convenient to write eq. 8 in symbolic form as:

$$s = \epsilon/a \tag{9}$$

where s is the seismogram sequence, ϵ is the reflection coefficient sequence, and a is the inverse reverberation filter sequence.

Most treatments of ARMA systems are concerned with systems where the MA part is invertible, so the entire ARMA system is invertible. However, as we have seen, the ARMA model for a seismogram in general is not invertible. We can observe the seismogram s. We would like to determine the sequences ϵ and a from the sequence s. The purpose of this paper is to give an algorithm which carries out this identification.

NUMERICAL EXAMPLE

First, let us give a numerical example of the algorithm. In order to construct a simple numerical example, let us assume that we use the coarse time grid given by $t_0 = 0, t_1 = 1, \ldots, t_n = n$ and that the two-way travel time in the water is $T = 1$ in terms of this grid. The value $t_0 = 0$ represents the arrival time of the first deep reflection (i.e., the reflection from deep interface 0), so the time origin is the arrival time of the first deep event. The transfer function of the seismogram (for a single surface layer) in terms of this time grid is:

$$S(z) = \frac{\epsilon_0 + \epsilon_1 z + \epsilon_2 z^2 + \ldots + \epsilon_n z^n}{(1 + cz)^2}$$

which we can write as:

$$S(z) = \frac{E(z)}{A(z)}$$

where:

$$E(z) = \epsilon_0 + \epsilon_1 z + \epsilon_2 z^2 + \ldots + \epsilon_n z^n$$

and:

$$A(z) = 1 + 2cz + c^2 z^2$$

Let us now give a numerical example. Suppose there are $n + 1 = 10$ deep interfaces, and suppose that the first 19 observations of the resulting marine seismogram are (reading consecutively as words on a page)

$s = (s_0, s_1, \ldots, s_{18}) =$ (1.0000, 0.0000, 0.1875, $-$0.9063, $-$0.7148,
0.1992, $-$0.6057, $-$0.8153, $-$0.1198, 0.9911,
0.5030, 0.1896, 0.0633, 0.0198, 0.0060,
0.0017, 0.0005, 0.0001, 0.0000)

Given these observations, the problem is to find the water bottom reflection coefficient c and the deep reflection sequence $\epsilon = (\epsilon_0, \epsilon_1, \epsilon_2, \ldots, \epsilon_9)$. Because the observed seismogram is not known in absolute terms but only to within an arbitrary scale factor, the resulting reflection coefficient sequence ϵ will be equal to the actual physical reflection coefficient sequence only to within a scale factor.

The method of solution we propose is an iterative scheme based on an algorithm which, for the kth step, has inputs s and $\epsilon^{(k-1)}$ and outputs $a^{(k)}$ and $\epsilon^{(k)}$. The seismogram sequence s is the numerical sequence of 19 observations given above, and remains fixed for each step. The outputs $a^{(k)}$ and $\epsilon^{(k)}$ of the kth step are supposed to converge to the sequence a and ϵ, respectively. In order to test whether we are getting convergence, we divide the z-transform of $a^{(k)}$ into the z-transform of $\epsilon^{(k)}$ to obtain the sequence $s^{(k)}$. We write the sequence $s^{(k)}$ symbolically as:

$$s^{(k)} = \epsilon^{(k)}/a^{(k)}$$

If the sequence $s^{(k)}$ computed at the end of the kth step is close to the seismogram sequence $s = \epsilon/a$, then we say that we have convergence, and stop the iteration. The computed $\epsilon^{(k)}$ and $a^{(k)}$ then represent the required identification of ϵ and a, respectively, in the ARMA model of the seismogram.

In order to start the iteration, we set $\epsilon^{(0)}$ equal to the zero-delay spike:

$$\epsilon^{(0)} = (1,0,0,\ldots,0)$$

The first iteration gives:
$a^{(1)} = (1, -0.32, 0.18)$
$\epsilon^{(1)} = (1, -0.32, 0.37, -0.97, -0.39, 0.27, -0.80, -0.58, 0.04, 0.88)$
The second iteration gives:
$a^{(2)} = (1, -0.37, 0.14)$
$\epsilon^{(2)} = (1, -.37, 0.33, -0.98, -0.35, 0.34, -0.78, -0.56, 0.10, 0.92)$

The third iteration gives:
$a^{(3)} = (1, -0.41, 0.12)$
$\epsilon^{(3)} = (1, -0.41, 0.30, -0.98, -0.32, 0.39, -0.77, -0.54, 0.14, 0.95)$
Continue iterating. The twentieth iteration gives:
$a^{(20)} = (1, -0.50, 0.624)$
$\epsilon^{(20)} = (1, -0.50, 0.25, -1.00, -0.25, 0.50, -0.75, -0.50, 0.25, 1.00)$
At this point the values of s and of $s^{(20)} = \epsilon^{(20)}/a^{(20)}$ are equal to within three decimal places. As a result we conclude that $\epsilon^{(20)}$ gives the deep reflection coefficients (to within a scale factor) and $a^{(20)} = (1, -0.50, 0.624) = (1, 2c, c^2)$ gives the water bottom reflection coefficient as $c = -0.25$.

DESCRIPTION OF THE ALGORITHM

The algorithm is based on the least-squares wave-form shaping filter, as derived in the first section. We recall that, in order to derive the shaping filter f, we must specify the input b and the desired output d. The shaping filter f is determined in such a way that the actual output $c = b \star f$ approximates the desired output d in a least-squares sense.

Let us now introduce a short-hand notation to describe the operation of a shaping filter. This short-hand notation has the general form

$$b \star f \doteq d$$

where we adhere to the convention that b and d are given, and f is determined in such a way that the convolution $b \star f$ approximates d in the least-squares sense. We remember the sequences on each end (i.e., b and d) are given, and the sequence in the middle (i.e., f) is determined. Subroutine SHAPE (Robinson, 1967) computes the least-squares shaping filter; in subroutine SHAPE the sequences b and d are subroutine inputs and the filter sequence f is the subroutine output.

Let us now describe the algorithm. At the beginning of step k we have the seismogram s and the approximate deep reflection coefficient sequence $\epsilon^{(k-1)}$. We apply subroutine SHAPE as:

$$s \star a^{(k)} \doteq \epsilon^{(k-1)}$$

to yield the preliminary estimate of $a^{(k)}$. However, we want to guarantee that $a^{(k)}$ is an invertible sequence, and in order to do so, we apply subroutine SHAPE as:

$$a^{(k)} \star [a^{-1}]^{(k)} \doteq (1,0,0,\ldots,0)$$

to yield the least-squares inverse $[a^{-1}]^{(k)}$. We then apply subroutine SHAPE as:

$$[a^{-1}]^{(k)} \star a^{(k)} \doteq (1,0,0,\ldots,0)$$

to yield the second estimate of $a^{(k)}$. Because of the minimum-delay property of least-squares inverses, this second estimate $a^{(k)}$ is necessarily invertible. Next we normalize this $a^{(k)}$ by dividing each element of $a^{(k)}$ by its leading element; the result is the final estimate of $a^{(k)}$. The final estimate of $\epsilon^{(k)}$ is given as the convolution of $a^{(k)}$ with s; that is:

$$\epsilon^{(k)} = a^{(k)} \star s$$

We thus have found $a^{(k)}$ and $\epsilon^{(k)}$, and the description of the algorithm is complete. Initially, we start with $\epsilon^{(0)} = (1,0,0,\ldots,0)$ and we end when each of $\epsilon^{(k)}$ and $a^{(k)}$ has stabilized.

The algorithm is given in a diagram as follows (Fig. 3):

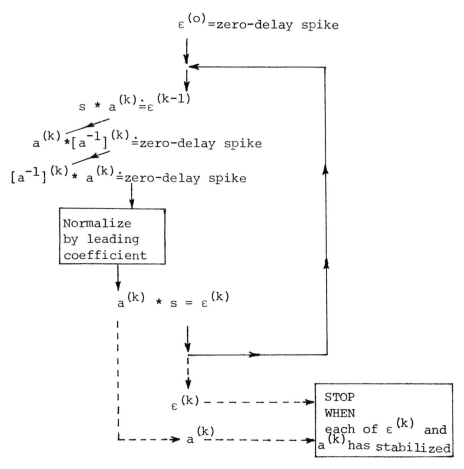

Fig. 3. Algorithm for a non-invertible system.

COMPARISON WITH DURBIN'S ALGORITHM

According to Kendall and Stuart (1966), Durbin has given an algorithm for finding the parameters ϵ and a of an invertible ARMA process $s = \epsilon/a$. Whereas in our algorithms we require only a to be invertible (which is a requirement for a stable causal ARMA system), Durbin in his algorithm requires both ϵ and a to be invertible, so s is invertible. The following diagram (Fig.4) gives a modified version of Durbin's algorithm. These modifications were made to express the essential content of such an invertible algorithm in a completely symmetrical form. We have not drawn the starting and stopping points of the algorithm, but only its internal workings.

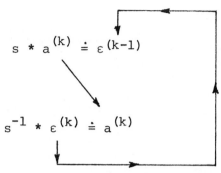

Fig. 4. Algorithm for an invertible system.

MAXIMUM ENTROPY

Let x_t (where the time index t takes on integer values) be a real stationary process. The autocorrelation function is defined as:

$$r_s = E(x_{t+s}x_t)$$

where E denotes expectation and the integer s is the time shift. For convenience, we normalize the autocorrelation function so that $r_0 = 1$. For each positive integer n we can define a prediction-error series ϵ_t and a hindsight-error series η_t associated with that value of n. The prediction-error time series is given by:

$$\epsilon_t = \sum_{s=0}^{n} a_s x_{t-s} \quad \text{(where } a_0 = 1\text{)},$$

and where the prediction-error operator coefficients $a_0 = 1, a_1, a_2, \ldots, a_n$ are chosen to minimize $E\epsilon_t^2$. If we go through this minimization procedure, we find that the required operator coefficients $1, a_1, \ldots, a_n$ can be found from the first part of the autocorrelation $1, r_1, \ldots, r_n$ by solving the *Toeplitz normal equations*:

$$\sum_{s=0}^{n} a_s r_{t-s} = 0 \quad \text{for } t = 1, 2, \ldots, n.$$

The minimum value of $E\epsilon_t^2$ is:

$$E\epsilon_t^2 = a_0 r_0 + a_1 r_1 + \ldots + a_n r_n = v_n \text{ (where } a_0 = 1, r_0 = 1\text{)}.$$

We call the quantity v_n the (prediction-error) variance. Let us now define the hindsight-error series η_t. The hindsight-error time series for a given value of n is:

$$\eta_t = \sum_{s=0}^{n} a_s x_{t+s} \quad \text{(where } a_0 = 1\text{)}.$$

If we minimize $E\eta_t^2$, we find that the required hindsight-error operator coefficients $1, a_1, \ldots, a_n$ satisfy the same set of normal equations as for the prediction-error operator, and the minimum value of $E\eta_t^2$ is also equal to v_n. Thus the operator coefficients of the prediction-error operator and the hindsight-error operator are identical, and in addition:

$$E\epsilon_t^2 = E\eta_t^2 = v_n.$$

The prediction error ϵ_t is the forecasting error resulting from approximating x_t in terms of the past values $x_{t-1}, \ldots, x_{t-n}$, whereas the hindsight error η_t is the retrospection error resulting from approximating x_t in terms of the future values $x_{t+1}, \ldots, x_{t+n}$. The difference between the two operators is that the prediction-error operator acts on past values of the time series, whereas the hindsight-error operator acts on future values.

Let us now consider a given set of data points $x_{t-n}, x_{t-(n-1)}, \ldots, x_{t-1}$ corresponding to the time interval from $t-n$ to $t-1$ inclusive. Let us also consider the corresponding prediction error and hindsight error associated with this fixed set of data points. The prediction error ϵ_t is the error in forecasting x_t from the past datum points $x_{t-n}, x_{t-n-1}, \ldots, x_{t-1}$. The hindsight error η_{t-n-1} is the error in retrospectively approximating x_{t-n-1} from the future datum points $x_{t-n}, x_{t-n-1}, \ldots, x_{t-1}$. Both sets of datum points are the same, and represent all the datum points between the points x_{t-n-1} and x_t that we wish to approximate. Thus η_{t-n-1} represents the error in x_{t-n-1} and ϵ_t represents the error in x_t, after we have removed the effect of the common intervening variables $x_{t-n}, x_{t-n-1}, \ldots, x_{t-1}$. As a result, the correlation between η_{t-n-1} and ϵ_t represents the net correlation between x_{t-n-1} and x_t after removal of the effects of all intervening variables. This net correlation is called the partial autocorrelation and is given by the partial autocorrelation coefficient c_{n+1} defined as:

$$c_{n+1} = \text{partial autocorrelation coefficient} = \frac{E(\epsilon_t \eta_{t-n-1})}{\sqrt{E\epsilon_t^2}\, \sqrt{E\eta_{t-n-1}^2}}$$

In order to find an expression for the partial autocorrelation coefficient in terms of well-known quantities, let us first consider the cross-correlation between the prediction error series ϵ_t and the given time series x_t. This cross-correlation, denoted by ψ_s, is:

$$\psi_s = E\ (\epsilon_t x_{t-s}) = E\left[\ \left(\sum_{j=0}^{n} a_j x_{t-j}\right) x_{t-s}\right] = \sum_{j=0}^{n} a_j E(x_{t-j} x_{t-s})$$

$$= \sum_{j=0}^{n} a_j r_{s-j}$$

The cross-correlation between the hindsight-error series η_t and the given time series x_t is:

$$E(\eta_t x_{t-s}) = \sum_{j=0}^{n} a_j r_{s+j}$$

which is equal to ψ_{-s} since $r_{-s-j} = r_{s+j}$. At this point let us observe that the Toeplitz normal equations require that $\psi_s = 0$ for $s = 1,2,3, \ldots, n$; that is, the Toeplitz normal equations require that the cross-correlation ψ_s vanishes in the interval $1 \leqslant s \leqslant n$.

Let us now find an expression for the covariance term in the numerator of the partial autocorrelation. We have:

$$E(\epsilon_t \eta_{t-n-1}) = E(\epsilon_t \sum_{s=0}^{n} a_s x_{t-n-1+s})$$

$$= \sum_{s=0}^{n} a_s E(\epsilon_t x_{t-n-1+s}) = \sum_{s=0}^{n} a_s \psi_{n+1-s}$$

$$= \psi_{n+1} + a_1 \psi_n + a_2 \psi_{n-1} + \ldots + a_n \psi_1.$$

Because of the Toeplitz normal equations, this equation becomes:

$$E(\epsilon_t \eta_{t-n-1}) = \psi_{n+1}.$$

In a similar way, we find:

$$v_n = E\epsilon_t^2 = E\eta_t^2 = \psi_0.$$

Thus the partial autocorrelation coefficient between x_t and x_{t-n-1} is:

$$c_{n+1} = \text{partial autocorrelation coefficient} = \frac{\psi_{n+1}}{\sqrt{\psi_0}\sqrt{\psi_0}} = \frac{\psi_{n+1}}{\psi_0} = \frac{\psi_{n+1}}{v_n}$$

$$= \frac{a_0 r_{n+1} + a_1 r_n + \ldots + a_n r_1}{a_0 r_0 + a_1 r_1 + \ldots + a_n r_n}$$

The prediction-error variance v_n is given by (Robinson, 1967, p.144):

$$v_n = r_0 (1-c_1^2)(1-c_2^2) \ldots (1-c_n^2)$$

If we let n toward infinity, we obtain the final prediction error as:

$$v_\infty = r_0 (1-c_1^2)(1-c_2^2)(1-c_3^2) \ldots$$

We now want to consider the class of all stationary processes having autocorrelations all with the same initial section $r_0, r_1, \ldots, r_n$. All members in this class have partial autocorrelations all with the same initial section $c_1, c_2, \ldots, c_n$. Thus all members of this class have final prediction errors of the form:

$$v_\infty = [r_0(1-c_1^2)(1-c_2^2) \ldots (1-c_n^2)][(1-c_{n+1}^2)(1-c_{n+2}^2) \ldots]$$

where the expression in the first set of brackets on the right is fixed. The final prediction error v_∞ is a measure of the entropy of the process, because the larger v_∞, the larger the ultimate unpredictability and hence the larger the entropy. Therefore, if we maximize v_∞, we obtain the maximum entropy member of this class. The maximization can be done by inspection; namely, the maximum is obtained by letting $c_{n+1} = c_{n+2} = \ldots = 0$, and the resulting maximum is:

$$v_\infty(\text{max}) = r_0(1-c_1^2)(1-c_2^2)\ldots(1-c_n^2).$$

FIXED ENTROPY ESTIMATE OF THE SEISMIC ACOUSTIC LOG

Often in geophysics we know the geologic structure well enough so that we can actually experiment with fixed entropy models. As an illustration let us turn to the marine seismic model; that is, the model of a layered medium with a perfect reflector at the upper interface ($c_0 = -1$) (Robinson, 1967, o.133).

As is well known, the initial portion of a seismogram is often the most noisy and the most difficult to work with. In the ideal case, the marine seismogram due to a downgoing unit spike has a downgoing component of the form 1, r_1, r_2, . . . and an upgoing component of the form r_1, r_2, . . . where the coefficients r_k make up an autocorrelation function with $r_0 = 1$. That is, the r_k constitute a positive definite function. We also know that the partial autocorrelation coefficients c_k are the reflection coefficients of the subsurface layers. As is well known, the Toeplitz recursion generates the partial autocorrelation coefficients c_k from the autocorrelation coefficients r_k in a sequential manner $k = 1, 2, 3, \ldots$. However, when we apply this Toeplitz method to an actual marine seismogram r_k, the errors due to noise in the initial portion of the seismogram are propagated sequentially in the computation of the reflection coefficients for $k = 1, 2, 3, \ldots$. As a result, the Toeplitz method results in larger and larger errors in the reflection coefficients as we go deeper and deeper into the earth, these errors being due to noise in the initial part of the seismogram.

In order to avoid this sequential generation of errors, we propose a simultaneous method of estimating the reflection coefficients from a marine seismogram, or equivalently a simultaneous method of estimating the partial autocorrelation coefficients from the autocorrelation coefficients. This method is an iterative method based on non-linear regression. The autocorrelation coefficient r_k is a non-linear function of the partial autocorrelation coefficients. We assume that all the partial autocorrelation coefficients c_1, c_2, . . ., c_n have fixed values except for a subset of m coefficients which can have arbitrary values. Usually these fixed values will be zero, corresponding to maximum entropy (i.e., no physical interface at a given depth), although in some instances certain non-zero values may be chosen on physical grounds. Let θ_1, θ_2, . . ., θ_m denote the subset of m partial autocorrelation coefficients with arbitrary values. Then the autocorrelation coefficients are non-linear functions of the unknown θ_1, θ_2, . . ., θ_m; let these functions be:

$$r_1 = f_1(\theta_1, \ldots, \theta_m)$$
$$r_2 = f_2(\theta_1, \ldots, \theta_m)$$
$$\cdots\cdots\cdots\cdots\cdots$$
$$r_n = f_n(\theta_1, \ldots, \theta_m)$$

These functions can be computed by the computer program (see Robinson, 1967, p.137) if we are given the values of $\theta_1, \ldots, \theta_m$. However, we are given the values of $r_1, r_2, \ldots, r_n$ and we want to find $\theta_1, \theta_2, \ldots, \theta_m$.

We let $\hat{\theta}_1, \hat{\theta}_2, \ldots, \hat{\theta}_m$ be the initial guesses as to the values of the partial autocorrelation coefficients in the subset. We then expand the function $f_k(\theta_1, \ldots, \theta_m)$ in a Taylor expansion and retain the linear terms only. We thereby obtain:

$$f_k(\theta_1, \ldots, \theta_m) \doteq f_k(\hat{\theta}_1, \ldots, \hat{\theta}_m) + \sum_{i=1}^{m} b_{ki}(\theta_i - \hat{\theta}_i)$$

where:

$$b_{ki} = \frac{\partial f_k(\theta_1, \ldots, \theta_m)}{\partial \theta_i} \bigg|_{\theta_1 = \hat{\theta}_1, \, \theta_2 = \hat{\theta}_2, \ldots, \theta_m = \hat{\theta}_m}$$

That is, the coefficient b_{ki} is the partial derivative evaluated at $\hat{\theta}_1, \hat{\theta}_2, \ldots, \hat{\theta}_m$. In practice, the b_{ki} are evaluated by a numerical approximation to the derivative instead of by an analytic expression. We want to choose $\theta_1, \theta_2, \ldots, \theta_m$ such that the mean square error:

$$\sum_{k=1}^{n} [r_k - f_k(\theta_1, \ldots, \theta_m)]^2$$

is a minimum. Using our Taylor approximation this mean square error becomes:

$$\sum_{k=1}^{n} [r_k - f_k(\hat{\theta}_1, \ldots, \hat{\theta}_m) - \sum_{i=1}^{m} b_{ki} u_i]^2$$

where the discrepancy u_i is defined as $u_i = \theta_i - \hat{\theta}_i$. If we differentiate the above expression for the mean square error with respect to the u_i and set the derivatives equal to zero, we get a set of normal equations which are linear in the unknowns u_i. We can solve these normal equations for the u_i. Using these values of the u_i we obtain the refined estimate of the partial autocorrelations given by $\theta_i = u_i + \hat{\theta}_i$. We can now use these refined estimates as our initial guesses and repeat the process. We keep iterating in this manner until successive iterations do not materially change the values of the partial autocorrelation coefficients $\theta_1, \ldots, \theta_m$.

In practice one can incorporate a source wavelet into the model as well as options that reduce or control the noise. Once the reflection coefficients c_i are determined the well-known relationship:

$$c_i = \frac{Z_i - Z_{i+1}}{Z_i + Z_{i+1}}$$

where Z_i is the acoustical impedance in layer i can be used to graph the acoustic log, i.e., the graph of acoustical impedance as a function of (two-way) travel time. The lower curve in Fig.5 shows a seismic trace as a function

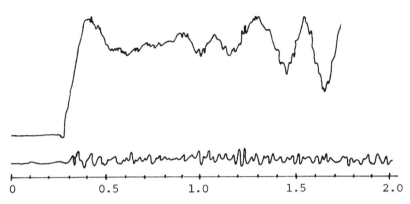

Fig. 5. A seismic trace (lower curve) and its corresponding acoustical log (upper curve).

of (two-way) travel time in seconds. The upper curve shows the corresponding seismic acoustical log computed from the seismic trace by the method given in this section. This seismic trace was recorded by Digicon Inc. on a marine survey in 1969 in the Arctic Ocean north of Canada.

SUMMARY AND CONCLUSIONS

We have given an algorithm to compute the parameters of the moving-average (MA) and the autoregressive (AR) components of a non-invertible ARMA system from its impulse response function. We have applied this algorithm to a marine seismogram, which can be regarded as the impulse response of a non-invertible ARMA system, in order to determine the reflection coefficients of the deep interfaces. A diagram of the algorithm is given and compared to the corresponding algorithm of Durbin for the case of an invertible ARMA system. From the general principles illustrated in these diagrams other algorithms along similar lines may be readily devised. Finally we have given an iterative method to compute the acoustical impedance log from a seismic trace taking into account all primary and multiple reflections.

REFERENCES

Box, G.E.P. and Jenkins, G.M., 1970. Time Series Analysis, Forecasting and Control. Holden-Day, San Francisco.
Robinson, E.A., 1967. Multichannel Time Series Analysis with Digital Computer Programs. Holden-Day, San Francisco.
Kendall, M.G. and Stuart, A., 1966. The Advanced Theory of Statistics, 3. Charles Griffin, London, 484 pp.

Appendix 8

Iterative and CDE ARMA Algorithms

(Paper by Enders A. Robinson in the *Proceedings of the First IEEE ASSP Workshop on Spectral Estimation,* McMaster University, Hamilton, Ontario, Canada, 1981)

8.1 Summary

The two algorithms are proposed for the estimation of the parameters of an ARMA process from observational data. The first is the iterative ARMA algorithm and the other is the CDE algorithm. The iterative ARMA algorithm consists of the following steps: (1) The AR(∞) parameters are estimated by means of the Yule-Walker equations. (2) The MA(∞) parameters are estimated as the least squares inverse of the AR(∞) parameters. (3) The ARMA parameters (i.e., the AR and MA parameters) are then estimated by iteration back and forth between two least-squares wave-shaping operations. The first shaping operation has the AR(∞) parameters as actual input, and the AR parameters as desired output, and it yields the MA parameters as the least-squares shaping filter. The second shaping operation has the MA(∞) parameters as actual input, and the MA parameters as desired output, and it yields the AR parameters as the least squares shaping filter. Iterations start with an initial guess of the AR parameters, and terminate when the AR and MA parameters stabilize.

The second algorithm presented in this paper is called the CDE algorithm, and it works as follows. Given a guess of the ARMA parameters, the CDE method generates the prediction error series, and the derivatives of the prediction error series with respect to each parameter. These derivative series form a multichannel actual input for a multichannel shaping operation, and the prediction error series forms the desired output. The resulting least-squares shaping filter represents the corrections to be made to the guess of the ARMA parameters. With the corrected guess, this process is then repeated. The iterations are stopped when the values of the ARMA parameters stabilize.

The value of these two new algorithms rests in the fact that they both use the LWR algorithm and thus are computationally more efficient than existing nonlinear regression methods for ARMA parameter estimation. Also, they make use of the engineering input-output approach which makes modification and extension of the algorithms easier than the conventional theoretical approach. LWR stands for Levinson-Wiggins-Robinson.

8.2 Introduction

The three basic finite-parameter time series models are the autoregressive (AR) model, the moving average (MA) model, and the autoregressive moving average (ARMA) model.[1,2,3] Given a finite number of observations of the time series, say $x(1), x(2), \ldots, x(N)$, there are two related questions: (1) What is the order of the process? and (2) What are the best estimates of the parameters of the process? In this paper, we will consider only question (2). Several efficient methods for estimating the parameters of an AR process are known.[4,5,6] Fortunately, AR parameter estimation can be formulated as a linear problem. In this paper, we consider the estimation of the parameters of MA and ARMA processes. The spectral estimates are then constructed from these parameters. The estimation of MA and ARMA models is more difficult than AR estimation because the problem is nonlinear.[7,8]

For the MA and ARMA estimation problem, Box and Jenkins[9] suggest a grid-search method. Parameters space is covered by a grid, so that each point on the grid corresponds to a particular set of numerical values of the parameters. From the given observations of the time series, the corresponding white noise process can be generated for each set of parameters. The sum of squares of each white noise process is computed, and then the entire grid is searched for that grid point that produces the smallest sum of squares. The grid point so found represents the least squares estimates of the parameters.

Box and Jenkins[9] also describe another procedure which they call nonlinear estimation. This description arises from the fact that the values of the white noise samples are nonlinear functions of the parameters. The nonlinear estimation procedure is a form of nonlinear regression analysis, and represents a gradient (or hill-descending) procedure to find the minimum sum of squares. Many computer programs to carry out this nonlinear estimation method are available commercially and at universities.

In this paper, we present two new methods for the estimation of MA and ARMA parameters. We call these two methods the *iterative ARMA algorithm* and the *CDE ARMA algorithm*. The corresponding MA algorithms are special cases of the ARMA algorithms. One may ask why two further estimation methods are proposed when the Box-Jenkins nonlinear regression method is available at nearly all computation centers and works well. One reason is computational cost, which is of prime importance in geophysical time series analysis. The nonlinear regression algorithm involves the solution of normal equations. A set of normal equations involving M regression coefficients requires the order of M^3 arithmetic operations for its solution. The proposed iterative ARMA algorithm and CDE ARMA algorithm, however, make use of Toeplitz normal equations and use the LWR algorithm[10] (given on pp. 241–249 of this book) for their solution. In this way, the number of arithmetic operations is of the order of M^2 instead of M^3. Because all the methods involve the solution of many sets of equations, this reduction in arithmetic operations results in significant savings.

Another reason for presenting the iterative and CDE algorithms is to illustrate the engineering approach to time series analysis as opposed to the theoretical approach. The engineering approach recognizes that there are certain fundamental input-output operations that keep recurring in time series theory. One such fundamental operation is the shaping filter. The shaping filter is embodied in the form of subroutine SHAPE for the single channel case and subroutine WIENER for the multichannel case. These subroutines and their description and examples of their use are documented,[11] so we will not repeat them here. The essential points to remember about the shaping filter are these. We are given an *actual input signal* and a *desired output signal*. These two signals go into subroutine SHAPE (or subroutine WIENER). What comes out is the *shaping filter coefficients*. These shaping filter coefficients are determined by requiring that the approximation

(actual input signal)*(shaping filter) $\approx$ (desired output signal)

holds in the least-squares sense. We call the shaping filter so computed the least-squares shaping filter. Note that the asterisk used above indicates convolution. In the computation of the least-squares shaping filter, both SHAPE and WIENER use the LWR algorithm.[10]

8.3 Iterative ARMA Algorithm

We will present the iterative ARMA algorithm for the case of a second order process. The invertible ARMA(2,2) process $x(k)$ is given by

$$x(k) + \alpha_1 x(k-1) + \alpha_2 x(k-2) = \epsilon(k) + \beta_1 \epsilon(k-1) + \beta_2 \epsilon(k-2) \quad (1)$$

where $\epsilon(k)$ is a white noise, where the AR parameters $(1, \alpha_1, \alpha_2)$ form a minimum-delay signal, and where the MA parameters $(1, \beta_1, \beta_2)$ also form a minimum delay signal. The AR(∞) representation of the ARMA process is

$$x(k) + \gamma_1 x(k-1) + \gamma_2 x(k-2) + \gamma_3 x(k-3) + \ldots = \epsilon(k) \quad (2)$$

where the AR(∞) parameters $(1, \gamma_1, \gamma_2, \ldots)$ satisfy the equations

$$
\begin{aligned}
\gamma_0 &= 1 \\
\gamma_1 + \beta_1 &= \alpha_1 \\
\gamma_2 + \beta_1\gamma_1 + \beta_2\gamma_0 &= \alpha_2 \\
\gamma_3 + \beta_1\gamma_2 + \beta_2\gamma_1 &= 0 \\
\gamma_4 + \beta_1\gamma_3 + \beta_2\gamma_2 &= 0 \\
\gamma_5 + \beta_1\gamma_4 + \beta_2\gamma_3 &= 0
\end{aligned}
\quad (3)
$$

$$\ldots$$

The AR(∞) parameters make up the prediction error operator $(1, \gamma_1, \gamma_2, \ldots)$ and the white noise series $\epsilon(k)$ is the prediction error, as shown by equation (2). The prediction distance is one time unit.

Given the observed numerical values $x(1), x(2), \ldots, x(N)$ of the time series, then estimators a_1, a_2, b_1, b_2 of the ARMA parameters $\alpha_1, \alpha_2, \beta_1, \beta_2$ respectively can be estimated in various ways. The first step of all the approaches that we will consider is the estimation of the first and significant part $(1, \gamma_1, \gamma_2, \ldots, \gamma_M)$ of the AR(∞) parameters. Let us denote this estimate by $(1, g_1, g_2, \ldots, g_M)$. This estimate is found as the solution of the Toeplitz normal equations (i.e., Yule-Walker equations) by use of the LWR algorithm. Note that we use Greek letters for parameter values and the corresponding Roman letters for their estimates.

Let us now describe the direct method of obtaining the ARMA parameters from $(1, g_2, g_2, \ldots, g_M)$. The empirical counterparts of the fourth and fifth equations of (3) are

$$\begin{aligned} g_3 + b_1 g_2 + b_2 g_1 &= 0 \\ g_4 + b_1 g_3 + b_2 g_2 &= 0. \end{aligned} \tag{4}$$

We solve these for the estimates b_1, b_2 of the parameters β_1, β_2. The empirical counterparts of the second and third of equations (3) are

$$\begin{aligned} g_1 + b_1 &= a_1 \\ g_2 + b_1 g_1 + b_2 &= a_2. \end{aligned} \tag{5}$$

These give the estimates a_1, a_2 of α_1, α_2.

Let us now describe the iterative algorithm. It uses the fact that the equations (3) tell us that $(1, \beta_1, \beta_2)$ is the shaping filter that transforms the input signal $(1, \gamma_1, \gamma_2, \ldots)$ into the output signal $(1, \alpha_1, \alpha_2)$. Given the estimate $(1, g_1, g_2, \ldots)$ of the input signal, we want to find the corresponding estimate $(1, b_1, b_2)$ of the shaping filter and estimate $(1, a_1, a_2)$ of the output signal. Because this is a problem of approximation we use least squares in the form of the least-squares shaping filter. We recall that we must specify an actual input signal and a desired output signal. The shaping-filter computer program then computes the least squares shaping filter coefficients.

Let us now say a word about normalization. For mathematical simplicity we prefer to have the leading coefficient of each of our filters and signals equal to unity. The least-squares shaping filter as computed will not generally have its leading coefficient equal to one. However, let us assume that we always divide all the coefficients by the leading coefficient, so that the resulting normalized least-squares shaping filter does have unity as its leading coefficient. In actual computations, not all these normalizations are required.

We know of no counterexample to the following conjecture, which we will soon use.

Conjecture: If the actual input and desired output are minimum-delay, then the least-squares shaping filter is minimum-delay.

Because the estimate $(1, g_1, \ldots, g_M)$ of the AR(∞) operator is a least-squares prediction error operator, it is necessarily minimum-delay. Let $(1, k_1, \ldots, k_M)$ be the least-squares inverse of $(1, g_1, g_2, \ldots, g_M)$, and hence $(1, k_1, \ldots, k_M)$ is also minimum-delay. The signal $(1, k_1, \ldots, k_M)$ is an estimate of the MA(∞) operator. Consider now the two approximations

$$(1, g_1, \ldots, g_M)*(1, b_1, b_2) \approx (1, a_1, a_2) \tag{6}$$

$$(1, k_1, \ldots, k_M)*(1, a_1, a_2) \approx (1, b_1, b_2). \tag{7}$$

In each of these approximations, the first set of parentheses enclose the actual input, the second set of parentheses enclose the shaping filter, and the third set enclose the desired output. We thus have the following iterative scheme which goes back and forth between these two equations. The respective actual inputs $(1, g_1, \ldots, g_M)$ and $(1, k_1, \ldots, k_M)$ in equations (6) and (7) are known quantities, and we wish to determine $(1, a_1, a_2)$ and $(1, b_1, b_2)$. We start with an initial guess $(1, a_1, a_2)$ as the desired output, and use subroutine SHAPE to compute the least-squares shaping filter $(1, b_1, b_2)$, as indicated in equation (6). We next use the $(1, b_2, b_2)$ as the desired output, and use subroutine SHAPE to compute the least-squares shaping filter $(1, a_1, a_2)$, as indicated in equation (7). We now use the $(1, a_1, a_2)$ as the desired output and use subroutine SHAPE to compute the least-squares shaping filter $(1, b_1, b_2)$, as indicated in equation (6). We next continue with equation (7), and keep going back and forth between the two equations. When the values of $(1, a_1, a_2)$ and $(1, b_1, b_2)$ stabilize, we stop the iterations. Assuming that our initial guess $(1, a_1, a_2)$ is minimum-delay, it follows from our Conjecture that all succeeding values of $(1, b_1, b_2)$ and $(1, a_2, a_2)$ are minimum-delay. The final values $(1, a_1, a_2)$ and $(1, b_1, b_2)$ are the estimates of the ARMA parameters $(1, \alpha_1, \alpha_2)$ and $(1, \beta_1, \beta_2)$ respectively.

Let us now review a similar iterative method.[12,13,14] Of course, many other possibilities are available, but they all depend upon the same general idea. We write the three approximations

$$(1, g_1, \ldots, g_M)*(1, b_1, b_2) \approx (1, a_1, a_2) \tag{8}$$

$$(1, b_1, b_2)*(1, c_1, c_2, \ldots, c_M) \approx (1, 0, 0, \ldots, 0) \tag{9}$$

$$(1, c_1, c_2, \ldots, c_M)*(1, a_1, a_2) \approx (1, g_1, \ldots, g_M). \tag{10}$$

Again, in each of these approximations, the first set of parentheses enclose the actual input, the second set of parentheses enclose the shaping filter, and the third set enclose the desired output. We start with an initial guess $(1, a_1, a_2)$ as desired output, and call subroutine SHAPE to compute the least-squares shaping filter $(1, b_1, b_2)$, as indicated in equation (8). We next use the $(1, b_1, b_2)$ as the actual input and the spike $(1, 0, 0, \ldots, 0)$ as desired output, and use subroutine SHAPE to compute the least-squares shaping filter $(1, c_1, \ldots, c_M)$, as indicated in equation (9). (In other words, $(1, c_1, \ldots, c_M)$ is the least-squares inverse of $(1, b_1, b_2)$. Thus $(1, c_1, \ldots, c_M)$ is minimum-delay, even though the initial guess $(1, a_1, a_2)$ may not have been minimum-delay.) We next use the $(1, c_1, \ldots, c_M)$ as the actual input and $(1, g_1, \ldots, g_M)$ as desired output, and use subroutine SHAPE to compute the least-squares shaping filter $(1, a_1, a_2)$, as indicated in equation (10). Because of the Conjecture the $(1, a_1, a_2)$ is minimum-delay. We next go back to equation (8) and repeat the process. All the following values of $(1, a_1, a_2)$ and $(1, b_1, b_2)$ will be minimum-delay because of the Conjecture. When things stabilize, we stop the iterations and use the final values of $(1, a_1, a_2)$ and $(1, b_1, b_2)$ as our estimates of the ARMA parameters.

8.4 CDE MA Algorithm

The letters CDE stand for *corrigitur dum erigitur,* which means "Corrected while erected." The reason for this name will soon be given. In this section, we want to treat *corrigitur-dum-erigitur* method (CDE method) to estimate the parameters of a MA time series. As an introduction to the CDE method, let us suppose that the time series $x(k)$ is generated by the invertible MA(1) model

$$x(k) = \epsilon(k) + \beta\epsilon(k - 1) \tag{11}$$

where the parameter β is less than one in magnitude and $\epsilon(k)$ is a white noise series. If we write this equation in the form

$$\epsilon(k) = -\beta\epsilon(k - 1) + x(k) \tag{12}$$

we find by recursive deductions that

$$\epsilon(k) = \sum_{j=0}^{\infty} (-\beta)^j x(k - j). \tag{13}$$

This equation represents the AR(∞) form of the MA(1) model. It shows that $\epsilon(k)$ is a nonlinear function of β. Let us expand the function $\epsilon(k)$ in a Taylor series around the point b. We obtain

$$\epsilon(k) = \epsilon(k)\Big|_{\beta=b} + \frac{\partial\epsilon(k)}{\partial\beta}\Big|_{\beta=b} (\beta - b) + \text{remainder}. \tag{14}$$

Let us define the time series $v(k)$ and $n(k)$ as

$$v(k) = -\frac{\partial\epsilon(k)}{\partial\beta}, \quad n(k) = v(k)\Big|_{\beta=b}. \tag{15}$$

That is, $n(k)$ is the time series obtained from $v(k)$ by replacing the parameter β by the value b. If we differentiate (11), we obtain

$$\frac{\partial \epsilon(k)}{\partial \beta} + \beta \frac{\partial \epsilon(k-1)}{\partial \beta} + \epsilon(k-1) = 0$$

which is

$$v(k) + \beta v(k-1) = \epsilon(k-1). \tag{16}$$

Because $\epsilon(k-1)$ is white, it follows that $v(k)$ is an AR(1) time series. Let us define $e(k)$ as the time series obtained by replacing β with b in $\epsilon(k)$; that is,

$$e(k) = \epsilon(k)\Big|_{\beta=b} = \sum_{j=0}^{\infty} (-b)^j x(k-j). \tag{17}$$

Thus equations (11) and (16) become

$$\begin{aligned} x(k) &= e(k) + be(k-1) \\ n(k) + bn(k-1) &= e(k-1). \end{aligned} \tag{18}$$

The Taylor series (14) is seen to be

$$e(k) = (\beta - b)n(k) + \text{error} \tag{19}$$

where the error is $\epsilon(k)$ minus the remainder. Equation (19) is in the form of the shaping filter equation, where $n(k)$ is the actual input signal and $e(k)$ is the desired output signal. We can thus use subroutine SHAPE to find the filter coefficient g_0. By the construction of the Taylor series, we know that

$$g_0 = \beta - b.$$

Thus the estimate of the parameter β is equal to the value b plus the filter coefficient g_0; that is,

$$\beta = b + g_0. \tag{20}$$

Let us now give the *corrigitur-dum-erigitur* algorithm for the MA(1) model. Let the numberical values of the given time series be $x(0)$, $x(1)$, . . . , $x(N)$. Let b be the guess of parameter β and let $e(-1)$ and $n(-1)$ be known initial values. (These initial values can be taken to be zero, or some extrapolation procedure can be used to estimate them. However, we will not dwell on how initial values are obtained, as this is the type of information which is so highly valued and closely guarded by practitioners of this art.) By use of the equations

$$\begin{aligned} e(k) &= x(k) - be(k-1) \\ n(k) &= e(k-1) - bn(k-1) \end{aligned} \tag{21}$$

we generate the values of the time series

$$
\begin{array}{ll}
e(0), e(1), \ldots, e(N) & \text{(the desired output)} \\
n(0), n(1), \ldots, n(N) & \text{(the actual input).}
\end{array}
\tag{22}
$$

We call subroutine SHAPE, and thus obtain the filter coefficient g_0. The corrected guess for the parameter β is thus $b + g_0$. We now repeat the algorithm with this corrected guess. Thus in an iterative fashion, we correct the model as we erect it, which explains the name *corrigitur dum erigitur*.

We will now state the *corrigitur-dum-erigitur* algorithm for the MA(q) model

$$
x(k) = \epsilon(k) + \beta_1\epsilon(k - 1) + \ldots + \beta_q\epsilon(k - q).
\tag{23}
$$

Let the given numerical time series be $x(0), x(1), \ldots, x(N)$. Let $b_1, b_2, \ldots, b_q$ be the respective guesses of the parameters $\beta_1, \beta_2, \ldots, \beta_q$. Let $e(-q), e(-q + 1), \ldots, e(-1)$ and $n(-q), n(-q + 1), \ldots, n(-1)$ be known initial values. By use of the equations

$$
\begin{array}{l}
e(k) = x(k) - b_1e(k - 1) - \ldots - b_qe(k - q) \\
n(k) = e(k - 1) - b_1n(k - 1) - \ldots - b_qn(k - q)
\end{array}
\tag{24}
$$

generate the values of the time series

$$
\begin{array}{ll}
e(0), e(1), \ldots, e(N) & \text{(the desired output)} \\
n(0), n(1), \ldots, n(N) & \text{(the actual input).}
\end{array}
\tag{25}
$$

Call subroutine SHAPE, and thus obtain the numerical values of the filter coefficients $g_0, g_1, \ldots, g_{q-1}$. We now repeat the algorithm with the corrected guesses

$$
b_1 + g_0, b_2 + g_1, \ldots, b_q + g_{q-1}.
\tag{26}
$$

We continue repeating the algorithm until the guesses converge to the moving average parameters $\beta_1, \beta_2, \ldots, \beta_q$.

8.5 CDE ARMA Algorithm

We now want to give the *corrigitur-dum-erigitur* (i.e., CDE) ARMA algorithm. As an introduction, let us suppose the time series $x(k)$ is generated by the invertible ARMA(2,2) model

$$
x(k) + \alpha_1x(k - 1) + \alpha_2x(k - 2) = \epsilon(k) + \beta_1\epsilon(k - 1) + \beta_2\epsilon(k - 2)
\tag{27}
$$

where the operators $(1, \alpha_1, \alpha_2)$ and $(1, \beta_1, \beta_2)$ are each minimum-delay and $\epsilon(k)$ is white noise. If we replace k by $k + 1$, this equation becomes

$$
x(k + 1) + \alpha_1x(k) + \alpha_2x(k - 1) = \epsilon(k + 1) + \beta_1\epsilon(k) + \beta_2\epsilon(k - 1).
\tag{28}
$$

The time series $\epsilon(k)$ is a function of the AR parameters α_1, α_2 and the MA parameters β_1, β_2. If we differentiate (27) and (28) with respect to α_1 and α_2 respectively, we obtain

$$x(k - 1) = \frac{\partial\epsilon(k)}{\partial\alpha_1} + \beta_1 \frac{\partial\epsilon(k - 1)}{\partial\alpha_1} + \beta_2 \frac{\partial\epsilon(k - 2)}{\partial\alpha_1}$$

$$x(k - 1) = \frac{\partial\epsilon(k + 1)}{\partial\alpha_2} + \beta_1 \frac{\partial\epsilon(k)}{\partial\alpha_2} + \beta_2 \frac{\partial\epsilon(k - 1)}{\partial\alpha_2} \qquad (29)$$

We see that both of these difference equations have the same left hand side and the same coefficients 1, β_1, β_2 on the right. Suppose they both have the same initial conditions in the remote past. We then see that they are equivalent if we define $\mu(k)$ as

$$\mu(k) = - \frac{\partial\epsilon(k)}{\partial\alpha_1} = - \frac{\partial\epsilon(k + 1)}{\partial\alpha_2}. \qquad (30)$$

The equivalent difference equation is thus

$$-x(k - 1) = \mu(k) + \beta_1\mu(k - 1) + \beta_2\mu(k - 2). \qquad (31)$$

Likewise, if we differentiate (1) and (2) with respect to β_1 and β_2 respectively, we obtain

$$\epsilon(k - 1) + \frac{\partial\epsilon(k)}{\partial\beta_1} + \beta_1 \frac{\partial\epsilon(k - 1)}{\partial\beta_1} + \beta_2 \frac{\partial\epsilon(k - 2)}{\partial\beta_1} = 0 \qquad (32)$$

$$\epsilon(k - 1) + \frac{\partial\epsilon(k + 1)}{\partial\beta_2} + \beta_1 \frac{\partial\epsilon(k)}{\partial\beta_2} + \beta_2 \frac{\partial\epsilon(k - 1)}{\partial\beta_2} = 0. \qquad (33)$$

If we define

$$\nu(k) = - \frac{\partial\epsilon(k)}{\partial\beta_1} = - \frac{\partial\epsilon(k + 1)}{\partial\beta_2} \qquad (34)$$

then each of equations (32) and (33) is equivalent to

$$\epsilon(k - 1) - \nu(k) - \beta_1\nu(k - 1) - \beta_2\nu(k - 2). \qquad (35)$$

When the ARMA parameters α_1, α_2, β_1, β_2 are replaced by the values of a_1, a_2, b_1, b_2, then the time series $\epsilon(k)$, $\mu(k)$, $\nu(k)$ are denoted by $e(k)$, $m(k)$, $n(k)$ respectively.

Let us now expand $\epsilon(k)$ in a Taylor series around the point a_1, a_2, b_1, b_2. We have

$$\epsilon(k) = e(k) - m(k)(\alpha_1 - a_1) - m(k - 1)(\alpha_2 - a_2)$$
$$- n(k)(\beta_1 - b_1) - n(k - 1)(\beta_2 - b_2) + R \qquad (36)$$

where R is the remainder. If we let the error be $\epsilon(k) - R$, and if we define the filter coefficients as

$$f_{10} = \alpha_1 - a_1, f_{11} = \alpha_2 - a_2,$$
$$f_{20} = \beta_1 - b_1, f_{21} = \beta_2 - b_2, \qquad (37)$$

then the Taylor series becomes

$$e(k) = f_{10}m(k) + f_{11}m(k-1) + f_{20}n(k) + f_{21}n(k-1) + \text{error}. \qquad (38)$$

This equation is in the form of a multichannel shaping filter (two input channels and one output channel). The two input signals are $m(k)$ and $n(k)$ and the desired output signal is $e(k)$. The filter coefficients are f_{10}, f_{11} on the first input channel and f_{20}, f_{21} on the second input channel. The multichannel shaping filter WIENER is used to compute the filter coefficients. Then the estimates of the ARMA parameters are given by

$$\begin{aligned}
\alpha_1 &= a_1 + f_{10}, \quad \alpha_2 = a_2 + f_{11}, \\
\beta_1 &= b_1 + f_{20}, \quad \beta_2 = b_2 + f_{21}.
\end{aligned} \qquad (39)$$

With this background we can now describe the *corrigitur-dum-erigitur* algorithm for finding the parameters of the ARMA(p,p) model

$$\begin{aligned}
x(k) + \alpha_1 x(k-1) + &\ldots + \alpha_p x(k-p) \\
&= \epsilon(k) + \beta_1 \epsilon(k-1) + \ldots + \beta_p \epsilon(k-p). \qquad (40)
\end{aligned}$$

Let the given numerical time series be $x(0), x(1), \ldots, x(N)$. Let $a_1, \ldots, a_p, b_1, \ldots, b_p$ be the respective guesses of the parameters $\alpha_1, \ldots, \alpha_p, \beta_1, \ldots, \beta_p$. Let sufficient initial values of the various time series be given so we can use the equations

$$\begin{aligned}
e(k) &= x(k) + a_1 x(k-1) + \ldots + a_p x(k-p) \\
&\quad - b_1 \epsilon(k-1) - \ldots - b_p \epsilon(k-p) \\
m(k) &= -x(k-1) - b_1 m(k-1) - \ldots - b_p m(k-p) \\
n(k) &= e(k-1) - b_1 n(k-1) - \ldots - b_p n(k-p)
\end{aligned} \qquad (41)$$

to generate the values

$$\begin{array}{ll}
e(0), e(1), \ldots, e(N) & \text{(desired output)} \\
m(0), m(1), \ldots, m(N) & \text{(first channel actual input)} \qquad (42) \\
n(0), n(1), \ldots, n(N) & \text{(second channel actual input)}.
\end{array}$$

We call subroutine WIENER to obtain the filter coefficients $f_{10}, f_{11}, \ldots, f_{1,p-1}, f_{20}, f_{21}, \ldots, f_{2,p-1}$. Subroutine WIENER uses the LWR algorithm for solving the block Toeplitz (Yule-Walker) multichannel normal equations, and so is computationally efficient. We now report the CDE algorithm with the corrected guesses

$$\begin{aligned}
a_1 + f_{10}, a_2 + f_{11}, &\ldots, a_p + f_{1,p-1}, \\
b_1 + f_{20}, b_2 + f_{21}, &\ldots, b_p + f_{2,p-1}
\end{aligned} \qquad (43)$$

for the ARMA parameters. We iterate until the process converges. We thus correct the ARMA model as we erect it. This procedure makes up the CDE method.

8.6 Concluding Remarks

Both the iterative algorithm and the CDE algorithm use the LWR recursion, so they are computational more efficiently than the existing nonlinear regression methods used to estimate ARMA parameters. The CDE ARMA algorithm, in fact, makes use of the multichannel LWR recursion. Although we have treated only single channel time series, the iterative and CDE algorithm can be extended to the case of multichannel time series.

Once the values of the ARMA(p,q) coefficients have been determined, the estimate of the spectral density is given by

$$\Phi(\omega) = \left| \frac{1 + b_1 e^{-i\omega} + \ldots + b_q e^{-i\omega q}}{1 + a_1 e^{-i\omega} + \ldots + a_p e^{-i\omega p}} \right|^2 \nu$$

where ν is the variance of the white noise process.

Additional note added July, 1982: In the use of these algorithms care must be taken to remove the mean values of all the time series. Also let us say a word about the CDE algorithm. One must start with a good initial guess. The critical step in the CDE algorithm is the truncation of the Taylor series to a first order approximation. A major problem could occur when this approximation is no longer valid. The classical problem of nonlinear regression, which is the method used in the CDE algorithm, is that, if the update terms yield estimates which are not near the initial values, then the neglecting of second and higher order terms in the Taylor series may invalidate the process. A solution of this problem is called damped least squares. The idea is to avoid very large update terms by providing a constant derived from the algorithm parameters to damp the updates. The damped least squares idea has been applied to the CDE algorithm by Dr. R. L. Cupo in his PhD thesis (June, 1982) in the Department of Electrical Engineering, Cornell University, Ithaca, New York 14853. The title of the thesis is *Computationally efficient methods of ARMA system identification and spectral estimation*. In addition to demonstrating the excellent empirical results of the CDE algorithm on time series data, the thesis develops other important theoretical and empirical methods, which include some new algorithms for spectral analysis. Computer programs are available with the thesis.

References

1. S. Haykin, *Nonlinear Methods of Spectral Analysis,* Berlin, Springer-Verlag, 1979.
2. E. Parzen, Some Recent Advances in Time Series Modeling. *IEEE Trans. Autom. Control,* vol. AC-19, pp. 723–730, 1974.
3. O. D. Anderson, *Time Series Analysis and Forecasting*. London: Butterworths, 1976.
4. J. P. Burg, *Maximum Entropy Spectral Analysis*. Stanford University Thesis, 1975.
5. T. J. Ulrych, Maximum Entropy Spectral Analysis and Autoregres-

sive Decomposition, *Rev. Geophysics and Space Physics,* vol. 13, pp. 183–200, 1975.

6. M. Kaveh and G. R. Cooper, An Empirical Investigation of the Properties of the Autoregressive Spectral Estimator, *IEEE Trans. Inform. Theory,* vol. IT-22, pp. 313–323, 1976.

7. S. L. Marple, *Conventional Fourier, Autoregressive, and Special ARMA Methods of Spectrum Analysis.* Stanford University Thesis, 1976.

8. O.L. Frost, *Power Spectrum Estimation.* NATO Advanced Study Institute, 1976.

9. G. E. P. Box and G. M. Jenkins, *Time Series Analysis, Forecasting and Control.* San Francisco, Holden-Day, 1970, Chapter 7.

10. M. Morf, A. Vieira, D. Lee and T. Kailath, Recursive Multichannel Maximum Entropy Spectral Estimation. *Modern Spectrum Analysis,* edited by D. G. Childers, New York: IEEE Press, 1978.

11. E. A. Robinson, *Multichannel Time Series Analysis with Digital Computer Programs.* San Francisco: Holden-Day, 1967. (Reprinted in this volume.)

12. E. A. Robinsin and S. Treitel, *Geophysical Signal Analysis,* Englewood Cliffs, New Jersey: Prentice-Hall, 1980, p. 449.

13. P. R. Gutowski, E. A. Robinson, and S. Treitel. Spectral Estimation: Fact or Fiction. *Modern Spectrum Analysis,* edited by D. G. Childers, New York, IEEE Press, 1978.

14. E. A. Robinson and M. T. Silvia. *Digital Foundations of Time Series Analysis* (2 vols). San Francisco: Holden-Day, 1979, 1981.

Appendix 9

A Historical Perspective of Spectrum Estimation

(Invited paper by Enders A. Robinson in the *Proceedings of the IEEE*, Vol. 70, No. 9, September 1982, pp. 885-907)

Abstract—The prehistory of spectral estimation has its roots in ancient times with the development of the calendar and the clock. The work of Pythagoras in 600 B.C. on the laws of musical harmony found mathematical expression in the eighteenth century in terms of the wave equation. The struggle to understand the solution of the wave equation was finally resolved by Jean Baptiste Joseph de Fourier in 1807 with his introduction of the Fourier series. The Fourier theory was extended to the case of arbitrary orthogonal functions by Sturm and Liouville in 1836. The Sturm–Liouville theory led to the greatest empirical success of spectral analysis yet obtained, namely the formulation of quantum mechanics as given by Heisenberg and Schrödinger in 1925 and 1926. In 1929 John von Neumann put the spectral theory of the atom on a firm mathematical foundation in his spectral representation theorm in Hilbert space. Meanwhile, Wiener developed the mathematical theory of Brownian movement in 1923, and in 1930 he introduced generalized harmonic analysis, that is, the spectral representation of a stationary random process. The common ground of the spectral representations of von Neumann and Wiener is the Hilbert space; the von Neumann result is for a Hermitian operator, whereas the Wiener result is for a unitary operator. Thus these two spectral representations are related by the Cayley–Möbius transformation. In 1942 Wiener applied his methods to problems of prediction and filtering, and his work was interpreted and extended by Norman Levinson. Wiener in his empirical work put more emphasis on the autocorrelation function than on the power spectrum.

The modern history of spectral estimation begins with the breakthrough of J. W. Tukey in 1949, which is the statistical counterpart of the breakthrough of Fourier 142 years earlier. This result made possible an active development of empirical spectral analysis by research workers in all scientific disciplines. However, spectral analysis was computationally expensive. A major computational breakthrough occurred with the publication in 1965 of the fast Fourier transform algorithm by J. S. Cooley and J. W. Tukey. The Cooley-Tukey method made it practical to do signal processing on waveforms in either the time or the frequency domain, something never practical with continuous systems. The Fourier transform became not just a theoretical description, but a tool. With the development of the fast Fourier transform the field of empirical spectral analysis grew from obscurity to importance, and is now a major discipline. Further important contributions were the introduction of maximum entropy spectral analysis by John Burg in 1967, the development of spectral windows by Emmanuel Parzen and others starting in the 1950's, the statistical work of Maurice Priestley and his school, hypothesis testing in time series analysis by Peter Whittle starting in 1951, the Box–Jenkins approach by George Box and G. M. Jenkins in 1970, and autoregressive spectral estimation and order-determining criteria by E. Parzen and H. Akaike starting in the 1960's. To these statistical contributions must be added the equally important engineering contributions to empirical spectrum analysis, which are not treated at all in this paper, but form the subject matter of the other papers in this special issue.

I. Introduction

SPECTRAL estimation has its roots in ancient times, with the determination of the length of the day, the phases of the moon, and the length of the year. The calendar and the clock resulted from empirical spectral analysis. In modern times, credit for the empirical discovery of spectra goes to the diversified genius of Sir Isaac Newton [1]. But the great interest in spectral analysis made its appearance only a little more than a century ago. The prominent German chemist

M SLOMOWITZ

SIR ISAAC NEWTON
1642-1727

Robert Wilhelm Bunsen (1811–1899) repeated Newton's experiment of the glass prism. Only Bunsen did not use the sun's rays as Newton did. Newton had found that a ray of sunlight is expanded into a band of many colors, the spectrum of the rainbow. In Bunsen's experiment, the role of pure sunlight was replaced by the burning of an old rag that had been soaked in a salt solution (sodium chloride). The beautiful rainbow of Newton did not appear. The spectrum, which Bunsen saw, only exhibited a few narrow lines, nothing more. One of the lines was a bright yellow.

Bunsen conveyed this result to Gustav Robert Kirchhoff (1824–1887), another well-known German scientist. They knew that the role of the glass prism consisted only in sorting the incident rays of light into their respective wavelengths (the process known as dispersion). The Newton rainbow was the extended continuous band of the solar spectrum; it indicates that all wavelengths of visible light are present in pure sunlight. The yellow line, which appeared when the light source was a burning rag, indicated that the spectrum of table salt contained a single specific wavelength. Further experiments showed that this yellow line belonged to the element sodium. No matter what the substance in which sodium appeared, that element made its whereabouts known by its bright yellow spectral line. As time went on, it was found that every chemical element has its own characteristic spectrum, and that the spectrum of a given element is always the same, no matter in what compound or substance the element is found. Thus the spectrum identifies the element, and in this way we can tell what elements are in substances from the distant stars to microscopic objects.

The successes of spectral analysis were colossal. However, the spectral theory of the elements could not be explained by classical physics. As we know, quantum physics was born and spectral theory was explained in 1925 and 1926 by the work of Werner Heisenberg (1901–1976) and Erwin Schrödinger (1887–1961). In this paper, we will show how spectral theory developed in the path to this great achievement.

Although most of the glamour of spectral theory has been associated with quantum physics, we will not neglect the parallel path taken in classical physics. Although the two paths began diverging with the work of Charles Sturm (1803–1855) and Joseph Liouville (1809–1882) on the spectral theory of differential equations, we will see that the final results, namely, the spectral representation of John von Neumann (1903–1957) for quantum physics, and that of Norbert Wiener (1894–1964) for classical physics, are intimately related.

Because light has high frequencies, our instruments cannot respond fast enough to directly measure the waveforms. Instead, the instruments measure the amount of energy in the frequency bands of interest. The measurement and analysis of the spectra of other types of signals, however, take different forms. With lower frequency signals, such as mechanical vibrations, speech, sonar signals, seismic traces, cardiograms, stock market data, and so on, we can measure the signals as functions of time (that is, as time series) and then find the spectra by computation. With the advent of the digital computer, numerical spectrum estimation has become an important field of study.

Let us say a few words about the terms "spectrum" and "spectral." Sir Isaac Newton introduced the scientific term "spectrum" using the Latin word for an image. Today, in English, we have the word *specter* meaning ghost or apparition, and the corresponding adjective *spectral*. We also have the scientific word *spectrum* and the dictionary lists the word *spectral* as the corresponding adjective. Thus "spectral" has two meanings. Many feel that we should be careful to use "spectrum" in place of "spectral" a) whenever the reference is to data or physical phenomena, and b) whenever the word modifies "estimation." They feel that the word "spectral," with its unnecessary ghostly interpretations, should be confined to those usages in a mathematical discipline where the term is deeply embedded.

The material in this paper through Section XII surveying the period from antiquity through Levinson and Wiener can be described as "The Prehistory of Spectrum Estimation" to emphasize that spectrum estimation is interpreted as estimation from data. The remaining sections may be described as "Some Pioneering Contributions to the Development of Methods of Spectrum Estimation."

Modern spectrum estimation began with the breakthrough for the analysis of short time series made by J. W. Tukey in 1949. This work led to a great blossoming forth of spectrum analysis techniques. Despite the advances in digital computing machinery, such computations were still expensive. The next great breakthrough occurred with the discovery of the fast Fourier transform in 1965 independently by J. W. Cooley and J. W. Tukey and by Gordon Sande. This development, in conjunction with silicon chip technology, has brought spectrum analysis to bear on a wide range of problems. Another breakthrough occurred with the introduction of maximum-entropy methods into spectrum analysis by John Burg in 1967.

II. TAYLOR SERIES

At the time when calculus was introduced in the seventeenth century by Newton and Leibnitz, the concept of a mathematical "function" entailed restricted properties, which in the course of time were gradually made less severe. In those days, the observations of natural events seemed to indicate that continuous relations always existed between physical variables. This view was reinforced by the formulation of the laws of nature on the basis of differential equations, as exemplified by Newton's laws. Thus it became commonplace to assume that any function describing physical phenomena would be differentiable. The idea of a function that changes in some capricious or random way, and thus does not allow any analytic formula for its representation, did not enter into the thinking of the mathematicians of that time. It was thus very natural for Brook Taylor (1685–1731) [2], a contemporary of Newton, to introduce the concept of "analytic function." The Taylor series expands an analytic function as an infinite summation of component functions. More precisely, the Taylor series expands a function $f(x)$, which is analytic in the neighborhood of a certain point $x = a$, into an infinite series whose coefficients are the successive derivatives of the function at the given point

$$f(a + h) = f(a) + \frac{1}{1!} f'(a) h + \frac{1}{2!} f''(a) h^2 + \cdots .$$

Thus analytic functions are functions which can be differentiated to any degree. We know that the definition of the derivative of any order at the point $x = a$ does not require more than knowledge of the function in an arbitrarily small neighborhood of the point $x = a$. The astonishing property of the Taylor series is that the shape of the function at a finite distance h from the point $x = a$ is uniquely determined by the behavior of the function in the infinitesimal vicinity of the point $x = a$. Thus the Taylor series implies that an analytic function has a very strong interconnected structure; by studying the function in a small vicinity of the point $x = a$, we can precisely predict what happens at the point $x = a + h$, which is at a finite distance from the point of study. This property, however, is restricted to the class of analytic functions. The best known analytic functions are, of course, the sine and cosine functions, the polynomials, and the rational functions (away from their poles).

III. THE DANIEL BERNOULLI SOLUTION OF THE WAVE EQUATION

The great Greek mathematician Pythagoras (ca 600 B.C.) was the first to consider a purely physical problem in which spectrum analysis made its appearance. Pythagoras studied the laws of musical harmony by generating pure sine vibrations on a vibrating string, fixed at its two endpoints. This problem

PYTHAGORAS   ARISTOTLE   EUCLID   ZENO OF ELEA

PYTHAGORAS (ca 580-500 B.C.)
ARISTOTLE (384-322 B.C.)
EUCLID (ca 300 B.C.)
ZENO (ca 490-430 B.C.)

excited scientists since ancient days, but the mathematical
turning point came in the eighteenth century when it was
recognized that the vertical displacement $u(x, t)$ of the vibrating string satisfies the wave equation

$$\frac{\partial^2 u}{\partial x^2} - \frac{1}{c^2}\frac{\partial^2 u}{\partial t^2} = 0.$$

Here x is the horizontal coordinate and t is the time. The constant c is a physical quantity characteristic of the material of
the string, and represents the velocity of the traveling waves on
the string. Because the endpoints $x = 0$ and $x = \pi$ are fixed, we
have the boundary conditions

$$u(0, t) = u(\pi, t) = 0.$$

(Note that for simplicity, we have taken the string to be of length π.) The problem of constructing the solution of the wave equation was then attacked by some of the greatest mathematicians of all time, and in so doing, they paved the way for the theory of spectrum analysis.

One of the finest results was that of Daniel Bernoulli (1700–1782) [3] in 1738. He introduced the method of separation of variables in which a trial solution is constructed as the product of a function of x alone, and a function of t alone. Thus, he wrote

$$u(x, t) = X(x)\, T(t).$$

Putting this trial solution in the differential equation and solving, he found the solutions

$$\cos kx \cos kct, \qquad \cos kx \sin kct$$

$$\sin kx \cos kct, \qquad \sin kx \sin kct.$$

However, the boundary condition at $x = 0$ excludes the solutions involving $\cos kx$, and so the possible solutions are reduced to the two choices

$$\sin kx \cos kct, \qquad \sin kx \sin kct.$$

The boundary condition at $x = \pi$ requires that the value of k to be an integer. In view of the linearity of the wave equation, any superposition of solutions gives a solution. Bernoulli thus gave the following solution:

$$u(x, t) = \sum_{k=1}^{\infty} \sin kx\, (A_k \cos kct + B_k \sin kct)$$

where the A_k and B_k are arbitrary constants. Bernoulli made the claim that this infinite sum is the general solution of the equation for the vibrating string. The implications of Bernoulli's claim were startling. From the principles of mechanics it was known that the initial displacement and initial velocity of the string could be prescribed in an arbitrary way. That is, it was known that at the initial time $t = 0$, both $u(x, 0)$ and $\dot{u}(x, 0)$ could have any functional form. (Note that the dot over a function indicates differentiation with respect to time, so $\dot{u}$ represents the velocity of the string in the vertical direction.) However, Bernoulli's solution gives explicit expressions for initial displacement and initial velocity, namely,

$$u(x, 0) = \sum_{k=1}^{\infty} A_k \sin kx$$

$$\dot{u}(x, 0) = c \sum_{k=1}^{\infty} k B_k \sin kx.$$

Thus Bernoulli's solution implied that each of two arbitrary functions $u(x, 0)$ and $\dot{u}(x, 0)$ could be expanded in the interval $0 \leqslant x \leqslant \pi$ in the form of an infinite series of sine functions. However, this result could not be explicitly demonstrated in Bernoulli's time.

Bernoulli's result can be expressed in the following way. Let the initial displacement $u(x, 0)$ be an arbitrary nonanalytic function $f(x)$. Then we have the expansion

$$f(x) = \sum_{k=0}^{\infty} A_k \sin kx$$

which says that a nonanalytic function $f(x)$ can be expressed as an infinite summation of analytic functions $\sin kx$ with weighting coefficients A_k. This result was a paradox at the time, and it led to a historical controversy of whether the function $f(x)$ could be freely chosen or must be restricted to the class of analytic functions. From the physical point of view, $f(x)$, which is the initial displacement of the string, could be freely chosen. From the then contemporary mathematical point of view, $f(x)$, which is an infinite summation of analytic functions, must be analytic. This view was believed by all the eminent mathematicians of the day.

Two of the greatest mathematicians who ever lived then set out to find the coefficients A_k of this expansion. Multiply each side by $\sin nx$ and integrate between 0 and π. Because

$$\int_0^\pi \sin kx \sin nx \, dx = \begin{cases} \pi/2, & \text{when } k = n \\ 0, & \text{when } k \neq n \end{cases}$$

the result found by L. Euler (1707–1783) [4] and J. L. Lagrange (1736–1813) [5] is

$$A_n = \frac{2}{\pi} \int_0^\pi f(x) \sin nx \, dx.$$

This is the point at which the question stood at the start of the nineteenth century.

IV. Jean Baptiste Joseph de Fourier and the Sinusoidal Spectral Theory

On December 21, 1807 the engineer Jean Baptiste Joseph de Fourier (1768–1830) [6] addressed the French Academy and made a claim that appeared incredible to the eminent mathematicians who were members of the Academy. As it turned out, one of the greatest advances in the history of mathematics, an innovation which was to occupy much of the attention of the mathematical community for over a century, was made by an engineer. Fourier said at that historic meeting that an arbi-

LEONHARD EULER
1707-1783

trary function, defined over a finite interval by any rough and even discontinuous graph, could be represented as an infinite summation of cosine and sine functions. The distinguished and brilliant academicians questioned the validity of Fourier's theorem, for they believed that any superposition of cosine and sine functions could only give an analytic function, that is, an infinitely differentiable function. An analytic function, of course, could never be discontinuous , and thus was very far removed from some arbitrarily drawn graph. In fact, Taylor's theorem stated that an analytic function had the property that, given its shape in an infinitesimal interval, the continuation of its course to the right and left by finite amounts was uniquely determined (the so-called process of analytic continuation). The academicians and the other great mathematicians of the time could not reconcile the property of analytic continuation with Fourier's theorem. How could the physical reasoning of an engineer stand up against the weight of the analytic reasoning of some of the most eminent mathematicians of all time?

These were the days when many great men were at the peak of their powers. Yet Fourier stood alone in defending his theorem.

As we have seen, the concept of analytic function requires a strong interconnection of the values of a function, where knowledge at one point allows us to predict the value at a point at a finite distance h. This prediction mechanism is embodied in the Taylor series expansion. However, a non-analytic function, such as a rough and discontinuous function, does not demand any such prediction mechanism between the immediate vicinity of a point and its wider surroundings. The Fourier series expansion is stated in terms of this wider concept of function. The coefficients of a Fourier series, as shown by the Euler–Lagrange result, are obtained by integration and not by differentiation as in the case of the Taylor series. Each Fourier coefficient A_n is obtained by integrating

JEAN BAPTISTE JOSEPH DE FOURIER
1768-1830

$f(x)$ sin nx over the entire range. Thus any modification of $f(x)$ in a limited portion of the range changes all of the Fourier coefficients. It follows that the interconnections operate in the Fourier series in a global sense and not in a local sense as in the case of the Taylor series. It is the behavior of $f(x)$ *in the large* that matters in the case of the Fourier series, and not so much the behavior in the vicinity of a point. How can we resolve the differences between these two types of expansions: the Taylor series, which is the expansion about a point which gives strict predictions a finite distance from the point, and the Fourier series, which is an expansion in the large and which gives knowledge of the function in the entire range. The Taylor series requires unlimited differentiability at a point, whereas the Fourier series does not demand any differentiability properties whatever.

Surprisingly enough, the chasm between the Taylor series and the Fourier series is bridged by means of the z-transform, which is the fundamental transform used in the theory of digital signal processing. Let us consider an analytic function $f(z)$ of the complex variable

$$z = x + jy = (re^{j\theta})^{-1}.$$

We now expand the function in a Taylor series (in the variable z^{-1}) about the point $z^{-1} = 0$, to obtain the z-transform

$$f(z) = \sum_{n=0}^{\infty} a_n z^{-n}.$$

The radius of convergence of this series extends from $z^{-1} = 0$ to the first singular point, say, z_0^{-1}. A singular point is a point where the function ceases to be analytic. The region of convergence of the Taylor series expansion of $f(z)$ is the region in the z-plane outside the circle of radius $|z_0|$; that is, the region of convergence is for all points z such that $|z^{-1}| < |z_0^{-1}|$ or equivalently $|z| > |z_0|$.

Let us now write the Taylor series expansion for points on the unit circle $z = \cos \theta - j \sin \theta$. We have

$$f(e^{-j\theta}) = \sum_{n=0}^{\infty} a_n (\cos n\theta - j \sin n\theta)$$

which is in the form of a complex Fourier series in the angle θ. Three cases can occur. In the first case, the singular point z_0 is inside the unit circle in the z-plane. In this case, the function is analytic on the unit circle and the Fourier series thus is an analytic representation of this analytic function. The French Academy believed this was the only case. In the second case, the singular point z_0 is outside the unit circle. In this case, the

Taylor series does not represent the function, and so we will not consider the case further. The third case is the interesting one, and is the case which resolves the mathematical controversy which led up to Fourier's discovery in 1807. When the singular point z_0 lies on the unit circle, the Taylor series will not converge at some or all of the points on the unit circle. Thus the Taylor series defines an analytic function, which is differentiable to any order outside the unit circle, but the function becomes nonanalytic at some or all of the points on the unit circle. The Fourier series in θ is the Taylor series for z on the unit circle, and thus the Fourier series represents a function in the variable θ, which is nonanalytic at some or all of the points in its range $-\pi \leqslant \theta \leqslant \pi$. A small modification of the Fourier coefficients that would move the singular point z_0 from on the unit circle to just inside the unit circle would change a nonanalytic Fourier representation to an analytic one. The amazing thing is that it is enough to move the singularity from the periphery of the unit circle to the inside by an arbitrarily small amount, in order to change the given nondifferentiable function in θ to one which can be differentiated any number of times. Thus the mistake of the great French mathematicians of the prestigious French Academy who wanted to restrict the validity of Fourier series to analytic functions depended entirely on that extremely small but finite distance from a point on the periphery to a point just inside the unit circle. A function can be extremely smooth right up to the unit circle, and then disintegrate into a rough and distorted image of its former self once it is on the unit circle. The Taylor series breaks down on the unit circle, but its counterpart, the Fourier series in θ, is still valid. The theorem of Fourier is true; science could blossom.

V. The Sturm-Liouville Spectral Theory of Differential Equations

Following the great innovation of Fourier in 1807, the remarkable properties of Fourier series were gradually developed throughout the nineteenth century and into the twentieth century. The Fourier series as introduced by Fourier is an expansion in terms of cosines and sines, which represent an orthogonal set of functions. However, there are many other sets of orthogonal functions, and so today any such expansion in terms of orthogonal functions is called a Fourier series. As we will see, some sets of orthogonal functions can be stochastic, and it turns out that the corresponding Fourier series play an important role in statistical spectral analysis.

First, however, let us look at the important generalizations made by the French mathematicians Charles Sturm (1803–

1855) [7] and Joseph Liouville (1809–1882) [8] in the decade of the 1830's. Let us now briefly look at the Sturm–Liouville theory of differential equations. The vibration of any infinitely long right circular cylinder of radius one can be described by a second-order differential equation. Let us consider a simple case, namely, the differential equation (the one-dimensional *Helmholtz equation*)

$$u''(x) + k^2 u(x) = 0.$$

The Helmholtz equation can be obtained by taking the temporal Fourier transform of the wave equation, which set off the search for the theory of Fourier. Here k is the wavenumber which is equal to ω/c where ω is the temporal frequency. In the Helmholtz equation, k^2 is some undetermined parameter. The variable x is the central angle of the cylinder, and so x lies in the range $-\pi$ and π. Because the points $x = -\pi$ and $x = \pi$ represent the same point on the cylinder, we must have the two boundary conditions

$$u(-\pi) = u(\pi)$$

$$u'(-\pi) = u'(\pi).$$

The general solution of the differential equation is

$$u(x) = A \cos kx + B \sin kx.$$

The two boundary conditions restrict the choice of the parameter k^2 to the discrete set of values

$$k^2 = 0, 1^2, 2^2, 3^2, \cdots$$

which are called the *eigenvalues* of the Helmholtz equation. The corresponding solutions of the equation, namely, the functions

$$u_k(x) = A \cos kx + B \sin kx$$

are called the *eigenfunctions*. These eigenfunctions are the cosine and sine functions which Fourier had used to construct his Fourier series. These functions represent the characteristic vibrational modes of the cylinder, which can only vibrate in this discrete set of wavenumbers $k = 0, 1, 2, \cdots$. Thus the Sturm–Liouville theory has given the answer to why the discrete set of cosine and sine functions were the correct ones for Fourier to use in a problem which stemmed from the wave equation.

Furthermore, the Sturm–Liouville theory gives us added insight to spectral analysis and, in fact, is the foundation of the spectral theory of differential equations. Most of the eigenvalue problems of mathematical physics are characterized by differential operators H of the form

$$H = \frac{d}{dx}\left[A(x)\frac{d}{dx}\right] + B(x).$$

The physical problems we consider require that the function $A(x)$ be positive within the given interval. Let us now form the operation $vHu - uHv$, which is

$$vHu - uHv = \frac{d}{dx}[A(x)(vu' - uv')].$$

We notice that the right-hand side is a total derivative, and so we have

$$\int_a^b (vHu - uHv)\,dx = [A(x)(vu' - uv')]_a^b.$$

Any differential operator H, which allows the transformation of such an integral (as on the left) into a pure boundary term (as on the right), is called *self-adjoint*. Thus the Sturm–Liouville operator H is self-adjoint. Often we may prescribe boundary conditions so that the right-hand side vanishes; such boundary conditions are called self-adjoint. We then have a self-adjoint problem, namely, a problem characterized by a self-adjoint operator H and self-adjoint boundary conditions. We then have the identity in the functions $u(x)$ and $v(x)$ given by

$$\int_a^b (vHu - uHv)\,dx = 0$$

which is called *Green's identity*.

The eigenvalue problem associated with the self-adjoint operator H starts with the differential equation

$$H\phi = \lambda\phi.$$

A solution satisfying the boundary conditions does not exist for all values of λ, but only for a certain selected set λ_i called the eigenvalues. This set consists of an infinite number of eigenvalues λ_i which are all real and which tend to infinity with i. We generally arrange these eigenvalues in increasing order to obtain the infinite sequence (called the *spectrum*)

$$\lambda_1, \lambda_2, \lambda_3, \cdots$$

together with the corresponding eigenfunctions

$$\phi_1, \phi_2, \phi_3, \cdots.$$

We now consider two different eigenvalues λ_j, λ_k and their corresponding eigenfunctions ϕ_j, ϕ_k. If we substitute $u = \phi_j$ and $v = \phi_k$ into Green's identity, we obtain

$$\int_a^b (\lambda_j \phi_j \phi_k - \lambda_k \phi_k \phi_j) \, dx = 0$$

which gives the orthogonality condition

$$\int_a^b \phi_j(x) \phi_k(x) \, dx = 0, \quad \text{for } j \neq k.$$

By normalization, we can require that

$$\int_a^b \phi_j^2(x) \, dx = 0$$

so that the eigenfunctions form an *orthonormal* set. The orthonormal property can be written more concisely as

$$\int_a^b \phi_j(x) \phi_k(x) \, dx = \delta_{jk}$$

where δ_{jk} is the Kronecker delta function.

Let us now represent an arbitrary function $f(x)$ in the form of the infinite expansion

$$f(x) = \sum_{k=1}^{\infty} c_k \phi_k(x).$$

As we have previously mentioned, such an expansion is called a *Fourier series* in honor of the pioneering work of Fourier. The Fourier coefficients c_k are obtained by multiplying both sides by $\phi_j(x)$ and integrating. The result is

$$c_j = \int_a^b f(x) \phi_j(x) \, dx.$$

Under certain general conditions, it can be shown that the orthonormal set is complete, so that the above Fourier expansion actually converges to the function $f(x)$. Suppose now that $f(x)$ is the solution to the inhomogeneous differential equation

$$Hf(x) = p(x).$$

In terms of linear system theory, $p(x)$ is the input and $f(x)$ is the output. Now substitute $u = f$ and $v = \phi_k$ into Green's identity. We obtain

$$\int_a^b (\phi_k Hf - fH\phi_k) \, dx = 0$$

which is

$$\int_a^b (\phi_k p - f \lambda_k \phi_k)\, dx = 0.$$

The above equation can be written as

$$\int_a^b f \phi_k\, dx = \frac{1}{\lambda_k} \int_a^b \phi_k p\, dx.$$

We recognize the left-hand side as the expression for the Fourier coefficient c_k. Thus

$$c_k = \frac{1}{\lambda_k} \int_a^b \phi_k(\xi)\, p(\xi)\, d\xi.$$

We now substitute this expression for c_k into the Fourier series to obtain

$$f(x) = \sum_{k=1}^{\infty} c_k \phi_k(x) = \int_a^b p(\xi) \left[\sum_{k=1}^{\infty} \frac{\phi_k(x)\, \phi_k(\xi)}{\lambda_k} \right] d\xi.$$

If we denote the expression in brackets by $G(x, \xi)$, then this equation is

$$f(x) = \int_a^b p(\xi)\, G(x, \xi)\, d\xi.$$

This is the integral form of the input–output relationship, and we recognize

$$G(x, \xi) = \sum_{k=1}^{\infty} \frac{\phi_k(x)\, \phi_k(\xi)}{\lambda_k}$$

as the *impulse response function* or *Green's function* (under the given boundary conditions), a concept originated by George Green (1793-1841) [9]. This equation exhibits the impulse response function of a linear system in terms of its spectrum $\lambda_1, \lambda_2, \lambda_3, \cdots$. We can confirm that the Green's function is indeed the impulse response by setting the input $p(x)$ equal to the impulse $\delta(x - x_0)$. Then the output is

$$\int_a^b \delta(\xi - x_0)\, G(x, \xi)\, d\xi = G(x, x_0)$$

and so $G(x, x_0)$ represents the output at x due to an impulse at x_0. Since the differential equation represents an input–output system, we see that the Green's function satisfies

$$HG(x, x_0) = \delta(x - x_0).$$

This equation shows that the Green's function $G(x, x_0)$ is the inverse of the differential operator H.

We have thus reviewed the spectral theory of differential operators, and now we can look at the most spectacular application of spectral estimation—quantum physics.

VI. SCHRÖDINGER SPECTRAL THEORY OF THE ATOM

The Sturm–Liouville theory of the expansion of functions in terms of orthogonal functions found numerous physical applications in the work of Lord Rayleigh (1842–1919). Such expansions occur throughout the study of the elastic vibrations of solids and in the theory of sound. In the history of physics, a decisive breakthrough occurred when Erwin Schrödinger (1887–1961) [10] showed in 1926 that the vibrations occurring within the atom can be understood by means of the Sturm–Liouville theory. Let us now explain how the wave mechanics of Schrödinger describes the spectral lines of the atom. An equivalent matrix mechanics was formulated a year before Schrödinger by Werner Heisenberg (1901–1976) [11].

Before quantum theory, classical physics was at an impasse. It could not explain the existence of atomic spectra. For example, the bright yellow spectral line of sodium discovered by Bunsen means that the radiation of its atoms produces a discrete frequency ω_0. If we assume that this line is emitted by an electron, then the laws of classical physics state that such an electron should emit not a discrete line at ω_0, but a whole spectrum of lines at all frequencies ω, and with no discontinuities in the spectrum. That is, classical physics predicts that the spectrum of an electron should be continuous as is the spectrum of the sun. Yet Bunsen observed the discrete spectrum of sodium as evidenced by the bright yellow line. (As we will soon see, this line observed by Bunsen is actually a doublet, which Bunsen was unable to resolve with the means available to him.)

Quantum mechanics allows us to see the atom from a new point of view. Quantum mechanics says that atomic electrons jump from one energy state to another, and that the difference of these energies is embodied as a quantum of electromagnetic energy, the photon. If the energy diminishes, a photon is born. If the energy increases, a photon or a quantum of energy from some other field has been absorbed just before the jump.

In quantum mechanics, an electron is represented by a probability density function. (The probability density function is found as the squared magnitude $|\phi|^2$ of a probability wave function ϕ.) An electron jump has a probability that depends upon the shapes of the probability density functions that correspond to the electron prior to and after the jump. The probability of a jump is, generally speaking, greater for the stronger overlapping or deeper interpenetration of these probability density functions. The laws that divide electron transitions in atoms into more probable and less probable ones are called selection rules. It is in this jumping of electrons that photons are born. These photons enter a spectroscope, get sorted into types, and produce the spectral lines.

The more photons that an atom emits in a second, the brighter the spectral lines. If the number of atoms remains constant, then the brightness of the spectral lines depends upon the statistical frequency of electron jumps in the atoms. And this statistical frequency is determined by the probability distribution of jumps. It is in this way that an atomic spectrum consisting of a number of lines of different brightnesses is generated.

One can make the observation that the spectrum estimation problem (the subject matter of this special issue of *Proceedings of the IEEE*) is not central to the spectral representation in quantum mechanics. This situation was brought forcibly to the writer's attention several years ago at the U.S. Air Force Geophysics Library at Hanscom Field, MA, which is one of the best scientific libraries in the world. The many shelves devoted to "spectra" consisted of a mixture of both kinds of books, but no book devoted to a discussion of the relationship between the two areas of spectral theory.

Spectral estimation in quantum mechanics is based on the edifice of spectroscopy, which is an instrumentational science. In 1891, the physicist A. A. Michelson developed an interferometer, a device producing the superposition of a light signal on top of itself with a prescribed delay. In one series of experiments, Michelson first bandpass filtered a light signal by passing it through a prism. He then used the interferometer to measure the visibility of the superimposed signal as a function of delay. The resulting curve was the autocovariance function of the original signal. Michelson then used a mechanical harmonic analyzer to compute the Fourier transform of the visibility curve; that is, he estimated the power spectrum of the signal. Michelson's experiments were done to examine the fine structure of spectral lines of light. Thus in those early days, the present day dichotomy of spectrum estimation had not yet materialized.

The technique of spectral analysis in physics developed rapidly in the twentieth century, and the instruments became more powerful and sensitive. The spectroscopists came up with the following question for theoreticians, namely, the question of why spectral lines are somewhat fat, not infinitesimally thin.

It was recognized that a photon corresponds to a line at one frequency ω. The question was why the lines on a photographic plate of a spectroscope come out somewhat broadened, not slender. The answer was found in the wave property of the electron and the Heisenberg uncertainty principle. The initial energy of an electron in an atom refers to a stationary state, and so does the final energy. However, an electron jump is in violation of some steady state. As soon as this occurs, the Heisenberg principle takes over. If we let Δt designate the lifetime of an electron between jumps, then the uncertainty of photon energy is $\Delta E \sim h/\Delta t$, where h is Planck's constant. Using Planck's formula for energy quanta, the uncertainty ΔE of the energy is proportional to the uncertainty $\Delta \omega$ of the frequency of the photon

$$\Delta E = \frac{h}{2\pi} \Delta\omega.$$

Thus the spectral lines have a width $\Delta\omega$ which is inversely proportional to the time of the "settled life" of the electron in the atom

$$\Delta\omega \sim \frac{2\pi}{\Delta t}.$$

In other words, the more "settled" or quiescent the life of the electron in the atom, the narrower the spectral lines. That is why at high temperatures and pressures, when many of the atomic electrons are unsettled, the spectral lines broaden out and become smeared. Thus an individual spectral line has a finite width associated with thermal motion and collision broadening. This is not only important in physics, but it relates very importantly to the topic of spectrum estimation in this special issue. Real "lines" have finite width. This means that real lines behave like narrow-band noises and not like either single frequencies or a constant-amplitude lightly frequency-modulated signal.

Let us now return the discussion of the yellow sodium line which Bunsen observed. The sodium D line is a doublet. Moreover the sodium spectrum contains four lines in the visible range, and two more in the near ultraviolet, strong enough to be useful for analytic chemistry. The sodium spectrum contains 29 lines of astrophysical interest between the D lines and 4390 Å (still in the visible).

We might say that Bunsen over a century ago was performing spectrum estimation. He was unable to resolve the two frequencies present in the doublet, even as today a person doing spectrum estimation might have the same problem in some other situation. Also Bunsen missed the many other lines in the sodium atom, even as today a person doing spectrum estimation might not find some features without the use of modern techniques. As spectrosopic instruments became better, these lines were discovered. Now another question, however, has come up. Many spectral lines, which, it would seem, should correspond to a single frequency, actually turned out to be the states of a number of very close-lying lines. The fact that the sodium D line is a doublet is a case in point. The fine structures of spectral lines (doublets, etc.) were revealed only because of the great advances in spectral techniques. In turn, electron spin was discovered in order to explain these "fine qualities" in spectra. Let us briefly give the reason. When spectra are generated, the states of two electrons with opposite spins can have slightly different energies. As a result, the spectral line is doubled; in place of one line we have twin lines with identical brightnesses. Such twins are usually born only when the outer electron shell has one electron. If the number of electrons in this shell increases, we can have triplets and even larger families of the former spectral line.

Let us now consider the quantum mechanical formulation of the harmonic oscillator problem. In terms of the nondimensional displacement x, the time-independent *Schrödinger equation* is

$$H\phi = \lambda\phi$$

where H is defined as the differential operator

$$H = \frac{d^2}{dx^2} - x^2$$

and λ is defined as

$$\lambda = \frac{2E}{\hbar\omega_0}.$$

Here ϕ is the probability wave function, the constant E is the energy, $h = 2\pi\hbar$ is Planck's constant, and the constant ω_0 is the natural frequency. The problem of finding the probability wave function ϕ is a Sturm–Liouville problem. The solution gives the eigenvalues as $1, 3, 5, 7, \cdots$, and so we write

$$\lambda_k = (2k + 1), \quad \text{for} \quad k = 0, 1, 2, \cdots.$$

Thus the eigenenergies are

$$E_k = \tfrac{1}{2}\hbar\omega_0\lambda_k = \hbar\omega_0(k + \tfrac{1}{2}), \quad \text{for} \quad k = 0, 1, 2, \cdots.$$

The corresponding eigenfunctions are

$$\phi_k = C_k h_k(x) e^{-x^2/2}, \quad \text{for} \quad k = 0, 1, 2, \cdots$$

where C_k is a normalization constant, and $h_k(x)$ is the Hermite polynomial of order k. The discrete set of eigenenergies E_0, $E_1, E_2, \cdots$ represent the discrete lines observed in the spectrum. Thus quantum mechanics, through the use of Sturm–Liouville theory, is able to explain the existence of atomic spectra. However, certain mathematical difficulties remained; the history of their resolution is given in the next section.

VII. The von Neumann Spectral Representation Theorem

In finite-dimensional space, the following eigenvalue problem is posed. Given an Hermitian matrix H, find all column-vector solutions ϕ of the characteristic equation

$$H\phi = \lambda\phi$$

where λ is a constant also to be determined. That is, given H, find ϕ and λ. The solutions $\phi_1, \cdots, \phi_n$ are called the eigensolutions (assumed to be normalized), and the corresponding real numbers $\lambda_1, \cdots, \lambda_n$ are called the eigenvalues of the matrix H. The totality of the eigenvalues $\lambda_1, \lambda_2, \cdots, \lambda_n$, in order of increasing magnitude, is called the spectrum. Now write the eigenequations

$$H\phi_k = \lambda_k \phi_k \quad \text{(for } k = 1, \cdots, n)$$

in the form of the matrix equation

$$HU = U\Lambda.$$

Because the eigensolutions are orthonormal, the matrix U (which has the eigensolutions as it columns) is unitary, i.e.,

$$UU^T = I$$

where I is the identity matrix. (The superscript T indicates complex conjugate transpose.) The matrix Λ is diagonal matrix, with the spectrum along its diagonal. Thus this eigenvalue problem can be described as the problem of finding a unitary matrix U that reduces H to a real diagonal matrix, i.e.,

$$U^{-1}HU = \Lambda.$$

(Note: In case H is real, then H is a symmetric matrix and U is an orthogonal matrix.)

Although the unitary matrix U, whose columns are the eigensolutions ϕ_i, is not uniquely determined by H, John von Neumann [12] in 1929 exploited the unitary nature of U to reformulate the eigenvalue problem. The von Neumann reformulation, which is called the *spectral representation problem*, yields the same results as the eigenvalue problem in finite-dimensional space, but has the advantage that it can be extended to Hilbert space.

JOHN VON NEUMANN
1903-1957

We recall that the diagonal matrix Λ is defined to be the matrix with the eigenvalues, ordered by increasing magnitude, along its main diagonal and zeros off the diagonal. Because of this ordering, the matrix Λ is uniquely determined for any given Hermitian matrix H. Because some eigenvalues may be repeated, let us relabel them as $\lambda_1, \lambda_2, \cdots, \lambda_m$ (with $m \leqslant n$), where each λ_i is now distinct. Consequently for a given H, we have the unique decomposition

$$\Lambda = \lambda_1 Q_1 + \lambda_2 Q_2 + \cdots + \lambda_m Q_m$$

where Q_i is a diagonal matrix with 1's in those places on its main diagonal in which λ_i occurs in Λ and 0's elsewhere. The sum of the Q_i gives the identity matrix

$$I = Q_1 + Q_2 + \cdots + Q_m.$$

We now define the matrix P_j as

$$P_j = UQ_jU^{-1} \quad \text{(for } j = 1, 2, \cdots, m\text{)}.$$

A projection matrix is defined as a Hermitian idempotent

matrix. Because Q_j is Hermitian ($Q_j = Q_j^T$) and idempotent ($Q_j Q_j = Q_j$), it follows that Q_j is a projection matrix. Because P_j is Hermitian ($P_j = P_j^T$) and idempotent

$$P_j P_j = U Q_j U^{-1} U Q_j U^{-1} = U Q_j Q_j U^{-1} = P_j$$

it follows that P_j is a projection matrix. Since for $i \neq j$

$$P_i P_j = U Q_i U^{-1} U Q_j U^{-1} = 0$$

it follows that $P_i + P_j$ is a projection matrix and the space spanned by P_i is orthogonal to the space spanned by P_j. Let us now define the function $\mathcal{H}(\lambda)$ of the continuous variable λ as

$$\mathcal{H}(\lambda) = P_1 \delta(\lambda - \lambda_1) + P_2 \delta(\lambda - \lambda_2) + \cdots + P_m \delta(\lambda - \lambda_m).$$

This function is the continuous representation of the suite of projection matrices $P_1, P_2, \cdots, P_m$.

We now consider the quadratic form uHv where u is a row vector and v is a column vector. We have

$$uHv = uU\Lambda U^{-1} v = uU(\lambda_1 Q_1 + \lambda_2 Q_2 + \cdots + \lambda_m Q_m) U^{-1} v$$

$$= u(\lambda_1 P_1 + \lambda_2 P_2 + \cdots + \lambda_m P_m) v$$

$$= \lambda_1 uP_1 v + \lambda_2 uP_2 v + \cdots + \lambda_m uP_m v.$$

The essence of the von Neumann spectral representation lies in the fact that the components $uP_j v$ are numerically invariant for given u, H, and v. In this way, the nonuniqueness of the unitary matrix U appearing in the eigenvalue decomposition is bypassed. We see that we can write the quadratic form as the integral

$$uHv = \int_{-\infty}^{\infty} \lambda u \mathcal{H}(\lambda) v \, d\lambda.$$

This equation represents the von Neumann *spectral representation of the Hermitian matrix H.*

Let us now analyze this equation. If we strip the u and v from this equation, we are left with

$$H = \int_{-\infty}^{\infty} \lambda \mathcal{H}(\lambda) \, d\lambda$$

which, in matrix notation, is

$$H = \lambda_1 P_1 + \lambda_2 P_2 + \cdots + \lambda_m P_m.$$

We can write the row vector u as

$$u = \int_{-\infty}^{\infty} u \mathcal{H}(\lambda) \, d\lambda$$

which is

$$u = uP_1 + uP_2 + \cdots + uP_m.$$

Finally, we can write

$$Hv = \int_{-\infty}^{\infty} \lambda \mathcal{H}(\lambda)\, v\, d\lambda$$

which is

$$Hv = \lambda_1 P_1 v + \lambda_2 P_2 v + \cdots + \lambda_m P_m v.$$

Let us now consider functions of the matrix H. First, we consider the square of H. We have

$$H^2 = (\lambda_1 P_1 + \cdots + \lambda_m P_m)^2 = \lambda_1^2 P_1 + \cdots + \lambda_m^2 P_m$$

$$= \int_{-\infty}^{\infty} \lambda^2 \mathcal{H}(\lambda)\, d\lambda.$$

We see that squaring H results in squaring the λ inside the integral. In general, if we form a function of H, then the result is that the same function of λ is taken within the integral sign; that is

$$f(H) = \int_{-\infty}^{\infty} f(\lambda)\, \mathcal{H}(\lambda)\, d\lambda.$$

The above spectral representation was derived for finite-dimensional space, that is, a space in which the elements u and v are vectors and the Hermitian operator H is a matrix. One of the major achievements of von Neumann was the development of the concept of the infinitely-dimensional space, which he called *Hilbert space* in honor of the great mathematician David Hilbert (1862–1943). We now let u and v represents elements in Hilbert space, and let H represent a Hermitian operator. A Hilbert space is characterized by an inner product (or dot product). The *inner product* of the elements u and v is denoted by $\langle u, v \rangle$. If we let H operate on the element v, we obtain a new element Hv. The inner product of the elements u and Hv is denoted by $\langle u, Hv \rangle$. This inner product is the counterpart of the quadratic form uHv in finite-dimensional space. Once we establish this connection, it turns out that the von Neumann spectral representation has exactly the same form in Hilbert space as it does in finite-dimensional space. Thus in Hilbert space, we also have an operator $\mathcal{H}(\lambda)$, which is the continuous representation of the suite of projection operators associated with the Hermitian operator H. Whereas in finite-dimensional space, we made use of the quadratic form $u\mathcal{H}(\lambda)\, v$, we now make use of its counterpart $\langle u, \mathcal{H}(\lambda)\, v \rangle$ in Hilbert space. Thus the von

Neumann *spectral representation* in Hilbert space is

$$\langle u, Hv \rangle = \int_{-\infty}^{\infty} \lambda \langle u, \mathcal{H}(\lambda)\, v \rangle \, d\lambda.$$

Let us now look at some history. In general, there is no quadratically integrable solution to the eigenvalue problem in Hilbert space. This circumstance, however, bothered no one working in physics. Wavelet solutions (i.e., quadratically integrable superpositions of eigenfunctions with eigenvalues in a small neighborhood) were used from the start, appearing in the works of de Broglie and Schrödinger from 1924.

One of the authors cited in the Reference Section knew von Neumann personally, studied his work assiduously, and certainly regards him as one of the truly great founders of quantum theory. However, there was never a "crisis in physics" that was resolved by the von Neumann spectral representation theorem. Most people doing the practical calculations to be compared with experiment had never heard of the theorem, which was for them at such a high level of abstraction that it had no bearing on what they were doing.

Throughout this essay we have traced the development of spectral theory, from the analytic functions of Brook Taylor, to the nondifferentiable functions of Jean Baptiste Joseph de Fourier, and now to the more general operators of Hilbert space. At each stage, these developments were mathematical in nature, but they laid the foundations for subsequent advances in physics. Reasoning in mathematics and reasoning in physics often appear quite different. When a major physical breakthrough occurs, such as in quantum mechanics in the 1920's, and a flood of exciting new physical results come out, certainly the work of mathematicians in establishing existence and uniqueness theorems might seem somewhat irrelevant.

For a moment let us go back to Sir Isaac Newton. It is often said that the unique greatness of Newton's mind and work consists in the combination of a supreme experimental with a supreme mathematical genius. It is also often said that the distinctive feature of Newtonian science consists precisely in the linking together of mathematics and experiment, that is, in the mathematical treatment of experimental or (as in astronomy, geophysics, or wherever experiments cannot be performed) observational data. Yet, although correct, this description does not seem to be quite complete; there is more in the work of Newton than mathematics and experiment. There is also a deep intuition and insight in his interpretation of nature.

In today's science, specialization has gone far. Physicists use mathematics; they formulate problems, devise methods of solution, and perform long derivations and calculations, but generally they are not interested in creating new mathematics. The discovery and purification of abstract concepts and principles is particularly in the realm of mathematics. John von Neumann (1903–1957) is a prime example of a mathematician doing physics. When he did physics, he thought and calculated like a physicist, only faster.· He understood all branches of physics, as well as chemistry and astronomy, but mainly he had a talent for introducing only those mathematical ideas that were relevant to the physics at hand. The introduction of abstract Hilbert space theory in quantum mechanics, chiefly by von Neumann, made possible the construction of a solid theory on the basis of the powerful intuitive ideas of Dirac and other physicists.

The physics of quantum theory cannot be mathematically formulated in finite-dimensional space but requires Hilbert space. After the work of Heisenberg and Schrödinger in 1925 and 1926, there was a crisis in abstract mathematics because the physics of quantum mechanics could not be adequately formulated in terms of the existing mathematical framework. This situation was rectified in 1929 by von Neumann [12] who laid the mathematical foundations of quantum mechanics in terms of Hilbert space. There is an apocryphal story that the young John von Neumann, who was barely past being a teenager, and had not yet earned his doctorate, was lecturing in Göttingen. Of course, most of the famous physicsts present regarded his work as too abstract, but the great mathematician Hilbert was in the audience. As the story goes, the elderly Hilbert leaned over and whispered into Professor Courant's ear: "What is this Hilbert space?" Another even more apocryphal story goes as follows. A group of physicists came to von Neumann and described a problem in physics which they could not solve. After thinking for a while, von Neumann in his head came up with the numerical answer which agreed with the experimental result, which the physicists knew but had not told him. They were very impressed and they blurted out "Dr. von Neumann, the general solution involves solving an infinite set of nonlinear partial differential equations. Certainly you have found some mathematical shortcut!" von Neumann answered "No, I solved the infinite set."

von Neumann [13] showed that from a mathematical point of view, it is the spectral representation that is required in quantum mechanics rather than the solution of the eigenvalue problem as such. In this sense, spectral theory represents the key to the understanding of the atom. In fact, von Neumann [13] has shown that the spectral representation enters so essentially into all quantum mechanical concepts that its existence cannot be dispensed with. His establishment of the spectral representation of the Hermitian operator H is one of the great achievements in mathematics, and a milestone in the history of spectral theory.

VIII. EINSTEIN-WIENER THEORY OF BROWNIAN MOTION

A highly interesting kinetic phenomenon known as Brownian movement was first reported in 1827 by the distinguished botanist, Robert Brown, who found that "extremely minute particles of solid matter when suspended in pure water exhibit motions for which I am unable to account and which, from their irregularity and seeming independence, resemble in a remarkable degree, the less rapid motions of some of the simplest animalcules of infusions." This type of irregular zigzag movement is typified by the dancing of dust particles in a beam of light. The cause of Brownian movement was long in doubt, but with the development of the kinetic theory of matter came the realization that the particles move because they are bombarded unequally on different sides by the rapidly moving molecules of the fluid in which they are suspended. The Brownian movement never ceases. The detailed physical theory of Brownian movement was worked out in 1904 by M. von Smoluchowski [14], and in a more final form in 1905 by Albert Einstein [15]. In 1923, Norbert Wiener [16] developed the mathematical theory of Brownian movement, which today is the basis of the mathematical model of white noise in continuous time. White noise is defined as a stationary random process which has a constant spectral power density. The concept of the white noise process, as given by the Einstein-Wiener theory of Brownian motion, is important in all theoretical studies of spectrum analysis.

In practice, a signal is of finite duration, and usually can be digitized on a grid fine enough for interpolation to be adequate. In this sense, the set of data representing a signal is really finite. Accordingly, we do not have to go to continuous time or to infinite time unless 1) we so wish or 2) we gain from it. In other words, as long as we stay finite, we do not need the Einstein-Weiner theory. With this *caveat emptor*, let us now discuss this theory.

A white noise process in continuous time cannot be represented by the ordinary types of mathematical functions which one meets in calculus. Instead, white noise can only be represented by what mathematicians call a *generalized function*. The most familiar example of generalized function is the *Dirac delta function*, which is often defined as

$$\delta(t - t_0) = \begin{cases} 0, & \text{for } t \neq t_0 \\ \infty, & \text{for } t = t_0 \end{cases}$$

$$\int_{-\infty}^{\infty} \delta(t - t_0) \, dt = 1.$$

The most important property of the delta function is its sifting property, that is, its ability to isolate or reproduce a particular value of an ordinary function $f(t)$ according to the convolution formula

$$\int_{-\infty}^{\infty} f(t - t_0) \, \delta(t) \, dt = f(t_0).$$

If one feels uncomfortable with generalized functions, then one can often avoid them by using Lebesgue–Stieltjes integrals. For example, the Heaviside step function $H(t)$ is an ordinary function equal to zero for $t < 0$ and to one for $t \geq 0$. Since

$$dH(t) = \delta(t) \, dt$$

the above convolution formula becomes the Lebesgue–Stieltjes integral

$$\int_{-\infty}^{\infty} f(t - t_0) \, dH(t) = f(t_0).$$

This Lebesgue–Stieltjes integral involves only ordinary functions.

Let us now look at a *white noise process* which we denote by $\epsilon(t)$. It is a generalized random function. Again let $f(t)$ be an ordinary function, and consider the convolution integral

$$\int_{-\infty}^{\infty} f(t - t_0) \, \epsilon(t) \, dt.$$

Let $\mathcal{E}(t)$ be the integrated white noise process, so that we may write

$$d\mathcal{E}(t) = \epsilon(t) \, dt.$$

The integrated white noise process $\mathcal{E}(t)$ is an ordinary random function, and the above convolution becomes the Legesgue–Stieltjes integral

$$\int_{-\infty}^{\infty} f(t - t_0) \, d\mathcal{E}(t).$$

Wiener formulated everything in terms of Lebesgue–Stieltjes integrals with ordinary functions. However, we are going to take a strictly engineering approach and formulate things in terms of ordinary integrals, but with generalized functions.

Without loss of generality in the discussion which follows, we can for convenience let $t_0 = 0$, so that the integral in question becomes

$$\int_{-\infty}^{\infty} f(t)\, \epsilon(t)\, dt.$$

As is usual statistical practice, let E denote the mathematical expectation operator. Since this operator is linear, it may be interchanged with integral signs (provided certain regularity conditions hold). The expectation of the above integral is

$$E\int_{-\infty}^{\infty} f(t)\, \epsilon(t)\, dt = \int_{-\infty}^{\infty} f(t)\, E\epsilon(t)\, dt.$$

Because we want white noise to have zero mean, we let $E\epsilon(t) = 0$, and so the above integral is zero. Let us next consider the variance given by

$$E\left[\int_{-\infty}^{\infty} f(t)\, \epsilon(t)\, dt\right]^2 = E\left[\int_{-\infty}^{\infty} f(t)\, \epsilon(t)\, dt \int_{-\infty}^{\infty} f(\tau)\, \epsilon(\tau)\, d\tau\right]$$

$$= \int_{-\infty}^{\infty} f(t)\, f(\tau)\, E[\epsilon(\tau)\, \epsilon(\tau)]\, dt\, d\tau.$$

Now we come to the key point. We want white noise to be uncorrelated at two different time points, but at the same time we want the variance of white noise to produce an impulse so as to make the above integral have a nonzero value. Thus the key element is to define the covariance $E[\epsilon(t)\, \epsilon(\tau)]$ as being equal to $\delta(t - \tau)$. Then the above integral becomes

$$\int_{-\infty}^{\infty} f(t)\, f(\tau)\, \delta(t - \tau)\, dt\, d\tau = \int_{-\infty}^{\infty} f^2(t)\, dt.$$

We can therefore make the following definition. A generalized random function $\epsilon(t)$ is white noise provided that $E\epsilon(t) = 0$ and $E\epsilon(t)\, \epsilon(\tau) = \delta(t - \tau)$. For a long time such a random process was regarded as improper. As we know, the delta function can be approximated arbitrarily close by ordinary functions. Likewise, the white noise process $\epsilon(t)$ can be approximated arbitrarily close by ordinary random processes.

Because one never uses the white noise process in isolation but only in integrals, the white noise process can be avoided by the use of the Lebesgue–Stieltjes integral, just as the Dirac delta function can be so avoided. However, as we have said, we will not follow the Lebesgue–Stieltjes approach here.

Let us now consider white noise $\epsilon(n)$ for discrete (integer) time n. White noise in discrete time is not a generalized random process, for $\epsilon(n)$ is merely a sequence of zero-mean, constant-variance, uncorrelated random variables. However, the Fourier transform of discrete white noise is a generalized random process, which we denote by $E(\omega)$. We have

$$E(\omega) = \sum_{n=-\infty}^{\infty} \epsilon(n)\, e^{-j\omega n} \qquad \text{(for } -\pi \leqslant \omega \leqslant \pi \text{)}.$$

We can easily verify that $E(\omega)$ has zero mean. The covariance of $E(\omega)$ is

$$\boldsymbol{E}[E^*(\omega)\, E(\mu)] = \boldsymbol{E} \sum_n \epsilon(n)\, e^{j\omega n} \sum_k \epsilon(k)\, e^{-j\mu k}$$

$$= \sum_n \sum_k [\boldsymbol{E}\epsilon(n)\,\epsilon(k)]\; e^{j(\omega n - \mu k)}.$$

Because $\boldsymbol{E}\epsilon(n)\,\epsilon(k) = \delta_{nk}$ (i.e., the Kronecker delta function, which is one when $n = k$ and zero otherwise), we have

$$\boldsymbol{E}[E^*(\omega)\, E(\mu)] = \sum_n \epsilon^{-jn(\mu - \omega)} = 2\pi\delta(\mu - \omega).$$

That is, the covariance is a Dirac delta function. Thus we come to an important result: The Fourier transform of a white noise process in (infinitely extended) discrete time n is a white noise process in the continuous variable ω. (It is easy to show that the corresponding result holds for the case of a white noise process in continuous time.) In other words, the Fourier transform of a very rough (white) process in time is a very rough (white) process in frequency. The Fourier transform preserves (saves) information and does not smooth (destroy) information. Today this result is second-nature to an engineer, but when Wiener obtained this result in 1923 it was startling. Wiener unlocked the spectral theory of the most random of processes (white noise), and now the stage was set for applying this result to the more smooth processes which are generated by many physical phenomena. Wiener made this application in 1930 under the name of generalized harmonic analysis, but before we give its history we will break our train of thought and look at the innovative work of Yule in 1927. Yule's work at the time seemed modest. While most mathematicians and physicists were developing general methods to deal with the infinite and the infinitesimal in spectrum analysis, Yule was developing a simple model with a finite number of parameters (i.e., a finite parameter model) in order to handle spectrum analysis in those cases where this model was appropriate. This model of Yule is known as the autoregressive (AR) process.

IX. YULE AUTOREGRESSIVE SPECTRUM ESTIMATION METHOD

At the turn of the twentieth century, Sir Arthur Schuster [17] introduced a numerical method of spectrum analysis for empirical time series. Let $x(n)$ represent the value of a time series at discrete (integer) time n. Given N observations of the time series from $n = 1$ to $n = N$, then Schuster's method consisted of computing the *periodogram* $P(\omega)$ defined as

$$P(\omega) = \frac{1}{N} |x(1) e^{-j\omega} + x(2) e^{-j\omega 2} + \cdots + x(N) e^{-j\omega N}|^2.$$

For example, suppose that the time series consists of a sinusoid of frequency ω_0 with superposed errors; then, the periodogram would show a peak at $\omega = \omega_0$. Thus by computing the periodogram, the peaks would show the location of the frequencies of the underlying sinusoidal motion. Until the work of Yule (1871–1951) in 1927 [18], the Schuster periodogram approach was the only numerical method of empirical spectrum analysis. However, many empirical time series observed in nature yielded a periodogram that was very erratic and did not exhibit any dominant peaks. This led Yule to devise his autoregressive method of spectrum analysis. In those days, empirical spectrum analysis was called the investigation of periodicities in disturbed series. His main application was the determination of the spectrum of Wolfer's sunspot time series.

G. Udny Yule in 1927 introduced the concept of a finite parameter model for a stationary random process in his fundamental paper on the investigation of the periodicities in time series with special reference to Wolfer's sunspot numbers. If we consider a curve representing a sinusoidal function of time and superpose on the ordinate small random errors, then the only effect is to make the graph somewhat irregular, leaving the suggestion of periodicity still quite clear to the eye. If the errors are increased in magnitude, the graph becomes more irregular, the suggestion of periodicity more obscure, and we have only sufficiently to increase the errors to mask completely any appearance of periodicity. But, however large the errors, Schuster's periodogram analysis is applicable to such a time series, and given a sufficient number of observations should yield a close approximation to the period and amplitude of the underlying sinusoidal wave.

Yule reasoned in the following way. Consider a case in which periodogram analysis is applied to a time series generated by some physical phenomenon in the expectation of eliciting one or more true periodicities. Then it seemed to Yule that in such a case there would be a tendency to start with the initial hypothesis that the true periodicities are masked solely by additive random noise. As we well know, additive random noise does not in any way disturb the steady course of the underlying sinusoidal function or functions. It is true that the periodogram itself will indicate the truth or otherwise of the hypothesis made, but Yule saw no reason for assuming it to be the hypothesis most likely *a priori*.

At this point, Yule introduced the concept of an input-output feed-back model. The amplitude of a simple harmonic pendulum with damping (in discrete approximation) can be represented by the homogeneous difference equation

$$b(n) + a_1 b(n - 1) + a_2 b(n - 2) = 0.$$

Here $b(n)$ is the amplitude at discrete (integer) time n. Errors of observation would cause superposed fluctuations on $b(n)$, but Yule observed that, by improvement of apparatus and automatic methods of recording, errors of observation can be practically eliminated: An initial impulse or disturbance would set the pendulum in motion, and the solution of the difference equation would give the impulse response. The initial conditions are $b(n) = 0$ for $n < 0$ and $b(0) = 1$. The characteristic equation of the difference equation is

$$E^2 + a_1 E + a_2 = 0.$$

From physical considerations, we know that the impulse response is a damped oscillation, so the roots E_1 and E_2 of the characteristic equation must be complex with magnitude less than one. This condition is equivalent to the condition that $a_2 < 1$ and $4a_2 - a_1^2 > 0$. The solution of the difference equation thus comes out to be

$$b(n) = e^{\lambda n} \frac{\sin(n + 1)\, \omega_0}{\sin \omega_0}$$

where

$$\lambda = 0.5 \ln a_2$$

$$\omega_0 = \tan^{-1}[-a_1^{-1} \sqrt{4a_2 - a_1^2}].$$

The damped oscillation $b(n)$ is the impulse response function. The frequency ω_0 is the fundamental frequency of the impulse response function.

As we mentioned above, Yule ruled out superposed errors. Now, however, he allows a driving function (or input) of white noise, which he describes in the following way. The apparatus is left to itself, and unfortunately boys get into the room and start pelting the pendulum with peas, sometimes from one side and sometimes from the other. He states that the motion is now affected, not by superposed fluctuations, but by driving disturbances. As a result, the graph will be of an entirely different kind than a graph in the case of a sinusoid with super-posed errors. The pendulum and pea graph will remain sur-prisingly smooth, but amplitude and phase will vary con-tinuously, as governed by the inhomogeneous difference equation

$$x(n) + a_1 x(n-1) + a_2 x(n-2) = \epsilon(n)$$

where $\epsilon(n)$ is the white noise input. The solution of this dif-ference equation is

$$x(n) = \sum_{k=0}^{\infty} b(k)\,\epsilon(n-k)$$

where $b(k)$ is the impulse response function given above.

Yule thus created a model with a finite number of param-eters, namely, the coefficients a_1 and a_2 of the difference equation. Given an empirical time series $x(n)$, he uses the method of regression analysis to find these two coefficients. Because he regresses $x(n)$ on its own past instead of on other variables, it is a self-regression or *autoregression*. The least squares normal equations involve the empirical autocorrelation coefficients of the time series, and today these equations are called the *Yule–Walker equations*.

Yule carried out his autoregressive analysis on Wolfer's sun-spot numbers, which are a sequence of yearly observations of sunspot observations. He used the numbers over the period 1749–1924 and obtained the autoregressive equation (with the mean value removed)

$$x(n) - 1.34254\,x(n-1) + 0.65504\,x(n-2) = \epsilon(n)$$

and thus

$$\lambda = 0.5 \ln 0.65504 = -0.21154$$

$$\omega_0 = 33.963° \text{ per year.}$$

Hence, the dominant period is $360°/\omega_0 = 10.60$ years. Yule states that his autoregressive method represents an alternative method of estimating the spectrum, as opposed to the Schuster periodogram. In fact, his autoregressive model gives him an estimate not only of the power spectrum but of an amplitude-and-phase spectrum

$$B(\omega) = \sum_{n=0}^{\infty} b(n)\,e^{-j\omega n} = \frac{1}{1 + a_1 e^{-j\omega} + a_2 e^{-2j\omega}}$$

which, for the sunspot numbers, is

$$B(\omega) = \frac{1}{1 - 1.34254\,e^{-j\omega} + 0.65504\,e^{-2j\omega}} \,.$$

The magnitude $|B(\omega)|$ and the phase $\theta(\omega)$ are given by the equation

$$B(\omega) = |B(\omega)|e^{j\theta(\omega)}.$$

The power spectrum is the square of the magnitude spectrum, that is, $|B(\omega)|^2$. The peak is close to the fundamental frequency $\omega_0 = 33.963°$ per year. Except in exploration geophysics [19], [20], where Yule's amplitude-and-phase spectrum $B(\omega)$ is physically the spectrum of the minimum-delay seismic wavelet, Yule's spectral estimation method received scant attention until the 1960's.

X. Wiener's Generalized Harmonic Analysis

Norbert Wiener [21] published in 1930 his classic paper, "Generalized Harmonic Analysis," which he personally considered his finest work. In his introduction, he states that he

NORBERT WIENER
1894-1964

was motivated by the work of researchers in optics, especially that of Rayleigh and Schuster. However, Wiener demonstrated that the domain of generalized harmonic analysis was much broader than optics. Among Wiener's results were the writing down of the precise definitions of and the relationship between the autocovariance function and the power spectrum. The theorem that these two functions make up a Fourier transform pair is today known as the Wiener–Khintchine theorem [22].

Mention should be made of the basic fact that the existence of the spectrum follows from the properties of positive definite functions. Bochner's theorem on the spectral representation of positive definite functions provides a direct mathematical unification of spectral theories in Hilbert space and in stationary time series.

The writer several times in the 1950's discussed with Professor Wiener why his 1930 paper was not more accepted and used by the mathematical profession at the time. As with all things, Wiener looked at history quite objectively and with his characteristic concern for and love of people. In retrospect, it seems it was not until the publication of Wiener's book *Cybernetics* [23] in 1948 and also the nonclassified publication of his book *Time Series* [24] in 1949 that the general scientific community was able to grasp the overall plan and implications of Wiener's contributions.

The following passage from Wiener's 1933 book *The Fourier Integral* [25] indicates the philosophy of Wiener's thinking and his great personal appeal:

"Physically speaking, this is the total energy of that portion of the oscillation lying within the interval in question. As this determines the energy-distribution of the spectrum, we may briefly call it the "spectrum." The author sees no compelling reason to avoid a physical terminology in pure mathematics when a mathematical concept corresponds closely to a concept already familiar in physics. When a new term is to be invented to describe an idea new to the pure mathematician, it is by all means better to avoid needless duplication, and to choose the designation already current. The "spectrum" of this book merely amounts to rendering precise the notion familiar to the physicist, and may as well be known by the same name."

Let us now define a stationary random process. We could either use discrete or continuous time, but for convenience let us use discrete (integer) time n. Let the process be denoted by $x(n)$, which, we will assume, has zero mean. The process is called (second-order) stationary, provided that its autocovariance function

$$\phi(k) = \boldsymbol{E} x^*(n) \, x(n+k)$$

depends only upon the time-shift k. Here, as always, the superscript asterisk indicates complex-conjugate. The normalized autocovariance function is called the autocorrelation function. However, Wiener generally used the term autocorrelation for $\phi(k)$, whether it was normalized or not. Nevertheless, it is confusing to keep using the term "autocorrelation" with two different meanings. It is better to use the term "autocovariance" wherever it is appropriate.

A white noise process is stationary. In the case of continuous time, its autocorrelation is $\delta(t)$ (the Dirac delta), whereas in the case of discrete time, its autocorrelation is δ_k (the Kronecker delta). As we have seen, the Fourier transform $E(\omega)$ of white noise in time is white in frequency; that is, the autocorrelation in frequency is the Dirac delta function

$$\boldsymbol{E} E^*(\omega) \, E(\omega + \mu) = 2\pi\delta(\mu).$$

The problems confronting empirical workers in spectral analysis in the first part of the twentieth century were centered around the Schuster periodogram. Schuster introduced this concept at the turn of the century, and until Yule's work in 1927, it was the only method available to carry out empirical spectral analysis. Suppose that we observe a stationary random process for a very long time, so that we obtain a time series $x(n)$ for $n = 1, 2, \cdots, N$, where N is very large. Schuster then computed the periodogram

$$P(\omega) = \frac{1}{N} \, |X(\omega)|^2$$

where $X(\omega)$ is the discrete Fourier transform

$$X(\omega) = \sum_{n=1}^{N} x(n) \, e^{-j\omega n}.$$

(Today we can compute $X(\omega)$ very rapidly by means of the Cooley–Tukey fast Fourier transform, but then it was a formidable task.) In the case when the stationary process is made up of sinusoidal waves with superimposed white noise, the periodogram is effective in picking out the discrete frequencies of the sinusoids. But a purely nondeterministic stationary process is generated by the convolution formula (input–output relation)

$$x(n) = \sum_{k=0}^{\infty} b(k) \, \epsilon(n-k).$$

(Here we interpret $b(k)$ as the impulse response function of a filter, the white noise process $\epsilon(n)$ as the input to the filter, and the stationary process $x(n)$ as the output). For such a process, the Schuster periodogram $P(\omega)$ is extremely rough, and often cannot readily be interpreted. Empirical spectral analysis was at an impasse. Most of the time series observed in nature could not be analyzed by the methods available in 1930.

Now comes Wiener in 1930 with generalized harmonic analysis. In brief, Wiener in 1930 knew how to take the Fourier transform of a stationary random process, a milestone in the use of Fourier methods. Wiener's generalized harmonic analysis makes use of a generalized random function, namely, the Einstein–Wiener (white noise) process. In order to put Wiener's work into context, we will now give a small digression on the most widely known generalized function: the Dirac delta function.

The *impulse (Dirac delta) function* had been known for many years prior to its use by Dirac [26] in 1928. It was known by Heaviside [27]. However, it took the stature of a great physicist, Paul Dirac, to decree in 1928 the use of the impulse function in physics. In those early days, people used to talk about $\delta(t)$ as a function of t in the ordinary sense whose integral with $f(t)$ produces $f(0)$; that is,

$$\int_{-\infty}^{\infty} \delta(t) f(t) \, dt = f(0).$$

This idea used to cause great distress to mathematicians, some of whom even declared that Dirac was wrong despite the fact that he kept getting consistent and useful results. The physicists rejected these extreme criticisms and followed their intuition. We can now see why the physicists succeeded despite the reservations of the mathematicians. It is true that the physicists spoke of $\delta(t)$ as an ordinary function, which it cannot be in any precise sense, and that they treated it as an ordinary function by integrating it and even differentiating it. But the physicists were justified because they only used $\delta(t)$ inside integrals with sufficiently-differentiable functions $f(t)$. For example, the derivative of $\delta(t)$ always appeared inside an integral, and the integral was integrated by parts as follows:

$$\int_{-\infty}^{\infty} \delta'(t) f(t) \, dt = - \int_{-\infty}^{\infty} \delta(t) f'(t) \, dt = -f'(0).$$

The physicists never used the delta function except to map functions to real numbers. In this sense, they employed the machinery but not the words of distribution theory, which was devised expressly in order to give delta functions a sound basis. It was the French mathematician L. Schwartz who after World War II created a systematic theory of generalized functions and explained it in his well-known monograph *Théorie des Distributions* in 1950 and 1951. From then on the theory of generalized functions was developed intensively by many mathematicians. This precipitate development of distribution theory received its main stimulus from the requirements of mathematics and theoretical physics, in particular the theory of differential equations and quantum physics. Generalized functions possess a number of remarkable properties that extend the capabilities of classical mathematical analysis. For example, any generalized function turns out to be infinitely differentiable (in the generalized meaning), convergent series of generalized functions may be differentiated termwise an infinite number of times, the Fourier transform of a generalized function always exists, and so on. For this reason, the uses of generalized function techniques substantially expand the range of problems that can be tackled and leads to appreciable simplifications that make otherwise difficult operations automatic.

As science advances, its theoretical statements seem to require an ever higher level of mathematics. When he gave his theoretical prediction of the existence of antiparticles in 1931 (*Proc. Roy. Soc. London, Ser.* A, vol. 133, pp. 60–72) Dirac wrote, "It seems likely that this process of increasing abstraction will continue in the future and that advance in physics is to be associated with a continual modification and generalization of the axioms at the base of mathematics rather than with a logical development of any one mathematical scheme on a fixed foundation." Subsequent developments in theoretical physics have corroborated this view. In this essay, we have seen that since the time of Newton, the search for and the study of mathematical models of physical phenomena have made it necessary to resort to a wide range of mathematical tools and have thus stimulated the development of various areas of mathematics. Now let us return to Norbert Wiener in 1930.

Physicists are concerned with unlocking the mysteries of nature, and the impulse (Dirac delta) function eases their task. The impulse function is the simplest of the generalized functions. One can imagine the plight of Wiener in the mathematical community when he introduced generalized random functions into the mathematical literature as early as 1923, and especially in his 1930 paper.

Let us now give the gist of Wiener's *generalized harmonic analysis*. As we know, convolution in the time domain corresponds to multiplication in the frequency domain. Thus in terms of Fourier transforms, the above input–output convolution integral becomes

$$X(\omega) = B(\omega) E(\omega).$$

In this equation, $E(\omega)$ is the Fourier transform of white noise, so that $E(\omega)$ is a generalized function that is white (i.e., very rough) in frequency. The filter's transfer function $B(\omega)$ is a smooth well-behaved (ordinary) function. The product $X(\omega)$ is also very rough.

Let us now take the inverse Fourier transform of $X(\omega)$. It is

$$x(n) = \frac{1}{2\pi} \int_{-\pi}^{\pi} e^{j\omega n} X(\omega) \, d\omega$$

which is

$$x(n) = \frac{1}{2\pi} \int_{-\pi}^{\pi} e^{j\omega n} B(\omega) E(\omega) \, d\omega.$$

This formula represents Wiener's generalized harmonic analysis of $x(n)$; that is, it is the *spectral representation* of the stationary random process $x(n)$. It involves the smooth filter transfer function $B(\omega)$ and the very rough (white in frequency) process $E(\omega)$. We thus see that the spectral representation requires Wiener's generalized random function $E(\omega)$, which came out of his studies of Brownian movement.

Wiener's generalized harmonic analysis (i.e., spectral representation) explains why the periodogram of Schuster did not work for convolutional processes. Because the periodogram (as the number of observations becomes large) is

$$P(\omega) = \frac{1}{N} |X(\omega)|^2$$

it follows that the periodogram has the intrinsic roughness of the $X(\omega)$ process. (It was not until the work of J. Tukey [34] in 1949 that a means was found to overcome this problem; Tukey's breakthrough was of epoch proportions.)

Wiener in his 1930 paper gave the following method, which was standard until the work of Tukey in 1949. Wiener's method was intended for very long time series. It consisted of computing the autocovariance function as the time average

$$\phi(k) = \frac{1}{N} \sum_{n} x^*(n) \, x(n+k)$$

for $-p \leqslant k \leqslant p$, where p is less than the data length N, and then computing the power spectrum $\Phi(\omega)$ as the Fourier transform

$$\Phi(\omega) = \sum_{k=-p}^{p} \phi(k) \, e^{-j\omega k}.$$

This Fourier transform relationship between autocovariance and power spectrum, as we have observed, is now called the *Wiener–Khinchin* theorem.

Whereas von Neumann's work in quantum physics in 1929 received instant acclaim and well-deserved recognition by physicists and mathematicians, Wiener's work in 1930 lay dormant. However, now with the benefit of hindsight, it is worthwhile for us to reconcile these two approaches to spectral estimation. This we will do in the next section.

XI. RECONCILIATION OF THE TWO SPECTRAL THEORIES

We have come a long way in the history of spectral estimation to this point. From the work of the ancients in deriving a calendar, to the work of the great mathematicians who formulated the wave equation in the eighteenth century, it took thousands of years. Then the work of Bernoulli, Euler, and Fourier came, and the result was a spectral theory in terms of sinusoidal functions, in place at the beginning of the nineteenth century. The theory was extended to the case of arbitrary orthogonal functions by Sturm and Liouville, and this led to the greatest empirical success of spectral analysis yet obtained: the physical results of spectral estimation that unlocked the secret of the atom. Credit for this result belongs to Heisenberg and Schrödinger in 1925 and 1926. Then in 1929, the work of von Neumann put the spectral theory of the atom on a firm mathematical foundation in his spectral representation theorem. The spectral work of von Neumann represents the cumulation of this line of research in quantum physics. Meanwhile, Rayleigh and Schuster at the beginning of the twentieth century were applying the original sinusoidal methods of Fourier to the analysis of data in the realm of classical physics. However, the periodogram approach of Schuster did not work well for purely nondeterministic stationary random processes, and this led Yule in 1927 to develop a spectral theory for a subclass known as autoregressive processes. Meanwhile, Wiener had developed the mathematical theory of Brownian movement in 1923, and in 1930 he introduced generalized harmonic analysis, that is, the spectral representation of a stationary random process. Thus in 1930, we have two spectral theories, one represented by the spectral representation theorem of von Neumann and the other by the spectral representation theorem of Wiener. It is the purpose of this section, with the benefit of hindsight, of course, to indicate the relationship between von Neumann and Wiener spectral theories.

The common ground is the Hilbert space. As we have seen, the von Neumann result is the spectral representation of a Hermitian operator H in Hilbert space. The Schrödinger equation is written in terms of a Hermitian operator, and this equation governs the spectrum of atoms and molecules. Now let us, however, leave this Hilbert space and look at another one. The other Hilbert space is one defined by the probability measure that governs the stationary random process in question. As we know, a Hilbert space is specified by an inner (or dot) product. The elements of the Hilbert space are random variables, and the inner product is defined as the expected value given by

$$\langle x, y \rangle = E x^* y.$$

(The superscript asterisk indicates the complex conjugate.) In this Hilbert space, a stationary process is defined as follows. We use discrete (integer) time n, although a similar development can be made in the case of continuous time. A sequence of random variables $x(n)$ in Hilbert space is called a *stationary random process* if its autocorrelation

$$\phi(k) = \langle x(n), x(n + k) \rangle$$

depends only upon the time-shift k and not on absolute time n. This definition implies that the elements $x(n)$ of the process are generated recursively by a unitary operator; that is,

$$U x(n) = x(n + 1)$$

so that

$$x(n + k) = U^k x(n).$$

Because a unitary operator represents a rotation, we see that a stationary random process traces out a spiral in Hilbert space, the so-called *Wiener spiral*. We now come to the connection that we are seeking, namely, the fact that the Cayley–Möbius transformation [28] of a Hermitian operator is a unitary operator. Thus there is a one-to-one correspondence between Hermitian operators and unitary operators in Hilbert space. The von Neumann spectral representation is for a Hermitian operator. If we take its Cayley–Möbius transformation, we obtain the corresponding spectral representation for the unitary operator U. This spectral representation has the form

$$U = \frac{1}{2\pi} \int_{-\pi}^{\pi} e^{j\omega} \mathcal{U}(\omega) \, d\omega$$

where $\mathcal{U}(\omega)$ represents a family of projection operators as a function of circular frequency ω. Thus the process has the representation

$$x(n) = U^n x(0) = \frac{1}{2\pi} \int_{-\pi}^{\pi} e^{j\omega n} \mathfrak{U}(\omega)\, x(0)\, d\omega.$$

We now make the identification

$$\mathfrak{U}(\omega)\, x(0) = X(\omega)$$

and we obtain

$$x(n) = \frac{1}{2\pi} \int_{-\pi}^{\pi} e^{j\omega n} X(\omega)\, d\omega.$$

This equation is Wiener's generalized harmonic analysis of the process. Thus we have the connection we sought; the two spectral representations are related by the Cayley–Möbius transformation.

XII. WIENER-LEVINSON PREDICTION THEORY

Early in 1940, Wiener became involved in defense work at MIT and, in particular, he became interested in the design of fire-control apparatus for anti-aircraft guns. The problem was to build into the control system of the gun some mechanical device to aim the gun automatically. The problem, in effect, was made up of two parts: a mathematical part, which consisted of predicting the future position of an airplane from its observed past positions, and an engineering part, which consisted of realizing the mathematical solution in the form of an actual physical device. Wiener recognized that it was not possible to develop a perfect universal predictor, and so he formulated the mathematical problem on a statistical basis. He defined the optimum predictor as the one that minimizes the mean-square prediction error. The minimization led to the Wiener–Hopf integral equation, which represented the completion of the mathematical part of the problem. As to the engineering part, Wiener immediately recognized that it was possible to devise a hardware apparatus that represents the solution to the Wiener–Hopf equation. As Wiener [29] states in his autobiography (p. 245): "It was not hard to devise apparatus to realize in the metal what we had figured out on paper. All that we had to do was make a quite simple assembly of electric inductances, voltage resistances, and capacitors, acting on a small electric motor of the sort which you can buy from any instrument company." Wiener's mathematical results [24] were published in 1942 as a classified report to Section D2 of the National Defense Research Committee. This report is Wiener's famous *Time Series* book, which we mentioned previously. Its full title is *Extrapolation, Interpolation, and Smoothing of Stationary Time Series with*

Engineering Applications, and it was republished as an unrestricted document in 1949 by MIT Press, Cambridge.

Although Wiener's "General Harmonic Analysis" did not have immediate influence, his *Time Series* book, which was written in a more understandable style, did among those who had access to the book in 1942 and the general public in 1949. As we will now see, a great deal of credit for the dissemination of Wiener's ideas belongs to his former student and his colleague, Professor N. Levinson.

Levinson's initial contact with Wiener was in Wiener's course in 1933–34 on Fourier Series and Integrals, which is described in Levinson's own words as follows:

"I became acquainted with Wiener in September 1933 while still an undergraduate student of electrical engineering, when I enrolled in his graduate course. It was at that time really a seminar course. At that level he was a most stimulating teacher. He would actually carry out his research at the blackboard. As soon as I displayed a slight comprehension of what he was doing, he handed me the manuscript of Paley–Wiener for revision. I found a gap in a proof and proved a lemma to set it right. Wiener thereupon set down at his typewriter, typed my lemma, affixed my name and sent it off to a journal. A prominent professor does not often act as a secretary for a young student."

N. Levinson, a dynamic and brilliant mathematician and a warm and kind person, made important and permanent contributions to engineering and applied science. The Levinson theorem in quantum mechanics illustrates his ability to grasp the relationship between physical concepts and mathematical structure. Few have this insight, and nowhere is it better demonstrated than in the two expository papers written in 1942 by Levinson soon after the restricted publication of Wiener's *Time Series* book. These two papers were published in 1947 in the *Journal of Mathematical Physics*, and thus they represented the first public disclosure of Wiener's time series results. Later these two papers also appeared as Appendices C and B in the unrestricted publication of Wiener's book in 1949 by MIT Press [24].

An appreciation of Levinson's contribution can be gained in historical perspective. The 1942 edition of Wiener's book was bound in a yellow paper cover, and because of its difficult mathematics, it came to be known among engineers as the "yellow peril" (a term familiar to mathematicians as applying to a famous series of advanced texts). However clear in a conceptual way the building of an actual device was to Wiener, there were few engineers at that time who were able to grasp

Wiener's mathematical solution, much less to realize it in the form of a physical device. At this point, Levinson stepped in and wrote "A heuristic exposition of Wiener's mathematical theory of prediction and filtering," [30], one of his two classic applied papers on explaining Wiener's work. Levinson describes his paper as an expository account of Wiener's theory. Levinson's earlier training was in electrical engineering, so he understood hardware design methods. In the paper, Levinson shows in an elementary way why the Wiener–Hopf equation cannot be solved by use of the Fourier transform theorem. Then, in a natural way, he introduces the spectral factorization and obtains the explicit solution for the prediction operator and, more generally, for the filter operator. This masterpiece of exposition opened up these methods to the engineering profession.

Levinson's other classic applied paper is entitled, "The Wiener RMS (root mean square) error criterion in filter design and prediction." [31] As before, let us try to put this paper in historical perspective. In 1942, the Army Air Force Weather Division negotiated a contract with MIT to perform statistical analyses of meteorological and climatological data, particularly in relationship to weather forecasting, and to conduct research into the application of statistical techniques to long-range forecasting [32]. Professor G. P. Wadsworth of the MIT Mathematics Department was in charge of this meteorological project. The basic idea was to collect and sort large amounts of numerical meteorological data and to forecast by analogy, much like the forecasts made on television today, in which the weatherman looks at the data appearing on the satellite picture of the earth. Wadsworth's method had merit, but the data required was just not available in the 1940's. Wiener's *Time Series* book was completed at about the same time as this MIT Meteorological Project was starting up. Since the weather data available occurred at discrete intervals of time, the continuous-time methods of Wiener were not directly applicable. As a result, Wadsworth asked Levinson to write up a discrete form of Wiener's theory. The result was Levinson's "Wiener RMS" paper with the Levinson recursion. However, use was never made of Wiener–Levinson prediction theory by the MIT Meteorological Project, and Levinson's paper sat dormant.

In order to understand why Levinson's methods were not used in the 1940's, one must look at the computing facilities available at the time. The actual realization of these methods would have to be carried out by people using hand calculators. A hand calculator could add, subtract, multiply, and divide, but had no memory except an accumulator. Thus the result of each separate calculation had to be transferred to paper by hand, a drawn-out, time-consuming process. In contrast to the hardware devices working in real time, as envisaged by Wiener, the hand calculator was a poor substitute. As Wiener [24, p. 102] states: "Much less important, though of real interest, is the problem of the numerical filter for statistical work, as contrasted with the filter as a physically active piece of engineering apparatus."

After Levinson wrote his two expository papers, which were completed in 1942, neither he nor Wiener took up research in the computational (software) aspect of Wiener's theory. Wiener was more interested in its realization by machines (hardware), and his research interest was already shifting to biological and medical problems. In fact, it was the union of these two research interests that led to his discovery and formulation of the science of cybernetics, which he describes as the problem of control and communication in machines and animals. Meanwhile Levinson had decided as early as 1940 to shift his field from the Fourier methods of Wiener to the field of nonlinear differential equations. He talked about this decision with his friends in 1940. Levinson worked hard over a period of two or three years (which included the period during which he wrote the two expository papers) before he felt that he had enough mastery in his new field. Such mastery he did achieve, and his outstanding contributions to differential equations were recognized by his receiving the prestigious Bocher Prize in Mathematics in 1954.

Despite their other research interests, both Wiener and Levinson were always ready to give their support and time to the MIT Meteorological Project directed by G. P. Wadsworth. Wiener was especially interested in seeing physical examples of autocorrelation functions. This interest led to the computation of several autocorrelation functions of ocean wave data by Wadsworth and by his friend and associate H. R. Seiwell [33], who was with the Woods Hole Oceanographic Institution. The interest in these computations led to the "Symposium on Autocorrelation Analysis Applied to Physical Problems" held at Woods Hole, MA in June 1949, sponsored by the Office of Naval Research. The high point of this meeting was the paper by Tukey [34]. Before Tukey's work, the power spectra computed from empirical autocorrelation functions were too erratic to be of any use in formulating physical hypotheses. Not only did Tukey show correctly how to compute power spectra from empirical data, but he also laid the statistical framework for the analysis of short-time series, as opposed to the very long ones envisaged by Wiener and Levinson.

Wadsworth was also director of the MIT section of the U.S. Naval Operations Evaluation Group, a project started in World War II which initiated the use of operations research in the

United States. By 1950, Wadsworth was applying operations research methods to industry and had established himself as one of the highest paid consultants in the United States. There were so many industrial people waiting to see him in his outer office at MIT that one had to make an appointment with his secretary many weeks in advance to see him in his inner office for just 5 or 10 minutes at the most. The writer began as one of Wadsworth's research assistants in the MIT Mathematics Department in September 1950, and he was assigned to work in seismology by Professor Wadsworth. Mobil Oil made available eight seismic records, and the writer immediately got a very lonely feeling, especially at MIT at night digitizing the Mobil seismic records with a ruler and pencil. Except for Wadsworth, in 1950 nobody at MIT or in the oil industry thought that the analysis of digital seismic data would ever be feasible.

Fortunately Tukey took an interest in the seismic project and conveyed his research ideas by mail. The first empirical results were the computation of the Tukey spectra for various sections of the Mobil records in the spring of 1951. From these spectral results, a seismic analysis based on prediction error was formulated in the summer of 1951. This analysis made use of Wiener prediction theory in digital form. Prior to this work, Wiener's procedures had only been realized in analog form. In hand plotting the first numerical results of what today is called linear predictive coding (LPC), the writer was so amazed that he could not believe his eyes, and he was sure that he would never see such good results again. But the second trace, and the third trace, and so on, were computed and confirmed what he saw. The digital processing method called deconvolution worked! As soon as possible, he made an appointment to see Wadsworth, which the secretary set three weeks from then, in September 1951. The result was that the digitally-processed seismic traces [35] were sent out to the oil industry, and the oil companies gave money to support a project. The MIT Geophysical Analysis Group was thus born, and the MIT Whirlwind digital computer was used to analyze seismic records throughout the lifetime of the GAG (1952–1957). During this period, Tukey freely gave his research advice [36], [37]. For example, Tukey's methods for estimating coherency (today called by various names, such as "semblance" by the oil industry) are vital in the estimation of seismic velocity as well as in other multichannel methods. Tukey's vision of a fast Fourier transform was always influential. In fact, S. M. Simpson [38], who later directed the Geophysical Analysis Group, eventually devised an efficient 24-point Fourier transform, which was a precursor to the Cooley–Tukey fast Fourier transform in 1965. The FFT made all of Simpson's efficient autocorrelation and spectrum programs instantly obsolete, on which he had worked the equivalent of half a lifetime. Wiener was very generous of his time [39]. Wiener's work [40], [41] on multichannel methods was helpful later in extending the Levinson recursion, which Levinson had devised for single channel time series, to the multichannel case [42]. The excellent seismic data and corresponding well logs supplied by the oil industry to the Geophysical Analysis Group made possible the development of the statistical minimum-delay model of the earth's stratigraphic layers, together with the theoretical justification of seismic deconvolution [19], [43].

In the late 1950's a digital revolution occurred because of the introduction of transistors in the building of digital computers, which made possible reliable computers at a much lower cost than previously. As a result, the seismic industry completely converted to digital technology in the early 1960's, a long ten years after the first digital results were obtained. Since then, nearly every seismic record taken in the exploration of oil and natural gas has been digitally deconvolved and otherwise digitally processed by these methods. The final result of the digital processing of seismic data was the discovery of great oil fields which could not be found by analog methods. These oil fields include most of the offshore discoveries, as in the North Sea, the Gulf of Mexico, the Persian Gulf, as well as great onshore discoveries in Alaska, Asia, Africa, Latin America, and the Middle East, made in the last twenty years. Today an oil company will deconvolve and process as many as one million seismic traces per day; it took a whole summer in 1951 to do 32 traces.

Whereas the digital revolution came first to the geophysical industry largely because of the tremendous accuracy and flexibility afforded by large digital computers, today we are in the midst of a universal digital revolution of epic proportions. One now realizes that the work of Wiener and Levinson is being appreciated and used by an ever-increasing number of people. Digital signal processing is a growing and dynamic field which involves the exploration of new technology and the application of the techniques to new fields. The technology has advanced from discrete semiconductor components to very large-scale integration (VLSI) with densities above 100 000 components per silicon chip. The availability of fast, low-cost microprocessors and custom high-density integrated circuits means that increasingly difficult and complex mathematical methods can be reduced to hardware devices as originally envisaged by Wiener, except the devices are digital instead of analog. For example, a custom VLSI implementation of linear predictive coding is now possible, requiring a small number of custom chips. Whereas originally digital methods were used at great expense only because the application demanded high flexibility and accuracy, we have now reached the point that anticipated long-term cost advantages have become a significant factor for the use of digital rather than analog methods.

XIII. TUKEY EMPIRICAL SPECTRAL ANALYSIS

As we have mentioned, a turning point in the empirical analysis of time series data began in 1949 at the Woods Hole Symposium on Applications of Autocorrelation Analysis. There Tukey presented the first of three papers [34], [36], [37], which he had written in the early years on spectrum analysis. These papers introduced the classic Tukey method of numerical spectral estimation, a method that has been used by most workers since that time. In addition, Tukey described an approximate distribution for the estimate. This distribution was required for the proper design of experiments for the collection of time series data. In a very interesting paper [44], Tukey describes the situation which led to his spectral work, including a discussion of Hamming's suggestion about the smoothing of the discrete Fourier transform of an empirical autocorrelation, which led to the joint work of Hamming and Tukey.

During the last four decades, Tukey [45]–[50] introduced a multitude of terms and techniques that are standard to the practice of the data analysis of time series. Such commonplace terms and concepts as "prewhitening," "aliasing," "smoothing and decimation," "tapering," "bispectrum," "complex demodulation," and "cepstrum" are due to Tukey. Very few papers in the literature of applied time series analysis do not give some acknowledgment of Tukey's ideas and methods, and most papers credit his ideas in some vital way. Moreover, Tukey [51]–[55] has made substantial contributions in the placing of the data analysis of time series into perspective with current research in the physical sciences, in statistics, and in computing and numerical analysis.

We have already mentioned the key influence Tukey had on the MIT group, which included Wadsworth, Simpson, the writer, and others. W. J. Pierson and L. J. Tick [56] at New York University used Tukey's methods in the analysis of oceanographic time series records. The outstanding thesis of Goodman [57], which extended the results of Tukey to the bivariate case, was written under Tukey's supervision. The group at La Jolla, CA, which included Munk, Rudnick, and Snodgrass, applied Tukey's spectral methods to estimate wave motion due to storms many thousands of miles away; a testimony to the power of his methods. Munk and McDonald wrote a remarkable book, *The Rotation of the Earth* [58], which used these spectral methods in several novel ways.

In this period, packages of computer programs for time series analysis were appearing. The collection of programs by Healy [59] of Bell Laboratories were circulated from 1960 on. The BOMM collection of programs [60] was developed at La Jolla. Some of the programs used by Parzen were included in his book [61]. The programs written at MIT are described in [38] and [62].

In econometrics, Granger's book [63] in 1964 described many of the techniques suggested by Tukey for the analysis of univariate and bivariate time series. The most successful application of spectrum techniques to economic series is its use for the description of the multitude of procedures of seasonal adjustment. In astronomy, Neyman and Scott [64] in 1958 carried out the analysis of two-dimensional data consisting of the positions of the images of galaxies on photographic plates.

Norbert Wiener remained active until his death in 1964. His later work included both empirical results, such as modeling and analyzing brain waves [66], [67], and theoretical results, such as his work with Masani on multivariate prediction theory [40], [41]. Wiener's death marks the end of an era in time series analysis and spectral theory.

XIV. THE COOLEY–TUKEY FAST FOURIER TRANSFORM

The present epoch of time series analysis began in 1965 with the publication of the fast Fourier transform by Cooley and Tukey [68]. The effect that this paper has had on scientific and engineering practice cannot be overstated. The paper described an algorithm for the discrete Fourier transform of $T = T_1 \cdots T_p$ values by means of $T(T_1 + \cdots + T_p)$ multiplications instead of the naive number T^2. Although such algorithms existed previously [69], they seem not to have been put to much use. Sande developed a distinct, symmetrically related algorithm simultaneously and independently.

The existence of such an algorithm meant, for example, that the following things could be computed an order of magnitude more rapidly: spectrum estimates, correlograms, filtered versions of series, complex demodulates, and Laplace transforms (see, for example, [70]). General discussions of the uses and importance of fast Fourier transform algorithms may be found in [71] and [72]. The Fourier transform of an observed stretch of series can now be taken as a basic statistic and classical statistical analyses—such as multiple regression, analysis of variance, principal components, canonical analysis, errors in variables, and discrimination—can be meaningfully applied to its values, [73] and references cited therein. Higher-order spectra may be computed practically [74]. Inexpensive portable computers for carrying out spectral analysis have appeared on the market and may be found in many small laboratories.

The years since 1965 have been characterized by the knowledge that there are fast Fourier transform algorithms. They have also been characterized by the rapid spread of type of data analyzed. Previously, the data analyzed consisted almost totally of discrete or continuous real-valued time series. Now the joint analysis of many series, such as the 625 recorded by the Large Aperture Seismic Array in Montana [75], has become common. Spatial series are analyzed [75]. The statistical analysis of point processes has grown into an entirely separate field [76]. The SASE IV computer program developed by Peter Lewis [77] has furthered such analysis considerably. We note that transforms other than the Fourier are finding interest as well [78], [79].

XV. BURG MAXIMUM ENTROPY SPECTRAL ANALYSIS

The discrete Fourier transform of the autocovariance is called the power spectrum. Thus the power spectrum of a stationary time series with autocovariance $\phi(n)$ is

$$\Phi(\omega) = \sum_{n=-\infty}^{\infty} \phi(n) e^{-j\omega n} \quad \text{(for } -\pi \leqslant \omega \leqslant \pi). \quad (1)$$

In this discussion, we do not require the autocovariance to be normalized, so $\phi(0)$ does not have to be one. If we know the entire autocovariance function, that is, if we know $\phi(n)$ for all values of n, then, of course, we can obtain the power spectrum by means of (1). However, in many applications, we know or can reliably measure the autocovariance only for a certain finite number of values of n, say for $n = 0, 1, 2, \cdots, p$. Because the autocovariance is symmetrical $\phi(n) = \phi(-n)$, we thus know the values of $\phi(n)$ for $n = 0, \pm 1, \pm 2, \cdots, \pm p$, and we do not know $\phi(n)$ for $|n| > p$. The question is how should we estimate the power spectrum (1) from only this partial knowledge.

In order to answer this question, we should first consider the phenomenon under study. As there are many different types of phenomena, there is a corresponding diversity in spectrum analysis. Brillinger and Tukey state that no distinction is more vital than that among a) noise-like processes, b) signal-like processes, and c) signal-plus-noise processes. While b) is ordinarily unrealistic, there are enough cases of c) with only a slight amount of noise so that b) is a helpful idealization.

A noise-like process produces time series quite different in character than those produced by a signal-like process. The regularity of a noise-like process does not lie in the shapes of its individual realizations, but in its underlying statistical structure. As a result, different realizations usually do not appear to resemble each other. A segment of one realization generally will neither look the same nor have the same empirical autocovariances as the corresponding segment of another realization. Anyone using the autocovariance from a given realization as a "known" autocovariance, and then fitting this "known" autocovariance exactly, is likely to be in worse error than if he does not. As Brillinger and Tukey point out, we often have only one distinct realization, and we need to make as good inferences as we can about the underlying population. We have to think statistically, and treat our numerical results with due consideration as to the tentative nature of the structural and stochastic assumptions built into the model. It is for data near the noise-process end of the continuum that many of the Fourier methods of spectrum estimation are intended and are most effective.

At the other extreme are the signal-like processes. Some of the best examples of such processes are found in exploration seismology. A concentrated energy source produces a seismic record. Because the random background noise is usually weak, the record will appear essentially the same as another one taken at the same place at a different time. As Brillinger and Tukey point out, the study of signal-like processes may well be done by quite different methods.

Also there is another aspect of spectrum analysis, one to which the limitations of the data have forced many applied research workers. Here the models are not narrowly restricted by reliable subject-matter knowledge. The time-series records are not long, and the appearance of the data is not distinctive. Corresponding records do not look alike. With almost nothing to work with, the research workers can do nothing much more than fitting a few constants. Thus they fit low-order AR, MA, and ARMA models usings the Box–Jenkins [93] methodology. As Brillinger and Tukey observe, this approach in a large number of applications seems to work much better than might be anticipated.

The basic issue in spectrum estimation is the proper choice of model and then the resulting choice of the method of spectrum estimation [102]. Application of a particular spectral estimator to an inappropriate model can result in serious specification errors.

Let us now return to the question in point, namely, how we should estimate the power spectrum from a limited section of the autocovariance. Most research workers who calculate and use only a limited number of autocovariances do not assume that all the later ones vanish. They use the earlier values to calculate a quadratic function of the data whose average value (across the ensemble), like all other quadratic functions of the data, is the integral of a knowable kernel with the spectrum. They then interpret their result accordingly. One must not charge these workers with making any assumption about the uncalculated autocovariances. What they usually do is to recognize that the empirical autocovariances that they do calculate will vary from realization to realization, and so they do not and should not take the empirical values as absolute truth.

One of the purposes of this historical essay is to try to give the flavor of important developments in spectrum estimation. Unfortunately, the writer did not attend the 37th Meeting of the Society of Exploration Geophysicists in 1967, although he attended the meetings in the years both before and after that one. It was at that meeting in Oklahoma City that John Burg presented a paper that was to shake the foundations of spectrum estimation. This fundamental work [80] is entitled *Maximum Entropy Spectral Analysis* and its abstract reads:

"The usual digital method of obtaining a power spectrum estimate from a measured autocovariance function makes the assumption that the correlation function is zero at all lags for which no estimate is available and uses some treatment of the estimated lags to reduce the effect of truncation of the autocovariance function. The method discussed in this paper instead retains all of the estimated lags without modification and uses a nonzero estimate for the lags not directly estimated. The particular estimation principle used is that the spectral estimate must be the most random or have the maximum entropy of any power spectrum which is consistent with the measured data. This new analysis technique gives a much higher resolution spectral estimate than is obtained by conventional techniques with a very little increase in computing time. Comparisons will illustrate the relative importance."

The estimation of the power spectrum of stationary time series from partial knowledge of its autocovariance function is a classical problem to which much attention has been given over the years. Almost all of this work is based on the use of window functions, whose properties can be analyzed by Fourier methods. Burg [80], [81], [82] in his pioneering work introduced a new philosophy in spectral analysis based on general variational principles, and, in particular, the *maximum entropy method* (MEM) which we will now discuss.

The conventional approach to estimating the power spectrum from $\phi(n)$, $|n| \leqslant p$, is to assume that $\phi(n) = 0$ for $n > p$ and to take the Fourier transform of $w(n) \phi(n)$, $|n| \leqslant p$, where $w(n)$ is a weighting function. We now want to describe the maximum entropy method of Burg.

Given a limited set of autocovariance coefficients together with the fact that a power spectrum $\Phi(\omega)$ must be non-negative, we know that there are generally an infinite number of power spectra in agreement with this information. Thus additional information is required, and a reasonable goal is to find a single function $\Phi(\omega)$, which is representative of the class of all possible spectra. In order to resolve this problem, some choice has to be made, and Burg made use of the concept of entropy. Maximum entropy spectral analysis is based on choosing that spectrum which corresponds to the most random or the most unpredictable time-series whose autocovariance coincides with the given set of values. This concept of maximum entropy is the same as that used in both statistical mechanics and information theory, and as we will see represents the most noncommittal assumption possible with regard to the unknown values of the autocovariance function.

Equation (1) gives the power spectrum $\Phi(\omega)$ as the discrete Fourier transform of the autocovariance function $\phi(n)$. From Fourier theory, we know that the autocovariance function can be obtained as the inverse Fourier transform of the power spectrum; that is

$$\phi(n) = \frac{1}{2\pi} \int_{-\pi}^{\pi} \Phi(\omega) e^{j\omega n} \, d\omega \qquad \text{(for all integers } n\text{).} \quad (2)$$

The fundamental assumption involved in maximum entropy spectral analysis is that the stationary process under consideration is the most random or the least predictable time series that is consistent with the given measurements. Specifically, the given measurements are the known autocovariance coefficients, namely

$$\phi(n) = \frac{1}{2\pi} \int_{-\pi}^{\pi} \Phi(\omega) e^{j\omega n} \, d\omega \qquad \text{(for } |n| \leqslant p\text{).} \quad (3)$$

In terms of information theory, we require that the entropy per sample of time series is a maximum. From the work of Shannon in 1948, it follows that the entropy is proportional to the integral of the logarithm of the power spectrum, that is, the entropy is

$$\int_{-\pi}^{\pi} \log \Phi(\omega) \, d\omega. \quad (4)$$

Therefore the required maximum entropy power spectrum is that function $\Phi(\omega)$ which maximizes (4) under the constraint equations (3).

One way to solve the problem of finding the maximum entropy power spectrum subject to fixed values of $\phi(n)$ for $|n| \leq p$ is by use of Lagrange multipliers. However, we may instead use the following approach. From (1) we see that the partial derivative of $\Phi(\omega)$ with respect to $\phi(n)$ is

$$\frac{\partial \Phi(\omega)}{\partial \phi(n)} = e^{-j\omega n}.$$

It follows that

$$\frac{\partial \log \Phi(\omega)}{\partial \phi(n)} = \frac{e^{-j\omega n}}{\Phi(\omega)} = [\Phi(\omega)]^{-1} e^{-j\omega n}. \tag{5}$$

Now let us maximize (4) with respect to the unknown values $\phi(n)$ where $|n| > p$. Thus we set the partial derivatives of (4) with respect to $\phi(n)$ for $|n| > p$ equal to zero; that is

$$\frac{\partial}{\partial \phi(n)} \int_{-\pi}^{\pi} \log \Phi(\omega) \, d\omega = \int_{-\pi}^{\pi} \frac{\partial \log \Phi(\omega)}{\partial \phi(n)} d\omega = 0,$$

$$\text{for } |n| > p. \quad (6)$$

Making use of (5), we see that (6) reduces to

$$\int_{-\pi}^{\pi} [\Phi(\omega)]^{-1} e^{-j\omega n} \, d\omega = 0, \quad \text{for } |n| > p. \tag{7}$$

This equation specifies the form of the inverse power spectrum $[\Phi(\omega)]^{-1}$ of a maximum entropy process. Let us explain.

Given any stationary process with positive power spectrum $\Phi(\omega)$, then its inverse power spectrum

$$[\Phi(\omega)]^{-1} = \frac{1}{\Phi(\omega)} \tag{8}$$

is also positive. We assume that the inverse power spectrum is integrable and bounded, so that it is a well-behaved power spectrum in its own right. Thus the inverse power spectrum (8) can be associated with an autocovariance function, which we designate by $\psi(n)$, such that the counterparts of (1) and (2) hold, namely

$$[\Phi(\omega)]^{-1} = \sum_{n=-\infty}^{\infty} \psi(n) e^{-j\omega n} \quad (\text{for } -\pi \leq \omega \leq \pi) \tag{9}$$

and

$$\psi(n) = \frac{1}{2\pi} \int_{-\pi}^{\pi} [\Phi(\omega)]^{-1} e^{j\omega n} \, d\omega \quad (\text{for all integers } n). \tag{10}$$

Because we do not normalize, the zero-lag value $\psi(0)$ does not have to be one.

Let us now return to the maximum entropy process. As we have seen, its inverse power spectrum satisfies (7) for $|n| > p$. In (7) replace n by $-n$, and also multiply each side of the equation by $1/2\pi$. Thus we obtain

$$\frac{1}{2\pi} \int_{-\pi}^{\pi} [\Phi(\omega)]^{-1} e^{j\omega n} \, d\omega = 0, \quad \text{for } |n| > N. \quad (11)$$

Comparing (11) with (10), we see that for a maximum entropy process we have

$$\psi(n) = 0, \quad \text{for } |n| > p. \quad (12)$$

Hence, using (12) in (9), we see that the inverse power spectrum of a maximum entropy process is

$$[\Phi(\omega)]^{-1} = \sum_{n=-p}^{p} \psi(n) e^{-j\omega n}. \quad (13)$$

The right-hand side of (13) is a finite trigonometric series. Thus we have shown that the maximum entropy process is one whose inverse power spectrum is a finite trigonometric series, or equivalently one whose power spectrum is the reciprocal of a finite trigonometric series, that is

$$\Phi(\omega) = \frac{1}{\displaystyle\sum_{n=-p}^{p} \psi(n) e^{-j\omega n}}. \quad (14)$$

If we let $z = e^{j\omega}$, then the finite trigonometric series (13) becomes

$$\frac{1}{\Phi(z)} = \sum_{n=-p}^{p} \psi(n) z^{-n}.$$

This can be factored by the Fejér method (Robinson [43, p. 194]) as

$$\sum_{n=-p}^{p} \psi(n) z^{-n} = \frac{1}{\sigma^2} [1 + \alpha_1 z^{-1} + \cdots + \alpha_p z^{-p}]$$

$$\cdot [1 + \alpha_1 z + \cdots + \alpha_p z^p] \quad (15)$$

where σ^2 is a positive constant and where

$$A(z) = 1 + \alpha_1 z^{-1} + \cdots + \alpha_p z^{-p} \quad (16)$$

is minimum-delay (i.e., where $A(z)$ has no zeros on or outside the unit circle). Thus the maximum-entropy process is specified by

$$\Phi(z) = \frac{\sigma^2}{A(z)\,A(z^{-1})}\,.$$

This result shows that the maximum entropy process is an AR process of order p.

Silvia and Robinson [83], through the use of lattice methods, have related the concept of maximum entropy to the geophysical inverse problem. Itakura and Saito [84] were responsible for introducing two important ideas into spectrum estimation that are now gaining wide acceptance in the engineering world. The first idea is that of using maximum likelihood in spectrum estimation. Although the idea itself was not new, their introduction of a particular spectrum distance measure is becoming more and more important for different applications, such as speech. Parzen [85] gives the name *information divergence* to this measure, which is the same as the Kullback–Leibler information number. He also shows its relation to the notion of cross-entropy. The second idea is that of using the lattice as a filter structure for the purpose of analysis (as an all-zero filter) and synthesis (as an all-pole filter). The idea of an adaptive lattice was first proposed by Itakura and Saito as a way of estimating the partial correlation (PARCOR) coefficients (a term they coined) adaptively. Makhoul [86] has shown how Burg's technique is really a special case of lattice analysis. Also, the lattice has become important because of its fast convergence and its relative insensitivity to roundoff errors.

XVI. STATISTICAL THEORY OF SPECTRUM ESTIMATION

Since the pioneering work of Tukey [34] in 1949, many important contributions have been made to the statistical theory of spectrum estimation. An adequate treatment would require a long paper in itself, and so all we can hope to do here is to raise the reader's consciousness concerning the statistical theory required to understand and implement spectrum estimation.

The writer has great admiration for the work of Parzen, who from the 1950's to the present time has consistently made bedrock contributions both in theory and applications [61], [85], [87], [88]. His long series of papers on time series analysis include the famous Parzen window for spectrum analysis. Another one of Parzen's important contributions is his formulation of the time series analysis problem in terms of reproducing kernel Hilbert spaces. A remarkable number of Ph.D. theses on time series analysis have been written under the direction of Parzen, more than any other person. The writer has had the good fortune to discuss geophysical time-series problems with Professor Parzen over the years, and in every case Parzen has been able to provide important physical insight in the application of the statistical methods. The Harvard lectures by Professor Parzen in 1976 represent one of the high points in time series analysis and spectrum estimation ever to be heard in those venerable halls.

The book by Grenander and Rosenblatt [65] in 1957 formalized many of the data analysis procedures and approximations that have come into use. They have an extensive treatment of the problem of choice of window and bandwidth. The further contributions to this problem by Parzen and by Jenkins are discussed in the 1961 paper of Tukey [51]. An accurate and informative account of the developments of spectrum estimation in the 1950's is given by Tukey [44].

Another important statistical development that deserves mention is the alignment issue in the estimation of coherence, worked on in the 1960's by Akaike and Yamanouch, by Priestley, and by Parzen. Discussions of this work and the references can be found in the book by Priestley [89]. This excellent book, which appeared in 1981, has already set a new standard. It can be recommended as an authoritative account of the statistical theory of spectrum estimation, which we only touch upon in this section.

H. Wold coined the names "moving average process" and "autoregressive process" in his 1938 thesis [90] under Professor Harald Cramér at Stockholm University. In his thesis, Wold computed a model of the yearly level of Lake Vaner in Sweden as a moving average of the current rainfall and the previous year's rainfall. He also computed an autoregressive model of the business cycle in Sweden for the years 1843–1913. In turn, Whittle wrote his 1951 thesis [91] under Professor Wold at Uppsala University. Whittle opened up and made important contributions to the field of hypothesis testing in time-series analysis. Whittle's careful work is exemplified by his autoregressive analysis of a seiche record [92] in which he fits a low level autoregressive model to the data and gives statistical tests to determine the appropriateness of the model. Professor Whittle used to return to Sweden for visits, and the writer remembers taking long walks with him through the Uppsala countryside exploring for old runestones and ancient Viking mounds. Although the writer had left the University of Wisconsin to work with Professor Wold in Sweden, it turned out that Wisconsin under the leadership of Professor G. Box became the real center of time series analysis. It was the joint work of Box with Professor G. M. Jenkins [93] that actually brought the autoregressive (AR) process and the moving average (MA) process to the attention of the general scientific community. The brilliance of this work has made the names Box–Jenkins synonymous with time-series analysis. No achievement is better deserved. No person understands data better than Box in the application of statistical methods to obtain meaningful results.

In the 1960's Parzen [87] and Akaike [94] discussed autoregressive spectrum estimation, and this work led to their crucial work on autoregressive order-determining criteria [88] and [95]. Such criteria have made possible the widespread application of autoregressive spectrum estimation by researchers in diverse scientific fields. Akaike has provided a link between statistics and control theory with deep and significant results, and his work is of the highest tradition that science can provide. Young research workers can learn much by studying his writings well.

We wish we had more space and knowledge to expand upon this section, and those many statisticians whom we have not mentioned should remember that this history is by no means the final word. Someday we hope to write more fully on this subject, and we welcome all comments and suggestions.

XVII. Engineering Use of Spectral Estimation

The purpose of this section is only to refer to the rest of the papers in this special issue of the *Proceedings of the IEEE*. These other papers cover the engineering use of spectral estimation much better than we could do here. There papers represent a living history of the present status of spectral estimation, and, in them and in the references which they give, the reader can find the works of the people who have made spectral analysis and estimation a vital scientific discipline today. As general references, we would especially like to mention the 1978 IEEE book edited by Childers [96], Haykin [97], the *RADC Spectrum Estimation Workshop* [98], the *First IEEE ASSP Workshop on Spectral Estimation* [99], and Ulrych and Bishop [100]. Although much progress has been made, much work yet remains to be done, and there is adventure for a research worker who sets his course in this rewarding and exciting field.

Acknowledgment

I want to express my sincere appreciation to Prof. D. R. Brillinger who let me freely use his paper, "Some history of data analysis of time series in the United States," in *History of Statistics in the United States*, edited by D. B. Owen and published by Marcel Dekker in 1976. I want to thank Dr. J. Makhoul for sending me notes on maximum likelihood and lattice networks. I want to especially thank the authors cited in the Reference Section whose constructive comments materially improved this paper. In writing an historical paper, we should include a thousand references instead of one hundred, so important statistical contributions have unfortunately been left out. Of course, we have purposely not included engineering contributions (as they are covered in the rest of this special issue) but there is never a clear cut line, and so in this sense other important work has also been left out. However, all such omissions are not intentional, and we will gladly try to rectify any situation in some appropriate future publication. Finally, most of all, I want to thank Prof. J. Tukey for the support and help he gave me on spectrum estimation thirty years ago at MIT for which I am forever grateful.

REFERENCES

[1] I. Newton, *Optics*. London, England, 1704.
[2] B. Taylor, *Methodus Incrementorum Directa et Inverse*. London, England, 1715.
[3] D. Bernoulli, *Hydrodynamics*. Basel, Switzerland, 1738.
[4] L. Euler, *Institutiones Calculi Differentialis*. St. Petersburg, Russia, 1755.
[5] J. L. Lagrange, *Théorie des Fonctions Analytiques*. Paris, France, 1759.
[6] J. Fourier, *Théorie Analytique de la Chaleur*. Paris, France: Didot, 1822.
[7] C. Sturm, "Memoire sur les équations différentielles linéaires du second ordre," *Journal de Mathématiques Pures et Appliquées*, Paris, France, Series 1, vol. 1, pp. 106–186, 1836.
[8] J. Liouville, "Premier mémoire sur la théorie des équations différentielles linéaries et sur le developpement des fonctions en séries," *Journal de Mathématiques Pures et Appliquées*, Paris, France, Series 1, vol. 3, pp. 561–614, 1838.
[9] G. Green, *Essay on the Application of Mathematical Analysis to the Theories of Electricity and Magnetism*. Nottingham, England, 1828.
[10] E. Schrödinger, *Collected Papers on Wave Mechanics*. London, England: Blackie, 1928.
[11] W. Heisenberg, *The Physical Principles of Quantum Theory*. Chicago, IL: University of Chicago Press, 1930.
[12] J. von Neumann, "Eigenwerttheorie Hermitescher Funcktional-operatoren," *Math. Ann.*, vol. 102, p. 49, 1929.
[13] ——, *Mathematische Grundlagen der Quantenmechanik*. Berlin, Germany: Springer, 1932.
[14] M. von Smoluchowski, *The Kinetic Theory of Matter and Electricity*. Leipzig and Berlin, Germany, 1914.
[15] A. Einstein, "On the theory of the Brownian movement," *Annalen der Physik*, vol. 19, pp. 371–381, 1906.
[16] N. Wiener, "Differential space," *J. Math. Phys.*, vol. 2, p. 131.
[17] A. Schuster," On the investigation of hidden periodicities with application to a supposed 26-day period of meterological phenomena," *Terr. Magnet.*, vol. 3, pp. 13–41, 1898.
[18] G. U. Yule, "On a method of investigating periodicities in disturbed series, with special reference to Wolfer's sunspot numbers," *Phil. Trans. Roy. Soc. London*, A, vol. 226, pp. 267–298.
[19] E. A. Robinson, *Predictive Decomposition of Time Series with Applications to Seismic Exploration*, MIT Geophysical Analysis Group, 1954; Reprinted in *Geophysics*, vol. 32, pp. 418–484, 1967.
[20] ——, *An Introduction to Infinitely Many Variates*. London, England: Griffin, 1959, p. 109.
[21] N. Wiener, "Generalized harmonic analysis," *Acta Math.*, vol. 55, pp. 117–258, 1930.

[22] A. Y. Khintchine, "Korrelations theorie der Stationären Stochastischen Prozesse," *Math. Ann.*, vol. 109, p. 604.

[23] N. Wiener, *Cybernetics.* Cambridge, MA: MIT Press, 1948.

[24] ——, *Extrapolation, Interpolation, and Smoothing of Stationary Time Series with Engineering Applications*, MIT NDRC Report, 1942, Reprinted, MIT Press, 1949.

[25] ——, *The Fourier Integral.* London, England: Cambridge, 1933.

[26] P. Dirac, *Principles of Quantum Mechanics.* New York: Oxford University Press, 1930.

[27] O. Heaviside, *Electrical Papers*, vol. I and II. New York: Macmillan, 1892.

[28] J. von Neumann, "Uber Funktionen von Funktional operatoren," *Ann. Math.*, vol. 32, p. 191.

[29] N. Wiener, *I Am a Mathematician.* Cambridge, MA: MIT Press, 1956.

[30] N. Levinson, "A heuristic exposition of Wiener's mathematical theory of prediction and filtering," *Journal of Math. and Physics*, vol. 26, pp. 110–119, 1947.

[31] N. Levinson, The Wiener RMS (root mean square) error criterion in filter design and prediction, *J. Math. Phys.*, vol. 25, pp. 261–278, 1947.

[32] G. P. Wadsworth, *Short-Range and Extended Forecasting by Statistical Methods*, Air Weather Service, Washington, DC, 1948.

[33] H. R. Seiwell, "The principles of time series analyses applied to ocean wave data," in *Proc. Nat. Acad. Sci., U.S..*, vol. 35, pp. 518–528, 1949.

[34] J. W. Tukey, "The sampling theory of power spectrum estimates," in *Proc. Symp. Appl. Autocorr. Anal. Phys. Prob. U.S. Off. Naval Res.* (NAVEXOS-P-725), 1949. Reprinted in *J. Cycle Res.*, vol. 6, pp. 31–52, 1957.

[35] G. P. Wadsworth, E. A. Robinson, J. G. Bryan, and P. M. Hurley, "Detection of reflections on seismic records by linear operators," *Geophys*, vol. 18, pp. 539–586, 1953.

[36] J. W. Tukey and R. W. Hamming, "Measuring noise color 1," *Bell Lab. Memo*, 1949.

[37] J. W. Tukey, *Measuring Noise Color*, Unpublished manuscript prepared for distribution at the Institute of Radio Engineers Meeting, Nov. 1951.

[38] S. M. Simpson, *Time Series Computations in FORTRAN and FAP.* Reading, MA: Addison–Wesley, 1966.

[39] N. Wiener, *Bull. Amer. Math. Soc.*, vol. 72, pp. 1–145.

[40] N. Wiener and P. Masani, "The prediction theory of multivariate stochastic processes," *Acta Math.*, vol. 98, pp. 111–150, 1957.

[41] ——, "On bivariate stationary processes," *Theory Prob. Appl.*, vol. 4, pp. 300–308.

[42] R. A. Wiggins and E. A. Robinson, "Recursive solution to the multichannel filtering problem," *J. of Geophys. Res.*, vol. 70, pp. 1885–1891, 1965.

[43] E. A. Robinson, *Statistical Communication and Detection with Special Reference to Digital Data Processing of Radar and Seismic Signals.* London, England: Griffin, 1967. Reprinted with new title, *Physical Applications of Stationary Time Series.* New York: Macmillan, 1980.

[44] J. W. Tukey, "An introduction to the calculations of numerical spectrum analysis," in *Spectral Analysis of Time Series*, B. Harris, Ed. New York: Wiley, 1967, pp. 25–46.

[45] H. Press and J. W. Tukey, "Power spectral methods of analysis and their application to problems in airplane dynamics," *Bell Syst. Monogr.*, vol. 2606, 1956.

[46] R. B. Blackman and J. W. Tukey, "The measurement of power spectra from the point of view of communications engineering," *Bell Syst. Tech. J.*, vol. 33, pp. 185–282, 485–569, 1958; also New York: Dover, 1959.

[47] J. W. Tukey, "The estimation of power spectra and related quantities," *On Numerical Approximation*, R. E. Langer, Ed. Madison, WI: University of Wisconsin Press, 1959, pp. 389–411.

[48] ——, "An introduction to the measurement of spectra," in *Probability and Statistics*, U. Grenander, Ed. New York: Wiley, 1959, pp. 300–330.

[49] ——, "Equalization and pulse shaping techniques applied to the determination of the initial sense of Rayleigh waves," in *The Need of Fundamental Research in Seismology*, Appendix 9, Department of State, Washington, DC, 1959, pp. 60–129.

[50] B. P. Bogert, M. J. Healy, and J. W. Tukey, "The frequency analysis of time series for echoes; cepstrum pseud-autocovariance, cross-cepstrum and shape-cracking," in *Time Series Analysis*, M. Rosenblatt, Ed. New York: Wiley, 1963, pp. 201–243.

[51] J. W. Tukey, "Discussion emphasizing the connection between analysis of variance and spectrum analysis," *Technometrics*, vol. 3, pp. 1–29, 1961.

[52] ——, "The future of data analysis," *Ann. Math. Statist.*, vol. 33, pp. 1–67, 1963.

[53] ——, "What can data analysis and statistics offer today?" in *Ocean Wave Spectra*, Nat. Acad. Sci., Washington, DC, and Prentice-Hall, Englewood Cliffs, NJ, 1963.

[54] ——, "Uses of numerical spectrum analysis in geophysics," *Bull. Int. Statist. Inst.*, vol. 39, pp. 267–307, 1965.

[55] ——, "Data analysis and the frontiers of geophysics," *Science*, vol. 148, pp. 1283–1289, 1965.

[56] W. J. Pierson and L. J. Tick, "Stationary random processes in meteorology and oceanography," *Bull. Int. Statist. Inst.*, vol. 35, pp. 271–281, 1957.

[57] N. R. Goodman, "On the joint estimation of the spectra, cospectrum and quadrature spectrum of a two-dimensional stationary Gaussian process," Science Paper no. 10, Engineering Statistics Laboratory, New York University, New York, 1957.

[58] W. H. Munk and G. J. F. MacDonald, *The Rotation of the Earth*. New York: Cambridge University Press, 1960.

[59] M. J. Healy and B. P. Bogert, "FORTRAN subroutines for time series analysis," *Commun. Soc. Computing Machines*, vol. 6, pp. 32–34, 1963.

[60] E. C. Bullard, F. E. Ogelbay, W. H. Munk, and G. R. Miller, *A User's Guide to BOMM*, Institute of Geophysics and Planetary Physics, University of California Press, San Diego, 1966.

[61] E. Parzen, *Time Series Analysis Papers*. San Francisco, CA: Holden-Day, 1967.

[62] E. A. Robinson, *Multichannel Time Series Analysis with Digital Computer Programs*. San Francisco, CA: Holden-Day, 1967.

[63] C. W. J. Granger, *Spectral Analysis of Economic Time Series*. Princeton, NJ: Princeton University Press, 1964.

[64] J. Neyman and E. L. Scott, "Statistical approach to problems of cosmology," *J. Roy. Statist. Soc.*, Series B, vol. 20, pp. 1–43, 1958.

[65] U. Grenander and M. Rosenblatt, *Statistical Analysis of Stationary Time Series*. New York: Wiley, 1957.

[66] N. Wiener, *Nonlinear Problems in Random Theory*. Cambridge, MA: MIT Press, 1958.

[67] ——, "Rhythm in physiology with particular reference to encephalography," *Proc. Roy. Roy. Virchow Med. Soc.*, NY, vol. 16, pp. 109–124, 1957.

[68] J. W. Cooley and J. W. Tukey," An algorithm for the machine calculation of Fourier series," *Math. Comput.*, vol. 19, pp. 297–301, 1965.

[69] J. W. Cooley, P. A. W. Lewis, and P. D. Welch, "Historical notes on the fast Fourier transform," *IEEE Trans. Audio Electroacoust.*, vol. AU-15, pp. 76–79, 1967.

[70] C. Bingham, M. D. Godfrey, and J. W. Tukey, "Modern techniques of power spectrum estimation," *IEEE Trans. Audio Electroacoust.*, vol. AU-15, pp. 56–66, 1967.

[71] E. O. Brigham and R. E. Morrow, "The fast Fourier transform," *IEEE Spectrum*, pp. 63–70, 1967.

[72] *IEEE Trans. Audio Electroacoust.* (Special issue on Fourier

transform), B. P. Bogert and F. Van Veen, Eds., vol. AU-15, June 1967 and vol. AU-17, June 1969.

[73] D. R. Brillinger, *Time Series: Data Analysis and Theory.* New York: Holt, Rinehart, and Winston, Inc., 1974; revised edition by Holden-Day, San Francisco, CA, 1980.

[74] D. R. Brillinger and M. Rosenblatt, "Computation and interpretation of k-th order spectra," in *Spectral Analysis of Time Series*, B. Harris, Ed. New York: Wiley, 1967, pp. 189–232.

[75] J. Capon, "Applications of detection and estimation theory to large array seismology," *Proc. IEEE*, vol. 58, pp. 760–770, 1970.

[76] *Stochastic Point Processes*, P. A. W. Lewis, Ed. New York: Wiley, 1972.

[77] P. A. W. Lewis, A. M. Katcher, and A. H. Weiss, "SASE IV—An improved program for the statistical analysis of series of events," *IBM Res. Resp.*, RC2365, 1969.

[78] Proc. Symp. Walsh Functions, 1970–1973.

[79] A. Cohen and R. H. Jones, "Regression on a random field," *J. Amer. Statist. Ass.*, vol. 64, pp. 1172–1182, 1969.

[80] J. P. Burg, *Maximum Entropy Spectral Analysis.* Oklahoma City, OK, 1967.

[81] ——, *Maximum Entropy Spectral Analysis.* Stanford, CA: Stanford University, 1975.

[82] R. T. Lacoss, "Data adaptive spectral analysis methods," *Geophysics*, vol. 36, pp. 661–675, 1971.

[83] M. T. Silvia and E. A. Robinson, *Deconvolution of Geophysical Time Series in the Exploration of Oil and Natural Gas.* Amsterdam, The Netherlands: Elsevier, 1979.

[84] F. Itakura and S. Saito, "Analysis synthesis telephony based on on the maximum-likelihood method," in *Proc. Sixth Int. Conf. on Acoustics*, (Tokyo, Japan), 1968.

[85] E. Parzen, "Modern empirical spectral analysis," Tech. Report N-12, Texas A&M Research Foundation, College Station, TX, 1980.

[86] J. Makhoul, "Stable and efficient lattice methods for linear prediction," *IEEE Trans. Acoust., Speech, Signal Processing*, vol. ASSP-25, pp. 423–428, 1977.

[87] E. Parzen, "An approach to empirical time series," *J. Res. Nat. Bur. Stand.*, vol. 68B, pp. 937–951, 1964.

[88] ——, "Some recent advances in time series modeling," *IEEE Trans. Automat. Contr.*, vol. AC-19, pp. 723–730, 1974.

[89] M. Priestley, *Spectral Analysis and Time Series*, 2 volumes, London, England: Academic Press, 1981.

[90] H. Wold, *A Study in the Analysis of Stationary Time Series.* Stockholm, Sweden: Stockholm University, 1938.

[91] P. Whittle, *Hypothesis Testing in Time-Series Analysis.* Uppsala, Sweden: Almqvist and Wiksells, 1951.

[92] ——, The statistical analysis of a seiche record, *J. Marine Res.*, vol. 13, pp. 76–100, 1954.

[93] G. Box and G. M. Jenkins, *Time Series Analysis, Forecasting, and Control.* Oakland, CA: Holden-Day, 1970.

[94] H. Akaike, "Power spectrum estimation through autoregressive model fitting," *Ann. Inst. Statist. Math.*, vol. 21, pp. 407–419, 1969.

[95] ——, "A new look at statistical model identification," *IEEE Trans. Autom. Contr.*, vol. AC-19, pp. 716–723, 1974.

[96] D. G. Childers, *Modern Spectrum Analysis.* New York: IEEE Press, 1978.

[97] S. Haykin, *Nonlinear Methods of Spectral Analysis.* Berlin, Germany: Springer, 1979.

[98] *Proc. of the RADC Spectrum Estimation Workshop*, Rome Air Development Center, Griffiss Air Force Base, NY, 1979.

[99] *Proc. of the First ASSP Workshop on Spectral Estimation*, McMaster University, Hamilton, Ontario, Canada, 1981.

[100] T. J. Ulrych and T. N. Bishop, "Maximum entropy spectral analysis and autoregressive decomposition," *Rev. Geophys.*, vol. 13, pp. 183–200, 1975.

[101] P. R. Gutowski, E. A. Robinson, and S. Treitel, "Spectral estimation: Fact or fiction," *IEEE Trans. Geosci. Electronics*, vol. GE-16, pp. 80–84, 1978. Reprinted in D. G. Childers, *Modern Spectrum Analysis.* New York: IEEE Press, 1978.

Appendix 10

Spectral Approach to Geophysical Inversion by Lorentz, Fourier, and Radon Transforms

(Invited paper by Enders A. Robinson in the *Proceedings of the IEEE*, Vol. 70, No. 9, September 1982, pp. 1039-1054)

Abstract—Geophysical inversion seeks to determine the structure of the interior of the earth from data obtained at the surface. In reflection seismology, the problem is to find inverse methods that give structure, composition, and source parameters by processing the received seismograms. The pioneering work of Jack Cohen and Norman Bleistein on general inverse methods has caused a revolution in the direction of research on long-standing unsolved geophysical problems. This paper does not deal with such general methods, but instead gives a survey of some production-type data processing methods in everyday use in geophysical exploration. The unifying theme is the spectral approach which provides methods for the approximate solution of some simplified inverse problems of practical importance.

This paper is divided into two parts, one dealing with one-dimensional (1-D) inversion, the other with two-dimensional (2-D) inversion. The 1-D case treated is that of a horizontally layered earth (Goupillaud model) with seismic raypaths only in the vertical direction. This model exhibits a lattice structure which corresponds to the lattice methods of spectral estimation. It is shown that the lattice structure is mathematically equivalent to the structure of the Lorentz transformation of the special theory of relativity. The solution of this 1-D inverse problem is the discrete counterpart of the Gelfand–Levitan inversion method in physics. A practical computational scheme to carry out the inversion process is the method of dynamic deconvolution. It is based on a generalization of the Levinson recursion, and involves the interacting recursions of two polynomials P and Q. This paper treats only much simplified 2-D models. One 2-D method gives the forward and inverse solution for a horizontally layered earth (Goupillaud model) with slanting seismic raypaths. This method involves the Radon transform which is often called "slant stacking" by geophysicists. The other 2-D methods given in this paper are concerned with the process of wavefield reconstruction and imaging known as "migration" in the geophysical industry. A major breakthrough occurred in 1978 when Stolt introduced spectral migration which makes the use of the fast Fourier transform. Another method, the slant-stack migration of Hubral, is based on the Radon transform.

I. INTRODUCTION

THE DIRECT problem in geophysics may be thought of as the determination of how seismic waves propagate on the basis of a known makeup of the subsurface of the earth. The inverse problem is to determine the subsurface makeup on the basis of wave motion observed at the surface of the earth. The inverse problem is not unique to geophysics. A large part of our physical contact with our surroundings depends upon an intuitive solution of inverse problems. In many other real-world problems, we must also infer the size, shape, and texture of remote objects from the way they transmit, reflect, and scatter traveling waves. For example, in X-ray computerized tomography [1], it is necessary to combine X-ray scans taken at different angles to form a cross-sectional image which represents the internal details of the scanned structure. In nondestructive testing [2], a reconstruction of three-dimensional (3-D) refractive-index field is made from holographic measurements taken at different angles. In electron microscopy [3], 3-D biological structures are deduced from 2-D electron micrographs taken at different tilt angles. Optimization techniques are being developed for digital image reconstruction from various types of projections [4].

In 1877, Lord Rayleigh [5] treated a physical inverse problem; he was one of the first scientists to do so. Rayleigh considered the problem of finding the density distribution of a string from knowledge of the vibrations. Kac [6] aptly described this inverse problem in the title of his well-known lecture "Can one hear the shape of a drum?" Because seismic waves are sound waves in the earth, we can describe our inverse problem (i.e., seismic exploration) as "Can we hear the shape of an oil field?"

With the introduction of the Schrödinger equation to describe the microphysical world, the scope of inverse problems in physics became enormously enlarged. Over the years, many general inversion procedures were formulated. One of the most elegant approaches was given by Gelfand and Levitan [7] on the solution of a differential equation by its spectral function. This solution leads to an integral equation, the Gelfand–Levitan equation. We will treat the discrete form of the Gelfand–Levitan integral equation in this paper, as well as give a computational scheme, known in geophysics as dynamic deconvolution, for its solution. The word "dynamic" is used to differentiate this deconvolution process from the usual time-invariant deconvolution methods.

The spectral methods used in geophysics are closely connected with the inverse problem [8]. Basically, the spectral approach provides methods for the approximate solution of many simplified inverse problems. We will be concerned in this paper with such specialized solutions and not with the general case. In this sense, this paper deals with the production-type data processing methods in everyday use in geohysical exploration, which serve not perfectly but well.

Since the energy crisis, a greatly increased research effort has been devoted to problems in the geophysical exploration for oil and natural gas. General inverse scattering methods from the mainstream of physics and applied mathematics have been introduced to the geophysical exploration industry. The pioneering work of Jack Cohen and Norman Bleistein has caused a revolution in the direction of research on the long-standing unsolved problems in the seismic exploration for oil. We do not treat these more powerful methods in this paper, but refer the reader to the recent work of Silvia [9], Silvia and Weglein [10], Cohen and Bleistein [11], [12], Mendel and Habibi-Ashrafi [13], Coen [14], Carroll and Santosa [15], Driessel and Symes [16], Stolt [17], Bube and Burridge [18], Zemanian and Subramaniam [19], Gazdag [20], Bamberger, Chavent, and Lailly [21], and Treitel, Gutowski, Hubral, and Wagner [22]. Larner [23] gives a balanced understanding of the entire field of exploration geophysics, from the most difficult physical and mathematical methods to the practical field implementation.

Because we are at a turning point in the methods used in seismic exploration, it is well to summarize where we stand today. Some of the methods presently in use will be replaced by the newer, more powerful methods now being developed, and others may survive, albeit in some modified form.

We divide this paper into two parts, 1-D and 2-D. The 1-D problems are concerned with a laterally homogeneous earth, so the only variation is in the depth dimension z. The basic method which we treat here is the Gelfand–Levitan solution of the inverse problem and the related dynamical-deconvolution scheme. These techniques are closely related to lattice approaches to spectral estimation [24], which use the Levinson recursion [25] and the Burg method [26]. Briefly, dynamic deconvolution is based on the interacting recursions of P and Q polynomials. These polynomials are related to the polynomial A appearing in the Levinson recursion by means of the equation $A_k = P_k - c_0 Q_k$, where $|c_0| = 1$.

We do not give any general solution of the 2-D problem, but instead treat special simplified cases which have proved useful. The 3-D problem is not treated at all because the simplified 2-D methods which we present can readily be extended to the 3-D case. Of course, in such an extension, many facets which depend upon dimension must be respected, but the basic ideas are the same. Today the exploration industry is using 3-D data (lateral dimensions x and y, and depth dimension z pointing downward) more and more, and eventually all exploration will be done with 3-D models. It is here that the general inverse approaches introduced by the pathfinding work of Cohen and Bleistein will reach their greatest effectiveness.

The specialized 2-D methods which we present make use of spectral analysis to solve a much simplified problem, known in the industry as migration. The two spectral techniques used are the 2-D Fourier transform and its related Radon transformation. The Fourier migration method is due to Stolt [27], and the Radon migration method is due to Hubral [28]. The Stolt method, which takes advantage of the efficiency of the fast Fourier transform, was a major breakthrough in seismic migration, and it has led to many other developments.

In brief, the limelight in geophysical exploration is on inverse methods. However, when one looks closer, one sees that underlying these methods are the associated spectral methods. Basically, the spectral approach can be used in conjunction with inversion theory to obtain solutions which give us both physical insight and practical exploration tools. The spectral approach, as exemplified by the 1-D lattice (i.e., layered-earth) methods and the 2-D Fourier and Radon migration methods, has provided practical computational schemes for seismic data processing. These spectral methods work and can be used routinely to solve exploration problems successfully in a large number of cases, even though the complete mathematical inverse solution is yet beyond our reach.

II. ONE-DIMENSIONAL INVERSION

A. The Goupillaud Layered-Earth Model

The determination of the properties of the earth from waves that have been reflected from the earth is the clasic problem of reflection seismology. As a first step in mathematical analysis, the problem is usually simplified by assuming that the earth's crust is made up of a sequence of sedimentary layers. The well-known *Goupillaud model* [29] (Fig. 1) approximates the heterogeneous earth with a sequence of horizontal layers, each of which is homogeneous, isotropic, and nonabsorptive. This stratified model is subjected to vertically traveling plane compressional waves, and thus it is a normal incidence model. It is assumed that the two-way travel time in each layer is the same and is equal to one time unit. In other words, the one-way

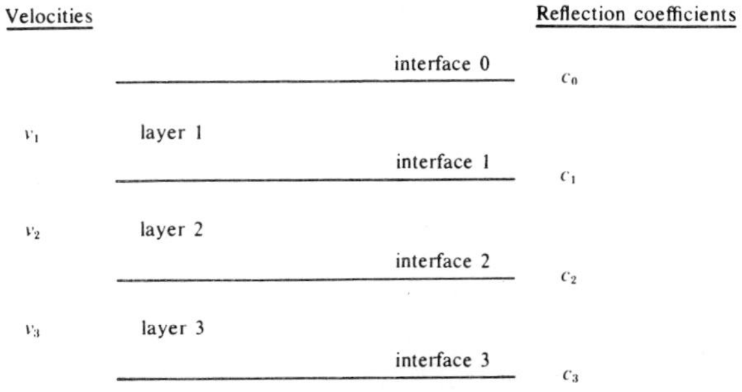

Velocities			Reflection coefficients
		interface 0	c_0
v_1	layer 1		
		interface 1	c_1
v_2	layer 2		
		interface 2	c_2
v_3	layer 3		
		interface 3	c_3

Fig. 1. The Goupillaud model.

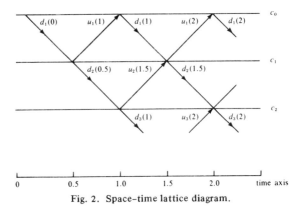

Fig. 2. Space–time lattice diagram.

travel time in each layer is taken to be one-half of the discrete unit of time. The upper half-space (the air) is called half-space 0, the first layer underneath is called layer 1, the next layer underneath is called layer 2, and so on. Interface 0 is the interface at the bottom of half-space 0, interface 1 is the interface at the bottom of layer 1, and so on. Let c_k be the reflection coefficient for downgoing waves striking interface k. The reflection coefficient for upgoing waves striking interface k is thus equal to $-c_k$. We will assume that the amplitudes of our waves are measured in units such that squared amplitude is proportional to energy. Then the transmission coefficient through interface k is equal to $(1 - c_k^2)^{1/2}$ for either upgoing or downgoing waves. All waves are digitized with unit time spacing. Although the waves exist throughout the layers, we will only be concerned with them as measured at the tops of the layers; see Fig. 2. This is done in order to keep the bookkeeping as simple as possible. If the number of the layer is odd, then time is measured at integer values: $n = 0, 1, 2, \cdots$. However, if the layer is even, then time is measured at integer-plus-one-half values: $n + 0.5 = 0.5, 1.5, 2.5, \cdots$. This is because it takes only 0.5 time unit for a wave to traverse a layer. For example, if a downgoing impulse is introduced at time 0 at the top of layer 1, then it arrives at the top of layer 2 at time 0.5, at the top of layer 3 at time 1, at the top of layer 4 at time 1.5, and so on. Because z is used for the depth dimension in geophysics, we will use the Laplace generating function instead of the z-transform. The variable s in the Laplace generating function corresponds to the variable z^{-1} in the z-transform. The downgoing wave at the top of layer k is denoted by $d_k(n)$ if k is odd, and by $d_k(n + 0.5)$ if k is even, where n is an integer. The respective generating functions are

$$D_k(s) = \sum_n d_k(n)s^n \qquad (k \text{ odd})$$

$$D_k(s) = \sum_n d_k(n + 0.5)s^{n+0.5} \quad (k \text{ even}).$$

The corresponding z transforms are obtained by letting $s = z^{-1}$. Similarly, the upgoing wave $u_k(n)$ for k odd, and $u_k(n + 0.5)$ for k even, is also measured at the top of the layer. Its generating function is $U_k(s)$.

We have thus described the Goupillaud-layered media. Besides its interest in exploration geophysics, the Goupillaud model is of interest in spectral estimation, for it is mathematically the same as a *lattice network*. These networks are useful in building models of many processes which occur in engineering practice, such as the acoustic tube model for digital speech processing, as developed by Gray and Markel [30], and others. As shown by Makhoul [31] and Durrani, Murukutla, and Sharman [32], the lattice model provides methods for adaptive spectral estimation. We now want to discuss some of the properties of this model that have been useful in exploration geophysics.

B. The Lorentz Transformation

When Maxwell derived the electromagnetic wave equation, it soon became known that it is not invariant under the Galilean transformation. However, it is invariant under the Lorentz transformation, and this observation was a key factor in Einstein's development of the special theory of relativity [33]. The *Lorentz transformation* can be written as

$$D_2 = \frac{1}{(1 - c_1^2)^{1/2}} [D_1 - c_1 U_1]$$

$$U_2 = \frac{1}{(1 - c_1^2)^{1/2}} [-c D_1 + U_1]$$

where D_1 and U_1 are, respectively, the time and space coordinates of an event in frame 1, where D_2 and U_2 are, respectively, the time and space coordinates of the event in frame 2, and c_1 (where $|c_1| < 1$) is the velocity (in natural units, such that the velocity of light is unity) between the two frames. The Lorentz transformation is a consequence of the invariance of the interval between events. By direct substitution, it can be shown that the coordinates of two events must satisfy the equation

$$D_2^2 - U_2^2 = D_1^2 - U_1^2$$

on transition from one frame of reference to the other.

We now want to find the relationship between the waves in the Goupillaud model. Instead of the conventional treatment, we will try to put this relationship in a more general setting. We know that the waves in each layer obey their respective wave equation. Let $D_1(s)$ and $U_1(s)$ be, respectively, the generating functions of the downgoing wave and the upgoing wave at the top of layer 1, and let $D_2(s)$ and $U_2(s)$ be the corresponding functions for layer 2. We then say that *wave motion* must be related by the *Lorentz transformation*

$$D_2(s) = \frac{1}{(1 - c_1^2)^{1/2}} \, [s^{1/2} D_1(s) - c_1 s^{-1/2} U_1(s)]$$

$$U_2(s) = \frac{1}{(1 - c_1^2)^{1/2}} \, [-c_1 s^{1/2} D_1(s) + s^{-1/2} U_1(s)] .$$

The constant c_1 (where $|c_1| < 1$) is the reflection coefficient of the interface between the two layers. This Lorentz transformation is a consequence of the invariance of the net downgoing energy in the layers. By direct substitution, it can be shown that

$$D_2 \overline{D}_2 - U_2 \overline{U}_2 = D_1 \overline{D}_1 - U_1 \overline{U}_1$$

(where the bar indicates that s is to be replaced by s^{-1}; i.e., $\overline{D}(s) = D(s^{-1})$). This equation says that the net downgoing energy in each layer is the same. Because there is no absorption, this energy relation is a physical fact implied by the model.

C. Polynomial Recursions

The Lorentz transformation between two adjacent layers can be written in matrix form as

$$\begin{bmatrix} D_{k+1} \\ U_{k+1} \end{bmatrix} = \frac{s^{-1/2}}{t_k} \begin{bmatrix} s & -c_k \\ -c_k s & 1 \end{bmatrix} \begin{bmatrix} D_k \\ U_k \end{bmatrix}$$

where we have used the symbol t_k to denote the transmission coefficient $(1 - c_k^2)^{1/2}$. Robinson [34] defines the polynomials $P_k(s)$ and $Q_k(s)$, and the reverse polynomials (with superscript R for reverse) given by

$$P_k^R(s) = s^k P_k(s^{-1})$$

$$Q_k^R(s) = s^k Q_k(s^{-1}).$$

These polynomials are defined by the equation

$$\begin{bmatrix} P_k^R & Q_k^R \\ Q_k & P_k \end{bmatrix} = \begin{bmatrix} s & -c_k \\ -c_k s & 1 \end{bmatrix} \begin{bmatrix} s & -c_{k-1} \\ -c_{k-1} s & 1 \end{bmatrix} \cdots \begin{bmatrix} s & -c_1 \\ -c_1 s & 1 \end{bmatrix} .$$

By inspection, we can find the first and last coefficients of these polynomials. We have

$$P_k(s) = 1 + \cdots + c_1 c_k s^{k-1}$$

$$Q_k(s) = -c_1 s + \cdots - c_k s^k$$

$$P_k^R(s) = c_1 c_k s + \cdots + s^k$$

$$Q_k^R(s) = -c_k + \cdots - c_1 s^{k-1}.$$

The polynomials for adjacent layers are related by

$$\begin{bmatrix} P_k^R & Q_k^R \\ Q_k & P_k \end{bmatrix} = \begin{bmatrix} s & -c_k \\ -c_k s & 1 \end{bmatrix} \begin{bmatrix} P_{k-1}^R & Q_{k-1}^R \\ Q_{k-1} & P_{k-1} \end{bmatrix}.$$

This equation gives the *Robinson recursion* [34]

$$P_k = P_{k-1} - c_k s\, Q_{k-1}^R$$

$$Q_k = Q_{k-1} - c_k s\, P_{k-1}^R$$

and its inverse recursion

$$P_{k-1} = \frac{1}{1 - c_k^2} (P_k + c_k\, Q_k^R)$$

$$Q_{k-1} = \frac{1}{1 - c_k^2} (Q_k + c_k\, P_k^R).$$

Let us now subtract the two recursion equations to obtain

$$(P_k - Q_k) = (P_{k-1} - Q_{k-1}) - c_k s(Q_{k-1}^R - P_{k-1}^R).$$

Let c_0 be the reflection coefficient of interface 0, where $|c_0| = 1$. To be definite, let $c_0 = 1$. If we define the polynomial A_k as $A_k = P_k - c_0 Q_k = P_k - Q_k$, we obtain the *Levinson recursion* [25]

$$A_k = A_{k-1} + c_k s\, A_{k-1}^R.$$

The *polynomial of the second kind* is defined as $B_k = P_k + c_0 Q_k = P_k + Q_k$, and we see it satisfies the recursion

$$B_k = B_{k-1} - c_k s\, B_{k-1}^R.$$

The inverse of the Levinson recursion is

$$A_{k-1} = \frac{1}{1 - c_k^2} (A_k - c_k\, A_k^R).$$

We will now make use of the two recursions given in this section for the analysis of layered-earth (lattice) models; the A recursion for the free-surface case and the P, Q recursion for the non-free-surface case.

D. Free-Surface and Non-Free-Surface Reflection Seismograms

We now want to consider an idealized seismic experiment. The source is a downgoing unit impulse introduced at the top

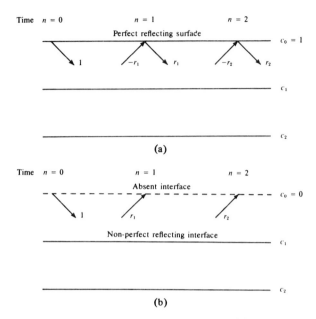

Fig. 3. (a) Free-surface siesmogram r_1, r_2, r_3, $\cdots$. (b) Non-free-surface
seismogram r_1, r_2, r_3, $\cdots$.

of layer 1 at time instant 0. This pulse proceeds downward
where it undergoes multiple reflections and refractions within
the layered system. Some of the energy is returned to the top
of layer 1, where it is recorded in the form of a seismic trace,
which we denote by the sequence $r_1, r_2, r_3, \cdots$, where the
subscript indicates the discrete time index; see Fig. 3.

There are two types of boundary conditions commonly imposed on the top interface (interface 0 with reflection coefficient c_0). One is the free-surface condition, which says that
interface 0 (the air-earth interface) is a perfect reflector; that
is, the free-surface condition is that $|c_0| = 1$. The free-surface
condition approximately holds in the case of a marine seismogram taken in a very smooth, calm sea, so the surface of the
water (interface 0) is virtually a perfect reflector.

The other condition is the non-free-surface case. For notational convenience, we will choose the non-free surface as
interface 1; that is, the air-earth interface is taken as interface 1,
which can have an arbitrary (nonperfect) reflection coefficient
c_1, where $|c_1| < 1$. Since interface 1 represents the surface of
the ground, it follows that interface 0 is not present, that is,
$c_0 = 0$. Thus the non-free-surface condition is that $c_0 = 0$ and
c_1 is arbitrary.

In summary, an ideal marine seismogram is generated by the

Goupillaud model with the free-surface condition $|c_0| = 1$. To be definite, we will use $c_0 = 1$. Thus the reflection coefficient for upgoing waves is $-c_0$, which is -1, so an upcoming pulse $-r_n$ is reflected into the downgoing pulse r_n. A typical land seismogram is generated by the Goupillaud model with the non-free-surface condition, which for convenience of notation, we take as $c_0 = 0$ and $|c_1| < 1$ (so interface 1 is the surface of the earth). The well-known acoustic tube model [35] for human speech may be described as a Goupillaud-type model with the free-surface condition at the lips.

Kunetz [36] gave the solution for the inversion of a free-surface reflection seismogram. This inversion method yields the reflection coefficient series $c_1, c_2, c_3, \cdots$, from which the impedance function of the earth as a function of depth may be readily computed. Robinson [34] reformulated the Kunetz solution in terms of the Levinson [25] recursion and gave a computer program to do both the forward process (generation of the synthetic seismogram) and the inverse process (inversion of the seismogram to obtain the reflection coefficients). The Kunetz method is covered in the next section.

The celebrated inversion method of Gelfand and Levitan [7] represents the solution of the inversion problem for non-free-surface reflection seismograms. This method has been in the mainstream of physics for many years, and has been further developed and extended by many physicists and mathematicians. The discrete form of the Gelfand–Levitan equation is derived by Aki and Richards [38] for the case of a finite inhomogeneous medium, that is, an inhomogeneous medium bounded by homogeneous media at both ends. In Section II-F, we treat the discrete Gelfand–Levitan equation and give a derivation which holds for an unbounded inhomogeneous medium. We then discuss dynamic deconvolution, which is a means of solving the Gelfand–Levitan equation. Dynamic deconvolution makes use of the interactive recursion of the P and Q polynomials [34]. This recursion for the non-free-surface case represents the counterpart of the Levinson recursion for the free-surface case.

E. The Kunetz Inversion of Free-Surface Reflection Seismograms

Let the source in the Goupillaud model with the free-surface condition $c_0 = 1$ be a unit spike at time 0; see Fig. 3(a). The source gives rise to an upgoing wave in the first layer as a result of reflections and refractions from the interfaces below. We denote this upgoing wave by $-r_1, -r_2, -r_3, \cdots$; that is,

$$u_1(n) = -r_n \quad \text{(for } n = 1, 2, 3, \cdots)$$

represents the wave motion striking the free surface from below. The free surface is a perfect reflector (with upgoing reflection coefficient $-c_0 = -1$). The upgoing wave is reflected back to produce the downgoing wave

$$d_1(n) = r_n \quad (\text{for} \quad n = 1, 2, 3, \cdots).$$

The entire downgoing wave at the top of layer 1 is made up of this reflected portion together with the initial source pulse

$$d_1(0) = 1.$$

We will call $r_1, r_2, r_3, \cdots$, the reflection seismogram. Thus

$$R(s) = r_1 s + r_2 s^2 + r_3 s^3 + \cdots$$

is the generating function of the reflection seismogram. Then it follows that

$$U_1(s) = -R(s)$$

$$D_1(s) = 1 + R(s).$$

We will now use the invariance property of the Lorentz transformation. The net downgoing energy in layer 1 is

$$D_1 \overline{D}_1 - U_1 \overline{U}_1 = (1 + R)(1 + \overline{R}) - R\overline{R} = 1 + R + \overline{R}.$$

Here we use the convention that a bar over a function indicates that each s is replaced by s^{-1}. If we go very deep, we can assume that we reach a depth where no waves are reflected upward, so we can write

$$U_\infty = 0.$$

Thus at this infinite depth, we have

$$D_\infty \overline{D}_\infty - U_\infty \overline{U}_\infty = D_\infty \overline{D}_\infty.$$

We now come to an important point, which makes the layered earth model (i.e., a lattice network) useful for spectral analysis. Because $\Phi(\omega)$ defined as

$$\Phi(\omega) = D_\infty(e^{-i\omega}) D_\infty(e^{i\omega})$$

is a *bona fide* spectral density function (i.e., nonnegative function of ω), we can use the invariance of the net downgoing energy from layer to layer to establish that

$$\Phi(\omega) = 1 + R(e^{-i\omega}) + R(e^{i\omega})$$

is the same spectral density function. Therefore, the seismogram, completed by the initial pulse and by symmetry

$$\cdots, r_{-3}, r_{-2}, r_{-1}, 1, r_1, r_2, r_3, \cdots$$

is a *bona fide* autocorrelation function. That *the seismogram*

is the right-half side of an autocorrelation function is the celebrated result of *Kunetz* [36].

The problem of finding the reflection coefficients $c_1, c_2, c_3,$
$\cdots$ from the free-surface reflection seismograms $r_1, r_2, r_3, \cdots$
represents the inverse problem. The earth's acoustic impedance function is readily computed from the reflection coefficient series.

The Lorentz transformation from layer 0 to layer $k + 1$ may
be written as

$$\begin{bmatrix} D_{k+1} \\ U_{k+1} \end{bmatrix} = \frac{s^{-k/2}}{\sigma_k} \begin{bmatrix} P_k^R & Q_k^R \\ Q_k & P_k \end{bmatrix} \begin{bmatrix} 1 + R \\ -R \end{bmatrix}$$

where $\sigma_k = t_1 t_2 \cdots t_k$ is the one-way transmission coefficient
through the k interfaces. Using this matrix equation, we solve
for D_{k+1}. Then, by replacing s by s^{-1}, we form $\overline{D}_{k+1}$. We also
solve for U_{k+1}. We thus find that

$$\overline{D}_{k+1} - U_{k+1} = \frac{s^{-0.5k}}{\sigma_k} A_k(1 + R + \overline{R})$$

where A_n is defined as $A_n = P_n - Q_n$. Since $\Phi = 1 + R + \overline{R}$, we
have

$$A_k \Phi = \sigma_k s^{0.5k} (\overline{D}_{k+1} - U_{k+1}).$$

Let us appeal to the physics of the situation; see Fig. 4. The
function D_{k+1} is the generating function of the downgoing
wave at the top of layer $k + 1$. This downgoing wave is made
up of the direct pulse $d_{k+1}(0.5k)$ together with the following
pulses: $d_{k+1}(0.5k + 1)$, $d_{k+1}(0.5k + 2), \cdots$. Because the
direct pulse is the result of only the transmissions through the
first k interfaces, we see that the direct pulse is the product of
these k transmission coefficients, that is,

$$d_{k+1}(0.5k) = t_1 t_2 \cdots t_k = \sigma_k.$$

Because the time instant of this direct pulse is $0.5k$, we see that

$$D_{k+1}(s) = \sigma_k s^{0.5k} + (\text{terms in higher powers of } s).$$

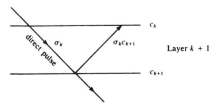

Fig. 4. Reflection of the direct pulse.

The function U_{k+1} is the generating function of the upgoing wave at the top of layer $k + 1$. The first pulse in the upgoing wave is the reflection of the direct downgoing pulse at interface $k + 1$. Thus the magnitude of this first upgoing pulse is $\sigma_k c_{k+1}$; that is, the magnitude is equal to the magnitude of the direct downgoing pulse times the reflection coefficient c_{k+1}. Because one time unit elapses for the round trip in layer $k + 1$, the first pulse of the upgoing wave in layer $k + 1$ occurs at one time unit later than the first pulse of the downgoing wave in layer $k + 1$. That is, the first upgoing pulse at the top of layer $k + 1$ occurs at time $0.5k + 1$. Thus

$$U_{k+1}(s) = \sigma_k c_{k+1} s^{0.5k+1} + \text{(terms in higher powers of } s\text{)}.$$

Using the above expressions, we obtain

$$A_k \Phi = \sigma_k s^{0.5k} \, [\text{(terms in lower powers of } s\text{)} + \sigma_k s^{-0.5k}$$

$$- \sigma_k c_{k+1} s^{0.5k+1} + \text{(terms in higher powers of } s\text{)}]$$

or

$$A_k \Phi = \sigma_k^2 \, [\text{(terms in negative powers)} + 1 - c_{k+1} s^{k+1}$$

$$+ \text{(terms in higher powers)}]$$

where $\sigma_k^2 = (t_1 t_2 \cdots t_k)^2$ is the two-way transmission coefficient through the k interfaces. Now comes the critical observation. The powers of s from 1 to k are missing on the right-hand side of the above equation. We will exploit this fact. We equate coefficients on each side of this equation for the powers of s from 0 to $k + 1$. We thus obtain the equations (one for each power from 0 to $k + 1$) given by

$$a_{k0} r_0 + a_{k1} r_1 + \cdots + a_{kk} r_k = \sigma_k^2$$

$$a_{k0} r_1 + a_{k1} r_0 + \cdots + a_{kk} r_{k-1} = 0$$

$$\cdots$$

$$a_{k0} r_k + a_{k1} r_{k-1} + \cdots + a_{kk} r_0 = 0$$

$$a_{k0} r_{k+1} + a_{k1} r_k + \cdots + a_{kk} r_1 = \sigma_k^2 c_{k+1}.$$

Here $a_{k0}, a_{k1}, \cdots, a_{kk}$ are the coefficients of the polynomial A_k. We note that $a_{k0} = 1$ and $r_0 = 1$. Now let us look at these equations. As we have seen, the Kunetz result says that r_k is an autocorrelation function. Thus these equations are *normal equations*, and hence the Levinson [25] recursion can be used to solve them. The result is the inversion program [34] that finds the reflection coefficients from the free-surface (marine) reflection seismogram.

F. The Gelfand–Levitan Inversion of Non-Free-Surface Reflection Seismograms

Let us now turn to the non-free-surface reflection seismogram, that is, the seismogram produced by the Goupillaud model with the non-free-surface condition $c_0 = 0$ and c_1 arbitrary; see Fig. 3(b). Let the source be a unit spike. The resulting seismogram is taken to be the upgoing wave in the first layer, that is, by

$$u_1(n) = r_n \quad \text{(for } n = 1, 2, 3, \cdots).$$

Because interface 0 is absent (i.e., $c_0 = 0$) the upgoing wave is not reflected back into the medium. Thus the downgoing wave at the top of layer 1 is simply the initial source pulse

$$d_1(0) = 1, \quad d_1(n) = 0 \quad \text{(for } n = 1, 2, 3, \cdots).$$

Let $R(s) = r_1 s + r_2 s^2 + \cdots$ be the generating function of the reflection seismogram. Thus $U_1(s) = R(s)$ and $D_1(s) = 1$. The Lorentz transformation is

$$\begin{bmatrix} D_{k+1} \\ U_{k+1} \end{bmatrix} = \sigma_k^{-1} s^{-0.5k} \begin{bmatrix} P_k^R & Q_k^R \\ Q_k & P_k \end{bmatrix} \begin{bmatrix} 1 \\ R \end{bmatrix}.$$

Thus we obtain

$$D_{k+1} = \sigma_k^{-1} s^{-0.5k} (P_k^R + Q_k^R R)$$

$$U_{k+1} = \sigma_k^{-1} s^{-0.5k} (Q_k + P_k R).$$

We add these two equations to obtain

$$D_{k+1} + U_{k+1} = \sigma_k^{-1} s^{-0.5k} (G_k^R + R G_k)$$

where G_k is defined as

$$G_k(s) = P_k(s) + Q_k^R(s)$$

$$= g_{k0} + g_{k1} s + \cdots + g_{k,k-1} s^{k-1}$$

$$= (1 - c_k) + g_{k1} s + \cdots + (c_1 c_k - c_1) s^{k-1}.$$

Because $g_{k0} = 1 - c_k$, we can find c_k as soon as we can determine g_{k0}. Thus the reflection coefficient series, and hence the impedance function of the earth, can be found directly from the sequence $g_{10}, g_{20}, g_{30}, \cdots$. Let us now show how this sequence is determined.

The direct pulse $d_{k+1}(k/2)$ is the product of the transmission coefficients $\sigma_k = t_1 t_2 \cdots t_k$ and it arrives at time $0.5k$. The first term of U_{k+1} arrives at time $0.5k + 1$. Thus $D_{k+1} + U_{k+1}$ has the form

$$D_{k+1} + U_{k+1} = \sigma_k s^{0.5k} + \text{(terms in higher powers of } s).$$

Thus we have

$$\sigma_k s^{0.5k} + \text{(higher power terms)} = \sigma_k^{-1} s^{-0.5k} (G_k^R + RG_k)$$

which gives

$$G_k^R + RG_k = \sigma_k^2 s^k + \text{(higher power terms)}.$$

This equation shows that the coefficients of $G_k^R + RG_k$ for the powers $1, 2, \cdots, k - 1$ are zero and the coefficient for the power k is equal to σ_k^2; that is,

$$g_{k,k-1} + g_{k0} r_1 = 0$$

$$g_{k,k-2} + g_{k0} r_2 + g_{k1} r_1 = 0$$

$$\cdots$$

$$g_{k1} + g_{k0} r_{k-1} + \cdots + g_{k,k-2} r_1 = 0$$

$$g_{k0} + g_{k0} r_k + \cdots + g_{k,k-2} r_2 + g_{k,k-1} r_1 = \sigma_k^2.$$

This set of equations is the discrete version of the *Gelfand–Levitan equation*.

Given the free-surface reflection seismogram $r_1, r_2, r_3, \cdots$, the Gelfand–Levitan inversion method involves solving the above set of equations for each of $k = 1, 2, \cdots N$. For $k = 1$ the set is

$$g_{10} + g_{10} r_1 = \sigma_1^2.$$

For $k = 2$ the set is

$$g_{21} + g_{20} r_1 = 0$$

$$g_{20} + g_{20} r_2 + g_{21} r_1 = \sigma_2^2.$$

After we solve for $g_{10}, g_{20}, \cdots :$, then we can find the reflection coefficients by means of

$$c_1' = 1 - g_{10}$$

$$c_2 = 1 - g_{20}$$

and so on.

If we define $a_{k1} = g_{k,k-1}$, $a_{k2} = g_{k,k-2}, \cdots, a_{k,k-1} = g_{k1}$, $a_{kk} = g_{k0} - 1$, then the Gelfand–Levitan equations are

$$\begin{bmatrix} a_{k1} \\ a_{k2} \\ \cdots \\ a_{kk} \end{bmatrix} + \begin{bmatrix} 0 & 0 & 0 & r_1 \\ 0 & 0 & r_1 & r_2 \\ & & & \\ r_1 & r_2 & r_{k-1} & r_k \end{bmatrix} \begin{bmatrix} a_{k1} \\ a_{k2} \\ \cdots \\ a_{kk} \end{bmatrix} + \begin{bmatrix} r_1 \\ r_2 \\ r_k \end{bmatrix} = 0$$

which we recognize as this discrete counterpart of the *Gelfand–Levitan integral equation* [7], [9], [38]

$$a(\tau, t) + \int_{-t}^{T} a(\tau, \beta)\, r(t + \beta)\, d\beta + r(t + \tau) = 0.$$

G. Seismic Inversion by Dynamic Deconvolution

The Gelfand–Levitan method of inversion, together with its many related methods, has received wide recognition. However, instead of the Gelfand–Levitan approach given in the preceding section, the seismic industry approaches the problem from a different point of view. This alternative inversion computational scheme is the method of *dynamic deconvolution* (dy-decon) [39], [40], [8]. Dy-decon inversion is based upon the physical structure of the reflection seismogram. The key fact is that the reflection seismogram is generated from the reflection coefficient by means of the Einstein addition formula [33]. The recognition of this fact makes the inversion of a reflection seismogram very simple from a computational point of view.

Let us now give the dy-decon computation scheme for the inversion of a non-free-surface reflection seismogram. We use the same conventions as in the preceding section. The field-recorded reflection seismogram $r_1, r_2, r_3, \cdots$ is represented by its generating function $R(s)$, which we now will denote by $R_1(s)$ because the field-recorded seismogram occurs in layer 1. We have

$$R_1(s) = r_1 s + r_2 s^2 + r_3 s^3 + \cdots$$

$$= c_1 s + (\text{terms in higher powers of } s).$$

We know $R_1(s)$ must have this form, because $c_1 s$ represents the first bounce from interface 1. No multiple reflections can appear at the time of the first bounce. Now suppose that layer 2 expands to fill the whole upper half-space, so there is no interface 1. Now the top interface is interface 2. Let the resulting seismogram in this expanded layer 2 be represented by its generating function

$$R_2(s) = c_2 s + (\text{terms in higher powers of } s).$$

Here $c_2 s$ represents the first bounce. Next, expand layer 3 to fill up the whole upper half-space. The resulting reflection seismogram has generating function

$$R_3(s) = c_3 s + (\text{terms in higher powers of } s)$$

where $c_3 s$ represents the first bounce. Thus conceptually we have a suite of reflection seismograms ($k = 1, 2, 3, \cdots$) with generating functions

$$R_k(s) = c_k s + (\text{terms in higher powers of } s)$$

where $c_k s$ represents the first bounce from interface k. We can, therefore, make the following important conclusion. Given the reflection seismogram for layer k, we can immediately find the reflection coefficient c_k for layer k, because c_k is simply the first coefficient appearing in the seismogram. This conclusion represents the solution of one-half of the inversion problem. The other half of the problem involves determining the suite of reflection seismograms. The given information is the top seismogram $R_1(s)$; this seismogram is the one physically recorded in the field by a seismic crew.

If the current in a river has velocity c_1, and if our motor boat in still water has a velocity R_1, then our motor boat headed upstream will have a velocity R_2 given by

$$R_2 = R_1 - c_1.$$

This equation is the *Newton addition formula*. However, if one attempts to apply Newtonian mechanical laws to ultra-high-speed charged particles, then an insurmountable contradiction is encountered. That is, the simple addition of velocities, as used in the boat example, does not apply in electrodynamics. Instead, one should use the Einstein addition formula for combining velocities. The Einstein formula guaranteed that the resulting velocity will never exceed the velocity of light. Thus the above Newton addition formula should be replaced by the *Einstein addition formula*, which is

$$R_2 = \frac{R_1 - c_1}{1 - R_1 c_1}.$$

Here we assume that all velocities are measured in natural units (i.e., in units such that the velocity of light is unity). Suppose $c_1 = -0.5$ and $R_1 = 0.8$. Then, according to the Newton formula, $R_2 = 1.3$, so R_2 is greater than unity; that is, R_2 is greater than the velocity of light. According to the Einstein formula

$$R_2 = \frac{0.8 + 0.5}{1 + 0.8(0.5)} = 0.929$$

which (necessarily) is less than the velocity of light. The Einstein formula is the correct one to use for ultra-high velocities.

Now let us make the following important observation, which led to the dynamic deconvolution process. A reflection coefficient in magnitude can never exceed unity. A reflection coefficient greater than unity in magnitude is just as impossible from the physics as a velocity greater than the velocity of light. Thus in combining the reflection coefficients of a system of layers, it follows that the Einstein addition formula must be used. As a result, the resulting reflectivity will never exceed unity in magnitude, as required in any physical system.

Now we want to head our boat upstream; that is, we want to dynamically deconvolve down into the earth. We could use the Newton addition formula and write

$$sR_2 = R_1 - c_1 s.$$

That is, the Newton formula says that we merely subtract the first bounce from R_1 in order to obtain R_2. (The s represents a time shift.) In fact, this formula is approximately true if the reflection coefficients are very small in magnitude, just as the Newton formula for velocities is true if the velocities are very small with respect to the velocity of light. Otherwise, we must use the Einstein addition formula

$$R_2 = \frac{R_1 - c_1 s}{s - R_1 c_1}.$$

Let us now give the inversion algorithm of dynamic deconvolution. We know R_1 (i.e., the field-recorded reflection seismogram). In step 1, we find c_1 as the first bounce of R_1, and then we compute R_2 by the above Einstein addition formula. This computation is easily done by making use of subroutine POLYDV in [34]. So ends step 1. In step 2, we find c_2 as the first bounce of R_2, and then we use the Einstein addition formula to find R_3

$$R_3 = \frac{R_2 - c_2 s}{s - R_2 c_2}.$$

So ends step 2. In step 3, we find c_3 as the first bounce of R_3, and then we find R_4 as

$$R_4 = \frac{R_3 - c_3 s}{s - R_3 c_3}.$$

So ends step 3. Thus given R_1, we can perform the entire deconvolution, and so obtain the sequence of reflection coefficients $c_1, c_2, c_3, \cdots$ and the suite of reflection seismograms $R_2, R_3, R_4, \cdots$. From the sequence of reflection coefficients, we can compute the impedance function of the earth.

Dynamic deconvolution gives the same impedance function as that found by the Gelfand–Levitan discrete inversion method. However, dynamic deconvolution is carried out in terms of physically meaningful quantities (i.e., reflection coefficients and reflection seismograms), so interactive computation can be used to reduce the effects of noise. Also, there are many other features of dynamic deconvolution which make it attractive, such as the option [39] of the determination of the reflection coefficients in the reverse order, i.e., in the order $c_n, c_{n-1}, \cdots, c_3, c_2, c_1$. This reverse order can be useful because in many cases, the most harmful noise appears at the beginning of the reflection seismogram. In such cases, it is better to work backwards in time on the reflection seismogram, leaving its noisy beginning to the end of the computations.

Let us now establish the Einstein addition formula by means of the Lorentz transformation. This proof can be found in most physics textbooks. We have

$$\begin{bmatrix} D_2 \\ U_2 \end{bmatrix} = \frac{s^{-1/2}}{t_1} \begin{bmatrix} s & -c_1 \\ -c_1 s & 1 \end{bmatrix} \begin{bmatrix} 1 \\ R_1 \end{bmatrix}$$

which gives

$$t_1 s^{1/2} D_2 = s - c_1 R_1$$
$$t_1 s^{1/2} U_2 = -c_1 s + R_1.$$

The reflection seismogram R_2 is the result obtained by deconvolving the upgoing wave U_2 by the downgoing wave D_2; that is,

$$R_2 = \frac{U_2}{D_2} = \frac{R_1 - c_1 s}{s - R_1 c_1}.$$

This equation is the Einstein addition formula.

H. Polynomial Recursion for Dynamic Deconvolution Inversion

Further insight on dynamic deconvolution can be obtained by examining the role played by the polynomials P_k and Q_k. Using the Lorentz transformation for the first k layers, we have

$$\begin{bmatrix} D_{k+1} \\ U_{k+1} \end{bmatrix} = \frac{s^{-k/2}}{\sigma_k} \begin{bmatrix} P_k^R & Q_k^R \\ Q_k & P_k \end{bmatrix} \begin{bmatrix} 1 \\ R_1 \end{bmatrix}.$$

As usual, σ_k is the one-way transmission factor

$$\sigma_k = t_k t_{k-1} \cdots t_1.$$

This equation gives

$$D_{k+1} = \sigma_k^{-1} s^{-k/2} (P_k^R + Q_k^R R_1)$$
$$U_{k+1} = \sigma_k^{-1} s^{-k/2} (Q_k + P_k R_1).$$

The direct downgoing pulse arrives at layer $k + 1$ at time $k/2$ and with a transmission loss of $\sigma_k = t_1 t_2 \cdots t_k$. Thus D_{k+1} has the form

$$D_{k+1} = \sigma_k s^{k/2} + (\text{terms in higher powers of } s).$$

This direct downgoing pulse is reflected at interface $k + 1$ at time $(k + 1)/2$ and produces the initial pulse of the upgoing wave. Because the incident pulse has amplitude σ_k and the reflection coefficient is c_{k+1}, it follows that the initial upgoing pulse has amplitude $\sigma_k c_{k+1}$. This initial upgoing pulse arrives at the top of layer $k + 1$ at time $(k/2) + 1$. Thus U_{k+1} has the form

$$U_{k+1} = \sigma_k c_{k+1} s^{(k/2)+1} + \text{(terms in higher powers of } s\text{)}.$$

We now have two equations for U_{k+1} Equating them, we have

$$\sigma_k c_{k+1} s^{(k/2)+1} + \text{(higher power terms)}$$

$$= \sigma_k^{-1} s^{-k/2} (Q_k + P_k R_1).$$

Let us now just pick out the $s^{(k/2)+1}$ term on the right-hand side. The right-hand side is

$$\sigma_k^{-1} s^{-k/2} [(q_{k1} s + \cdots + q_{kk} s^k)$$

$$+ (p_{k0} + \cdots + p_{k,k-1} s^{k-1})(r_1 s + \cdots + r_{k+1} s^{k+1} + \cdots)]$$

so the $s^{(k/2)+1}$ term is displayed as

$$\sigma_k^{-1} s^{-k/2} [(p_{k0} r_{k+1} + \cdots + p_{k,k-1} r_2) s^{k+1}$$

$$+ \text{(higher power terms)}].$$

Equating the $s^{(k/2)+1}$ terms on the left and right, we have

$$\sigma_k c_{k+1} s^{(k/2)+1} = \sigma_k^{-1} s^{-k/2} (p_{k0} r_{k+1} + \cdots + p_{k,k-1} r_2) s^{k+1}$$

which gives

$$c_{k+1} = \frac{p_{k0} r_{k+1} + p_{k1} r_k + \cdots + p_{k,k-1} r_2}{\sigma_k^2}.$$

We thus have the following scheme based on the Robinson [34] recursion for P and Q in order to invert the non-free-surface reflection seismogram $r_1, r_2, r_3, \cdots$. As the initial step, we set $c_1 = r_1$, $\sigma_1^2 = 1 - c_1^2$, $P_1(s) = 1$, $Q_1(s) = -c_1 s$. Then we perform the following DO loop from $k = 1$ to the total number of layers that we wish to consider

Compute c_{k+1} by the above formula

Compute $\sigma_{k+1}^2 = (1 - c_{k+1}^2) \sigma_k^2$

Compute $P_{k+1}(s) = P_k(s) - c_{k+1} s \, Q_k^R(s)$

Compute $Q_{k+1}(s) = Q_k(s) - c_{k+1} s \, P_k^R(s)$.

We thus obtain the reflection coefficient series $c_1, c_2, c_3, \cdots$ from which the required impedance function can be calculated.

Finally, let us write down the expression for the reflection seismogram R_{k+1} at layer $k + 1$. It is

$$R_{k+1} = \frac{U_{k+1}}{D_{k+1}} = \frac{Q_k + P_k R_1}{P_k^R + Q_k^R R_1}$$

$$= \frac{\sigma_k c_{k+1} s^{(k/2)+1} + \text{(higher power terms)}}{\sigma_k s^{k/2} + \text{(higher power terms)}}$$

$$= c_{k+1} s + \text{(higher power terms)}.$$

We have thus confirmed the statement made in the preceding section that the first bounce of R_{k+1} is c_{k+1} s.

In closing our discussion of 1-D inversion, let us mention the *fixed-entropy estimate* [41] of the seismic acoustic log. This scheme is an autocorrecting iterative method, based on a forward model, to compute the acoustic impedance of the earth from the reflection seismogram. This method was offered commercially by Digicon Inc. during 1968–1969 under the trade name S.A.L. (for seismic acoustic log), and it has proved successful as a practical inversion scheme in seismic data processing centers.

III. Two-Dimensional Inversion

A. Plane-Wave Decomposition and Migration

We will now consider two spatial dimensions: lateral coordinate x and depth coordinate z, where the z axis points downward. The other dimension is that of time t. The 2-D methods discussed here involve extremely simple models, so these methods are not truly 2-D in any general sense. We discuss two methods. One treats the forward and inverse problem for a horizontally layered media. This method involves the Radon transform [42], which is often called "slant stacking" by geophysicists. The Radon transform produces a plane-wave decomposition of a wavefield, and thus we can operate on each plane wave separately in order to produce our desired results. The other method we present is a process for wavefield reconstruction and imaging. This process is known as "migration" in geophysics. Although various migration methods have been in constant use by the seismic industry for about forty years, a major breakthrough occurred in 1978, when Stolt [27] disclosed his spectral method of migration. This pioneering work of Stolt is based upon the fast Fourier transform, and it is often called frequency-domain migration or f–k migration (frequency–wavenumber migration). Several universities have seismic research projects which devote large efforts to migration and related problems.

B. The Radon Transform

Let $u(x, t)$ represent the wave motion observed on the surface of the ground ($z = 0$). For fixed horizontal position x, the 1-D function $u(x, t)$ of time t represents a seismic trace. The entire suite of seismic traces for all positions x represents the seismic section.

The *Radon transform* [42] of $u(x, t)$ is defined as

$$U_R(p, \tau) = \int_{-\infty}^{\infty} u(x, px + \tau) \, dx.$$

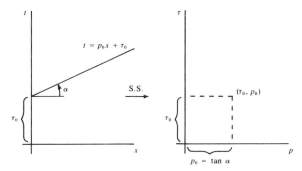

Fig. 5. The slant stack of a line is a point.

We see that the Radon transform is a function of two variables; τ is called the *intercept* and p is called the *slope*. The reason is that $t = \tau + px$ represents a line in the (x, t) plane (where x is the horizontal axis and t is the vertical axis). This line has slope $p = \tan \alpha$ (i.e., the line makes an angle α with the x axis) and t-intercept τ (i.e., the line cuts the t axis at τ). Geophysicists call the Radon transformation a *slant stack*, as this concept has been in use in exploration seismology since the work of the MIT Geophysical Analysis Group [43] in the 1950's. We may regard the terms *Radon transform* and *slant stack* as meaning the same thing.

The reason for the name "slant stack" is the following. We can perform the Radon transform by sweeping over the wavefield $u(x, t)$ with lines, each given by its slope p and intercept τ. We then add (integrate) all the values on each line and associate the sum (integral) with its slope p and intercept τ. That is, we "stack" all the values of the wavefield on each "slant" line; that is, we "slant stack."

Thus the Radon transform involves summing all the amplitudes $u(x, t)$ along a given line of slope p_0 and intercept τ_0, and plotting that sum at the corresponding point (p_0, τ_0) on the p, τ plane. In brief, the Radon transform has this characteristic; it takes a line of intercept τ_0 and slope p_0 in the x, t space and transforms it into a point (p_0, τ_0) in the new space. That is, the Radon transform converts a line into a point; see Fig. 5. No information is lost because a line is completely described by its intercept and slope.

Now let us look at the *inverse Radon Transform*. This is an inverse slant stack. To be mathematically correct, we must first take the time derivative of the Hilbert transform of $U_R(p, \tau)$. We then slant stack along lines of slope $\tan \beta$ and intercept t; that is, lines $\tau = t + (\tan \beta)p$. Let us find the inverse slant stack of the point (p_0, τ_0). The only slant lines that will contribute are the ones that go through this point. Such a contributing line satisfies

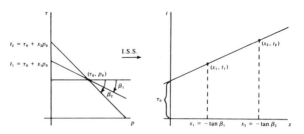

Fig. 6. The inverse slant stack of the point is the original line.

$$\tau_0 = t + (\tan \beta)p_0$$

so its intercept is $t = \tau_0 - p_0 \tan \beta$. For the inverse slant stack, we let x be the negative slope, that is,

$$x = -\tan \beta.$$

Thus the point (p_0, τ_0) for each β gets transformed into the point $(x, t) = (-\tan \beta, \tau_0 - p_0 \tan \beta)$ in the original (x, t) plane. As β sweeps out all values, the locus of all these points is the line $t = \tau_0 + p_0 x$, that is, the line of slope p_0 and intercept τ_0 in the (x, t) plane. This is the original line, so we see that the inverse slant stack works; see Fig. 6.

The above heuristic explanation of the inverse Radon transform must be made more precise mathematically. An equation for our heuristic description is

$$u(x, t) = \int_{-\infty}^{\infty} \frac{d}{dt} H U_R(p, t - px) \, dp$$

where H denotes the Hilbert transform.

C. The Fourier Transform

The Radon transform takes a line into a point, and the inverse Radon transform takes the point back into the original line. The 2-D Fourier transform takes a line into another line, and the inverse Fourier transform takes it back into the original line.

Let the function be a delta function $\delta(t - px - \tau)$ along the line $t = px + \tau$ in the (x, t) plane. This line has slope $p = \tan \alpha$ and intercept τ. The *Fourier transform* is

$$\int_{-\infty}^{\infty} \int_{-\infty}^{\infty} \delta(t - px - \tau)e^{-i(\omega t - k_x x)} \, dx \, dt$$

$$= \int_{-\infty}^{\infty} e^{-i[\omega(px+\tau) - k_x x]} \, dx$$

$$= 2\pi e^{-i\omega\tau} \delta(p\omega - k_x).$$

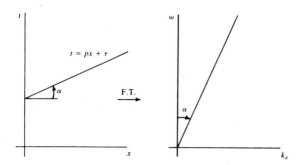

Fig. 7. The Fourier transform of a line is a line through the origin with reciprocal slope. The intercept of the original line is contained in the phase spectrum of the transform line.

Thus the Fourier transform has magnitude given by a delta function along the line $\omega = k_x/p$, and has phase given by $-\omega\tau$. The line makes an angle α with the ω axis and goes through the origin (intercept = 0). The slope of the given line is the reciprocal of the slope of the tranformed line, and the intercept of the given line is locked up in the phase spectrum; see Fig. 7.

By taking the *inverse Fourier transform*, we regain the original line; that is,

$$\frac{1}{2\pi} \int_{-\infty}^{\infty} \int_{-\infty}^{\infty} e^{-i\omega\tau} \delta(p\omega - k_x) e^{i(\omega t - k_x x)} \, dk_x \, d\omega$$

$$= \delta(t - px - \tau)$$

see Fig. 8.

Because of this interplay between lines, the Radon transform is closely related to the Fourier transform. Let us evaluate the Fourier transform $U(k_x, \omega)$ of the seismic wavefield $u(x, t)$ along the line $\omega = k_x/p$. We have $k_x = p\omega$ so $U(k_x, \omega)$ becomes

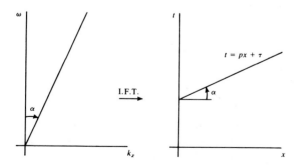

Fig. 8. The inverse Fourier transform gives back the original line.

$$U(p\omega, \omega) = \int_{-\infty}^{\infty} \int_{-\infty}^{\infty} u(x, t) e^{-i(\omega t - p\omega x)} \, dx \, dt.$$

Because $\tau = t - px$, we have

$$U(p\omega, \omega) = \int_{-\infty}^{\infty} e^{-i\omega\tau} \left[\int_{-\infty}^{\infty} u(x, \tau + px) \, dx \right] d\tau.$$

We recognize the expression within the brackets as the Radon transform $U_R(p, \tau)$. Thus

$$U(p\omega, \omega) = \int_{-\infty}^{\infty} e^{-i\omega\tau} \, U_R(p, \tau) \, d\tau$$

which says that *the Fourier transform of the Radon transform with respect to the intercept variable τ is equal to the 2-D Fourier transform evaluated on the line $k_x = p\omega$.*

D. The Ray Parameter p and the Intercept Parameter τ

Let us now consider a horizontally stratified layered medium in 2-D space (x, z). We assume that the depth axis z points downward, with $z = 0$ indicating the surface. Each interface is represented by a flat (i.e., nontilted) line; line $z =$ positive constant. Let us assume there are N earth layers in total, with interfaces at $z_0 = 0, z_1, z_2, \cdots, z_N$. Layer k lies between interface z_{k-1} (on top) and z_k (on bottom). The thicknesses of the layers are

$$h_1 = z_1 - z_0, h_2 = z_2 - z_1, \cdots, h_N = z_N - z_{N-1}.$$

We let $v_1, v_2, \cdots, v_N$ denote the compressional velocities in the respective layers.

Let an impulsive source be initiated at the surface. Waves will travel down into the earth where they will suffer reflections and refractions at the interfaces. At each surface point $(x, z = 0)$, the resulting wave motion can be recorded in the form of a seismic trace. The seismic trace will include primary reflections (i.e., impulses that have traveled paths directly down and back up) and multiple reflections (i.e., impulses that have bounced back and forth within various layers and combinations of layers before returning to the surface). Because the interfaces are flat, there is a symmetry; for each downgoing leg there is a corresponding upgoing leg. Thus we can consider merely the upgoing legs of the ray paths. We thus work with one-way times. The complete times, or two-way times, would then be twice the one-way times that we obtain.

The primary reflection from layer k would have one leg from each layer from interface k up to the surface. A multiple reflection includes extra bounces, so it would have more than

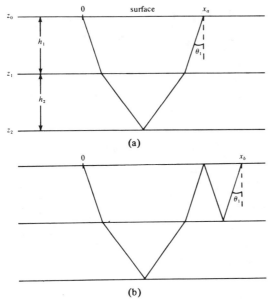

Fig. 9. Primary (a) and peg-leg multiple (b) each with the same value
θ_1 of the emergence angle but with different offsets x_a and x_b.

one leg in some or all of the layers. For example, a peg-leg
multiple has one long leg (corresponding to the primary) and
a short leg (corresponding to an extra bounce); see Fig. 9.

Using geometric seismics, we can say that the waves travel
along rays. At a given receiver point $(x_1, z = 0)$ on the surface
of the earth, the waves will come in from all directions. Let
θ_1 represent the angle of emergence of a ray. (All angles are
measured from the normal; that is, all angles are measured
from the z-axis to the ray.) For example, at a given receiver
point $(x_1, 0)$, the primary from interface k would come in at
one angle, the primary from another interface would come in
at a different angle, and each possible multiple would come
in at its own angle. At a different receiver point $(x_2, 0)$, all
the angles would be different. To make any sense at all from
the received signals, we must do some sorting.

One way to sort is by angle. Let us pick one given angle θ_1,
and then move along the horizontal x-axis, and pick out each
ray that comes in at that given angle. We throw away all the
other rays. We now appeal to Snell's law, which says that p is
a constant where

$$p = \frac{\sin \theta_1}{v_1} = \frac{\sin \theta_2}{v_2} = \cdots = \frac{\sin \theta_N}{v_N}.$$

All the ray paths that we have picked out have the same value
of the parameter p, which is called the *ray parameter* or *Snell's*

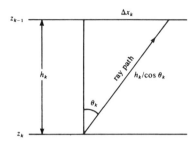

Fig. 10. Upgoing ray path in layer k.

parameter. A wave which travels along a path with a fixed value of p is called a *Snell wave.* Thus we have sorted out all the Snell waves for one given value of p, namely, $p = \sin \theta_1 / v_1$. What good does this do us?

The answer is that we can find an associated parameter τ which has nice properties. Each ray path that we have saved is characterized by the same value of p. We are going to construct our model (i.e., we are going to pick the interface positions $z_1, z_2, \cdots, z_N$) to fit this value of p. In other words, we are going to pick a model (characterized by the value p) to fit our data (all the received signals with a fixed value p).

Let us look at the ray path of one leg in layer k; see Fig. 10. The thickness of the layer is h_k, and the angle that the ray makes with the vertical is θ_k. Thus we have a right triangle with angle θ_k and adjacent, or vertical, side h_k. The travel distance of the wave is the slant distance (i.e., the hypotenuse). The offset distance Δx_k is the projection of the travel distance on the x-axis (i.e., Δx_k is the opposite, or horizontal, side).

The offset distance Δx_k is

$$\Delta x_k = h_k \tan \theta_k.$$

The slant distance is $h_k / \cos \theta_k$, so the travel time is

$$\Delta t_k = \frac{h_k}{v_k \cos \theta_k}.$$

Let us now consider the parameter τ. Its increment $\Delta \tau_k$ for layer k is defined as

$$\Delta \tau_k = \Delta t_k - p \Delta x_k.$$

Let us compute $\Delta \tau_k$. It is

$$\Delta \tau_k = \frac{h_k}{v_k \cos \theta_k} - p h_k \frac{\sin \theta_k}{\cos \theta_k} = \frac{h_k \cos \theta_k}{v_k}.$$

The angle θ_k is fixed because $\sin \theta_k = v_k p$. We will now choose the interfaces of our model so that the thicknesses of the layers are

$$z_k - z_{k-1} = h_k = \frac{v_k}{\cos \theta_k}.$$

In other words, we fit the model to the data; the data consist of all the ray paths with a fixed value of p. Thus for the chosen model, we have

$$\Delta \tau_k = 1$$

for each layer k. The primary from interface k goes through k layers; thus the τ value for this primary is

$$\tau = \sum_{j=1}^{k} \Delta \tau_j = k.$$

Suppose a multiple path goes through layer 1 four times, layer 2 three times, and layer 3 once. Then the τ value for this multiple reflection is

$$\tau = 4\Delta \tau_1 + 3\Delta \tau_2 + \Delta \tau_3 = (4 + 3 + 1) = 8.$$

Thus the τ parameter is an integer that gives the sum of the total number of legs in each layer that a multiple path makes. The name of the τ parameter is the *intercept parameter*.

E. The Time–Distance Curve

Let us now plot travel time t versus offset distance x for any given type of reflection path (primary or multiple). For example, we might consider the multiple path $(2, 1)$ which goes through layer 1 two times and layer 2 one time; see Fig. 11. We consider this type of path (a path with 2, 1 bounces in layers 1, 2, respectively) for all values of the ray parameter p; that is, for all possible emergence angles θ_1. For each value of offset x there will be a travel time t. A plot of travel time t versus offset x is called the *time–distance curve* for the multiple

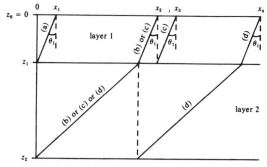

Fig. 11. Upgoing paths only are shown: (*a*) first primary (1 bounce in layer 1); (*b*) second primary (1, 1 bounces in layers 1, 2, respectively); (*c*) multiple (2, 1 bounces in layers 1, 2, respectively); (*d*) multiple (1, 2 bounces in layers 1, 2, respectively).

path $(2, 1)$. Let us designate this curve as $t = f(x; 2, 1)$. This curve is shown in Fig. 12. Also shown are the time–distance curve $t = f(x; 1)$ for the primary from interface 1, the time–distance curve $t = f(x; 1, 1)$ for the primary from interface 2, and the time–distance curve $t = f(x; 1, 2)$ for the multiple with 1, 2 bounces in layers 1, 2, respectively. Except for the case of the first primary $t = f(x; 1)$, there is no explicit formula for such a curve. However, we can find a parametric representation in terms of the ray parameter p. Since $\sin \theta_k = p v_k$, it follows that $\cos \theta_k = (1 - p^2 v_k^2)^{1/2}$ and $\tan \theta_k = p v_k / (1 - p^2 v_k^2)^{1/2}$. Thus the parametric representation of the above time–distance curve $t = f(x; n_1, n_2, \cdots, n_k)$ is

$$x = \sum_k \Delta x_k = \sum_k \frac{h_k p v_k}{(1 - p^2 v_k^2)^{1/2}}$$

$$t = \sum_k \Delta t_k = \sum_k \frac{h_k}{v_k(1 - p^2 v_k^2)^{1/2}}$$

where the index k runs over the value $k = 1$, n_1 times; $k = 2$, n_2 times; and so on, up to $k = k$, n_k times.

Because the ray emerges at angle θ_1 with the vertical, it follows that the wavefront makes an angle θ_1 with the horizontal, as the wavefront is at right angles to the ray. In a small increment of time dt, the wave travels a distance $v_1 dt$ along the ray path. In the same amount of time, the wavefront sweeps out a distance dx along the x-axis, where $dx \sin \theta_1 = v_1 \, dt$, as shown in Fig. 13. Thus the slope of the time–distance curve is

$$\frac{dt}{dx} = \frac{\sin \theta_1}{v_1}.$$

That is, *the slope of the time–distance curve at any point x is equal to the ray parameter p of the ray path that emerges at that point*; i.e.,

$$\frac{dt}{dx} = p.$$

In summary, each type of multiple path has a time–distance curve whose slope at any value of x is equal to the ray parameter characterizing the ray emerging at that point. For example, for the time–distance curve $t = f(x; 2, 1)$, we have

$$p = \frac{dt}{dx} = \frac{df(x; 2, 1)}{dx}$$

where the ray emerging at x has angle $\theta_1 = \sin^{-1} (p v_1)$.

Let us now find out what the parameter τ is. We know that the slope of the curve $f(x; 2, 1)$ is p. That is, the tangent to this curve is a line with slope p. Let τ be the t-intercept of this

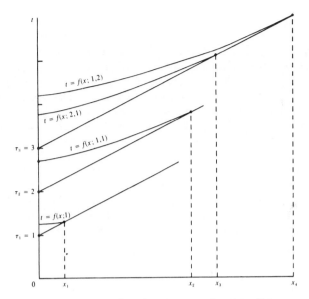

Fig. 12. The hyperbolic-shaped curves are the time–distance curves for the primaries $f(x; 1)$ and $f(x; 2)$ and the multiples $f(x; 2, 1)$ and $f(x; 1, 2)$. The offsets x_1, x_2, x_3, x_4 correspond to the same value of the ray parameter p. When we slant stack at this value of p, the first primary (one leg) gives intercept $\tau_1 = 1$, the second primary (two legs) gives $\tau_2 = 2$, and each of the multiples (each three legs) gives $\tau_3 = 3$.

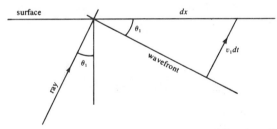

Fig. 13. Geometric demonstration that the slope of the time–distance curve is p.

tangent line, so the equation of the tangent line is

$$t = px + \tau.$$

In the preceding section, we defined $\Delta \tau_k$ as

$$\Delta \tau_k = \Delta t_k - p \Delta x_k$$

so

$$\sum_k \Delta \tau_k = \sum_k \Delta t_k - p \sum_k \Delta x_k$$

which is

$$\tau = t - px.$$

Thus we see that the parameter τ given in the preceding section is the same as the τ given in this section. This explains why we have called τ the *intercept parameter*. The parameter τ is the intercept of the tangent line with the t-axis.

What happens if we slant stack a time–distance curve? A time–distance curve may be thought of as the envelope of its tangent lines. Slant stacking converts each tangent line into a point (p, τ), where p is the slope and τ is the intercept of the line. As an example, let us consider the case of the first primary reflection. The ray-path travel time is t, so the ray-path distance is $v_1 t$, which is the hypotenuse of a right triangle with sides h_1 and x. Thus by the Pythagorean theorem, we have

$$v_1^2 t^2 = x^2 + h_1^2$$

so

$$t = \frac{1}{v_1} (x^2 + h_1^2)^{1/2}.$$

which shows that the first-primary time-distance curve is a hyperbola. This is the one time–distance curve we can write explicitly (instead of implicitly in parametric form). The curve in parametric form is

$$x = \frac{h_1 p v_1}{(1 - p^2 v_1^2)^{1/2}}$$

$$t = \frac{h_1}{v_1 (1 - p^2 v_1^2)^{1/2}}.$$

The intercept parameter τ is

$$\tau = t - px = \frac{h_1 \cos \theta_1}{v_1}$$

where

$$\cos \theta_1 = (1 - p^2 v_1^2)^{1/2}.$$

Thus the above equation for τ together with the Snell equation are

$$\frac{\tau}{h_1} = \frac{\cos \theta_1}{v_1}$$

$$p = \frac{\sin \theta_1}{v_1}$$

which give

$$\frac{\tau^2}{h_1^2} + p^2 = \frac{1}{v_1^2}.$$

Thus the (p, τ) curve is an *ellipse*. This ellipse is the Radon transform (i.e., slant stack) of the time–distance hyperbola

$$t^2 - \frac{x^2}{v_1^2} = \frac{h_1^2}{v_1^2}.$$

F. Dynamic Deconvolution (Inversion) and Dynamic Reconvolution (Construction)

A seismic section $u(x, t)$ gives the amplitude of the received waves as a function of receiver position x and time t. A seismic section represents the received data on the surface of the earth.

Each type of path (primary and multiple) appear as an event on the seismic section. These events lie along the time–distance curves of the respective paths.

Given the seismic data $u(x, t)$, we now want to pick out all the paths that have the same value of the ray parameter p. That is, we want to pick out all the ray paths that emerge at some given angle. As we have said, if we fix the receiver position x, then all the different types of paths come in at different angles. On the other hand, if we fix the angle, then all the different types of ray paths with that emergent angle come in at different receiver positions x.

We recall that we choose the layers in our model for a particular value of p. Consider all the ray paths with the value p. Each ray path will emerge at a different x value. At that x value, the slope of the corresponding time–distance curve will be p. Thus the tangent line at this point will have slope p and intercept τ. The value of τ will depend upon the type of ray path. More specifically, τ is an integer equal to the sum of the number of legs through each layer. For example, for the multiple path with four passes through layer 1, three passes through layer 2, and one pass through layer 3, the value of τ is $4 + 3 + 1 = 8$.

Let us now slant stack the data with slope p. Then the stacked data as a function of τ will be as follows. Every one of the paths has ray parameter with the given value p:

$\tau_1 = 1$: (1) First primary

$\tau_2 = 2$: (1) Second primary, and
(2) multiple with two passes through layer 1

$\tau_3 = 3$: (1) Third primary,
(2) multiple with three passes through layer 1,

(3) multiple with two passes through layer 1 and
one pass through layer 2, and

(4) multiple with one pass through layer 1 and
two passes through layer 2.

Thus for fixed p, we obtain a trace as a function of τ. This slant-stack trace satisfies the requirement that the timing of all primaries and multiples are integer valued. Thus this slant-stack trace is the same as a normal incidence trace generated by a Goupillaud model where the reflection coefficients are the ones specified by the ray parameter p. In particular, the multiple arrivals of the slant-stack trace have the same time structure as the 1-D seismic trace generated by the Goupillaud model.

It follows, therefore, we can take this slant stack and invert it by the 1-D methods given in the 1-D part of this paper. In particular, we can use Gelfand–Levitan inversion as implemented by the dynamic deconvolution method.

Conversely, we can construct a forward scheme which generates a seismic section $u(x, t)$ from a given layered model. For each ray parameter p, we find the non-normal-incidence reflection coefficients for each of the layers. We then use the forward Gelfand–Levitan scheme (i.e., dynamic reconvolution) and generate the 1-D seismic trace. This seismic trace will be a function of τ for the given p. Repeating this process for many p values, we obtain $U_R(p, \tau)$. We then apply the inverse Radon transform to obtain the synthetic seismic section $u(x, t)$.

G. Migration

So far we have considered flat layers. Now we want to consider a sloping interface in a constant velocity medium. Suppose the first interface is a line which makes the angle β with the horizontal. We consider a source and receiver at the same surface point x. By Fermat's theorem of least time, the ray path must be a *least time path*. Thus the ray path will be a straight line from the source to the reflecting point on the interface. The same path is used by the reflected wave back to the receiver, and this common ray path will be at right angles to the interface. Thus the ray path will make an angle β with the vertical.

Let the medium have constant velocity v, which for simplicity we take to be $v = 1$. Let us refer to Fig. 14. The interface cuts the surface of the ground at point ξ. We call ξ the intercept. Let x be the coordinate of the receiver. Thus we have a right triangle with hypotenuse $x - \xi$ and angle β. The side opposite β is the ray path $vt = t$. Here t is the one-way travel time along the ray path. Thus

$$\sin \beta = \frac{t}{x - \xi}.$$

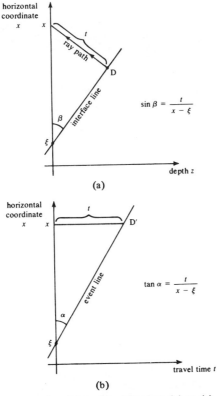

(a)

(b)

Fig. 14. Wave propagation (a) to (b). Migration (b) to (a). (a) Earth cross section. With velocity $v = 1$, a wave takes time t to travel up from depth point D to receiver x. (b) Seismic section. The depth point appears at D' on the seismic section. The interface with dip $\tan \beta$ and intercept ξ appears as the event with dip $\tan \alpha$ and same intercept. We see that $\sin \beta = \tan \alpha$.

On the seismic section, we will plot t versus x. Then the seismic trace at receiver position x will have an event at t. As we vary x, these events will fall on a straight line which intercepts the x axis at ξ; that is, the intercept of the interface line and the intercept of the event line are the same. Let the event line make an angle α with the x-axis. Again we have a right triangle. The side opposite α has length t and the (non-hypotenuse) side adjaccent to α has length $x - \xi$. Thus we have

$$\tan \alpha = \frac{t}{x - \xi}.$$

Comparing the above two equations, we have

$$\sin \beta = \tan \alpha.$$

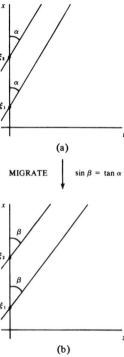

Fig. 15. Mechanical migration: (a) events on a seismic section with dips
tan α; (b) each event is rotated about its intercept from tan α to tan β
to produce interfaces of dip tan β.

This is the basic equation of migration. *Migration* is the conversion of the event line in the (x, t) plane to the interface line in the (x, z) plane. Each of these lines have the same x-intercept ξ. Thus migration involves rotating the event line around this intercept ξ so as to change the event angle α to the interface angle β, where

$$\beta = \sin^{-1} \tan \alpha.$$

Prior to 1960, migration was performed by mechanical devices; see Fig. 15.

H. Spectral Migration

Each of the events on the seismic section (i.e., the observed data) is represented by a curve in the (x, t) space. Each curve may be considered as the envelope of its tangent lines. Let the equation for a given tangent line be

$$x = \frac{1}{\tan \alpha} t + \xi.$$

Let us now Fourier transform the data; see Fig. 16. The above line will be transformed to line

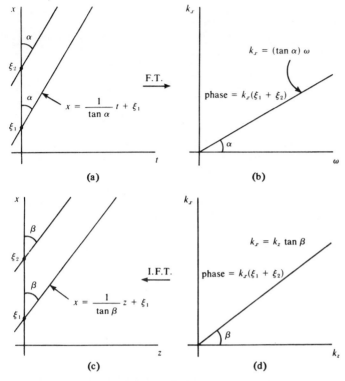

Fig. 16. Spectral migration: (a) events on seismic section with dips
tan α; (b) Fourier transform converts all events into same line, with
intercepts preserved in the phase; (c) migration changes dip from tan
α to tan β; (d) inverse Fourier transform produces interfaces of dip
tan β.

$$k_x = (\tan \alpha) \omega$$

and with phase spectrum $k_x \xi$. The process of migration transforms the above line into the line

$$k_x = (\tan \beta) k_z$$

and with same phase spectrum. We now inverse Fourier transform. The result gives the corresponding line

$$x = \frac{1}{\tan \beta} z + \xi$$

in the (x, z) space. The interfaces appear as the envelopes of
these lines. We have thus described the process of *spectral
migration*, or *Stolt migration* [27].

I. Slant-Stack Migration

Each of the events on the seismic section (i.e., the observed
data) is represented by a curve in (x, t) space. Each curve may

be considered as the envelope of its tangent lines. Let the
equation for a given tangent line be

$$\tan \alpha = \frac{t}{x - \xi}$$

which is

$$x = \frac{1}{\tan \alpha} t + \xi.$$

Let us now slant stack the data; see Fig. 17. The above line
will be transformed into the point $(1/\tan \alpha, \xi)$. All the tangent lines with slope $\tan \alpha$ will fall along the transform line
$(1/\tan \alpha) = $ constant in the transform plane. We now move
this line left to the position $1/\tan \beta$. We thus shift all such
transform lines. This shifting is the process of migration; i.e.,
the changing of dips. We then inverse slant stack. The result
gives the corresponding lines

$$x = \frac{1}{\tan \beta} z + \xi$$

in the (x, z) space. The interfaces appear as the envelopes
of these lines. We have thus described the process of *slant-
stack migration* (often called *S-two migration*) which is due to
Hubral [28].

IV. Conclusion

The problem of the geophysicist is to determine the structure of the interior of the earth from data obtained at the
surface of the ground. Ultimately the problem is to find a
method that will give structure, composition, and source parameters by processing the whole seismogram. Such a problem
is an inverse problem. The forward problem is one which a
model of the earth structure and seismic source is used to give
properties of seismic motion. When the solution of the forward problem is known, an iteration based on trial and error
represents one method of inversion. The parameters of the
model are readjusted according to some criterion until some
satisfying agreement between the data and the computed wave
motion is discovered. This iterative type of approach to the inverse problem has proven to be successful in many applications.
Today far more sophisticated inversion methods are being
developed for seismic data. In this paper, we have described
the present state of the art in which spectral methods in the
form of lattice methods, the Fourier transform, and the Radon
transform play the key role. An understanding of these spectral methods will provide a firm basis for the appreciation of
the exciting new inversion methods which the future holds.

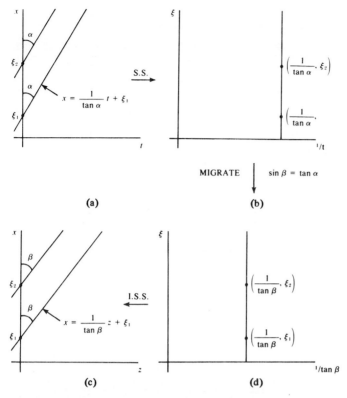

Fig. 17. Slant-stack migration: (a) events on seismic section with dips tan α; (b) slant stacking converts all events into same vertical line; (c) migration moves vertical line to left, from 1/tan α to 1/tan β; (d) inverse slant stacking produces interfaces of dip tan β.

REFERENCES

[1] H. J. Schudder, "Introduction to computer aided tomography," *Proc. IEEE*, vol. 66, pp. 628–637, 1978.

[2] D. W. Sweeney and C. H. West, "Reconstruction of three-dimensional refractive index fields from multidimensional interferometric data," *Appl. Opt.*, vol. 11, pp. 2649–2664, 1973.

[3] P. F. Gilbert, "The reconstruction of a three-dimensional structure from projections and its applications to electron microscopy," *Proc. R. Soc. London*, ser. B, vol. 182, pp. 89–102, 1972.

[4] T. S. Durrani and C. E. Goutis, "Optimization techniques for digital image reconstruction from their projections," *Proc. Inst. Elec. Eng.*, vol. 127, pp. 161–169, 1980.

[5] Lord Rayleigh, *The Theory of Sound.* New York: Dover, 1950.

[6] M. Kac, "Can one hear the shape of a drum?" *Amer. Math. Monthly*, vol. 73, pp. 1–23, 1966.

[7] I. M. Gelfand and B. M. Levitan, "On the determination of a differential equation by its spectral function," *Amer. Math. Soc. Trans.*, vol. 1, pp. 253–304, 1955.

[8] M. T. Silvia and E. A. Robinson, *Deconvolution of Geophysical Time Series in the Exploration for Oil and Natural Gas.* Amsterdam, The Netherlands: Elsevier, 1979.

[9] M. T. Silvia, "Application of statistical filtering techniques to inverse scattering problems," in *Proc. 2nd Int. Symp. on Computer Aided Seismic Analysis and Discrimination at Southeastern Massachusetts University* (IEEE Computer Society), pp. 20-27, 1981.

[10] M. T. Silvia and A. Weglein, "Method for obtaining a nearfield inverse scattering solution to the acoustic wave equation," *J. Acoust. Soc. Amer.*, vol. 69, pp. 478-489, 1981.

[11] J. Cohen and N. Bleistein, "A velocity inversion procedure for acoustic waves," *Geophysics*, vol. 44, pp. 1077-1087, 1979.

[12] N. Bleistein and J. Cohen, "Velocity inversion. A tool for seismic exploration," presented at the *SIAM Conf.*, Tucson, AZ, 1981.

[13] J. Mendel and F. Habibi-Ashrafi, "A survey of approaches to solving inverse problems for lossless layered media systems," *IEEE Trans. Geosci. Remote Sensing*, vol. GE-18, pp. 320-330, 1980.

[14] S. Coen, "Complete acoustic and elastic layered modeling for seismic reflection data," presented at the SIAM Conf., Tucson, AZ, 1981.

[15] R. Carroll and F. Santosa, "Scattering techniques for a one-dimensional inverse problem in geophysics," *Math. Meth. in the Appl. Sci.*, vol. 3, pp. 145-171, 1981.

[16] K. Driessel and W. Symes, "Coefficient identification problems for hyperbolic partial differential equations. Some fast and accurate algorithms for the seismic inverse problem in one space dimension," presented at the SIAM Conf., Tucson, AZ, 1981.

[17] R. H. Stolt, "Imaging and inversion of seismic data," presented at the SIAM Conf., Tucson, AZ, 1981.

[18] K. P. Bube and R. Burridge, "Solution of the one-dimensional inverse problem of reflection seismology by downward continuation of surface data," presented at the SIAM Conf., Tucson, AZ, 1981.

[19] A. H. Zemanian and P. Subramaniam, "The application of the theory of infinite networks to the geophysical exploration of layered strata," presented at the SIAM Conf., Tucson, AZ, 1981.

[20] J. Gazdag, "Migration of seismic data by phase shift plus interpolation," presented at the SIAM Conf., Tucson, AZ, 1981.

[21] A. Bamberger, G. Chavent, and P. Lailly, "About the stability of the inverse problem in 1-D wave equations. Application to the Interpretation of Seismic Profiles," *Appl. Math. Optim.*, vol. 5, pp. 1-47, 1979.

[22] S. Treitel, P. Gutowski, P. Hubral, and D. Wagner, "Plane wave decomposition of seismograms," presented at the SEG Meet., Los Angeles, CA, 1981.

[23] K. L. Larner, "Computational problems resulting from the discreteness of data sets obtained in seismic exploration," presented at the SIAM Conf., Tuscon, AZ, 1981.

[24] J. Makhoul, "Stable and efficient lattice methods for linear prediction," *IEEE Trans. Acoust., Speech, Signal Processing*, vol. ASSP-25, pp. 423-428, Oct. 1977.

[25] N. Levinson, "The Wiener RMS error criterion in filter design and prediction," *J. Math. Phys.*, 1947.

[26] J. P. Burg, "Maximum entropy spectral analysis," presented at the Soc. Exploration Geophysicists Meet., Oklahoma City, OK, 1967.

[27] R. H. Stolt, "Migration by Fourier transform," *Geophysics*, vol. 43, pp. 23-48, 1978.

[28] P. Hubral, "Slant stack migration," in *Festischrift Theodor Krey*. Hannover, Germany: Prakla-Seismos, 1980, pp. 72-78.

[29] P. Goupillaud, "An approach to inverse filtering of near surface layer effects from seismic records," *Geophysics*, vol. 26, pp. 754-760, 1961.

[30] A. Gray and J. Markel, "Digital lattice and ladder filter synthesis," *IEEE Trans. Audio Electroacoust.*, vol. AU-21, pp. 491-500, 1973.

[31] J. Makhoul, "A class of all-zero lattice digital filters: Properties and applications," *IEEE Trans. Acoust., Speech, Signal Processing*, vol. ASSP-26, pp. 304-314, Aug. 1978.

[32] T. Durrani, N. Murukutla, and K. Sharman, "Constrained algorithms for multi-input adaptive lattices in array processing," in *IEEE ICASSP Proc.*, 1981.

[33] H. Lorentz, A. Einstein, H. Minkowski, and H. Weyl, *The Principles of Relativity: A Collection of Original Memoirs.* London, England: Methuen, 1923 (reprinted by Dover Publ., New York, 1958).

[34] E. A. Robinson, *Multichannel Time Series Analysis with Digital Computer Programs.* San Francisco, CA: Holden-Day, 1967. (Revised edition, 1978.)

[35] H. Wakita, "Direct estimation of the vocal tract shape by inverse filtering of acoustic speech waveforms," *IEEE Trans. Audio Electroacoust.*, vol. AU-21, pp. 417-427, 1973.

[36] G. Kunetz, "Généralisation des opérateurs d'antirésonance à un nombre quelconque de réflecteurs," *Geophys. Prospecting*, vol. 12, pp. 283-289, 1964.

[37] G. Kunetz and I. D'Erceville, "Sur certaines propriétés d'une onde plane de compréssion dans un milieu stratifié," *Ann. Geophysique*, vol. 18, pp. 351-359, 1962.

[38] K. Aki and P. G. Richards, *Quantitative Seismology*, vol. 2. San Francisco, CA: W. H. Freeman, 1980.

[39] E. A. Robinson, "Dynamic predictive deconvolution," *Geophys. Prospecting*, vol. 23, pp. 779-797, 1975.

[40] V. Bardan, "Comments on dynamic predictive deconvolution," *Geophys. Prospecting*, vol. 25, pp. 569-572, 1977.

[41] E. A. Robinson, "Iterative identification of non-invertible autoregressive moving-average systems with seismic applications," *Geoexploration*, vol. 16, pp. 1-19, 1978.

[42] J. Radon, "Uber die Bestimmung von Funktionen durch ihre Integralwerte langs gewisser Manningfaltigkeiten," *Berichte der Sächsischen Akademie der Wissenschaften*, vol. 69, pp. 262-277, 1917.

[43] "The MIT Geophysical Analysis Group Reports," *Geophysics*, vol. 32, 1967.

Index

BOOKS BY ENDERS A. ROBINSON

1954 Predictive Decomposition of Time Series with Applications to Seismic Exploration
1959 An Introduction to Infinitely Many Variates
1962 Random Wavelets and Cybernetic Systems
1967 Statistical Communication and Detection with special reference to Digital Data Processing of Radar and Seismic Signals
1967 Multichannel Time Series Analysis with Digital Computer Programs
1967 Forecasting on a Scientific Basis (with H. Wold, G. Orcutt, D. Suits, P. de Wolf)
1969 The Robinson-Treitel Reader (3 editions) (with S. Treitel)
1978 Digital Signal Processing and Time Series Analysis (with M. T. Silvia)
1979 Deconvolution of Geophysical Time Series in the Exploration for Oil and Natural Gas (with M. T. Silvia)
1979 Digital Foundations of Time Series Analysis
      Volume 1. The Box-Jenkins Approach (with M. T. Silvia)
1980 Geophysical Signal Analysis (with S. Treitel)
1980 Physical Applications of Stationary Time Series
1980 University Course in Digital Seismic Methods used in Petroleum Exploration
1981 Digital Foundations of Time Series Analysis
      Volume 2. Wave-Equation Space-Time Processing (with M. T. Silvia)
1981 Time Series Analysis and Applications
1981 Least Squares Regression Analysis in Terms of Linear Algebra
1981 Statistical Reasoning and Decision Making
1983 Migration of Geophysical Data
1983 Multichannel Time Series Analysis with Digital Computer Programs (Second Edition)